Structure & Methods
Volume 3:
DNA & RNA

Proceedings of the Sixth Conversation in the Discipline Biomolecular Stereodynamics held at the State University of New York at Albany, June 6-10, 1989

Edited by

R.H. Sarma & M.H. Sarma

Institute of Biomolecular Stereodynamics,
Department of Chemistry
State University of New York at Albany and
National Foundation for Cancer Research

Adenine Press
2066 Central Avenue
Schenectady, NY 12304
(518) 456-0784
Fax: (518) 452-4955

Adenine Press
Post Office Box 355/340
Guilderland, New York 12084

The computer graphics illustrations on the cover & the frontispiece were generated by Teresa Larsen, using the program RMS by David Goodsell.

Frontispiece and Cover Illustration: Unrolled helix diagram of the B-DNA decamer of sequence: C-G-A-T-C-G-A-T-C-G, by Kazimierz Grzeskowiak, Kazunori Yanagi, and Richard Dickerson. Atoms of the sugar-phosphate backbone, and oxygens of water molecules within the minor grove, have been projected on a cylinder of radius 8 Å, which then has been unrolled. The helix axis is vertical. Note how the water molecules within the minor groove (blue spheres) alternate between a single spine of hydration and two ribbons of hydration, as the groove narrows and widens.

Library of Congress Cataloging-in-Publication Data

Conversation in Biomolecular Stereodynamics (6th : 1989 : State University of New York at Albany)
Structure & methods : proceedings of the Sixth Conversation in the Discipline Biomolecular Stereodynamics held at the State University of New York at Albany, June 6-10, 1989 / edited by R.H. Sarma & M.H. Sarma.
p. cm.
Includes bibliographical references.
Contents: v. 1. Human genome initiative & DNA recombination -- v. 2. DNA protein complexes & proteins -- v. 3. DNA & RNA.
ISBN 0-940030-32-2 (set) : $290.00
1. Nucleic acids--Structure--Congresses. 2. Proteins--Structure--Congresses. 3. Biomolecules--Structure--Congresses. 4. Stereochemistry--Congresses. I. Sarma, Ramaswamy H., 1939- . II. Sarma, M.H. (Mukti H.), 1940- . III. State University of New York at Albany. IV. Title. V. Title: Structure and methods.
QP620.C67 1989a
574.87'328--dc20 90-474
CIP

Manufactured in the United States by Adenine Press, Inc., set in type by Adenine on Digitek 5000 typesetting system manufactured by Itek Graphix Corp., USA.
Printed in the United States

Made in New York, USA

Preface

These are the proceedings of the Sixth Conversation in Biomolecular Stereodynamics, held at the State University of New York at Albany, June 6-10, 1989 under the auspices of the Department of Chemistry and organized by the University's Institute of Biomolecular Stereodynamics. These volumes essentially constitute the invited presentations as well as the deliberations at the panel discussions.

The conference and these volumes were made possible by generous support from public and private institutions. We are immensely grateful to the following institutions for suppporting the congress.

State University of New York
State University of New York at Albany, Office of the President, Office of Vice President for Research, Dean, College of Science and Mathematics, Departments of Biological Sciences and Chemistry
Adenine Press, Inc.
Applied Biosystems
Bristol-Myers Copmany
Burroughs Wellcome Company
Domtar, Inc.
E.I. du Pont de Nemours & Co.
General Electric Company
Hoffmann-La Roche, Inc.
Merck Sharp & Dohme
National Foundation for Cancer Research
National Institutes of Health
National Science Foundation
Sterling-Winthrop
Wilmad Glass Company

We thank our friends and colleagues who have either served in the Organizing Committee or have provided valuable suggestions or have physically helped us in several ways. We must particularly mention: D.L. Beveridge, C.W. Hilbers, N.R. Kallenbach, D.M.J. Lilley, W.D. Phillips, A.G. Redfield, A. Rich, N.C. Seeman, M. Soumpasis, E.N. Trifonov and A.H.-J. Wang. We acknowledge with gratitute the help from Virginia Dollar and Charles Heller of Chemistry, John Elliot of Biology, Al Dasher of the College of Science and Mathematics and Don Bielecki of the Conference Department of SUNYA.

Most of all we thank, congratulate and applaud the participants of the Sixth Conversation for their notable contribuitons and their continuing and unabated dedication to the discipline of biological structure, dynamics, interactions and expression.

We are looking forward to the pleasure of being your hosts for the Seventh Conversation June 4-8, 1991.

Ramaswamy H. Sarma & Mukti H. Sarma
Albany, New York
March 7, 1990

CONTENTS

Structure & Methods
Volume 3: DNA & RNA

CONTENTS

Structure & Methods
Volume 1: Human Genome Initiative & DNA Recombination

CONTENTS

Structure & Methods
Volume 2: DNA Protein Complexes & Proteins

Structure & Methods, ISBN 0-940030-32-2
Volume 3: DNA & RNA, ISBN 0-940030-31-4
Eds., Ramaswamy H. Sarma & Mukti H. Sarma, © Adenine Press 1990

What Do We Really Know About B-DNA?

Richard E. Dickerson
Molecular Biology Institute
University of California
Los Angeles CA 90024

Abstract

Thirty-one B-DNA oligomer crystal structures have been solved over the past decade. Seventeen of these are of the "Drew" dodecamer sequence, C-G-C-G-A-A-T-T-C-G-C-G, or its mismatch variants and complexes with drug molecules. Another 5 dodecamer structures have different sequences but are crystallographically isomorphous with the Drew set. New departures are a phosphorothioate analogue of G-C-G-C-G-C and four related decamers. These decamers have the advantage of stacking in an especially ordered manner as continuous helices in the crystal, and give unusually high resolution diffraction patterns, at best out to 1.3 Å. A comparison of dodecamers, hexamer, and decamers has led to a set of structural principles: 1) The minor groove in B-DNA tends to be narrower in regions of AT base pairs than in GC regions, and wider when BII phosphate conformations occur on both strands. 2) CG base pairs have low propeller twist; AT pairs can have high propeller twist but need not do so. 3) High propeller twist often accompanies a narrow minor groove but is not required for its narrowing. 4) High propeller twist in regions of successive adenines (A-tract DNA) is stabilized by interbasepair hydrogen bonds in the major groove. 5) Narrow regions of minor groove contain a spine of hydration; wide regions of minor groove contain two ribbons of waters along the walls. The stoichiometry is the same: two bound waters per base pair. 6) Sugar conformation in B-DNA is distributed about C2′-endo and C1′-exo, but is broader than in A-DNA, whose sugar pucker clusters tightly around C3′-endo. 7) Bending in B-DNA occurs by rolling adjacent base pairs around their long axes, in a direction that compresses the broad major groove. 8) A-tract B-DNA tends to be straight, with flexible hinge bends occurring at junctions with general-sequence DNA. Alternating poly-AT DNA shows regular alternation of twist and roll.

Introduction

Just ten years ago this December, in 1979, there appeared the first report of a single crystal x-ray structure analysis of a short length of DNA double helix (T2). (References associated with Tables II - V will be cited with a leading "T"; general references will be cited by number only.) The results were somewhat of a shock, as the helix was observed to be in neither of the canonical A or B forms anticipated by fiber diffraction analysis. Instead, the C-G-C-G-C-G oligomer adopted an entirely new, left-handed zig-zag Z-DNA structure, whose occurrence in nature has been reasonably well documented since that time, but whose biological relevance is still unproven.

The first single crystal analysis of the biologically dominant B-DNA helix appeared

Table I
Single Crystal X-Ray Structure Analyses of Synthetic Oligonucleotides, First Five Years

Sequence	Temp.	Unit Cell Dimensions a	b	c	Unique Base Pairs	Research Group	Publ. Date
I. A-Helical Family							
a. Space group $P4_32_12$							
iCCGG	5°C	41.10	41.10	26.70	4	UCLA (CIT)	1981
GGCCGGCC	−8°C	42.06	42.06	25.17	4	MIT	1982
GGCCGGCC	−18°C	40.51	40.51	24.67	4	MIT	1982
b. Space group $P6_1$							
GGbrUAbrUACC	RT	45.05	45.05	41.72	8	Weiz/Camb	1981
GGTATACC	RT	45.01	45.01	41.55	8	Weiz/Camb	1981
c. Space group $P2_12_12_1$							
r(GCG)d(TATACGC)	0°C	24.20	43.46	49.40	10	MIT	1982
II. B-Helical Family -- Space group $P2_12_12_1$ only							
CGCGAATTCGCG	RT	24.87	40.39	66.20	12	UCLA (CIT)	1980
CGCGAATTCGCG	16°K	23.44	39.31	65.26	12	UCLA (CIT)	1982
CGCGAATTbrCGCG	20°C	24.71	40.56	65.62	12	UCLA	1982
CGCGAATTbrCGCG	7°C	24.20	40.09	63.95	12	UCLA	1982
CGCGAATTCGCG/Cisplatin	4°C	24.16	39.93	66.12	12	UCLA	1984
III. Z-Helical Family							
a. Space group $C222_1$							
CGCG	RT	19.50	31.27	64.67	4	UCLA (CIT)	1980
b. Space group $P2_12_12_1$							
CGCGCG/spermine	RT	17.88	31.55	44.58	6	MIT	1979
meCGmeCGmeCG	−8°C	17.76	30.57	45.42	6	MIT	1982
meCGTAmeCG	−10°C	17.91	30.43	44.96	6	MIT	1984
c. Space group $P6_5$							
CGCG disordered	?	31.25	31.25	44.06	6	MIT	1980
IV. Irregular Helices							
pATAT ($P2_1$)	?	12.12	21.29	8.77	2	Camb/Weiz	1978
CGTACG/Daunomycin ($P4_12_12$)	?	27.92	27.92	52.89	3	MIT	1980
CGTACG/Triostin A (F222)	−16°C	31.35	62.38	61.26	3	MIT	1984

Only structures published in 1984 or earlier are listed. For further information and references, see Tables II - V.

the following year (T6), with what has come to be known as the "Drew sequence": C-G-C-G-A-A-T-T-C-G-C-G, an embedding of the Eco RI restriction site in an alternating CG matrix. Other examples of A, B and Z helices followed in rapid succession in 1980-1 (T4, T8, T12), and the field of single crystal DNA structure analysis could be said to be fairly launched. The First Conversation in Biomolecular Stereodynamics in April of 1979 took place just on the eve of these new developments, and in a sense the Conversations and the field have grown up together.

What has been achieved in DNA single crystal structure analysis since that date, and what have we learned for our ten years of effort? Progress at first was slow. Table I shows what was accomplished during the first five years: several A-DNA octamers and a DNA-RNA hybrid decamer, several variants of alternating pyrimidine-purine Z-DNA, including methylation of cytosine and in one case the presence of AT base pairs. But only *one* example of B-DNA, the Drew sequence, albeit in several variations. The rate-limiting step was the synthesis, purification, and more especially the crystallization of oligomers. When one worker in the field announced plans to synthesize and study a particular DNA sequence, a colleague chided, "That's not the way to operate; you set up 100 sequences and solve what crystallizes." The streetlight syndrome[1] was in full operation.

The logjam has been broken in the last five years, thanks to improved methods of DNA synthesis and purification. Now, within limits, it is possible to set synthetic goals and study predefined sequences. Tables II through V list all of the oligonucleotide structures of the last decade, for A, B, Z and irregular helices respectively. There are 23 entries for A-helices, 31 for B, 16 for Z and 8 structures with irregular helices, for a grand total of 78! Surely DNA by now is one of the best-known of biological molecules?

The situation is not quite as optimistic as these numbers would suggest, and the Tables have been set up to illustrate this. Structure analyses in the Tables that share the same space group, the same unit cell dimensions (within a few Ångstroms) and the same number of unique base pairs per asymmetric unit constitute an *isomorphous set* of structures. The first nine A-helical structures in Table II form such an isomorphous set, as do the next nine in space group $P6_1$, and the first 22 B structures in Table III. If one had the (x,y,z) coordinates for any one member of such an isomorphous set, one could immediately use them as a starting model with any of the other members

---

[1]Old vaudeville routine:

Q: "What are you looking for out here in the street?"
A: "I lost a silver dollar."
Q: "Where did you lose it?"
A: "About half a block down the road."
Q: "So why are you looking for it here under the streetlight?"
A: "The light's better here!"

Table II
Single Crystal X-Ray Structure Analyses of Synthetic A-Helical Oligonucleotides

Sequence	Temp.	Unit Cell Dimensions a	b	c	Unique Base Pairs	Volume/ Base Pair (Å^3)	Resolution, d
a. Space group $P4_32_12$							
iCCGG	5°C	41.10	41.10	26.70	4	1409	2.0
CCCCGGGG	15°C	43.36	43.36	24.83	4	1459	2.25
GCCCGGGC	RT	43.25	43.25	24.61	4	1439	1.8
GGCCGGCC	−8°C	42.06	42.06	25.17	4	1391	2.25
GGCCGGCC	−18°C	40.51	40.51	24.67	4	1265	2.25
GGGCGCCC	RT	43.28	43.28	24.66	4	1444	1.8
GGGCGCCC	115°K	42.74	42.74	24.57	4	1403	1.7
CTCTAGAG	RT	42.53	42.53	24.33	4	1375	2.15
GTGTACAC	4°C	42.43	42.43	24.75	4	1392	2.0
b. Space group $P6_1$							
GGbrUAbrUACC	RT	45.05	45.05	41.72	8	1528	1.7
GGTATACC	RT	45.01	45.01	41.55	8	1519	1.8
GGGATCCC	RT	46.83	46.83	44.49	8	1525	2.5
GGGCGCCC	RT	46.96	46.96	44.31	8	1763	2.9
GGGCGCCC	110°K	43.62	43.62	41.49	8	1424	1.9
GGGGCCCC	18°C	45.32	46.32	42.25	8	1566	2.5
GGGGCTCC GT mis.	2°C	45.20	45.20	42.97	8	1584	2.25
GGGGTCCC GT mis.	2°C	44.71	44.71	42.40	8	1529	2.1
GGGTGCCC GT mis.	RT	45.62	45.62	40.99	8	1539	2.5
c. Space group $P4_3$							
GGATGGGAG	RT	45.29	45.29	24.73	9	1409	3.0
d. Space group $P6_122$							
GTGTACAC		32.4	32.4	79.5	4	1505	2.0
CpsCGTACGTACGG		46.2	46.2	71.5	6	1836	2.5
e. Space group $P2_12_12_1$							
r(GCG)d(TATACGC)	0°C	24.20	43.46	49.40	10	1299	2.0
UUAUAUAUAUAUAA RNA	RT	34.11	44.61	49.11	14	1334	2.25

of the set, and refine that new structure to completion without difficulty. In fact, this is just the method of *molecular replacement*. (But note that two further B structures in the same $P2_12_12_1$ space group in Table III are *not* isomorphous with the preceeding 22. Although they share the same symmetry, they have quite different cell dimensions and different numbers of independent base pairs. They represent truly distinct structures, and cannot be solved so easily via molecular replacement from a knowledge of one of the first 22.)

The differences among the structures in an isomorphous set are of interest, of

Table II
continued

R	Sigma Level	No. Data	No. Solvent	Research Group	Public. Date	Deposited in Public Domain? Data	Coords.	Refs.
16.5%	2	1486	86	UCLA (CIT)	1981	R1ANASF	1ANA	8,13,23
15%	0	1018	82	Weiz/MIT	1987	No	No	51
17.1%	3	1359	34	Berlin	1987	R9DNASF	9DNA	52
17.4%	3	920	75	MIT	1982	No	No	17,19
15.8%	3	874	84	MIT	1982	No	No	17,19
15.9%	2	2082	88	Weizmann	1988	No	No	67
21%	2	1694	62	Weizmann	1989	No	No	61
14.7%	1	931	35	Cambridge	1989	No	No	78
11.5%	0	1214	43	Wisconsin	1987	No	No	54,79
14%	2	4669	84	Weiz/Camb	1981	No	No	12,22,46
19.8%	2	3251	66	Weiz/Camb	1981	No	No	12,22
16.6%	3	1428	9	Berlin	1988	R3ANASF	3ANA	64
12%	2	1068	45	Weizmann	1989	No	No	81
16%	2	2827	100	Weizmann	1989	No	No	81
14%	2	1283	106	Cambridge	1985	R2ANASF	2ANA	35
13.6%	2	1924	52	Camb/Weiz	1985	No	No	28,43
14.5%	2	2486	104	Camb/Weiz	1985	No	No	32
15.2%	2	1362	63	Weizmann	1988	No	No	67
33%	0	1032	0	Cambridge	1986	No	1DN6	47
12.5%		1561	50	Wisconsin	1989	No	No	82
13.6%	0	2415	71	Wisconsin	1989	No	No	70
16%	1.5	2521	179	MIT	1982	No	No	17,20
13.1%	2	2492	91	Strasbourg	1988	No	No	60

course, because their sequences are different. But if one worries about the effects of crystal packing forces and crystallizing conditions (as one must), then all the 22 B-DNA structures in the "Drew" set experience the same influences from crystal packing forces, and will be subject to the same crystal deformations.

How can we sort out the two additive effects: the one arising from base sequence itself, and the other from the manner in which the oligomer is "packaged" in the crystal? One approach is to examine many isomorphous sequences in the same crystal setting, where crystal packing becomes at least a common factor. The other

Table III
Single Crystal X-Ray Structure Analyses of Synthetic B-Helical Oligonucleotides

Sequence	Temp.	Unit Cell Dimensions a	b	c	Unique Base Pairs	Volume/ Base Pair (Å^3)	Resolution, d
a. Space group $P4_32_12$							
CGCGAATTCGCG	16°K	23.44	39.31	65.26	12	1253	2.7
CGCGAATTCGCG	RT	24.87	40.39	66.20	12	1385	1.9
CGCGAATTCGCG	RT	24.87	40.39	66.20	12	1385	1.9
CGCGAATTCGCG Aniso	RT	24.87	40.39	66.20	12	1385	1.9
CGCGAATTbrCGCG	20°C	24.71	40.56	65.62	12	1370	3.0
CGCGAATTbrCGCG	7°C	24.20	40.09	63.95	12	1293	2.3
CGCGAATTTGCG GT mis.	4°C	25.53	41.22	65.63	12	1433	2.5
CGCGAATTAGCG GA mis.	5°C	25.69	41.96	65.19	12	1464	2.5
CGCAAATTGGCG GA mis.	4°C	25.23	41.16	65.01	12	1406	2.25
CGCAAATTCGCG AC mis.	4°C	25.37	41.44	65.20	12	1428	2.5
CGCGAmeATTCGCG	RT	25.62	40.70	67.32	12	1462	2.0
CGCGAATTCGCG/Cisplatin	4°C	24.16	39.93	66.12	12	1329	2.6
CGCGAATTbrCGCG/Netropsin	4°C	24.27	39.62	63.57	12	1273	2.2
CGCGAATTCGCG/Hoechst33258	RT	25.04	40.33	65.85	12	1385	2.2
CGCGAATTCGCG/Hoechst33258	15°C	25.23	40.58	66.08	12	1409	2.25
CGCGAATTCGCG/DAPI	RT	25.35	40.71	66.53	12	1430	2.4
CGCGAATTCGCG/Berenil	7°C	25.29	41.78	64.76	12	1426	2.5
CGCAAAAAAGCG	4°C	25.4	40.7	65.8	12	1417	2.5
CGCAAAAATGCG	12°C	24.54	40.32	65.86	12	1358	2.6
CGCATATATGCG	6°C	23.54	38.86	66.57	12	1269	2.2
CGCAAATTTGCG/Distamycin	15°C	25.20	41.07	64.65	12	1393	2.2
GCGCATATCGCG/Netropsin	10°C	25.48	41.26	66.88	12	1464	2.4
GpsCGpsCGpsC	18°C	34.90	39.15	20.64	6	1175	2.17
CGATCGATCG	0°C	38.86	39.58	33.19	10	1276	1.8
b. Space group C2							
CCAAGCTTGG GA mis.	5°C	32.52	26.17	34.30	5	1278	1.3
		beta = 118.9					
CCAACGTTGG	4°C	32.25	25.49	34.65	5	1301	1.4
		beta = 114.0					
CCAGGCCTGG	RT	32.15	25.49	34.82	5	1275	1.6
		beta = 116.71					
CGCTTAAGCG	RT	77.27	25.97	79.17	30	1324	
		beta = 104.5					
CGCAGAATTCGCG A bulge	123°K	78.48	42.85	25.16	12	1739	2.8
		beta = 99.36					
c. Space group I222							
CGCGAAATTTACGCG A bulge	4°C	37.0	53.7	101.6	14	1802	3.0
d. Space group R3							
ACCGGCGCCACA	--	65.9	65.9	47.1	12	1640	2.8

Table III
continued

R	Sigma Level	No. Data	No. Solvent	Research Group	Public. Date	Deposited in Public Domain? Data	Coords.	Refs.
15.1%	2	1051	83	UCLA (CIT)	1982	R2BNASF	2BNA	14
17.8%	2	2725	80	UCLA (CIT)	1980	R1BNASF	1BNA	6-9,11
18.8%	?	3979	64	Strasbourg	1987	No	No	58
14.9%	2	2728	80	Berkeley	1985	R7BNASF	7BNA	30
17.3%	2	1515	44	UCLA	1982	R3BNASF	3BNA	15,21
17.3%	2	2919	115	UCLA	1982	R4BNASF	4BNA	15,21
13%	2	2000	71	Cambridge	1985	No	No	53
17.0%	2	2028	83	Cambridge	1986	No	No	39,44
16%	2	2262	94	Edinburg	1989	No	No	71
19.0%	2	2029	82	Cambridge	1986	No	No	45
16.9%	2	2379	86	MIT	1988	No	4DNB	62
11.2%	2	2088	128	UCLA	1984	R5BNASF	5BNA	26
21.1%	2	2528	75	UCLA	1985	R6BNASF	6BNA	33,34
14.0%	2	1569	175	UCLA	1987	R8BNASF	8BNA	56
15.7%	2	2000	126	MIT	1988	R1DNHSF	1DNH	68
21.5%	2	2428	24	UCLA	1989	No	No	84
	2			InstCanRes	1989	No	No	92
20%	0.5	2003	27	Cambridge	1987	No	No	55
20.1%	2	1975	23	Yale	1989	R1BDNSF	1BDN	74
18.7%	1	1915	43	UCLA	1989	R1DN9SF	1DN9	69
19.6%	2	2369	70	MIT	1987	No	2DND	50
20.1%	2	1848	60	MIT	1988	No	1DNE	72
14.5%	2	1327	72	Cambridge	1987	No	No	42
16.5%	2	3209	80	UCLA	1989	No	No	94
16.4%	2	4016	68	UCLA	1987	R3DNBSF	3DNB	57,66
17.9%	1	4707	71	UCLA	1989	No	No	93
16.9%	1	2420		Berlin	1989	No	No	77
				UCLA	1989	No	No	91
15%	2	?	50	Weizmann	1988	No	No	63
26.3%	1.5	1943	?	NCI/Weiz.	1988	No	No	65
15.3%	3	1101	20	Strasbourg	1989	No	No	83

Table IV
Single Crystal X-Ray Structure Analyses of Synthetic Z-Helical Oligonucleotides

Sequence	Temp.	Unit Cell Dimensions a	b	c	Unique Base Pairs	Volume/ Base Pair ($Å^3$)	Reso- lution, d
a. Space group $P4_32_12$							
CGCG	RT	19.50	31.27	64.67	4	1232	1.5
b. Space Group $P2_12_12_1$							
CGCGCG/spermine	RT	17.88	31.55	44.58	6	1048	0.9
CGCGCG	RT	18.01	31.03	44.80	6	1043	1.0
meCGmeCGmeCG	−8°C	17.76	30.57	45.42	6	1027	1.3
brCGbrCGbrCG	18°C	18.01	30.88	44.76	6	1037	1.4
brCGbrCGbrCG	37°C	17.93	30.83	44.73	6	1030	1.4
meCGTAmeCG	−10°C	17.91	30.43	44.96	6	1021	1.2
meCGATmeCG	?	18.30	31.10	44.10	6	1046	1.54
CGCGTG GT mis.	15°C	17.45	31.63	45.56	6	1048	1.0
CGCGflUG	10°C	17.38	31.06	45.39	6	1021	1.5
brUGCGCG GbrU mis.	4°C	17.94	30.85	49.94	6	1152	2.25
c. Space group $P6_5$							
CGCG disordered	?	31.25	31.25	44.06	6	1035	1.5
CGCGCGCG disordered	?	31.27	31.27	43.56	6	1025	1.6
CGCATGCG disordered	?	30.90	30.90	43.14	6	991	2.5
CGTACGTACG disordered	?	17.93	17.93	43.41	2	1007	1.5
d. Space group C2							
CGCGCGTTTTCGCGCG hairpin	7°C	57.18	21.63 beta = 95.22	36.40	8	1400	2.1

equally necessary approach is to look at the same sequences or segments of sequences in quite different crystal setting, to see how they differ and what common features always recur. This is illustrated well for A-DNA by the sequence G-G-G-C-G-C-C-C, which has been examined in two different space groups and at both room temperature and low temperature (T61, T67, T78). Surprising differences are found in the structure of the helix under differing conditions, including large changes in width of the minor groove. These differences can be related to hydration and water activity, and themselves are fascinating topics for study (T78).

Hence one must treat with caution a simple "head count" of DNA structure analyses, and ask in each case what new conditions were used, what new crystal environment the helix experienced, and what new information resulted. Just over half of the 31 DNA structure analyses in Table III are of the same C-G-C-G-A-A-T-T-C-G-C-G "Drew" sequence, and another five represent sequence variants that are crystallographically isomorphous with the Drew structure. It was known from the very first analysis in this 22-structure isomorphous set that the double helices crys-

Table IV
continued

R	Sigma Level	No. Data	No. Solvent	Research Group	Public. Date	Deposited in Public Domain? Data	Coords.	Refs.
21%	2	1900	84	UCLA (CIT)	1980	R1ZNASF	1ZNA	4,8,10
13%	2	15000	68	MIT	1979	No	2DGC	2,17,76
17.5%	2	10893	88	MIT	1989	No	1DCG	76
15.6%	1.5	4208	98	MIT	1982	No	Paper	16,17
13.3%	2	2919	61	Strasbourg	1986	R1DN4SF	1DN4	41
12.5%	2	3765	83	Strasbourg	1986	R1DN5SF	1DN5	41
16%	1.5	5412	98	MIT	1984	No	Paper	24
19.3%	1.5	2386	88	MIT	1985	No	No	37
19.5%	1	10964	91	MIT	1985	No	No	31
20.0%	2	3008	64	MIT	1989	No	No	73
15.6%	2	1105	64	Cambridge	1986	No	No	40
19.3%	?	?	85	MIT	1980	No	No	?
19%	?	?	85	MIT	1985	No	No	29
16%	?	?	?	MIT	1985	No	No	29
25.5%	2	506	7	Wis/Stras.	1985	No	1DN8	27,38
20.0%	2	1509	70	UCLA	1988	R1D16SF	1D16	59

tallized around a 2_1 screw axis, with the last two base pairs of one helix being hydrogen-bonded, via minor groove base edges, to the first two base pairs of the next (Figure 2 of ref. 1). As a consequence the minor groove is blocked by intermolecular contacts at both ends of the dodecamer helix, and probably artifically widened as well. This must be kept in mind when interpreting the results of any of the first 22 structures listed in Table III.

The Z-DNA structures in Table IV tend to stack end-upon-end instead, in a manner that simulates a continuous helix through the crystal. Because the hexamers in space group $P2_12_12_1$ constitute exactly half a turn of Z helix, they stack with 180° rotation so that two hexamers build a complete turn. (See Figure 2 of ref. T2.) The unconnected step from the top of one hexamer to the bottom of the next is as typical a helix step as are any of those interior steps that are connected by phosphate groups. This illustrates the strong effect of base pair stacking in defining helix structure; one could almost believe that the helix structure still would result even if the connecting phosphates were absent.

The A-helical crystals also exhibit a characteristic behavior, in which the flat surface of the final base pair of one helix packs against one wall of the shallow minor groove of another helix in the crystal. This end-against-groove packing persists whether four molecules spiral around a screw axis, as in space group $P4_32_12$ (Figure 6 of ref. T51) or six as in $P6_1$ (Figures 4-6 of ref. T12). Indeed, it is encountered in every other space group listed in Table II, and must be regarded as one of the most persistent and characteristic features of crystals of A-helical oligonucleotides.

There is an old chestnut in academia (with applications elsewhere as well) about the man "who claimed to have 20 years' experience, but who in fact only had one year's experience 20 times." As one looks at the first half of Table III, one gets the impression that it is about time to break new ground. The first B-DNA structure to break this new ground was a phosphorothioate analogue of G-C-G-C-G-C, with sulfur replacing one oxygen at the R position (extending toward the major groove) on each phosphate group that preceeded a cytosine in the standard 5′-to-3′ chain direction. Its B-helical hexamers stack atop one another in columns through the crystal parallel to the *c* axis (Figure 11 of ref. 1). The length of that axis, 20.64 Å, is just six times the typical base pair rise of 3.44 Å. But because the natural repeat of B-DNA is ten base pairs rather than six, a twist dislocation must occur at every junction between two stacked hexamers.

The "logical" length for stacking B-DNA oligomers would be a decamer, and indeed the recent series of decamer structures listed in Table III all exhibit end-upon-end stacking in the crystal that is an excellent simulation of a continuous helix, even to such matters as twist and roll angles and groove hydration (Figure 1). Three of these new B structures, C-C-A-A-G-A-T-T-G-G, C-C-A-A-C-G-T-T-G-G, and C-C-A-G-G-C-C-T-G-G, constitute a new isomorphous set in space group C2, with 5 base pairs or half the double helix as the asymmetric unit. But the fourth helix, C-G-A-T-C-G-A-T-C-G, is independent. It adopts the same $P2_12_12_1$ symmetry as the 22 members of the Drew set, but is quite distinct from them in structure and crystal packing, and has an asymmetric unit of 10 base pairs.

A few words about evaluating DNA x-ray structure analyses may be useful to the noncrystallographic reader. The significance of isomorphous sets of structures, sharing common space group, cell dimensions, and number of base pairs per asymmetric unit, has already been discussed. The number of crystallographically unique base pairs is a convenient rough measure of the information content of the results; a decamer with 10 unique base pairs obviously will contain twice the structure information of a decamer whose two ends are related by a twofold axis. The number of intensity data, conversely, is the best measure of the information going into a structure analysis. The ratio of *number of data per base pair determined* is an excellent measure of how much we actually know about each base pair. For example, the Drew 16 K dodecamer used 1051 two-sigma F_o's to determine 12 independent base pairs, or 88 reflections per base pair. The GA decamer used 4016 two-sigma F_o's to determine 5 independent base pairs, or 803 reflections per base pair. The higher quality of the GA decamer map is obvious if one compares figure 1 of ref. T57 with Figure 2 of ref. T14.

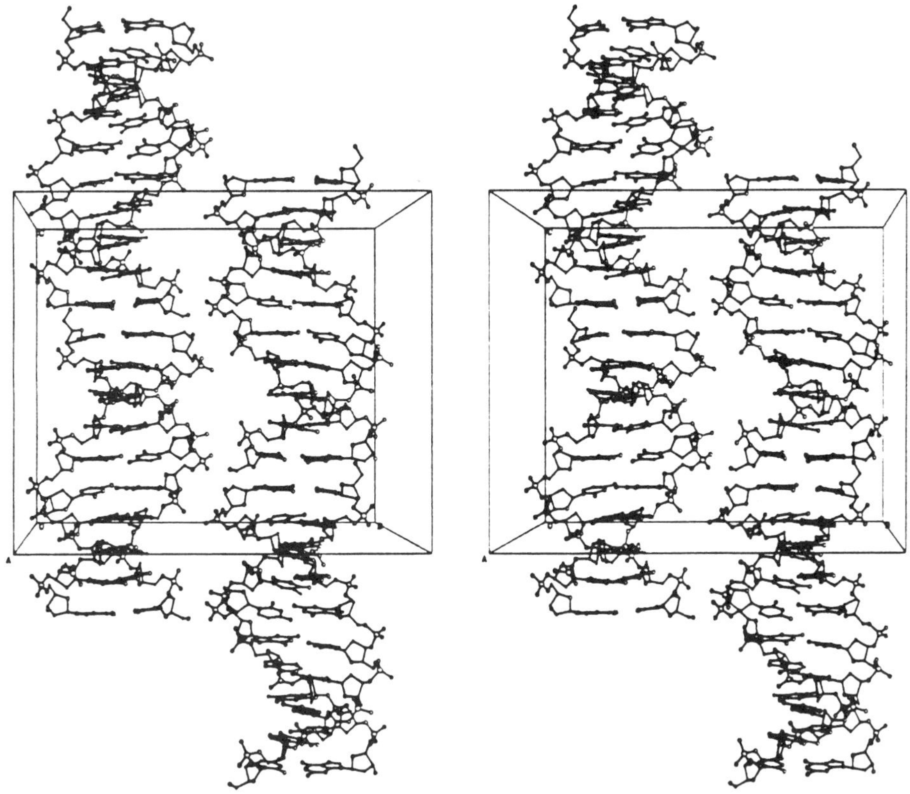

Figure 1: Packingof double helical decamer molecules of C-G-A-T-C-G-A-T-C-G in the orthorhombic unit cell. Successive helices are stacked atop one another along the (vertical) *c* axis, whose length of 33.19 Å is just ten times the typical rise per base pair. The step between helices, which has no connecting phosphates, is in no way distinguished from other internal helix steps. This emphasizes the importance of base pair stacking in determining helix structure. Two adjacent columns of helices are packed with wide groove against narrow groove, and narrow against wide, meaning that the two columns would be related by a simple horizontal translation if they were continuous and if all base pairs were alike. But the continuity of the columns is interrupted by removal of every tenth phosphate group. Note that the closest lateral contacts between columns occur where a backbone phosphate from one column approaches a gap between molecules in the neighboring column, thus minimizing charge-charge repulsion of phosphates. This requires a 5 base pair stagger between helices in the two columns, and generates the observed 2_1 screw axes of symmetry.

The ratio of number of x-ray intensities or reflections per water molecule located also is a good rough assessment of the degree of conservatism of the water search. The two Hoechst 33258 complexes with the Drew dodecamer had only 9 and 16 measured intensities F_0 for every water molecule reported, which is pushing the limit. In contrast, the C-G-C-A-A-A-A-A-A-G-C-G dodecamer and the DAPI complex with the Drew sequence had as many as 74 and 97 reflections per water molecule located, which perhaps verges on the overly conservative.

Table V
Single Crystal X-Ray Structure Analyses of Synthetic Oligonucleotides with Irregular Helices

Sequence	Temp.	Unit Cell Dimensions a	b	c	Unique Base Pairs	Volume/ Base Pair (Å^3)	Resolution, d
pATAT ($P2_1$)	?	21.12	21.29	8.77	2	986	1.0
CGTACG/Daunomycin ($P4_12_12$)	?	27.92	27.92	52.89	3	1718	1.5
CGATCG/Daunomycin ($P4_12_12$)	4°C	27.98	27.98	52.87	3	1724	1.5
CGATCG/Daunomycin ($P4_12_12$)	15°C	28.11	28.11	53.08	3	1748	1.5
CGATCG/Adriamycin ($P4_12_12$)	15°C	28.21	28.21	53.19	3	1764	1.7
CGTACG/Triostin A (F222)	−16°C	31.35	62.38	61.26	3	2496	1.67
CGTACG/Echinomycin (F222)	10°C	30.71	62.56	61.70	3	2470	1.8
GCGTACGC/Trios. A ($P6_322$)	15°C	40.9	40.9	80.7	4	2436	2.25

The sigma level cutoff indicates how much of the observed data the investigator elected to use in refinement. A 0-sigma cutoff means that every reflection was used; a 2-sigma cutoff indicates that all data that measured below twice the standard error threshold were eliminated. Obviously the more data one rejects, the lower the residual error or R factor can be made to fall, to a limit of zero when the number of data remaining is as small as the number of parameters being refined. For example, the GA decamer refined to 17.8% for the 5072 1-sigma data, and down to 16.4% for the 4016 data above 2-sigma. R factor comparisons are only meaningful for refinements at the *same* sigma level. A 2-sigma cutoff is most widely used, with 3-sigma cutoff as an alternative. Higher sigma cutoff levels mean that one has had to discard more and more of the medium intensity reflections, and may indicate serious trouble with the data set.

The penultimate two columns in Tables II through IV indicate whether either the observed x-ray data (the measured F_o's) or the results (the atomic coordinates) have been made available to the general scientific public, usually by deposition with the Brookhaven Protein Data Bank. Serial numbers are identification codes in the Brookhaven Data files. "Paper" means that the coordinates were printed in the journal.

The "Drew" Dodecamer

For the first eight years, the isomorphous set of Drew variants constituted our entire knowledge of crystalline B-DNA structures. Several important conclusions about B-DNA were drawn from these, but the more recent hexamer and decamer studies have required modifications in these conclusions. Figure 2 shows the original Drew dodecamer, C-G-C-G-A-A-T-T-C-G-C-G, and illustrates some of its most characteristic features:

1. Groove Width. The minor groove is narrower in the A-A-T-T center of the double helix than in the C-G-C-G ends.

Table IV
continued

R	Sigma Level	No. Data	No. Solvent	Research Group	Public. Date	Deposited in Public Domain? Data	Coords.	Refs.
15.2%	1.5	2717	43	Camb/Weiz	1978	No	No	1,18
20%	2	2108	40	MIT	1980	No	No	5
25%	5(!)	1845	40	Cambridge	1989	No	No	80
17.5%	2	----	47	MIT	1989	No	No	75
17.7%	2	----	53	MIT	1989	No	No	75
18%	1	2995	135	MIT	1984	No	No	25,36
19.9%	1	2015	88	MIT	1985	No	No	36
20%	1.5	1130	91	MIT	1986	No	No	48,49

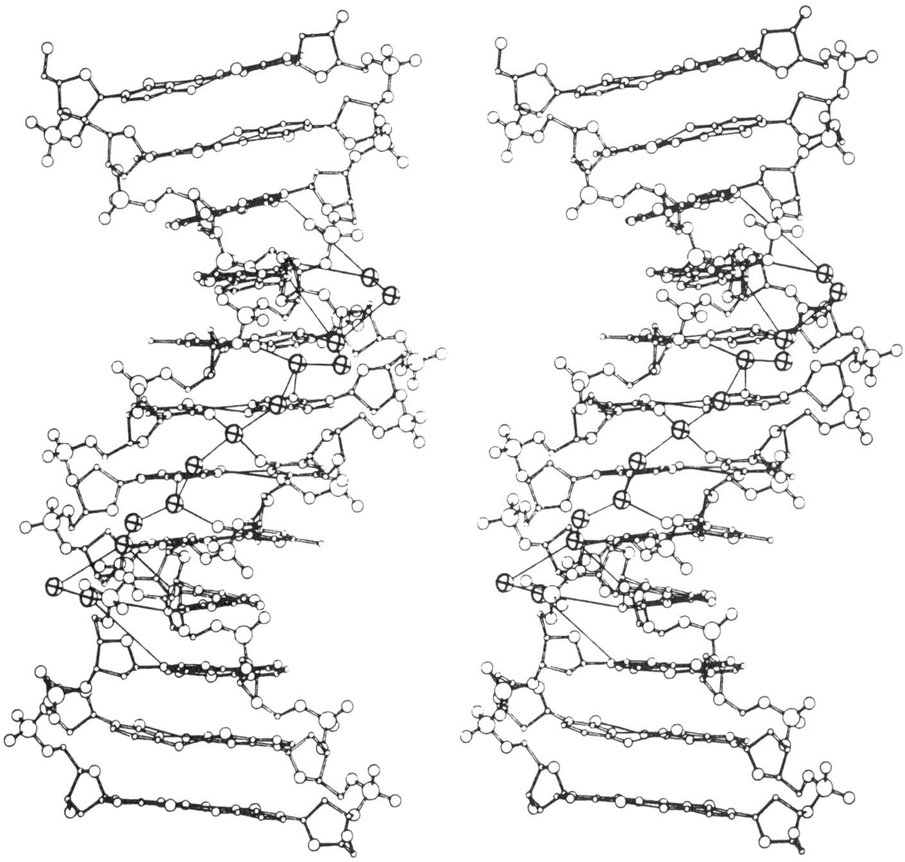

Figure 2: Stereo view of the structure of the Drew dodecamer of sequence C-G-C-G-A-A-T-T-C-G-C-G (T6-T9), showing the spine of water molecules (crossed spheres) down the narrow minor groove in a region of large propeller twist, and the bend to the left of the top of the molecule.

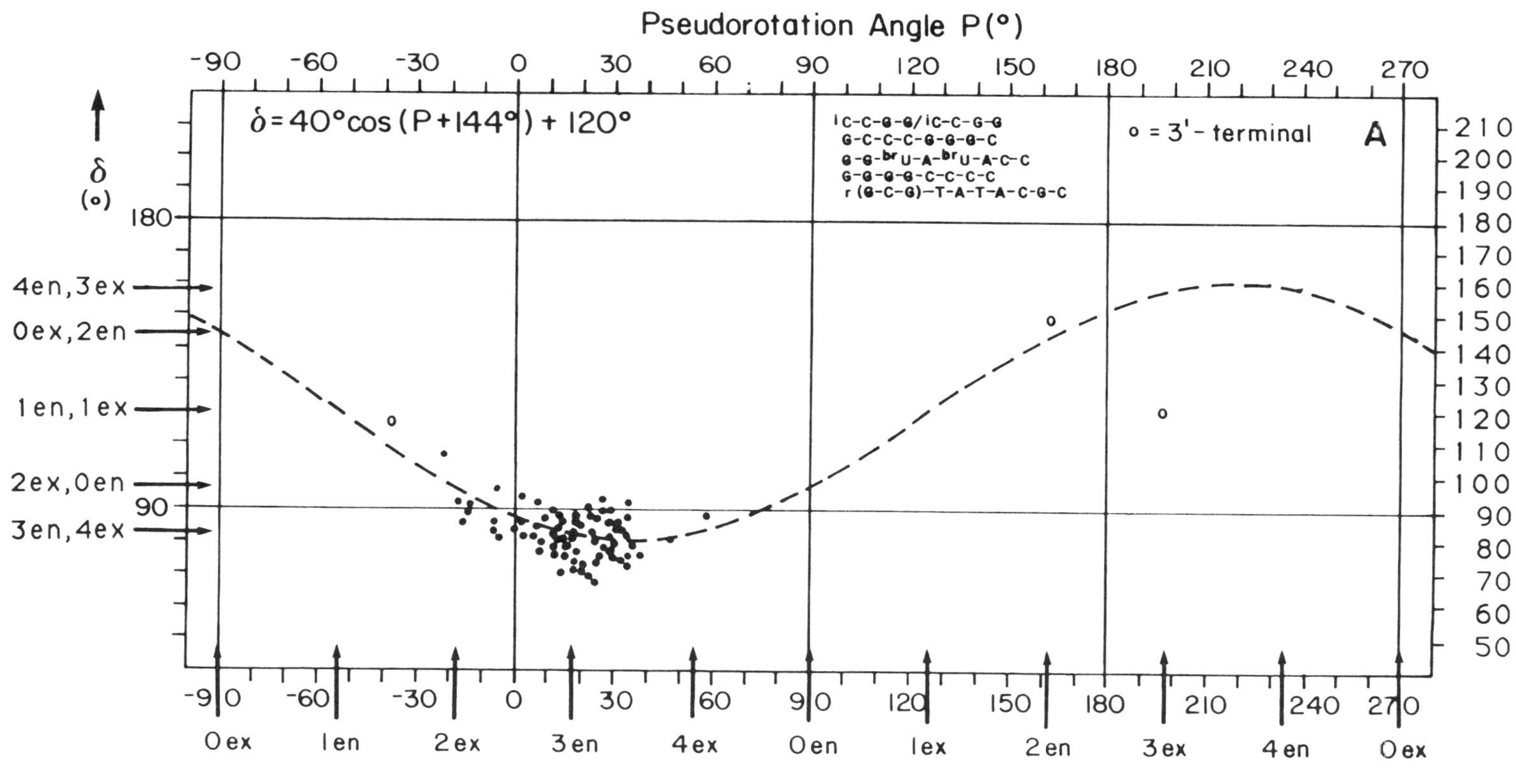

Figure 3: Plot of pseudorotation angle P (2,3) versus main chain torsion angle *delta* (C5′-C4′-C3′-O3′) for five typical A-helical octamers and decamers from Table II. Note the pronounced clustering around a C3′-*endo* sugar conformation, except for the occasional 3′-terminal sugar ring, which is less subject to helical restraints and can relax to the C2′-*endo* domain.

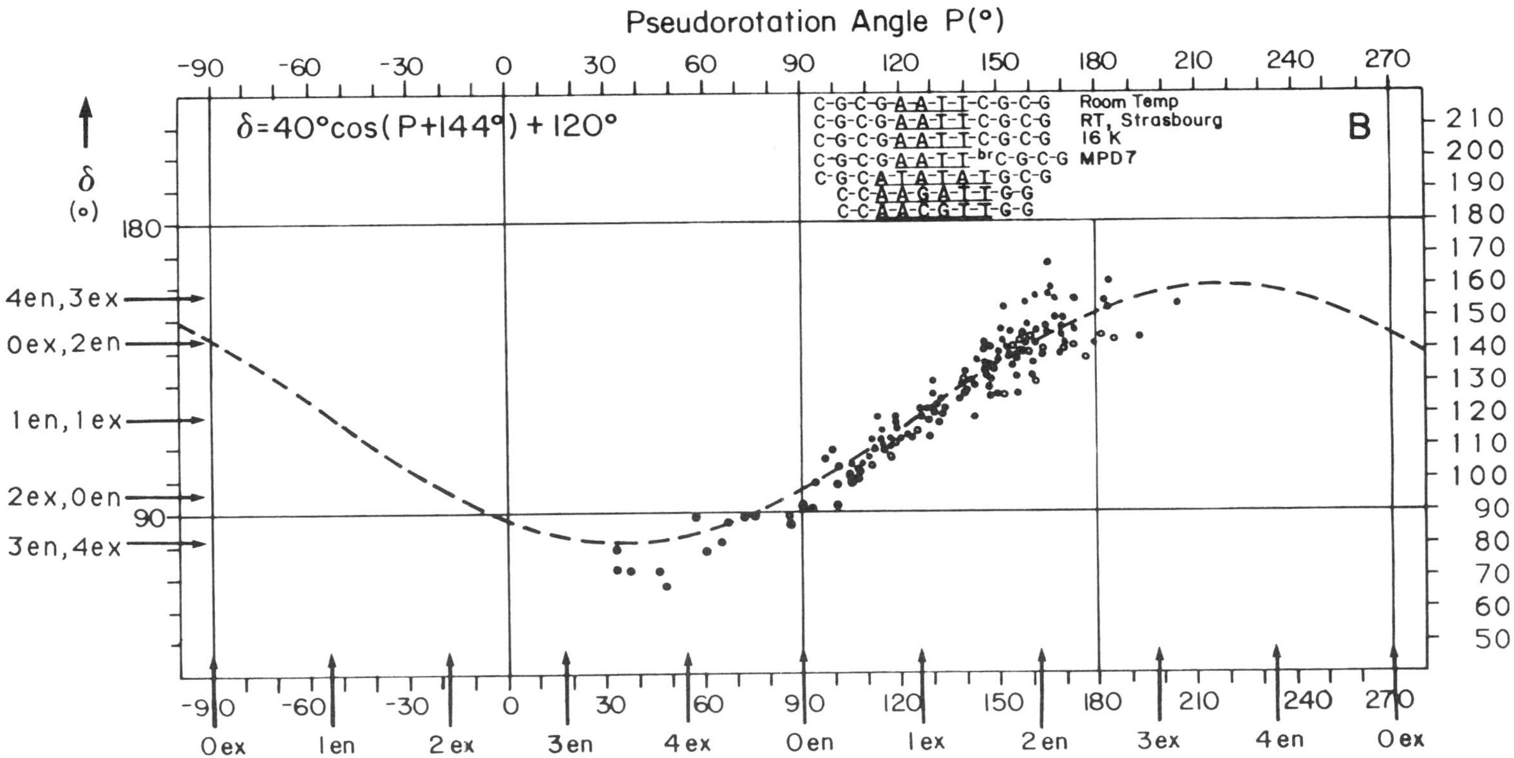

Figure 4: Plot of P vs. *delta* for seven typical B-DNA dodecamers and decamers from Table III. Now the distribution is much less clustered, extending from just short of C3′-*exo*, to the left nearly to C3′-*endo*. Conformations outside the range from C3′-*exo* at right to C2′-*exo* at left are not expected on theoretical grounds for A, B or Z helices because of the high energies involved, and indeed are never encountered in well-refined crystal structures.

2. Minor Groove Hydration. A zig-zag *spine of hydration* fills the narrow A-A-T-T region of the minor groove. Water molecules in a first hydration shell make diagonal connections between O2 atoms of thymines and N3 atoms of adenines via hydrogen bonds. These first shell waters are themselves connected into a continuous zig-zag chain by second shell waters. The spine breaks up and disappears in the wider C-G-C-G regions.

Both the groove width and spine of hydration must be regarded with caution in the light of known intermolecular packing forces. Overlap of ends of the helix could be responsible both for the wider minor groove at the ends, and for disappearance of the spine of hydration. It could be that the normal pattern for all B-DNA in isolation is of a narrow minor groove filled by the water spine. This conclusion indeed held sway in the early days of the Drew dodecamer analysis, but had to be modified later.

3. Propeller Twist. Base pairs in the central A-A-T-T region have distinctly larger propeller twists than in the flanking C-G-C-G ends, typically 15° or greater, rather than 0° to 10°. One reason for this could be that propeller twisting greatly increases stacking of bases along each strand of the double helix, and that the two hydrogen bonds in A-T pairs are less restrictive of propeller rotation than are the three H-bonds of G-C pairs.

4. Deoxyribose Ring Conformation. Although sugar pucker tends to favor the C2′-*endo* conformation expected from fiber diffraction studies, the distribution of conformations is much broader than in crystal structures of A and Z-DNA, extending down into the C1′-*exo* and O4′-*endo* range. Figure 3 gives the distribution of pseudorotation angle P and main chain torsion angle *delta* (C5′-C4′-C3′-O3′) for several A-helical crystal structures, and Figure 4 provides the equivalent plot for B-helical dodecamers and decamers. The difference in clustering of points is striking.

5. Helix Bending. The C-G-C-G-A-A-T-T-C-G-C-G helix exhibits a distinct *bend* at its upper end in Figure 2, localized at the junction between the C-G-C-G end and the A-A-T-T center. The bend is a result purely of rolling of one base pair atop the next along their long axes, with no tilt component that would involving separating the base pairs at one end. The roll bend is in the direction that compresses the wide major groove.

A comparable bend is not found at the other end of the helix, demonstrating that the bend is permitted but not required. The two ends of the helix are sequentially and chemically identical, but occupy different crystal environments. As Figure 9 of reference 1 illustrates, asymmetry of local crystal environment is almost inevitable in this space group, in the interest of more efficient side-to-side contacts between molecules. Hence the crystal structure analysis provides two separate "experiments" to show how this particular sequence responds to different local stresses. The answer is that the junction between GC and AT regions is a *flexible hinge* capable of adopting more than one conformation.

Intermolecular interactions and crystal packing forces therefore can be both a hindrance (as with groove width and hydration) and a source of new information (as with bending). But the role of such forces must always be kept in mind.

6. Twist and Roll Variations. Considerable local variations are observed in the Drew dodecamer in the helical twist angle and in the roll angle between successive base pairs. Twist varies between 28° and 41°, although with an average of 35.9° that is almost precisely that expected for B-DNA from fiber diffraction. Roll varies between +7° (opening of roll angle toward the minor groove) and −10° (opening toward the major groove). Y-R steps (Y = pyrimidine; R = purine) tend to have positive roll angles, and R-Y roll angles tend to be negative. Calladine (5) attempted to explain the observed twist and roll behavior in terms of the steric clash of purine rings across the helix at successive base pairs, and Dickerson (6) quantified these principles and found that they explained successfully all of the then known crystal structures, as listed in Table I. But later structure results violated "Calladine's rules", which are now perceived to be incomplete and to neglect other factors that are important in determining sequence-structure relationships. A new and expanded set of "Calladine's rules" has not been found, but the search for principles governing twist and roll behavior continues.

Table VI

Summary Comparison of Properties of B-DNA Helices

Nucleotide Sequence	I.D. Code	Resolution (A)	Minor Groove Width	Mean Propeller Twist	Minor Groove Hydration	Helix Bend at / (if present)
CGCGAATTCGCG	HD	1.9	W N W	L H L	b S b	Bent, CGCG/AATTCGCG
CGCAAATTTGCG	MC	2.2	W N W	L H L	b u b	Bent, CGC/AAATTTGCG
CGCAAAAAAGCG	HN	2.5	W N W	L H L	b u b	Bent, CGC/AAAAAAGCG
CGCAAAAATGCG	AD	2.6	W N W	L H L	b u b	Bent, CGC/AAAAATGCG
CGCGAATTbrCGCG	MK	2.3	W N W	L H L	b S b	Straight
CGCATATATGCG	CY	2.2	W N W	I	b u b	Bent, CGC/ATATATGCG
CGCGATATCGCG	ZS	2.2	W N W	L I L	b S b	Bent, CGCG/ATATCGCG
GpsCGpsCGpsC	WC	2.2	W	L	R	Straight
CCAAGATTGG	GA	1.3	I W W W I	L H L	R	Straight
CCAACGTTGG	CG	1.4	W W N W W	L I L	R S R	Straight
CGATCGATCG	KK	1.8	W N W N W	L I L	S R S	Straight
CCAGGCCTGG	UH	1.6	I W I W I	L (I) L	R S R	Straight

W = wide minor groove (> 12 Å)
I = intermediate minor groove
N = narrow minor groove (< 10 Å)

H = high propeller twist (> 15°)
I = intermediate propeller twist
L = low propeller twist (< 10°)

S = central spine of hydration
R = two ribbons along groove walls
d = hydration irregular or disordered
b = groove blocked, no information
u = hydration state uncertain because of lack of resolution

Although the helix bend, /, has been positioned between GC and AT base pairs, the bend in practice cannot be localized closer than one or two base pairs.

Identification code usually from initials of first Author: HD = Horace Drew; MC = Miquel Coll; HN = Hillary Nelson; AD = Anna DiGabrieli; MK = Mary Kopka; CY = Chun Yoon; ZS = Zippora Shakked (personal communication); WC = William Cruse; GA, CG = Gilbert Prive; KK = Kazunori Yanagi and Kasimierz Grzeskowiak; UH = Udo Heinemann.

Other Members of the Drew Isomorphous Set

The subsequent 21 analyses in Table III have amplified our knowledge about the B helix, as indicated in Table VI.

1. Groove Width. The Wide-Narrow-Wide pattern of minor groove width in the HD helix (see identification codes in Table VI) persists in all cases, but this cannot be separated absolutely from the issue of intermolecular overlap in the crystal, since all 22 structures have virtually identical crystal environments. The new decamer structures will clarify the groove-width issue.

2. Minor Groove Hydration and Drug Binding. The spine of hydration down the central narrow minor groove is observed in the HD, MK and ZS dodecamers, but lack of resolution prevents definite statements about minor groove hydration in the other examples listed in Table VI. In all cases the minor groove in the outer GC ends is blocked by overlap with neighbors up the 2_1 axis.

The minor groove is the binding site for several antitumor drug molecules that are formed by the linking of flat aromatic rings and/or planar amide groups. Netropsin and distamycin essentially are short oligomers of alternating -CO-NH- amides and five-membered pyrrole rings, with neutral or cationic ends. Netropsin binds within the narrow AT region of the minor groove in the Drew dodecamer by displacing the spine of hydration (Figure 5). The three amide NH groups use bifurcated hydrogen bonds to bridge exactly the same adenine N3 and thymine O2 atoms that were connected by waters in the first hydration shell. The size of the binding site is dictated by the length of the netropsin molecule. The observed specificity for regions of AT base pairs probably comes from a combination of (a) The absence of a blocking C2 amine group on the bottom of the groove with adenines, as contrasted with guanines, (b) The inherently narrower minor groove for AT regions by comparison with GC (about which more later), permitting better hydrophobic packing interactions, and (c) the deeper negative electrostatic potential at the bottom of the minor groove in AT regions compared with GC (7), again probably a consequence of the absence of the more electropositive -NH_2 groups. The gain of entropy resulting from the dispersal of water atoms of the spine of hydration certainly contributes to the free energy of binding, and may play a role in AT specificity as well. The binding of netropsin serves as a paradigm for the binding of many other drug molecules of similar general structure, including distamycin, Hoechst 33258, DAPI and berenil (see Table III). Even intercalating drugs that have nonplanar components such as sugar molecules tend to fit these nonplanar elements within the minor groove of the double helix (see Table V).

3. Propeller Twist. Propeller twist remains high in AT regions of all of those dodecamers that have runs of two or more successive adenines. The investigators of the MC and HN dodecamers propose that this large propeller twist is stabilized by inter-basepair hydrogen bonds in the major groove, connecting an adenine N6 with an O4 from the thymine that is paired with the next adenine down the chain. One such H bond can be formed at each A-A step along the sequence, and as Figure 6 demonstrates, five

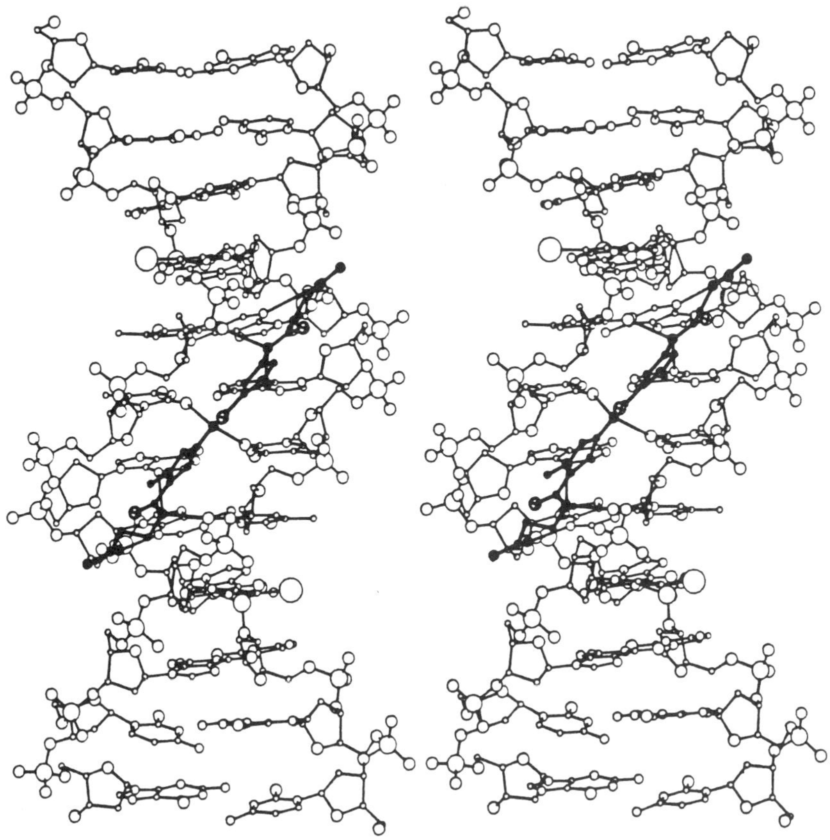

Figure 5: Structure of the complex between the MK dodecamer, C-G-C-G-A-A-T-T-^{br}C-G-C-G, and the antitumor antibiotic *netropsin* (T33, T34). The drug molecule replaces the spine of hydration in the minor groove. Two large spheres are bromine atoms at the C5 ring position of cytosines 9 and 21, whose presence in the major groove induces a straightening of the helix axis.

such bonds are possible for the HN helix, four for the MC, and two for the HD dodecamer. Conversely, the CY dodecamer with its alternation of A and T bases is systematically unable to make a single one of these major groove inter-basepair hydrogen bonds, and it exhibits a smaller propeller twist at AT base pairs. Evidently a large propeller twist is possible at AT pairs, but not mandatory. The HN and MC workers suggest that it is these inter-basepair H-bonds that make poly-A tracts of DNA especially stiff and resistant to bending. Significantly, in every example of a bent dodecamer listed in Table III, the bending occurs at the junction between GC and AT regions, while the central AT region is unbent.

4. Sugar Conformation. Most structure analyses of other B-DNA dodecamers show a slightly lower spread of sugar conformations than in the original Drew refinement. But the trend visible in Figures 3 and 4 persists: B-DNA is inherently more flexible with respect to sugar conformation than is A-DNA. This very suppleness of the B

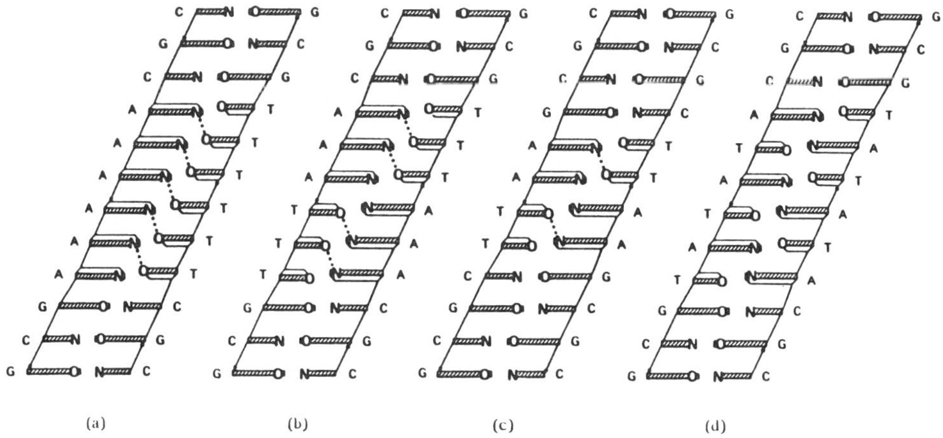

Figure 6: Unrolled major groove ladder diagrams of base pair edges in (a) HN: C-G-C-A-A-A-A-A-A-G-C-G, (b) MC: C-G-C-A-A-A-T-T-T-G-C-G. (c) HD: C-G-C-G-A-A-T-T-C-G-C-G, and (d) CY: C-G-C-A-T-A-T-A-T-G-C-G. A cross-chain hydrogen bond between adenine N6 and thymine O4 is possible at every A-A step along the sequence: 5 for HN, 4 for MC, 2 for HD and none for CY. From reference T69. (See Table VI for helix identification codes.)

helix may be significant in its biological role, by allowing it to respond to sequence variations more easily, in a manner that can be recognized by sequence-specific binding proteins.

5. Helix Bending. It was found in the MK helix that the bend in helix axis could be removed by introducing a bulky bromine atom into the major groove at the 5 position of cytosine 9 in each strand (Figure 5). This produces minor adjustments of intermolecular contacts, and with the Drew sequence leads to a straight helix, reinforcing the idea that the GC/AT junction in this sequence is indeed a flexible hinge rather than a static kink.

Both the HN and AD duplexes have the special property of being non-selfcomplementary, with two strands of different sequence:

HN: C-G-C-A-A-A-A-A-A-G-C-G and C-G-C-T-T-T-T-T-T-G-C-G

AD: C-G-C-A-A-A-A-A-T-G-C-G and C-G-C-A-T-T-T-T-T*-G-C-G

DiGabrieli *et al.* also substituted 5-bromouracil for T* at the ninth position in the second strand, corresponding to the Br position in the MK helix. They then crystallized the duplex and looked for bromine positions. To their surprise, they found two half-bromine sites at the two ends of the helix, rather than a single full-weight bromine. This indicates end-for-end disorder of molecules within the crystal, or an equal distribution of "up" and "down" orientations. Since the bend in helix axis is observed to occur only at one end of the helix in the crystal, this establishes that the bend must be purely a crystal packing effect, and that it can occur with equal facility at the A9-G10 step of strand 1 or the T21-G22 step of strand 2 (which corresponds to the C3-A4 step of strand 1). Note that in this case, the added single bromine did not induce a straightening of helix axis as with the MK helix. Hence the hinges between GC and AT regions at both ends of the AD helix are equally flexible, and whether a hinge is bent or not depends on local crystal conditions. This of necessity is also the case in all of the self-complementary dodecamers where the two hinges are chemically identical, and might be expected in the HN helix as well.

6. *Twist and Roll Variation.* The new members of the Drew isomorphous set often fail to follow the simple Calladine's rules for twist and roll behavior (4,5). There remains a tendency for twist angle to be especially low at C-G and at A-T steps, and for roll to be positive at Y-R steps and negative at R-Y steps. But these are only trends, with specific exceptions known.

One striking and characteristic feature of the CY helix with its alternating -A-T-A-T-A-T- center was actually predicted a decade earlier: the alternating of twist angles, low at A-T steps and high at T-A. Figure 7 shows these five base pair steps, and illustrates how extensive the base overlap is in the A-T pairs and how deficient it is for the T-A pairs. Klug *et al.* (8) predicted this alternation of twist when they proposed an "alternating-B" model for poly(dA-dT) · poly(dA-dT), based on the crystal structure of pA-T-A-T (T1), a tetramer with a 5′ phosphate. Their interpretation was that the inherently better A-T stacking was reinforced at the expense of T-A stacking, which is poorer even in a perfectly regular 36° helix. The alternation of roll angles found in earlier decamers (and also implicit in the coordinates of the alternating-B model)--positive at Y-R steps and negative at R-Y steps--persists in the CY alternating-AT helix.

The Phosphorothioate Hexamer

One would conclude from the foregoing isomorphous set of structures that the narrowing of the minor groove was a property of tracts of AT base pairs, while the groove in GC regions retained a width that was more similar to that obtained for idealized B-DNA from fiber diffraction studies. This was confirmed by the first truly new departure in B-DNA structure in eight years, the phosphorothioate hexamer: GpsC-GpsC-GpsC. The minor groove is wide throughout its length, and base pairs have low propeller twist. One feature of minor significance in the dodecamers assumes prominence in the new hexamer: B_I versus B_{II} phosphate conformation (Figure 8). In the B_I conformation, torsion angle *epsilon* (C4′-C3′-O3′-P) is *trans*, while torsion angle *zeta* (C3′-O3′-P-O5′) is *gauche*$^-$. The elbow angle formed by C3′-O3′-P lies nearly flat on the cylindrical surface of the helix. In contrast, in the B_{II} conformation the two torsion angle domains are reversed, and the O3′ atom points inward toward the helix axis. This pushes the P atom out away from the helix axis slightly, and turns the phosphate so the O1-P-O2 plane is nearly vertical and the O3′-P-O5′ plane is nearly horizontal. One consequence is an opening-out of helix rotation at that step and a tendency toward destacking of the two bases at that end of the base pair. Another consequence, as we shall see with the decamers, is a widening of the minor groove.

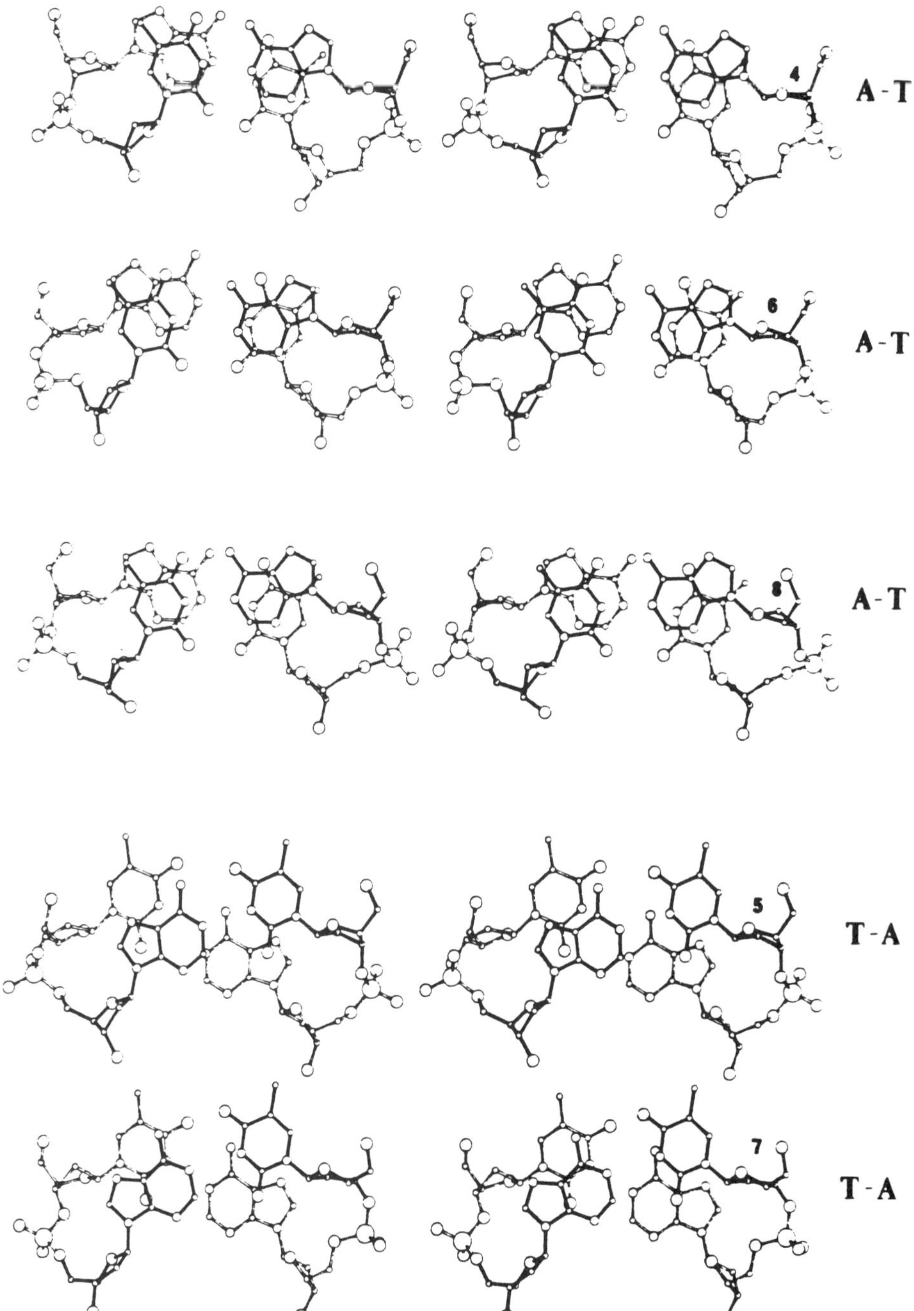

Figure 7: Stacking of two successive base pairs at A-T and T-A steps of the CY helix, of sequence: C-G-C-A-T-A-T-A-T-G-C-C. Overlap of bases is much greater for A-T than for T-A, because the helical twist angle is smaller. Twist angles at the steps displayed are, from top to bottom: A4-T21, 32°; A6-T19, 29°, A8-T17, 34°; T5-A20, 41°; and T7-A18, 42°.

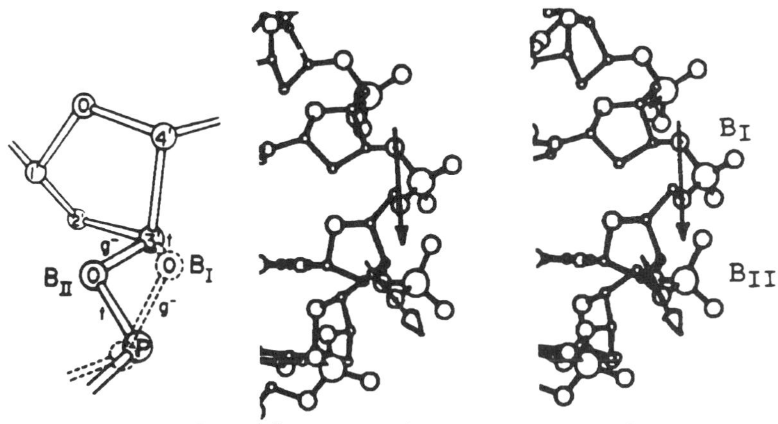

	Epsilon	Zeta	Ep-Ze
B_I	*trans* 180°	*gauche*⁻ 240°	-120°
B_{II}	*gauche*⁻ 240°	*trans* 180°	+120°

Figure 8: B_I vs. B_{II} phosphate conformations. Left: Diagram showing motion of the O3′ atom between conformations. Right: Stereo drawing of phosphates P9-P12 in the HD helix, with B_{II} conformation at P11. In the more common B_I phosphate conformation, the angle formed by C3′-O3′-P lies roughly in the cylindrical surface of the helix, whereas in the B_{II} conformation it points inward toward the helix axis. As a consequence the vector between phosphate atoms O3′ and O5′ (arrows) lies more nearly in the plane of the base pairs in B_{II}, rather than along the direction of the main chain. The phosphate group in B_{II} is rotated out slightly farther from the helix axis. Torsion angle difference *epsilon - zeta* is a useful analytical marker of the two phosphate conformations.

The B_{II} conformation is in a decided minority in the isomorphous set of dodecamer structures, occurring consistently at positions P11 and P23 on the two strands and only occasionally at the phosphate nearest the 5′ end of each chain. P11 and P23 occur at G-C steps in all of the dodecamers, but the G-C step at the other end of the helix is never B_{II}. Nor does crystal packing suggest a reason for the altered conformations at P11 and P23 (1).

In the phosphorothioate hexamer, B_I and B_{II} phosphate conformations alternate along each strand and also across the helix; no two phosphates at the same base pair step adopt the B_{II} conformation. In the schematic below, B_{II} phosphates are in bold face:

		P2		**P3**		P4		**P5**		P6	
Strand 1	5'-G1		C2		G3		C4		G5		C6-3'
	|		|		|		|		|		|
Strand 2	3'-C12		G11		C10		G9		C8		G7-5'
		P12		P11		**P10**		P9		P8	

It is interesting to note that in this setting the two phosphate conformations fail to correlate with base sequence. Their behavior is precisely reversed in the two chains, with B_{II} at C-G steps in strand 1 and at G-C steps in strand 2. But there may be a correlation with crystal packing, as noted in reference 1.

The destacking of bases at B_{II} phosphates is shown dramatically in figure 5 of ref. T42. Because of the asymmetry of phosphate conformations in the two chains, pyrimidines consistently are well-stacked 3′ to purines in strand 1, whereas purines stack well on the 3′ side of pyrimidines in strand 2. Hence phosphate conformation with GC base pairs cannot be a rigidly sequence-determined phenomenon, but can only be a tendency, subject to local variations. The intrinsic B_I vs. B_{II} tendencies at both G-C and C-G steps must be roughly the same.

Hydration of the minor groove in the phosphorothioate hexamer illustrates a new and important principle, but the discussion will be deferred until consideration of the C-C-A-A-G-A-T-T-G-G decamer since it was first noticed in that structure.

The Decamer Story

A. C-C-A-A-G-A-T-T-G-G

The stacked decamers comprise a set of related structures, remarkable both for the fidelity with which they simulate infinite B helices through the crystal (Table VII), and their high resolution: 1.8 Å to 1.3 Å. Of course these two effects are related; it is the precise ordering of molecules in the crystal lattice that permits collection of such high-resolution data. The precision of analysis of these decamers surpasses that of any of the previous B structures.

The GA decamer, C-C-A-A-G-A-T-T-G-G, is shown in Figure 9. Because the double helix sits on a twofold axis in the crystal, the asymmetric unit contains only five base pairs or half the helix. The minor groove is wide down its entire length, but this is expected in view of the introduction of two purine-purine G-A mispairs in the center. These two mispairs have an unusually large propeller twist, in part because of inter-basepair hydrogen bonds in the *minor* groove between the N2 of guanine and the O2 of thymine on the next base pair out toward the end of the helix. This high 24° propeller twist in base pair G5-A16 and the linking minor groove H bond induce a 17° propeller in the adjacent A4-T17, but propeller twist for the other three base pairs toward each end of the helix is small.

Table VII
"Helix" Parameters Across Unconnected Steps in Stacked Decamers in the Crystal

	Sequence	Twist	Rise	Roll	Slide
GA:	C-C-A-A-G-A-T-T-G-G	41.6°	2.90 Å	+3.3°	+0.02 Å
CG:	C-C-A-A-C-G-T-T-G-G	40.4°	3.17 Å	+2.9°	−0.03 Å
KK:	C-G-A-T-C-G-A-T-C-G	24.9°	3.91 Å	−1.0°	+0.03 Å
UH:	C-C-A-G-G-C-C-T-G-G	40.1°	2.95 Å	+3.7°	−0.16 Å

Slide is relative displacement along the long axis of the base pairs.

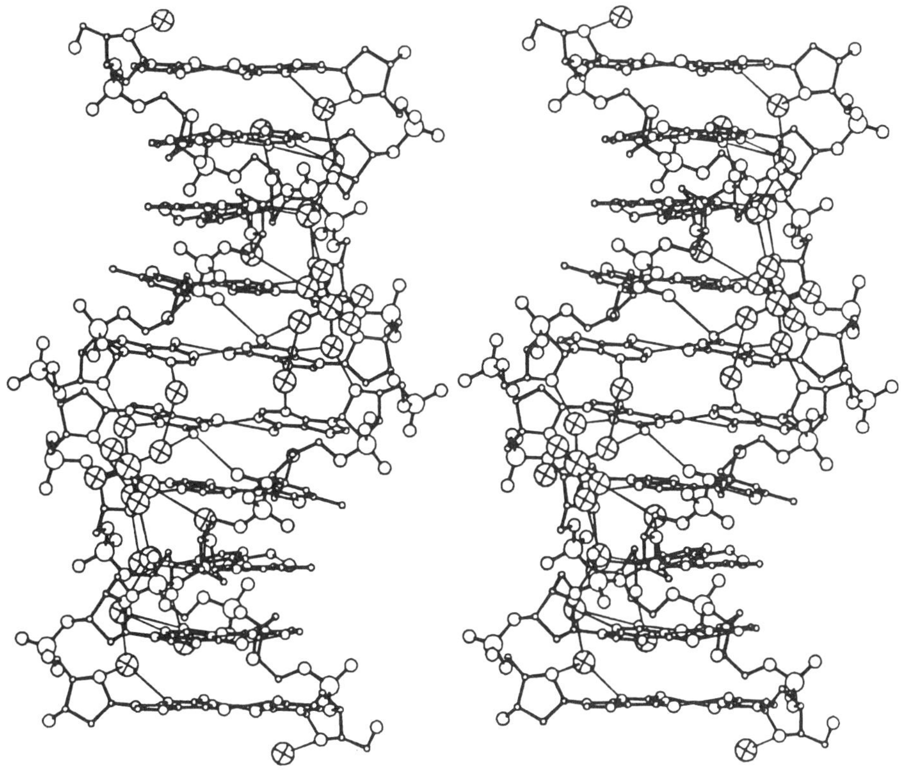

Figure 9: Structure of the GA decamer, C-C-A-A-G-A-T-T-G-G. Crossed spheres in the minor groove are water molecules or hydrated magnesium ions (two octahedral clusters). Hydrogen bonds involving bases, sugar O4′ atoms and water molecules are drawn as thin solid lines.

The GA decamer exhibits an important new pattern of minor groove hydration that appears to be typical of wide grooves. As Figure 9 shows, the central region of the minor groove around the two GA mispairs is occupied by two octahedral $Mg(H_2O)_6^{2+}$ ions, with hydrogen bonds from magnesium waters to adenine N3, guanine N2 and N3, sugar O4′ and to other waters. But toward both ends of the helix, two ribbons of waters run along the two walls of the wide minor groove, forming local bridges between purine N3 or pyrimidine O2, and the next sugar O4′ atom in the 5′-to-3′ chain direction. These ribbons of hydration are schematized in Figure 10.

Exactly the same pattern of wide groove hydration is present in the phosphorothioate hexamer structure, although this was not realized at first. If the solvation data of Table VII of ref. T42 are represented on an unrolled minor groove plot, the result is Figure 11. All but two of the expected ribbon waters are present.

These wide groove ribbons may be of quite general significance. If one were imagine the two walls of the minor groove in Figure 10 being squeezed together so that pairs of waters such as 21+3, 13+30 and 33+14 are brought into coincidence, then the

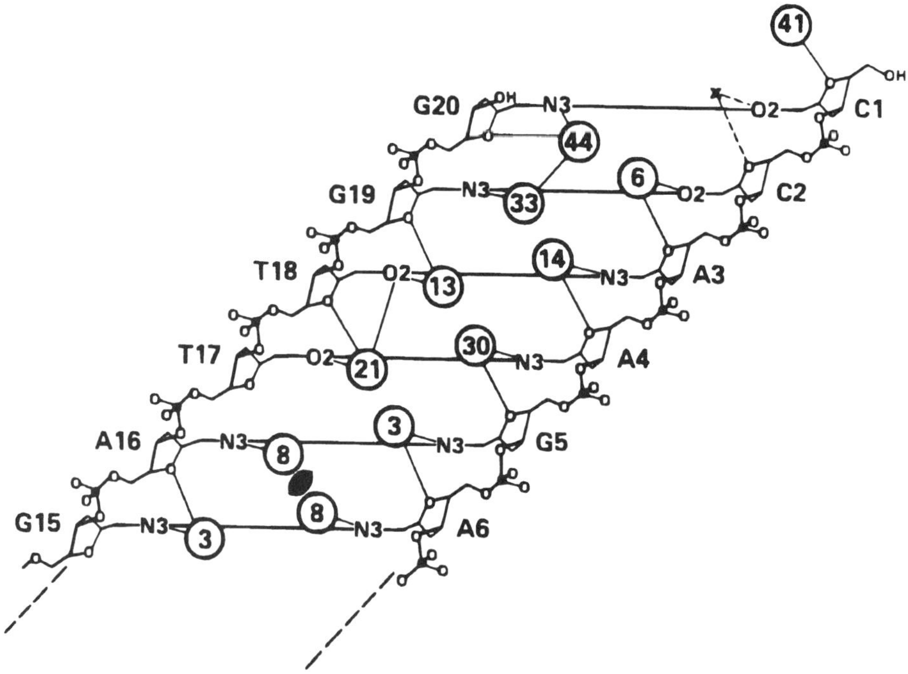

Figure 10: Unrolled minor groove diagram of the GA decamer, showing two ribbons of water molecules (numbered circles) down the walls of the wide groove. Only the top half of the groove is shown; the other half is identical, and is related to this by 180° rotation about the twofold axis indicated between waters no. 8. From ref. T57.

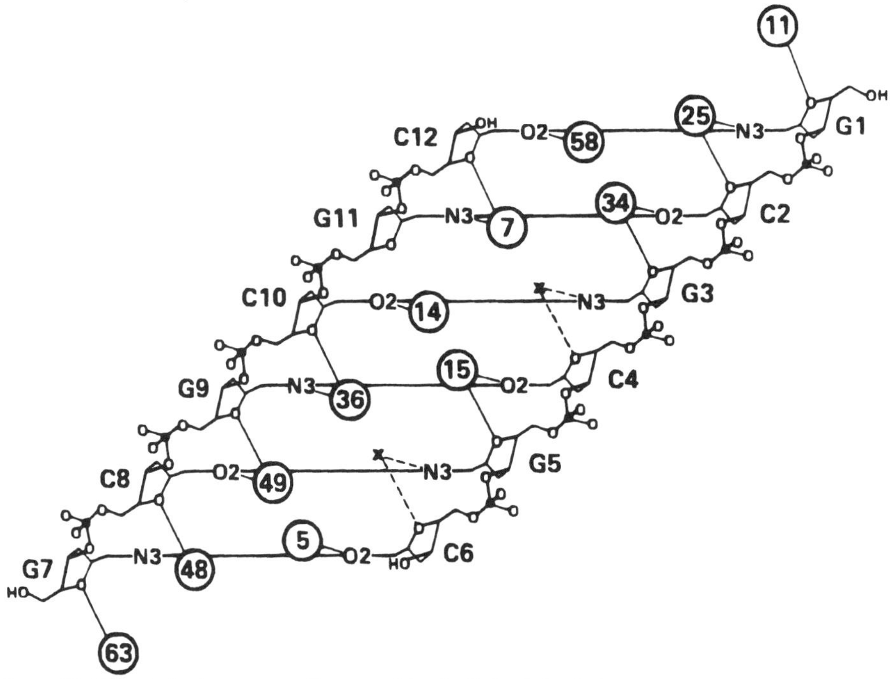

Figure 11: Unrolled minor groove diagram of the GpC-GpC-GpC phosphorothioate hexamer, showing the same two ribbons of hydration along the walls. No waters were reported at two positions marked "x". From ref. T57.

first shell of a spine of hydration would result. Bridging these with second shell waters would complete a normal spine. Both the narrow groove spine and the wide groove ribbons have the same number of waters per base pair: two. Hence one can regard the spine and ribbons as representing two extreme states of a possible continuum of hydration structures, determined by minor groove width.

B. C-C-A-A-C-G-T-T-G-G

The CG decamer (Figure 12) lacks the minor groove inter-basepair hydrogen bonds of the GA decamer, and has a uniformly low propeller twist. In spite of this, the minor groove narrows in the center in a manner reminiscent of the dodecamer family. The water structure in the CG decamer is remarkable: the narrow minor groove in the middle has a quite regular zig-zag spine of hydration like that of the dodecamers, whereas the wide minor grooves toward the ends exhibit two ribbons of water molecules of the type that has just been described for GA and the hexamer. The two modes of minor groove hydration are "coupled" by hydrated magnesium ions, each of which contributes one of its liganded waters to the spine and two other waters as anchors for the ribbons.

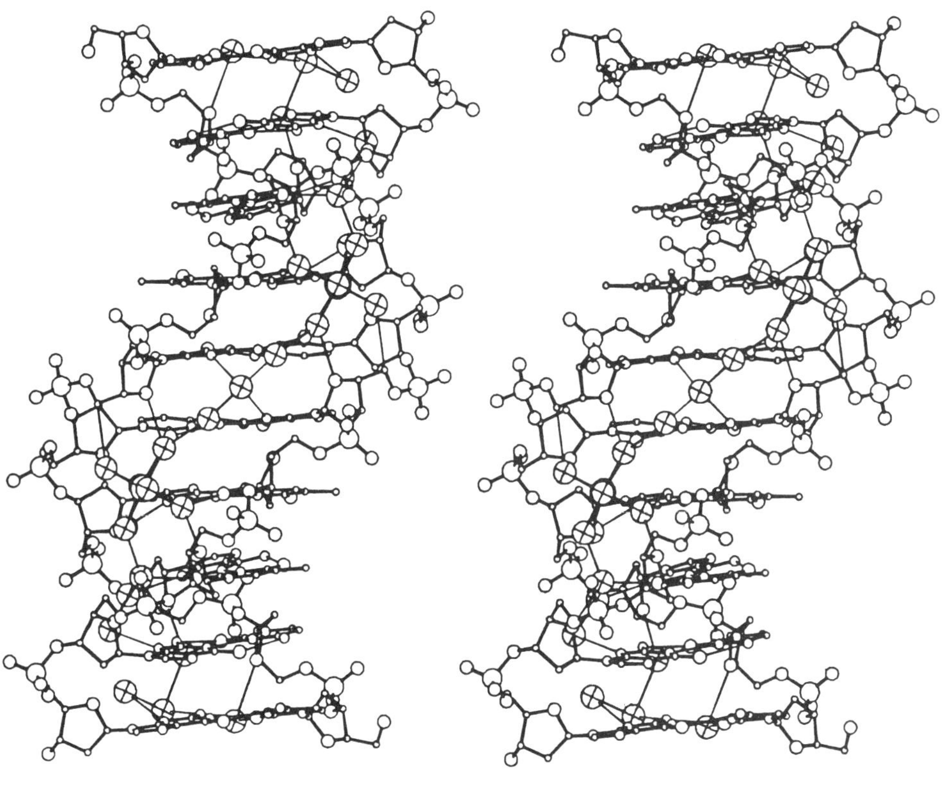

Figure 12: Structure of the CG decamer, C-C-A-A-C-G-T-T-G-G. Crossed spheres are waters or magnesiums as before. Note the spine of hydration down the narrow central region of the minor groove, terminating at the two octahedral $Mg(H_2O)_6^{2+}$ clusters. Hydrogen bonds involving bases, sugar O4′ atoms and water molecules are drawn as thin solid lines, as are a few close contacts between magnesium waters and DNA $-CH_2$-groups.

This CG decamer is significant in emphasizing three structural features of B-DNA:

a. The narrow groove spine and wide groove ribbons of hydration appear to be general properties of B-DNA.

b. High propeller twist is not required for narrowing of the minor groove, as had once been suggested (e.g.; Figure 9 of ref. T15).

c. High propeller twist also is not necessarily required for hydrogen-bond bridging by the first hydration shell of the spine.

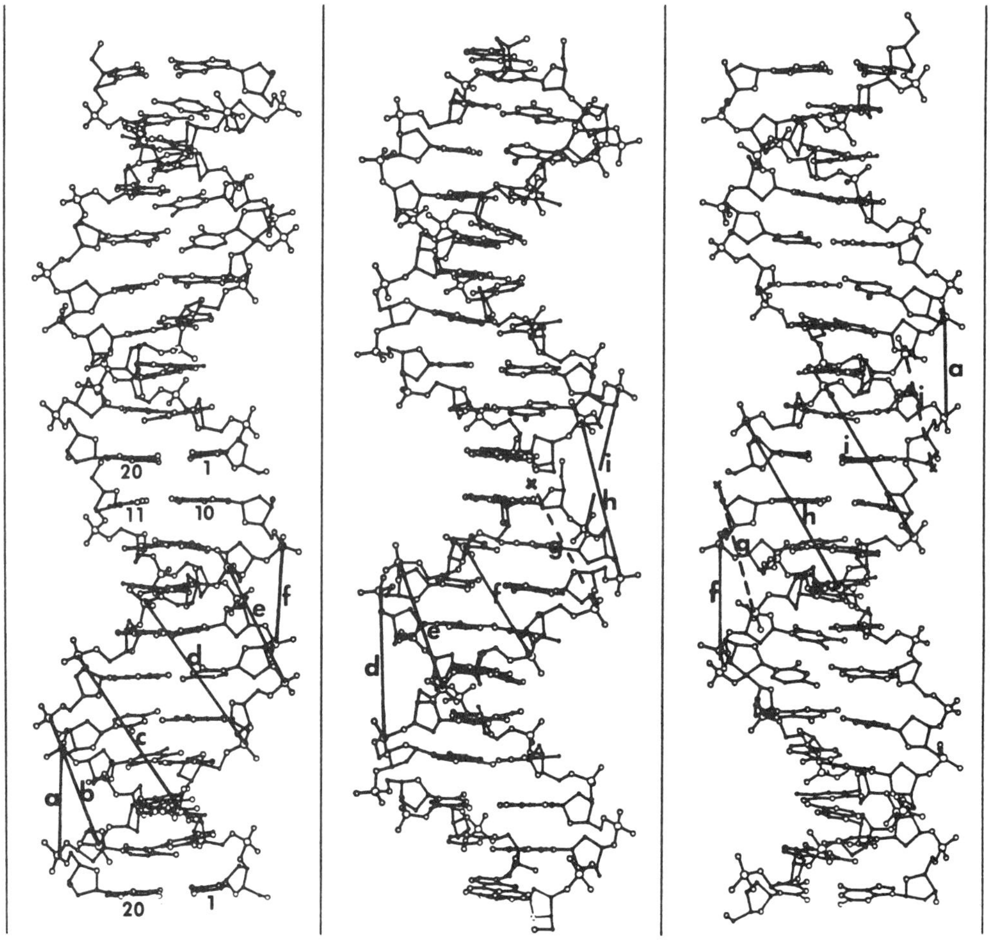

Figure 13: Three view of two KK decamers of sequence: C-A-T-C-G-A-T-C-G stacked atop one another as they are found in the crystal. The left panel is an enlargement of the leftmost column in Figure 1. The shortest P-P distances across the minor groove are drawn as diagonal lines labeled a through j. Distance g and j are dashed because they are only hypothetical, involving the missing phosphates that would connect these two decamers into a continuous helix. Observed P-P distances are plotted in Figure 14.

The important factor in stabilizing the spine of hydration appears to be the narrowness of the groove itself.

C. C-G-A-T-C-G-A-T-C-G

The KK helix carries forward the minor groove width hydration story, and provides new information on the relation of groove width to base sequence. Like the other three decamer structures, its molecules are stacked in the crystal in a manner that simulates a continuous helix, as seen in Figure 13. But unlike the other three decamers, it crystallizes in space group $P2_12_12_1$ with all ten base pairs as the asymmetric unit, thus providing twice as much information about helix geometry.

The minor groove of the KK helix shows surprising oscillations. As seen in Figures 13 and 14, the groove is widest in the CG center of the helix, narrower in the flanking AT zones, and widens again at the ends if one generates the relevant continuous helix. This periodicity of groove width of five base pairs was totally unexpected, and contrasts with the GA and CG helices, which only show local groove narrowing in their centers. It is surprising to realize that minor groove width can vary so rapidly, and that as few as two successive base pairs can exhibit their characteristic "signature".

Hydration in the KK helix continues the spine/ribbon dichotomy. Two rows of water molecules are found in the wide minor groove regions of the helix, coalescing to a single central spine in the narrow regions. Ribbons and spine maintain their integrity even under such rapidly fluctuating conditions.

D. C-C-A-G-G-C-C-T-G-G

The last member of the decamer family, the UH helix, is isomorphous with the GA and CG helices, and like them has five base pairs per asymmetric unit (T77). Its minor groove behavior is the precise opposite of that of KK, although less extreme: somewhat narrow in the center (ca. 5 Å), wider in the flanking regions, and narrow again in the region where P-P vectors such as h and i (Figure 13) bridge two stacked helices. This for the first time calls into question the association of AT regions with narrow minor grooves and GC regions with wide grooves. Why should a G-G-C-C center be narrow? In fact the "narrow" regions of the UH groove still are nearly as wide as that in the fiber-derived B-DNA model; it is the regions between them that are widened. The UH plot resembles that of the GA helix, but with a somewhat greater range of fluctuation. What is causing this widening?

Phosphate Conformation and Minor Groove Widening

A suggestive correlation is found between widening of the minor groove and occurrence of B_{II} phosphates. The B_{II} conformation occurs at P3, P5, P6 and P9 in the GA helix, at P3 and P9 in the GC helix, at P2 and P7 in KK, and at P3, P5 and P9 in UH. As Figure 14 illustrates, the minor groove is widest at those positions (1) where a B_{II} phosphate occurs at a given helix step on one strand, and (2) another is found on the other strand at the next base pair step in the 5′-to-3′ direction. Conversely, the minor

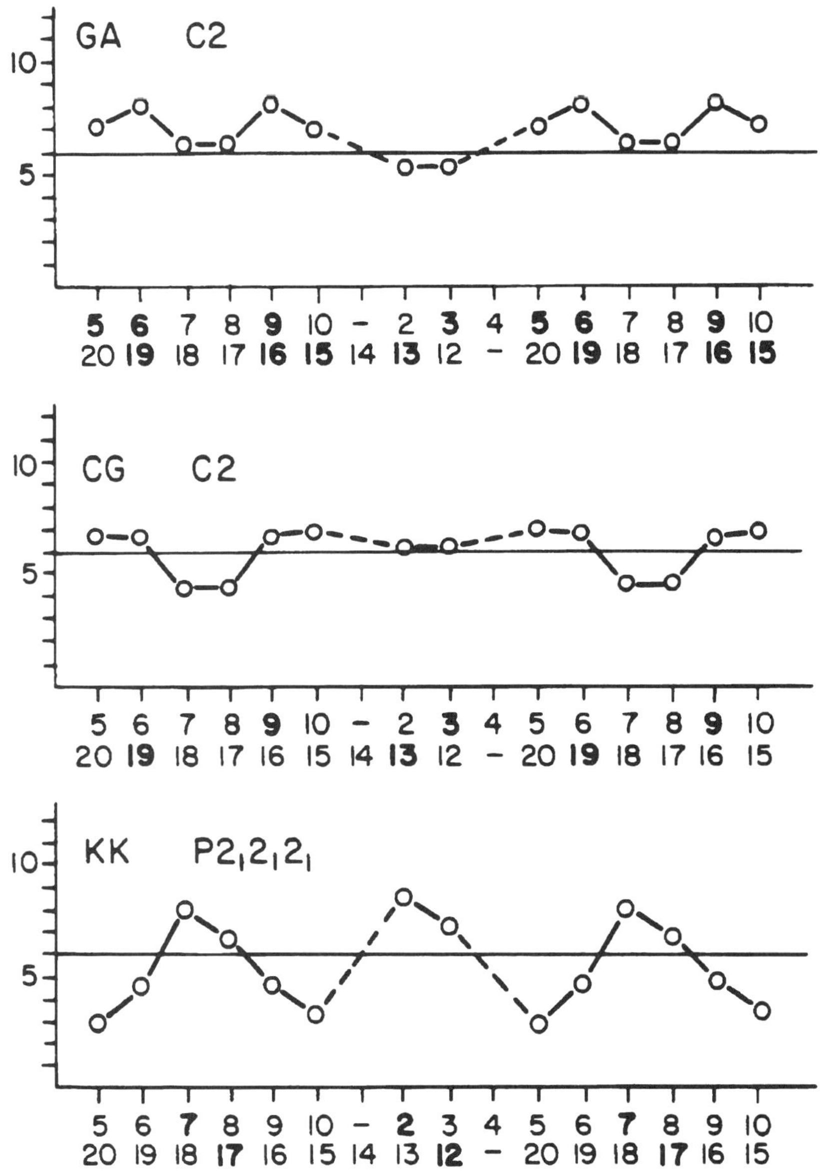

Figure 14: Minor groove width in three decamers: GA, CG and KK, when helices are stacked atop one antoher as observed in the crystal. (See example for KK helix in Figure 13.) Plotted are minimum P-P distances less 5.8 Å, or the effective opening between the walls of the minor groove. Horizontal line is expected groove width from fiber diffraction. Dashed lines bridge regions where phosphates are missing at the junctions between decamer molecules (g and j in Figure 13). Phosphate numbers in strands 1 and 2 are given below each plot, with B_{II} phosphates distinguished by bold face numerals. Note that in each helix the minor groove is widest when B_{II} phosphates occur at two adjacent helix steps in the 5′-proximal positions (e.g.; 5/19 and 9/15 for helix GA, but not 13\3).

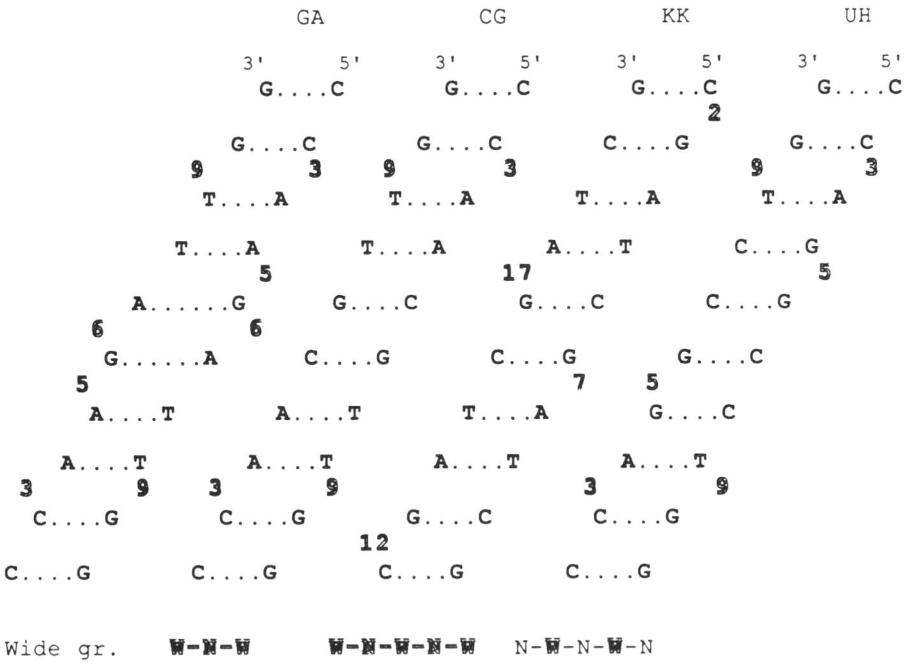

Figure 15: Unrolled minor groove ladder diagrams of GA, CG, KK and UH helices, with bold face numerals to indicate locations of B_{II} phosphates. Groove width behavior is summarized below each helix, where W and N indicate wide and narrow grooves. Narrow grooves in UH helix in reality are of intermediate width. Minor groove is narrowest in regions that are most free of B_{II} conformations.

groove is especially narrow when no B_{II} conformations are encountered at two or more successive base pair steps.

These ideas on phosphate conformation and groove width are schematized in Figure 15. The minor groove in GA is uniformly wide because B_{II} conformation are distributed continuously along the helix. The CG helix has a long zone free of B_{II} phosphates in the center, and a narrow minor groove in the same region. The Wide-Narrow-Wide-Narrow-Wide fluctuations in the KK helix occur because of the regular placement of B_{II} phosphates at the ends of the helix and in the center, and the inverse behavior of the UH helix arises because the distribution of B_{II} phosphates is virtually the inverse of that in KK.

This analysis of course only answers half the sequence/structure question. If a wide minor groove accompanies B_{II} phosphate conformations, how are these conformations related to base sequence, if indeed they are? The phosphorothioate hexamer illustrates that when two steps such as C-G and G-C have comparable intrinsic tendency toward the B_{II} conformation, crystal packing can tip the balance. But are there sequence-determined effects also?

A striking feature of Figure 15 is that no B_{II} conformation ever is found at a purine-pyrimidine (R-Y) or pyrimidine-pyrimidine (Y-Y) step along a chain. Y-R and R-R steps are encountered with both B_{II} and B_I phosphates. There seems to be a tendency for B_{II} not to be found at two successive positions along a chain, with Y-R exerting a stronger B_{II} tendency than R-R. Specifically, three principles seem to govern the distribution observed in the decamers:

1. B_{II} phosphates are observed only at Y-R and R-R steps.

2. Within these two classes a hierarchy of B_{II} tendency is found: Y-R (except C-G) > R-R > C-G.

3. B_{II} conformations are rarely found at successive steps along a chain. One conformation will supersede its neighbor, with the hierarchy listed in Point 2.

This three-point algorithm explains the observed B_{II} locations in the four decamers completely, except that it predicts a B_{II} conformation in the KK helix at P3 rather than P2. It is highly suggestive; but in view of the fate of Calladine's rules it must be regarded as only a working hypothesis, subject to future testing against new sequences. The ratio of adjustable parameters to data in this algorithm may be close to 1:1.

What Do We Really Know About B-DNA?

Now we can try to answer the question posed as the title of this article. We know that the old fiber-derived B-DNA model was an excellent first draft of reality, but that the crystalline B-helical oligomers have a variety that was unsuspected before 1980. The general structural principles that have emerged are:

1. All B-DNA (and A-DNA also) base pairs have appreciable propeller twist, in a direction that improves stacking of bases down each strand of the helix. CG base pairs have low propeller twist; AT pairs can have low or high propeller twist depending on their setting.

2. High propeller twist in AT pairs is stabilized by inter-basepair hydrogen bonds in the major or minor groove. A major groove bond of this type is possible whenever two adenines (or two thymines) follow one another along a strand.

3. The minor groove tends to be narrower in regions of AT base pairs than in GC regions. Clusters of B_{II} phosphate conformations rotate the phosphate group out and widen the minor groove. High base pair propeller twist often accompanies a narrow minor groove but is not required for its presence.

4. Narrow regions of the minor groove contain an ordered zig-zag spine of hydration. Wide minor groove regions have two ribbons of waters along the walls of the groove instead, bridging from base edge N and O atoms to the O4′ atoms of sugar rings. Many groove-binding drug molecules bind in a similar fashion, replacing the hydrogen-bonded spine by a covalently-bonded drug backbone, but making comparable hydrogen bonds to N and O atoms on the floor of the minor groove.

5. Sugar rings in B-DNA have a preference for C2′-*endo* or C1′-*exo* conformations, but the distribution is broader than for A-DNA, where conformations cluster tightly around C3′-*endo*.

6. A-tract B-DNA (AT base pairs only) tends to be straight, with bends occurring at junctions with mixed-sequence B-DNA. Regions of alternating A and T bases also show alternation of twist and roll angles, with small twist and negative roll at A-T steps, and large twist and positive roll at T-A steps.

7. Bending of B-DNA occurs by a rolling of one base pair over another around their long axes. The tilt component to bending is small. This roll bending seems to be unidirectional, with compression of the wide major groove. Bending at the AT to mixed DNA junctions mentioned above is permitted but is not mandatory.

Those aspects of structure that relate to binding of antitumor drugs in the minor groove are summarized in Figure 16. The seven principles listed above have the virtue of consistency, but it remains to be demonstrated that they also possess that of universality. It is hoped that they can be tested against a plethora of new oligonucleotide

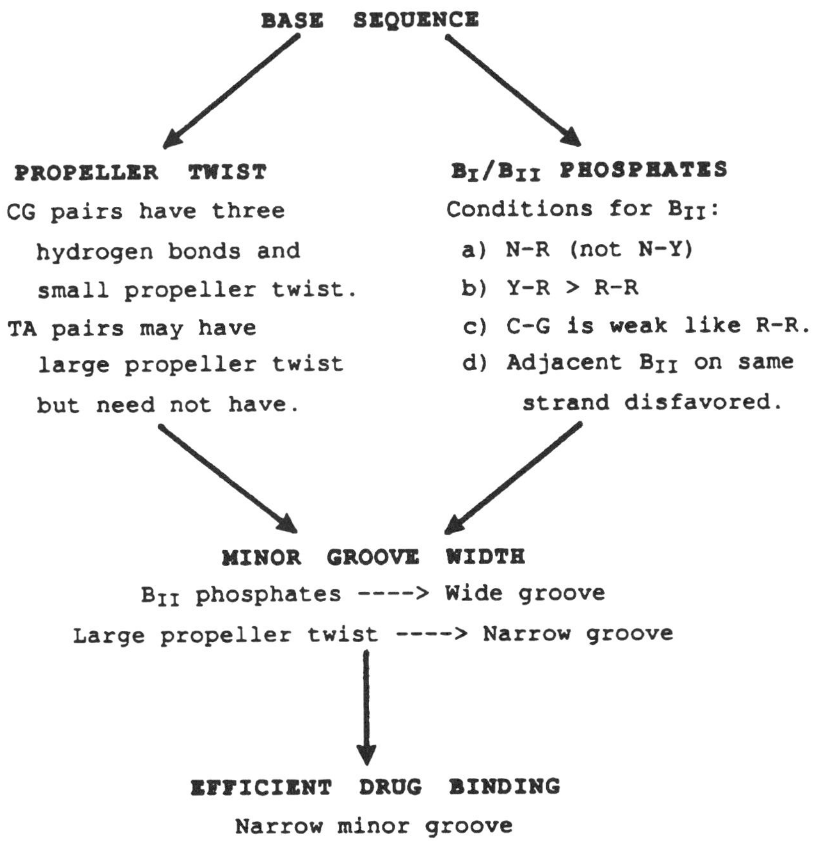

Figure 16: Summary of progression from DNA base sequence, through groove width, to drug binding.

structures in the coming five years, and that out of this testing, secure principles can arise.

Acknowledgments

I would like to thank Udo Heinemann, Gilbert Privé, Kazunori Yanagi, Kazimierz Grzeskowiak and Mary Kopka for ongoing discussions of DNA geometry and hydration, and the rest of my research group for their patience in enduring drafts of parts of this paper. The DNA structure studies were supported by NSF grant DMB 85-01682, and the DNA-drug studies by NIH grant GM-31299 and American Cancer Society grant NP-504.

Afterword

There is a dark side to Tables II through V that must be considered in closing. The second and third columns from the right in each table indicate whether, at any time from initial publication to the present day, either the original x-ray data or the final atomic coordinates have been deposited in a form that is available to the public. This traditionally has meant placing the data and the coordinates on file with the Brookhaven Protein Data Bank. The cryptic serial numbers in Tables II - V are Data Bank reference identification numbers. In two cases the coordinates have been printed in the journal, and these are indicated by the entry "Papers".

The unfortunate reality is that for only 29 of the 78 published structures have the atomic coordinates been placed in the public domain, and for only 20 of these 29 are the x-ray data public as well. For 49 of the 78 published structures, the general scientific community has access neither to the *data* from the research nor the *results* of that research. All that one has are discussions of those results by the authors in scientific journals. The validity of those discussions, and the authors' conclusions, must be accepted without proof, an unusual and disturbing circumstance for a field of science.

Year by year cumulative statistics on disclosure are given in Table VIII, and are plotted in Figure 17. The number of sets of atomic coordinates deposited is growing year by year, but the number of new structures determined is growing at an even faster rate, so that the information gap is worsening. Five years ago, coordinates were available for 53% of the published oligonucleotide structures. Today the same information is available for only 40% of the structures published. The problem is not just a lack of time in which to deposit information on current oligonucleotide structures. Twenty-one of the 49 undocumented structures were published three or more years ago, and nine of the "ancient" structures listed in Table I are still undocumented. One begins to wonder whether there is any hope for the proper disclosure and publication of these structures in a true scientific sense.

The above discussion has been in terms of atomic coordinates. Although these sometimes are referred to as the "data", in reality they are not the *data* from a structure analysis, but only the *results*. The situation with regard to the true data, the x-ray

Table VIII

Cumulative Listing of Oligonucleotide Structures and Level of Publication

Year: Deposited:	78	79	80	81	82	83	84	85	86	87	88	89	Unp
XYZ + F_o:	0	0	2	3	6	6	7	10	12	15	18	20	20
XYZ only:	0	1	1	1	2	2	3	4	5	6	8	9	9
Total XYZ:	0	1	3	4	8	8	10	14	17	21	26	29	29
Nothing:	1	1	3	5	8	8	9	17	21	26	31	44	49
Total:	1	2	6	9	16	16	19	31	38	47	57	73	78
% Avail.:	0	50	50	44	50	50	53	45	45	45	46	40	37

Tabulated are cumulative numbers of olignucleotide crystal structures published in scientific journals. Deposition information is compiled from Tables II - V, and includes:

F_o = Deposition of primary *data*: X-ray diffraction intensity data, available from the Brookhaven Protein Data Bank.

XYZ = Deposition of *results*: Final refined atomic coordinates, usually available from Brookhaven, but in a few cases printed directly in the journal.

% Avail. = Percent of structures for which XYZ coordinates are available to the public.

Unp = Unpulished recent work.

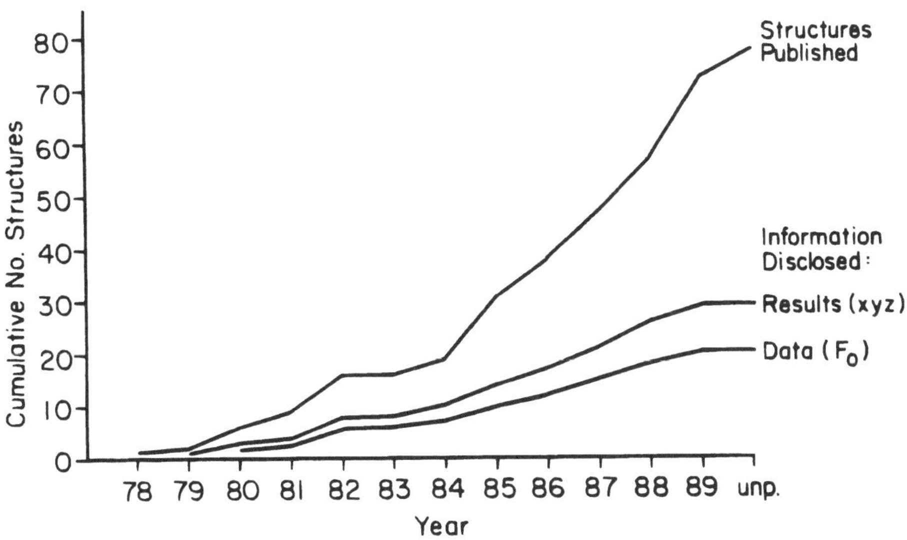

Figure 17: Cumulative record of single crystal oligonucleotide structure analyses since 1979, showing (a) how many structures have been published, (b) how many of these have included public deposition of their results (atomic coordinates x, y, z) at any time between the date of publication and the present day, and (c) how many have also made public their original x-ray data (F_o). F_o disclosure has always meant deposition with the Brookhaven Protein Data Bank; atomic coordinates have been deposited there, or in two instances have been printed in the journal instead. For 49 of the 78 oligonucleotide structures, extending back the full ten years, neither data nor results have ever been made available to the public. Data from Table VIII.

intensities, is even more grim. No F_0 data are available for 58 of the 78 structures known today, and nearly half of these 58 were published three or more years ago. For only 7 of the "ancient" structures in Table I can one obtain F_0 information. This makes impossible, in general, the kind of testing that was carried out on the Drew C-G-C-G-A-A-T-T-C-G-C-G dodecamer, which was refined three times in three different ways by three independent laboratories, fortunately with comparable results (T7,T30,T58). It also means that the scientific community will gain *nothing* from the research other than the slowly aging commentaries of the authors in their original journal publications. A situation has arisen that should give pause to granting agencies as well as scientific journals and the community at large. The field could benefit greatly from a measure of *glasnost*.

References and Footnotes

I. References to Tables I through V in chronological order; cited with a leading T in the text:

1. M.A. Viswamitra, O. Kennard, P.G. Jones, G.M. Sheldrick, S. Salisbury, L. Falvello and Z. Shakked (1978). Nature 273, 687-688.
2. A.H.-J. Wang, G.J. Quigley, F.J. Kolpak, J.L. Crawford, J.H. van Boom, G. van der Marel and A. Rich, *Nature 282*, 680-686 (1979).
3. J.L. Crawford, F.J. Kolpak, A.H.-J. Wang, G.J. Quigley, J.H. van Boom, G. van der Marel and A. Rich, *Proc. Natl. Acad. Sci. USA 77*, 4016-4020 (1980).
4. H.R. Drew, T. Takano, S. Tanaka, K. Itakura and R.E. Dickerson, *Nature 286*, 567-573 (1980).
5. G.J. Quigley, A.H.-J. Wang, G. Ughetto, G. van der Marel, J.H. van Boom and A. Rich, *Proc. Natl. Acad. Sci. USA 77*, 7204-7208 (1980).
6. R.M. Wing, H.R. Drew, T. Takano, C. Broka, S. Tanaka, K. Itakura and R.E. Dickerson, *Nature 287*, 755-758 (1980).
7. R.E. Dickerson and H.R. Drew, *J. Mol. Biol. 149*, 761-786 (1981).
8. R.E. Dickerson, H.R. Drew and B.N. Conner, *Biomolecular Stereodynamics*, (R. H. Sarma, Ed.), Adenine Press, New York, Vol. 1, pp. 1-34 (1981).
9. H.R. Drew and R.E. Dickerson, *J. Mol. Biol. 151*, 535-556 (1981).
10. H.R. Drew and R.E. Dickerson, *J. Mol. Biol. 152*, 723-736 (1981).
11. H.R. Drew, R.M. Wing, T. Takano, C. Broka, S. Tanaka, K. Itakura and R.E. Dickerson, *Proc. Natl. Acad. Sci. USA 78*, 2179-2183 (1981).
12. Z. Shakked, D. Rabinovich, W.B.T. Cruse, E. Egert, O. Kennard, G. Sala, S.A. Salisbury and M.A. Viswamitra, *Proc. Roy. Soc. London B213*, 479-487 (1981).
13. B.N. Conner, T. Takano, S. Tanaka, K. Itakura and R.E. Dickerson, *Nature 295*, 294-299 (1982).
14. H.R. Drew, S. Samson and R.E. Dickerson, *Proc. Natl. Acad. Sci. USA 79*, 4040-4044 (1982).
15. A.V. Fratini, M.L. Kopka, H.R. Drew and R.E. Dickerson, *J. Biol. Chem. 257*, 14686-14707 (1982).
16. S. Fujii, A.H.-J. Wang, G. van der Marel, J.H. van Boom and A. Rich, *Nucl. Acids Res. 10*, 7879-7892 (1982).
17. S. Fujii, A.H.-J. Wang, J. van Boom and A. Rich, *Nucl. Acids Res. Symp Series 11*, 109-112 (1982).
18. M.A. Viswamitra, Z. Shakked, P.G. Jones, G.M. Sheldrick, S.A. Salisbury and O. Kennard, *Biopolymers 21*, 513-533 (1982).
19. A.H.-J. Wang, S. Fujii, J.H. van Boom and A. Rich, *Proc. Natl. Acad. Sci. USA 79*, 3968-3972 (1982).
20. A.H.-J. Wang, S. Fujii, J.H. van Boom, G.A. van der Marel, S.A.A. van Boeckel and A. Rich, *Nature 299*, 601-604 (1982).
21. M.L. Kopka, A.V. Fratini, H.R. Drew and R.E. Dickerson, *J. Mol. Biol. 163*, 129-146 (1983).
22. Z. Shakked, D. Rabinovich, O. Kennard, W.B.T. Cruse, S.A. Salisbury and M.A. Viswamitra, *J. Mol. Biol. 166*, 183-201 (1983).
23. B.N. Conner, C. Yoon, J.L. Dickerson and R.E. Dickerson, *J. Mol. Biol. 174*, 663-695 (1984).
24. A.H.-J. Wang, T. Hakoshima, G. van der Marel, J.H. van Boom and A. Rich, *Cell 37*, 321-331 (1984).
25. A.H.-J. Wang, G. Ughetto, G.J. Quigley, T. Hakoshima, G.A. van der Marel, J.H. van Boom and A. Rich, *Science 225*, 1115-1121 (1984).

26. R.M. Wing, P. Pjura, H.R. Drew and R.E. Dickerson, *EMBO Journal 3*, 1201-1206 (1984).
27. R.G. Brennan and M. Sundaralingam, *J. Mol. Biol. 181*, 561-563 (1985).
28. T. Brown, O. Kennard, G. Kneale and D. Rabinovich, *Nature 315*, 604-606 (1985).
29. S. Fujii, A.H.-J. Wang, G.J. Quigley, H. Westerink, G. van der Marel, J.H. van Boom and A. Rich, *Biopolymers 24*, 243-250 (1985).
30. S.R. Holbrook, R.E. Dickerson and S.-H. Kim, *Acta Cryst. B41*, 255-262 (1985).
31. P.S. Ho, C.A. Frederick, G.J. Quigley, G.A. van der Marel, J.H. van Boom, A.H.-J. Wang and A. Rich, *EMBO Journal 4*, 3617-3623 (1985).
32. G. Kneale, T. Brown, O. Kennard and D. Rabinovich, *J. Mol. Biol. 186*, 805-814 (1985).
33. M.L. Kopka, C. Yoon, D. Goodsell, P. Pjura and R.E. Dickerson, *Proc. Natl. Acad. Sci. USA 82*, 1376-1380 (1985).
34. M.L. Kopka, C. Yoon, D. Goodsell, P. Pjura and R.E. Dickerson, *J. Mol. Biol. 184*, 553-563 (1985).
35. M. McCall, T. Brown and O. Kennard, J. Mol. Biol. 183, 385-396 (1985).
36. G. Ughetto, A.H.-J. Wang, G.J. Quigley, G.A. van der Marel, J.H. van Boom and A. Rich, *Nucl. Acids Res. 13*, 2305-2323 (1985).
37. A.H.-J. Wang, R.V. Gessner, G.A. van der Marel, J.H. van Boom and A. Rich, *Proc. Natl. Acad. Sci. USA 82*, 3611-3615 (1985).
38. R.G. Brennan, E. Westhof and M. Sundaralingam, *J. Biomol. Str. Dynam. 3*, 649-665 (1986).
39. T. Brown, W.N. Hunter, G. Kneale and O. Kennard, *Proc. Natl. Acad. Sci. USA 83*, 2402-2406 (1986).
40. T. Brown, G. Kneale, W.N. Hunter and O. Kennard, *Nucl. Acids Res. 14*, 1801-1809 (1986).
41. B. Chevrier, A.C. Dock, B. Hartmann, M. Leng, D. Moras, M.T. Thuong and E. Westhof, *J. Mol. Biol. 188*, 707-719 (1986).
42. W.B.T. Cruse, S.A. Salisbury, T. Brown, R. Cosstick, F. Eckstein and O. Kennard, *J. Mol. Biol. 192*, 891-905 (1986).
43. W.N. Hunter, G. Kneale, T. Brown, D. Rabinovich and O. Kennard, *J. Mol. Biol. 190*, 605-618 (1986).
44. W.N. Hunter. T. Brown and O. Kennard, *J. Biomol. Str. Dynam. 4*, 173-191 (1986).
45. W.N. Hunter, T. Brown, N.N. Anand and O. Kennard, *Nature 320*, 552-555 (1986).
46. O. Kennard, W.B.T. Cruse, J. Nachman, T. Prange, Z. Shakked and D. Rabinovich, *J. Biomol. Str. Dyn. 3*, 623-647 (1986).
47. M. McCall, T. Brown, W.N. Hunter and O. Kennard, *Nature 322*, 661-664 (1986).
48. G.J. Quigley, G. Ughetto, G.A. van der Marel, J.H. van Boom, A.H.-J. Wang and A. Rich, *Science 232*, 1255-1258 (1986).
49. A.H.-J. Wang, G. Ughetto, G.J. Quigley and A. Rich, *J. Biomol. Str. Dynam. 4*, 319-342 (1986).
50. M. Coll, C.A. Frederick, A.H.-J. Wang and A. Rich, *Proc. Natl. Acad. Sci. USA 84*, 8385-8389 (1987).
51. T.E. Haran, Z. Shakked, A.H.-J. Wang and A. Rich, *J. Biomol. Str. Dynam. 5*, 199-217 (1987).
52. U. Heinemann, H. Lauble, R. Frank and H. Bloeker, *Nucl. Acids Res. 15*, 9531-9550 (1987).
53. W.N. Hunter, T. Brown, G. Kneale, N.N. Anand, D. Rabinovich and O. Kennard, *J. Biol. Chem. 21*, 9962-9970 (1987).
54. S. Jain, G. Zon and M. Sundaralingam, *J. Mol. Biol. 197*, 141-145 (1987).
55. H.C.M. Nelson, J.T. Finch, B.F. Luisi and A. Klug, *Nature 330*, 221-226 (1987).
56. P.E. Pjura, K. Grzeskowiak and R.E. Dickerson, *J. Mol. Biol. 197*, 257-271 (1987).
57. G.G. Privé, U. Heinemann, S. Chandrasegaran, L.-S. Kan, M.L. Kopka and R.E. Dickerson, *Science 238*, 498-504 (1987).
58. E. Westhof, *J. Biomol. Str. Dynam. 5*, 581-600 (1987).
59. R. Chattopadhyaya, S. Ikuta, K. Grzeskowiak and R.E. Dickerson, *Nature 334*, 175-179 (1988).
60. A.C. Dock-Bregeon, B. Chevrier, A. Podjarny, D. Moras, J.S. deBear, G.R. Gough, P.T. Gilham and J.E. Johnson, *Nature 335*, 375-378 (1988).
61. M. Eisenstein, H. Hope, T.E. Haran, F. Frolow, Z. Shakked and D. Rabinovich, *Acta Cryst. B44*, 625-628 (1988).
62. C.A. Frederick, G.J. Quigley, G.A. van der Marel, J.H. van Boom, A.H.-J. Wang and A. Rich, *J. Biol. Chem. 263*, 17872-17879 (1988).
63. L. Joshua-Tor, D. Rabinovich, H. Hope, F. Frolow, E. Appella and J.L. Sussman, *Nature 334*, 82-84 (1988).
64. H. Lauble, R. Frank, H. Bloecker and U. Heinemann, *Nucl. Acids Res. 16*, 7799-7816 (1988).
65. M. Miller, R.W. Harrison, A. Wlodawer, E. Appella and J.L. Sussman, *Nature 334*, 85-86 (1988).

66. G.D. Privé, U. Heinemann, S. Chandrasegaran, L.-S. Kan, M.L. Kopka and R.E. Dickerson, *Structure and Expression, Vol. 2: DNA and its Drug Complexes*, (R.H. Sarma and M.H. Sarma, Eds.), Adenine Press, New York, pp. 27-47 (1988).
67. D. Rabinovich, T. Haran, M. Eisenstein and Z. Shakked, *J. Mol. Biol. 200*, 151-161 (1988).
68. M. Teng, N. Usman, C.A. Frederick and A.H.-J. Wang, *Nucl. Acids Res. 16*, 2671-2690 (1988).
69. C. Yoon, G.G. Privé, D.S. Goodsell and R.E. Dickerson, *Proc. Natl. Acad. Sci. USA 85*, 6332-6336 (1988).
70. C.A. Bingman, S. Jain, D. Jebaratnam and M. Sundaralingam, *Abstracts, Sixth Conversation in Biomolecular Stereodynamics*, Albany, NY, p. 28 (1989).
71. T. Brown, G.A. Leonard, E.D. Booth and J. Chambers, *J. Mol. Biol. 207*, 455-457 (1989).
72. M. Coll, J. Aymami, G.A. van der Marel, J.H. van Boom, A. Rich and A.H.-J. Wang, *Biochemistry 28*, 310-320 (1989).
73. M. Coll, D. Saal, C.A. Frederick, J. Aymami, A. Rich and A.H.-J. Wang, *Nucl. Acids Res.* (1989).
74. A.D. DiGabriele, M.R. Sanderson and T.A. Steitz, *Proc. Natl. Acad. Sci. USA 86*, 1816-1820 (1989).
75. C.A. Frederick, L.D. Williams, G. Ughetto, G.A. van der Marel, J.H. van Boom, A. Rich and A.H.-J. Wang, *Biochemistry*, submitted (1989).
76. R.V. Gessner, C.A. Frederick, G.J. Quigley, A. Rich and A.H.-J. Wang, *J. Biol. Chem. 264*, 7921-7935 (1989).
77. U. Heinemann and C. Alings, *J. Mol. Biol. 210*, 369-381 (1989).
78. W.N. Hunter, B.L. D'Estaintot and O. Kennard, *Biochemisty 28*, 2444-2451 (1989).
79. S. Jain, G. Zon and M. Sundaralingam, *Biochemistry 28*, 2360-2364 (1989).
80. M.H. Moore, W.N. Hunter, B.L. D'Estaintot and O. Kennard, *J. Mol. Biol. 206*, 693-705 (1989).
81. Z. Shakked, G. Guerstein-Guzikevich, F. Frolow and D. Rabinovich, *Nature*, submitted (1988).
82. M. Sundaralingam and S. Jain, *Abstracts, Sixth Conversation in Biomolecular Stereodynamics*, Albany, NY, p. 341 (1989).
83. Y. Timsit, E. Westhof, R.P.P. Fuchs and D. Moras, submitted (1989).
84. T. Larsen, D. Goodsell, D. Cascio, K. Grzeskowiak and R.E. Dickerson, *J. Biomole. Struct. Dyn. 7*, 477-491 (1989).

Unpublished:

91. T. Larsen and R.E. Dickerson, unpublished.
92. D. Brown, M.R. Sundaram, J.V. Skelly, T.C. Jenkins, T. Brown, E. Garman, D.I. Stuart and S. Neidel, submitted (1990).
93. G. Privé and R.E. Dickerson, submitted (1989).
94. K. Yanagi, K. Grzeskowiak and R.E. Dickerson, in preparation.

II. General references; cited by number alone:

1. R.E. Dickerson, D.S. Goodsell, M. L. Kopka and P.E. Pjura, *J. Biomol. Str. Dyn. 5*, 557-579 (1987).
2. A.H.-J. Wang and M.-K. Teng, *J. Crystal Growth 90*, 295-310 (1988).
3. C. Altona and M. Sundaralingam, *J. Am. Chem. Soc. 94*, 8205-8208 (1972).
4. S.T. Rao, E. Westhof and M. Sundaralingam, *Acta Cryst. A36*, 421-425 (1981).
5. C.R. Calladine, *J. Mol. Biol. 161*, 343-362 (1982).
6. R.E. Dickerson, *J. Mol. Biol. 166*, 419-441 (1983).
7. K. Zakrzewska, R. Lavery and B. Pullman, *J. Biomol. Str. Dynam. 4*, 833-843 (1987).
8. A. Klug, A. Jack, M.A. Viswamitra, O. Kennard, Z. Shakked and T.A. Steitz, *J. Mol. Biol. 131*, 669-680 (1979).

Structure & Methods, ISBN 0-940030-32-2
Volume 3: DNA & RNA, ISBN 0-940030-31-4
Eds., Ramaswamy H. Sarma & Mukti H. Sarma, © *Adenine Press 1990*

Structural Features of G/C-Rich DNA Going A or B

Udo Heinemann, Claudia Alings and Hanspeter Lauble*
Abteilung Saenger, Institut für Kristallographie
Freie Universität Berlin
Takustraβe 6, D-1000 Berlin 33

Abstract

G/C-rich DNA which contains oligo d(G) · oligo d(C) sequences or many isolated GG/CC base pair steps may adopt either the A form or the B form of DNA depending on solution conditions. Oligonucleotides containing these sequence elements frequently crystallize in the A form even if their solution structure as determined by NMR or Raman spectroscopy is predominantly B-DNA. Two crystal structures of G/C-rich A-DNA fragments determined in our laboratory show quite significant differences in their global helical structures and in local conformational features. They represent snapshots out of a quasi-continuous spectrum of different A-DNA structures analysed in the past few years. Recently, the crystal structure of the decamer d(CCAGGCCTGG) has been solved as well. This oligonucleotide is the first DNA fragment which contains only isolated A · T base pairs and crystallizes as B-DNA. Its helical structure is distinct from A-tract DNA as present in the Dickerson/Drew type dodecamers. However, the variability of B-DNA structures characterized so far is not as large as for the A-DNA family.

Comparing the published A-DNA and B-DNA crystal structures, it becomes evident that certain structural features such as base pair inclination, major groove width and rise per base pair change in an almost continuous fashion when going from A to B-DNA. This does not imply that the A and B forms cannot be distinguished any more. The lateral displacement of base pairs from the helix axis, no matter how it is defined, changes discontinuously between the two right-handed helical families. It is around zero for B-DNA and around 4 Å for A-DNA placing the helix axis in the major groove. This global change is associated with the bimodal change of local structural parameters such as sugar pucker and base-pair slide.

Introduction

A considerable number of crystal structures of DNA fragments has been solved in the 1980's, but a simple comparison with the number of known protein structures shows that the DNA data base is still rather small. If one disregards all unusual or perturbed structures, i.e., chemically modified DNA, DNA with mismatched or looped-out bases and DNA complexed with drugs or proteins, one is left with about 10 sequences that formed A-DNA double helices in the crystal (1-11) and even fewer

*Present address: Scripps Clinic Research Institute, 10666 North Torrey Pines Road, La Jolla, CA 92037.

B-DNA structures (12-19). Even these structures are not strictly independent since many are closely related by sequence and crystallize nearly isomorphously with others (20,21). For instance, most A-DNA structures are based on octamers crystallized in either of two space groups ($P6_1$ or $P4_32_12$) and crystallographic studies of B-DNA have for a long time been limited to variants of the Dickerson/Drew dodecamer d(CGCGAATTCGCG). Since crystal packing may have a profound effect on the three-dimensional structure of oligonucleotides (22) it is important that many new sequences be analysed in new crystal environments in the near future. Even the limited data base on DNA crystal structures available today provides some insight into the mechanics of DNA molecules and the relatedness and interconversion of different helix types.

Here we describe the helical structures of two A-DNA fragments, d(GCCCGGGC) and d(GGGATCCC), and the B-DNA decamer d(CCAGGCCTGG) and compare them with published structural data for other oligodeoxyribonucleotides. The structures were determined by X-ray diffraction methods (2,6,19,23). All of them represent G/C-rich DNA which is abundant in GG/CC base pair steps. As all A-DNA fragments crystallized so far, the octamers adopt a global conformation quite distinct form canonical A-DNA as defined by fiber diffraction methods (24). In contrast, the decamer closely resembles classical B-DNA but differs in important structural aspects, such as minor groove width, from crystalline A/T-rich DNA. We will demonstrate that, despite the large structural variability in either helical family, a distinction between A-DNA and B-DNA still can and should be made since some structural parameters change in a bimodal fashion when going from one helix form to the other, although others change quasi-continuously. We will discuss the relation between structures determined in the crystal and those determined in solution and comment on the influence of DNA sequence on the A-B equilibrium.

Experimental

The experimental procedures involved in the determination of the three crystal structures are published (2,6,19) and will be summarized here briefly to allow assessment of the accuracy of the results and possible bias introduced by the crystallographic techniques applied. All three DNA fragments crystallized quasi-isomorphously with oligonucleotides the structures of which had already been determined. To solve the structures, models of the DNA helices with the given sequence and in the expected type were constructed from ideal coordinates (24) and positioned in the unit cell according to their quasi-isomorphous reference structures (d(^{I}CCGG) and d(GGGGCCCC) (25,5) for the octamers and d(CCAAGATTGG) (26,27) for the decamer). A rigid-body refinement of the position and orientation of the model helix usually confirmed the choice of helix type and reference structure and provided a starting point for the subsequent restrained least-squares refinement. This simple approach failed to succeed in the case of d(GGGATCCC) where a more complicated procedure had to be used (28).

The initial least-squares refinement was usually carried out with the program CORELS (29,30) which devides the molecules into constrained groups that are linked by

Table I
Crystal Data

	d(GCCCGGGC)	d(GGGATCCC)	d(CCAGGCCTGG)
Helix type	A	A	B
Space group	$P4_32_12$	$P6_1$	C2
Cell constants	a = 43.25 Å c = 24.61 Å	a = 46.83 Å c = 44.49 Å	a = 32.15 Å b = 25.49 Å c = 34.82 Å β = 116.71 °
Contents of asymmetric unit	one strand	double helix	one strand
Resolution	1.8 Å	2.5 Å	1.6 Å
Reflections per base pair	369	195	484
R value	17.8%	17.2%	16.9%

bonds with restrained geometry. Convergence of the refinement was then reached after the incorporation of solvent molecules by further cycles with the stereochemically restrained least-squares procedure of Hendrickson and Konnert (31,32) as adapted for nucleic acids (NUCLIN, 33). Here, bond lengths, bond angles, planar groups, chiral volumes and non-bonded contacts were restrained to standard geometry and the temperature factors of bonded atoms were kept from deviating unreasonably. Restraints for backbone torsion angles and sugar pucker were applied for neither structure. Yet most deoxyribose units adopt the expected sugar pucker ($C_{3'}$-*endo* for the A-DNA octamers and $C_{2'}$-*endo* for the B-DNA decamer) and the torsion angles fall into their normal ranges (34) with exceptions that can be explained on the basis of base-pair stacking or crystal packing. The crystallographic parameters of the three structures are summarized in Table I.

G/C-Rich A-DNA

The conformational parameters of DNA helices discussed in the following section are those of Dickerson and colleagues (13,35) and were determined with the HELIB program package. The sign conventions conform to the standard adopted at the 1988 Cambridge meeting (36). Some structures have also been analysed with the CURVES algorithm (37,38) which does not depend on a straight DNA axis. Most helical parameters follow the same trend when determined with either program, but the absolute numbers may vary significantly.

Fiber and single crystal X-ray diffraction studies have defined a broad range of possible global A-DNA structures which may be characterized by average conformational parameters such as the inclination of base pairs relative to the helix axis, the width of the deep (major) groove and the rise per base pair. In the fiber structure of mixed-sequence A-DNA (24), inclination is 22°, the rise per base pair is 2.56 Å

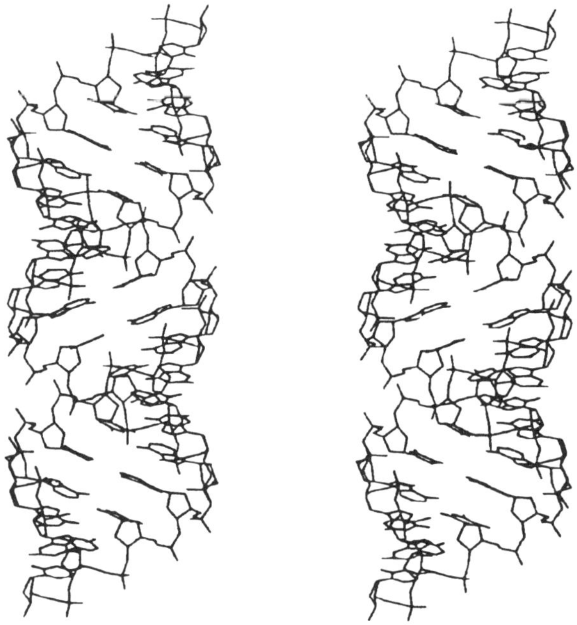

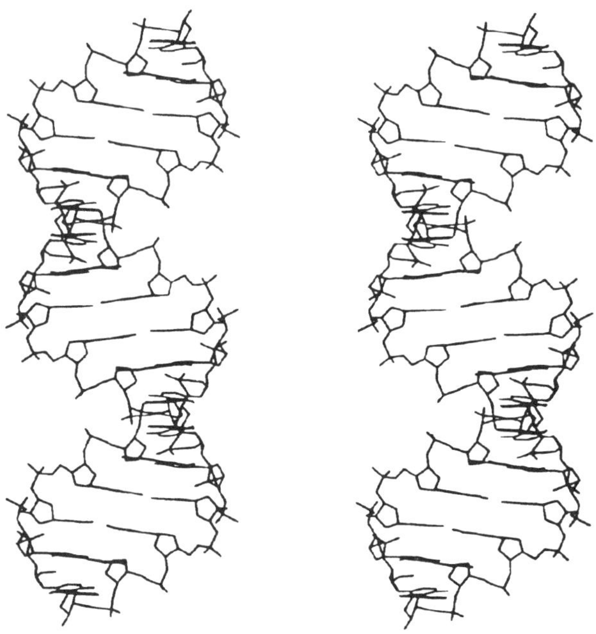

Figure 1: Stereo drawings of 18 base pairs of standard A-DNA (top) and of an extended helix built from the central 6 base pairs of the oligonucleotide d(GCCCGGGC) as found in the crystal structure (bottom). In the center of each helix, the view is into the major groove which is extremely narrow in standard A-DNA but wide open in the crystalline oligonucleotide.

and the major groove width is only 2.3 Å (closest phosphorus-phosphorus approach minus 5.8 Å to account for the van der Waals radii of the phosphate groups). These values are usually not found in oligonucleotide crystal structures. With a 7.2° average inclination, a 3.2 Å rise per base pair and a major groove separation of 9.8 Å the octamer d(GCCCGGGC) was found to have a conformation at the opposite end of the A-DNA spectrum. The degree of divergence in A-helical DNA is obvious from a comparison of an 18 base-pair canonical A-DNA helix with an extended double helix based on the crystal structure of d(GCCCGGGC) (Figure 1). The latter was constructed from the central 6 base pairs of the octamer by rotation around and translation along the best helix axis to give a continuous double helix. The structure of the other octamer investigated, d(GGGATCCC), is intermediate between these two extremes.

All A-DNA structures, whether determined by fiber diffraction from polymeric samples or by single crystal diffraction methods from oligonucleotides, have in common the position of the helix axis in the deep major groove, as opposed to B-DNA where the axis passes through the base pairs. The average displacement of the base pairs from the helix axis found in oligonucleotide crystals is between −3.3 and −4.8 Å (9,6). Another important common feature of A-DNA is the $C_{3'}$-*endo* sugar pucker. The few deoxyribose units in A-DNA structures that deviate substantially from this pucker are usually found at the 3′-end of a strand.

G/C-Rich B-DNA

Most oligonucleotides that were crystallized to date have an excess of G · C over A · T base pairs simply because the low melting temperature of short A/T-rich DNA fragments precludes formation of stable double helices. In a formal sense, the Dickerson/Drew dodecamer d(CGCGAATTCGCG) would have to be considered C/G-rich. Its helical structure, however, is dominated by the A/T-rich center which causes a narrow minor groove ideally suited to bind drug molecules (39-41). The only remaining G/C-rich B-DNA structures determined in the crystalline state then are d($G_{ps}CG_{ps}CG_{ps}C$) (18) and the decamer d(CCAGGCCTGG) (19). In the former, every second phosphodiester linkage is replaced by a phosphorothioate group, the presence of which, however, does not seem to perturb the helical structure significantly. The purine-pyrimidine alternation of the sequence causes a characteristic alternation of B_I and B_{II} backbone types along either strand (18).

In the crystal, d(CCAGGCCTGG) molecules stack end to end forming continuous double helices (Figure 2). The inter-helical stacking of a C · G onto a G · C base pair very closely resembles the intra-helical stacking between the central base pairs number 5 and 6. The formation of a quasi-endless double helix in the crystal requires an exact 10-fold helical repeat of the decamer. Helix twist angles indeed average 36°, but they vary enormously between 24° and 51°. The large twist occurs at the CpA dinucleotide step and is compensated by small twist values of the adjacent steps. Since the decamer helix propagates all through the crystal, it also has to be perfectly straight. This is an important distinction from the Dickerson/Drew type structures in which A-tract sequences induce various degrees of bending (12-16,42).

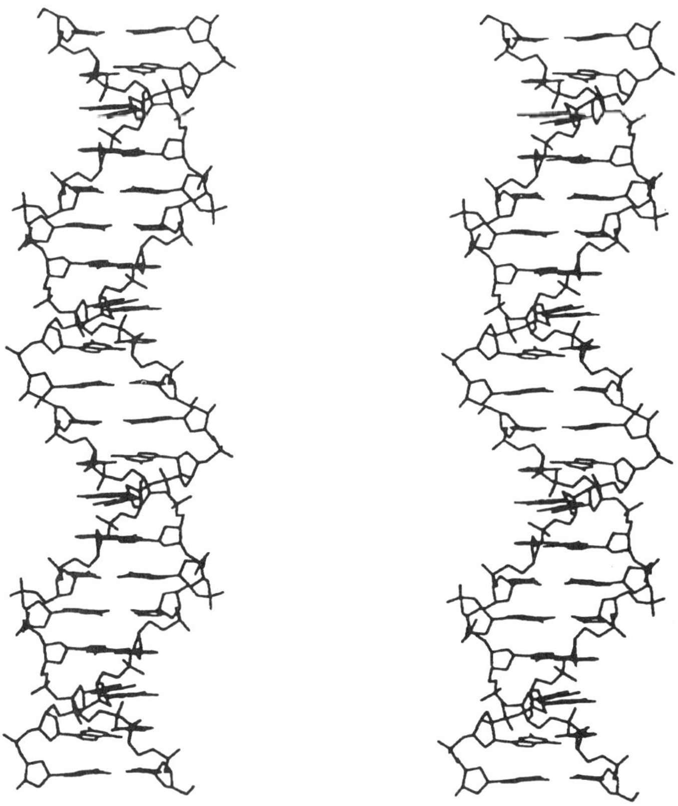

Figure 2: Stereo drawing of two double-helical B-DNA decamer fragments as they stack end to end in crystals of d(CCAGGCCTGG).

In Figure 3, the structure of d(CCAGGCCTGG) is compared with an ideal B-BNA helix of the same sequence, with the MPD7 variant of the Dickerson/Drew dodecamer (13) and with the isomorphous decamer d(CCAAGATTGG) containing two successive *anti-anti* G · A base-pair mismatches (26,27). The ends of the mismatched decamer, sharing a common sequence with d(CCAGGCCTGG), also have very similar helical structure. One can see that the decamer global structure is closer to fiber diffraction B-DNA than either A-tract or the mismatched DNA structure. The main differences from canonical B-DNA are the presence of both B_I and B_{II} backbone types which are averaged in fibers, a reduced average propeller twist ($-8°$ *versus* $-15°$) and a slightly narrower minor groove in the center (5.2 Å *versus* 5.9 Å). It seems to us that the G/C-rich decamer, due to its overall similarity with canonical B-DNA, is a good model for general-sequence B-DNA. The degree of structural variability observed in this oligonucleotide is large (e.g., helix twist values between 51° and 24°) and may define the range in which sequence or environmentally induced conformational fluctuations manifest themselves.

At present, the B-DNA family appears to be more homogeneous than A-form DNA because the differences in global helix structure between the fiber model and oligonucleotide structures and among these are more subtle in the former. This notion may change as more B-DNA crystal structures are solved in the future.

Bimodal Change Between A-DNA and B-DNA

Considering the broad range of possible global conformations present in B-DNA and especially in A-DNA, one may ask whether a classification in these two archetypal right-handed helix forms is still justified or whether there is a smooth transformation from one form into the other. The distinction has to be maintained as long as there are conformational parameters that change in a bimodal fashion when going from the A to the B form and *vice versa* as opposed to a continuous change of values. As mentioned above, the average displacement of base pairs from the helix axis is such a parameter that changes between two widely separated allowed ranges of −3.3 Å to −4.8 Å in A-DNA and 0.2 Å to 1.1 Å in B-DNA. No intermediate values have been reported so far and there is no reason to anticipate that the large gap of 3.5 Å between these ranges will be bridged by some DNA structures to be determined. The displacement of the base pairs from the axis is strongly correlated with the average slide of the base pairs (Figure 4). Other correlations can be found which will also reflect a bimodal structural change between A-DNA and B-DNA.

The DNA backbone structure, as well, shows bimodal behaviour in the nearly exclusive presence of $C_{3'}$-*endo* sugar pucker in A-DNA and a restriction around $C_{2'}$-*endo* of sugar puckers in B-DNA. This restriction may be more severe than previously thought (43) since a recent re-refinement of the Dickerson/Drew dodecamer found most sugar puckers in their expected $C_{2'}$-*endo* range and demonstrated the possible influence on torsion angle values of the refinement algorithm used (44).

There is evidence from a variety of sources that runs of guanines or isolated GG/CC base pair steps may favour the A form over the B form under suitable conditions (45-48). Therefore it is interesting to compare the stacking geometries at GG/CC steps in A-DNA and in B-DNA. Figure 5 shows the GG/CC stacking of base pairs number 2 and 3 in A-DNA d(GCCCGGGC) and base pairs number 4 and 5 in B-DNA d(CCAGGCCTGG). As usually observed at homopurine-homopyrimidine steps in A-DNA, there is partial overlap between the five-membered ring of the guanine base at the 3′-side and the six-membered guanine ring at the 5′-side of the step, while the cytosines are totally unstacked in the octamer structure. The stacking pattern is very different at the B-DNA CC/GG step which shows approximately equal overlap of cytosine and guanine bases. Simple consideration of geometric overlap between base pairs certainly cannot explain the presumed higher stability of CC/GG steps in A-DNA. Indeed, calculations of stacking energies in A-DNA indicate that CC/GG steps may be less stable than most others in this helix form (1,49). It is conceivable that differences in hydration energies have to be considered to explain its propensity to adopt the A form of DNA.

Continuous Change Between A-DNA and B-DNA

We have argued above that A-DNA and B-DNA are distinct entities characterized

(a)

(b)

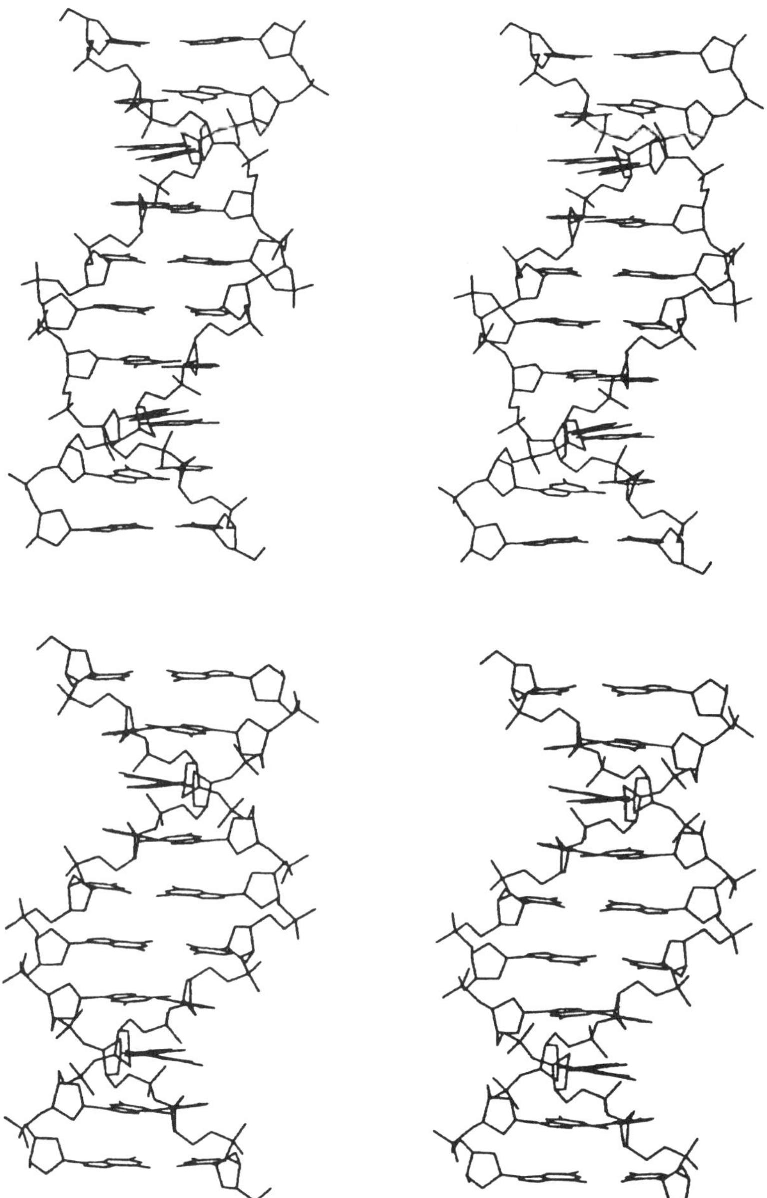

Figure 3: Stereo drawings of the decamer d(CCAGGCCTGG) (a), a model of the same sequence constructed from ideal B-DNA coordinates (24) derived from X-ray fiber diffraction (b), the MPD7 form of the Dickerson/Drew dodecamer d(CGCGAATT^{Br}CGCG) (13; Protein Data Bank entry 4BNA) (c), and the G · A mismatch decamer d(CCAAGATTGG) (26) (d). The view is into the minor grooves of the helices.

by structural parameters that change in a bimodal fashion when going from one helix form to the other. However, there is another set of important conformational parameters which do in fact show a continuous change between the A and B forms of DNA. Among these are the average inclination of base pairs with respect to the

(c)

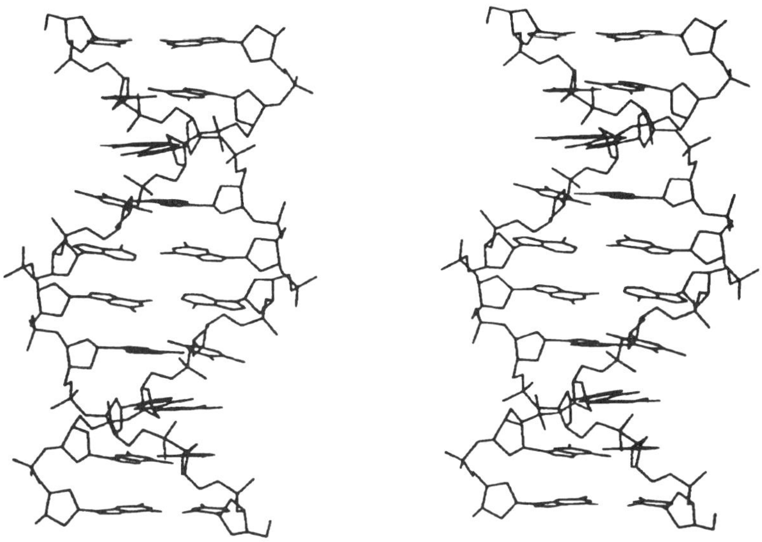

(d)

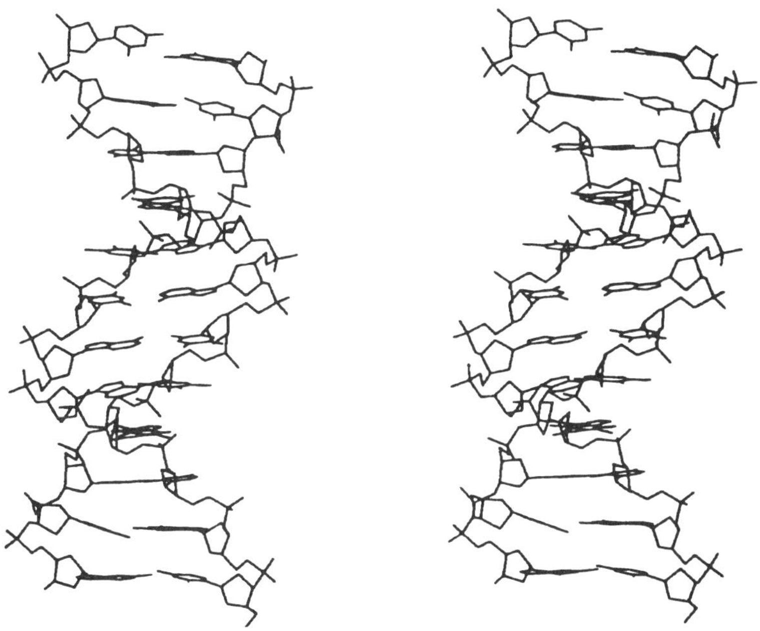

Figure 3: *continued*

helix axis, the width of the major groove and the rise per base pair (Figure 6). The correlation plot shows that the gap between A-DNA and B-DNA crystal structures is small. Looking at these structural features, there is less difference between most A-DNA and B-DNA oligonucleotide crystal structures than between the A-DNA oligonucleotide structures and the fiber diffraction model for mixed-sequence A-DNA or the

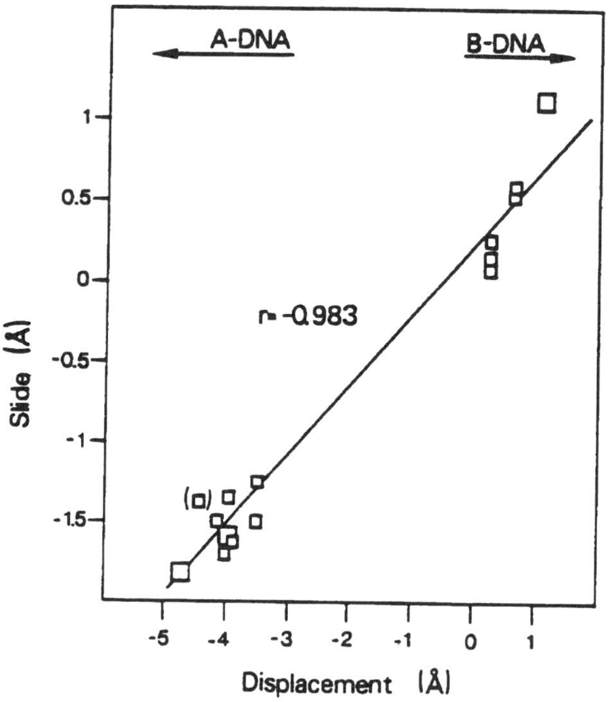

Figure 4: Dependence of the average base-pair slide fromthe average displacement of base pairs from the helix axis in DNA crystal structures. Parameters for d(CCCCGGGG), d(GGCCGGCC) (−8°), d(GGGGCCCC), d(GGTATACC), d(CTCTAGAG), d(GGATGGGAG), r(GCG)d(TATACGC) (in parentheses), the B-DNA fiber model, d(CGCGAATTCGCG) (native and MPD7 forms), d(CGCAAA-AAAGCG) and d($G_{ps}CG_{ps}CG_{ps}C$) were taken from (21) or from the original literature. The enlarged symbols mark the oligonucleotides described in this paper, d(CCAGGCCTGG), d(GCCCGGGC) and d(GGGATCCC) going to negative values of displacement. *r* is the linear correlation coefficient.

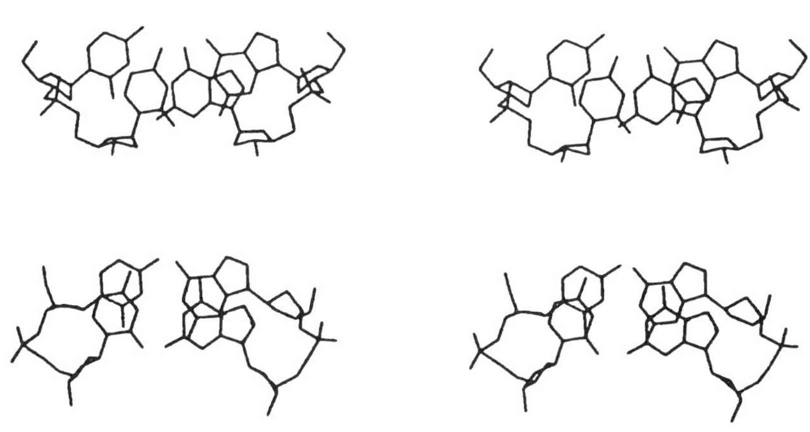

Figure 5: Stereo drawings of CC/GG base pair stacks in A-DNA (top) and in B-DNA (bottom). In both cases, the view is down the helix axis.

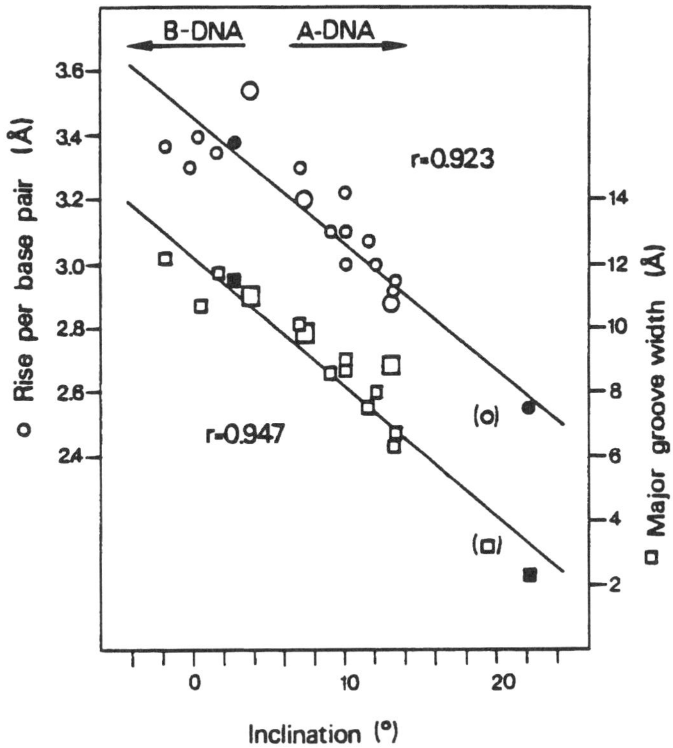

Figure 6: Correlation of the major groove width and the rise per base pair withthe average inclination of base pairs against the helix axis. The filled symbols mark the fiber diffraction models of mixed-sequence A-DNA and B-DNA. Structural parameters for the oligonucleotides d(CCCCGGGG), d(GGCCGGCC) (−8°C and room temperature structures), d(GGGCGCCC), d(GGGGCCCC), d(GGTATACC), d(CTCT-AGAG), d(GTGTACAC), d(GGATGGGAG), r(GCG)d(TATACGC) (in parentheses), and d($G_{ps}CG_{ps}CG_{ps}C$) were taken from (21) or from the original literature. Enlarged symbols mark the DNA structures discussed in this paper, d(GGGATCCC), d(GCCCGGGC) and d(CCAGGCCTGG) going to decreasing absolute values of inclination. The linear correlation coefficients for the least-squares lines are given as *r*.

structure of an RNA/DNA hybrid (11). It must be stressed that the most important conformational parameter with regard to biological function, namely the width of the major groove, changes in a continuous way from B to A-DNA. Hence, proteins that like to read out the information content of the major groove can do so in B-DNA and in many subtypes of A-DNA helices.

A-DNA in Crystals and in Solution

There is an apparent paradox in that G/C-rich oligonucleotides often crystallize as A-DNA while their solution structure at moderate ionic strength as determined by NMR or Raman spectroscopy is predominantly B-DNA (47,50-53). The evidence, however, is not unequivocal since data from CD spectroscopy can be correlated very well with global structural parameters determined by X-ray crystallography (54). One might suspect that spectroscopic methods may mistake some of the

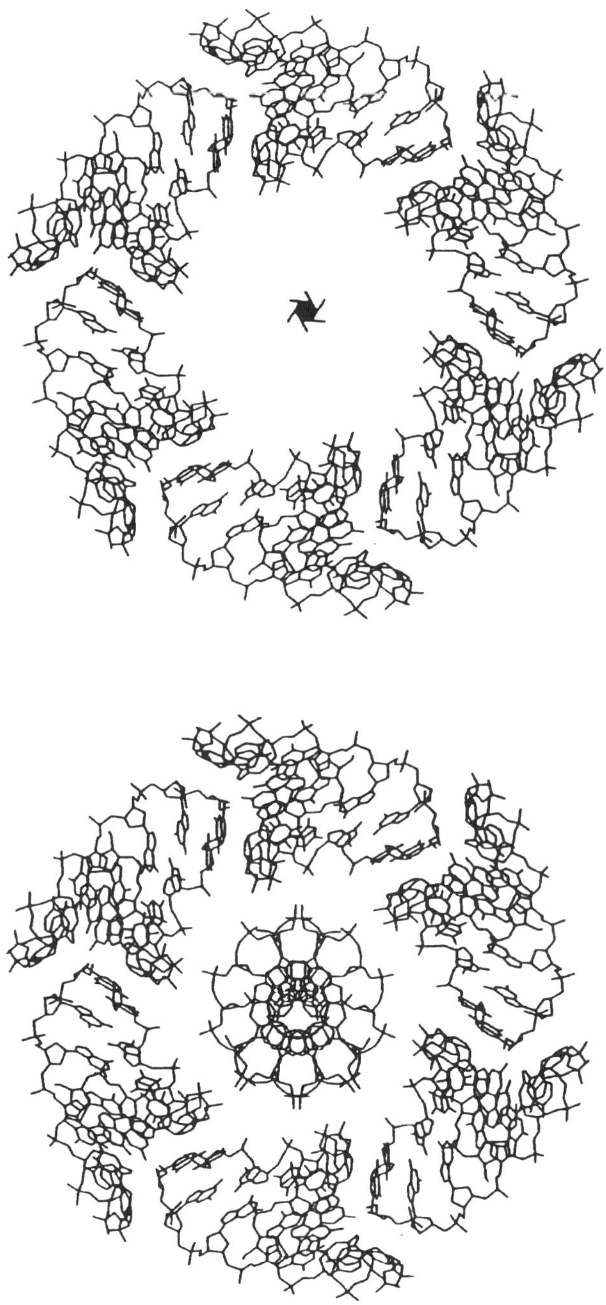

Figure 7: Possible coexistence of A-DNA and B-DNA in crystals of d(GGGATCCC). A-DNA helical fragments pack in endless spirals around the sixfold screw axis of space group $P6_1$ (a). The solvent channel in the center is large enough to accomodate the same DNA fragment in the B form (b).

unconventional A-DNA structures with small base-pair inclination and wide open major groove for B-DNA. This is not the case, however, since both NMR and Raman spectroscopy rely heavily on sugar pucker which belongs to the parameters that change discontinuously between the helix forms: A-DNA is always $C_{3'}$-*endo* and B-DNA is usually around $C_{2'}$-*endo*. Furthermore, calculation of inter-proton NMR marker distances (55) in crystalline d(GCCCGGGC) shows that this oligonucleotide would still be recognized as A-DNA by NMR spectroscopy. Thus, the differences found between crystal and solution conformations have to be real. The key to the problem may lie in the limited sensitivity of the spectroscopic methods. An NMR study of d(CCCGGG) concludes that 70% or more of the DNA has sugar puckers indicative of B-DNA, that inter-proton distances within nucleotide units are as expected for B-DNA, but that some inter-nucleotide distances are intermediate between A-DNA and B-DNA (53). Since this oligonucleotide may be prone to adopt the A form due to its sequence containing many GG/CC steps, the possibility remains that on time average a substantial fraction of the DNA is in the A form. It could therefore crystallize as A-DNA if this would provide a more favourable way of crystal packing than the B form.

There is direct crystallographic evidence that at least some of the A-DNA oligonucleotides have been crystallized from solutions near the A-B equilibrium. Diffraction patterns of d(GG^{Br}UA^{Br}UACC) recorded with Synchrotron radiation showed diffuse scattering at 3.4 Å spacing perpendicular to the *c*-axis in space group $P6_1$, reminiscent of the strong meridional reflection in B-DNA (56). Careful analysis of the X-ray diffraction pattern revealed a complicated B-DNA fiber pattern superimposed on the single crystal pattern originating from the ordered A-DNA helices. The fiber diffraction pattern could be interpreted as indicating the presence of the B-DNA form of d(GG^{Br}UA^{Br}UACC) in the large solvent channels running along the *c*-axis. The octamer d(GGGATCCC) crystallizes isomorphously with d(GG^{Br}UA^{Br}UACC) and also displays large contiguous solvent channels around which the A-DNA fragments pack in endless spirals as dictated by the 6_1 screw axis. The diffuse scattering perpendicular to the *c*-axis mentioned above is observed on all X-ray photographs of the octamer, but the off-meridional parts of the B-DNA fiber pattern were never observed. Packing analysis shows that the solvent channel could easily accommodate the B-DNA helix of d(GGGATCCC) (Figure 7). Therefore it is possible, although not proven, that A-DNA and B-DNA coexist in crystals of this DNA fragment. This coexistence may be a common feature of all DNA octamers crystal lized in this space group.

References and Footnotes

1. T.E. Haran, Z. Shakked, A.H.-J. Wang and A. Rich, *J. Biomol. Struct. Dyn. 5*, 199-217 (1987).
2. U. Heinemann, H. Lauble, R. Frank and H. Blöcker, *Nucleic Acids Res. 15*, 9531-9550 (1987).
3. A.H.-J. Wang, S. Fujii, J.H. van Boom and A. Rich, *Proc. Natl. Acad. Sci. USA 79*, 3968-3972 (1982).
4. D. Rabinovich, T. Haran, M. Eisenstein and Z. Shakked, *J. Mol. Biol. 200*, 151-161 (1988).
5. M. McCall, T. Brown and O. Kennard, *J. Mol. Biol. 183*, 385-396 (1985).
6. H. Lauble, R. Frank, H. Blöcker and U. Heinemann, *Nucleic Acids Res. 16*, 7799-7816 (1988).
7. Z. Shakked, D. Rabinovich, W.B.T. Cruse, E. Egert, O. Kennard, G. Sala, S.A. Salisbury and M.A. Viswamitra, *Proc. Roy. Soc. ser. B, 213*, 479-487 (1981).

8. W.N. Hunter, B. Langlois D'Estaintot and O. Kennard, *Biochemistry 28*, 2444-2451 (1989).
9. S. Jain, G. Zon and M. Sundaralingam, *Biochemistry 28*, 2360-2364 (1989).
10. M. McCall, T. Brown, W. Hunter and O. Kennard, *Nature 322*, 661-664 (1986).
11. A.H.-J. Wang, S. Fujii, J.H. van Boom, G.A. van der Marel, S.A.A. van Boeckel and A. Rich, *Nature 299*, 601-604 (1982).
12. R. Wing, H. Drew, T. Takano, C. Broka, S. Tanaka, K. Itakura and R.E. Dickerson, *Nature 287*, 755-758 (1980).
13. A.V. Fratini, M.L. Kopka, H.R. Drew and R.E. Dickerson, *J. Biol. Chem. 257*, 14686-14707 (1982).
14. M. Coll, C.A. Frederick, A.H.-J. Wang and A. Rich, *Proc. Natl. Acad. Sci. USA 84*, 8385-8389 (1987).
15. H.C.M. Nelson, J.T. Finch, B.F. Luisi and A. Klug, *Nature 330*, 221-226 (1987).
16. A.D. DiGabriele, M.R. Sanderson and T.A. Steitz, *Proc. Natl. Acad. Sci. USA 86*, 1816-1820 (1989).
17. C. Yoon, G.G.Privé, D.S. Goodsell and R.E. Dickerson, *Proc. Natl. Acad. Sci. USA 85*, 6332-6336 (1988).
18. W.B.T. Cruse, S.A. Salisbury, T. Brown, R. Cosstick, F. Eckstein and O. Kennard, *J. Mol. Biol. 192*, 891-905 (1986).
19. U. Heinemann and C. Alings, *J. Mol. Biol.*, in press.
20. Z. Shakked and D. Rabinovich, *Prog. Biophys. Mol. Biol. 47*, 159-195 (1986).
21. O. Kennard and W.N. Hunter, in *Landolt-Börnstein, New Series, Group VII, Volume 1a*, Ed., W. Saenger, Springer, Berlin, Heidelberg, New York, pp. 255-360 (1989).
22. R.E. Dickerson, D.S. Goodsell, M.L. Kopka and P.E. Pjura, *J. Biomol. Struct. Dyn. 5*, 557-579 (1987).
23. U. Heinemann, H. Lauble, R. Frank and H. Blöcker, *Nucleosides and Nucleotides 7*, 699-702 (1988).
24. R. Chandrasekaran and S. Arnott, in *Landolt-Börnstein, New Series, Group VII, Volume 1b*, Ed., W. Saenger, Springer, Berlin, Heidelberg, New York, pp. 31-170 (1989).
25. B.N. Conner, T. Takano, S. Tanaka, K. Itakura and R.E. Dickerson, *Nature 295*, 294-299 (1982).
26. G.G. Privé, U. Heinemann, S. Chandrasegaran, L.-S. Kan, M.L. Kopka and R.E. Dickerson, *Science 238*, 498-504 (1987).
27. G.G. Privé, U. Heinemann, S. Chandrasegaran, L.-S. Kan, M.L. Kopka and R.E. Dickerson, in *Structure and Expression. Volume 2: DNA and Its Drug Complexes*, Eds., R.H. Sarma and M.H. Sarma, Adenine Press, Schenectady, pp. 27-47 (1988).
28. D. Rabinovich and Z. Shakked, *Acta Cryst. A40*, 195-200 (1984).
29. J.L. Sussman, *Methods Enzymol. 115*, 271-303 (1985).
30. J.L. Sussman, S.R. Holbrook, G.M. Church and S.-H. Kim, *Acta Crystallogr. sect. A, 33*, 800-804 (1977).
31. W.A. Hendrickson, *Methods Enzymol. 115*, 252-270 (1985).
32. W.A. Hendrickson and J.H. Konnert, in *Computing in Crystallography*, Eds., R. Diamond, S. Ramaseshan and K. Venkatesan, The Indian Academy of Sciences, Bangalore, pp. 13.01-13.23 (1980).
33. E. Westhof, P. Dumas and D. Moras, *J. Mol. Biol. 184*, 119-145 (1985).
34. W. Saenger, *Principles of Nucleic Acid Structure*, Springer Verlag, New York (1984).
35. R.E. Dickerson, in *Biological Macromolecules and Assemblies: Vol. 2, Nucleic Acids and Interactive Proteins*, Eds., F. Jurnak and A. McPherson, Wylie, New York, Appendix, pp. 471-494 (1985).
36. R.E. Dickerson, M. Bansal, C.R. Calladine, S. Diekmann, W.N. Hunter, O. Kennard, E. von Kitzing, R. Lavery, H.C.M. Nelson, W.K. Olson, W. Saenger, Z. Shakked, H. Sklenar, D.M. Soumpasis, C.-S. Tung, A.H.-J. Wang and V.B. Zhurkin, *EMBO J. 8*, 1-4 (1989).
37. R. Lavery and H. Sklenar, *J. Biomol. Struct. Dyn. 6*, 63-91 (1988).
38. R. Lavery and H. Sklenar, *J. Biomol. Struct. Dyn. 6*, 655-667 (1989).
39. M.L. Kopka, C. Yoon, D. Goodsell, P. Pjura and R.E. Dickerson, *Proc. Natl. Acad. Sci. USA 82*, 1376-1380 (1985).
40. M.L. Kopka, C. Yoon, D. Goodsell, P. Pjura and R.E. Dickerson, *J. Mol. Biol. 183*, 553-563 (1985).
41. P.E. Pjura, K. Grzeskowiak and R.E. Dickerson, *J. Mol. Biol. 197*, 257-271 (1987).
42. R.E. Dickerson, M.L. Kopka and P. Pjura, *Proc. Natl. Acad. Sci. USA 80*, 7099-7103 (1983).
43. H.R. Drew and R.E. Dickerson, *J. Mol. Biol. 151*, 535-556 (1981).
44. E. Westhof, *J. Biomol. Struct. Dyn. 5*, 581-600 (1987).
45. S. Arnott and E. Selsing, *J. Mol. Biol. 88*, 551-552 (1974).
46. S. Bram, *Nature New Biology 233*, 161-164 (1971).
47. W.L. Peticolas, Y. Wang and G.A. Thomas, *Proc. Natl. Acad. Sci. USA 85*, 2579-2583 (1988).

48. H.-Y. Mei and J.K. Barton, *Proc. Natl. Acad. Sci. USA 85*, 1339-1343 (1988).
49. T.E. Haran, Z. Berkovich-Yellin and Z. Shakked, *J. Biomol. Struct. Dyn. 2*, 397-412 (1984).
50. D.G. Reid, S.A. Salisbury, S. Bellard, Z. Shakked and D.H. Williams, *Biochemistry 22*, 2019-2025 (1983).
51. L.J. Rinkel, M.A. Sanderson, G.A. van der Marel, J.H. van Boom and C. Altona, *Eur. J. Biochem. 159*, 85-93 (1986).
52. M.J. Benevides, A.H.-J. Wang, A. Rich, Y. Kyogoku, G.A. van der Marel, J.H. van Boom and G.J. Thomas, *Biochemistry 25*, 41-50 (1986).
53. S. Wolk, W.N. Thurmes, W.S. Ross, C.C. Hardin and I. Tinoco, Jr., *Biochemistry 28*, 2452-2459 (1989).
54. L. Fairall, S. Martin and D. Rhodes, *EMBO J. 8*, 1809-1817 (1989).
55. C.A.G. Haasnoot, H.P. Westerink, G.A. van der Marel and J.H. van Boom, *J. Biomol. Struct. Dyn. 2*, 345-360 (1984).
56. J. Doucet, J.-P. Benoit, W.B.T. Cruse, T. Prange and O. Kennard, *Nature 337*, 190-192 (1989).

Structure & Methods, ISBN 0 940030 32 2
Volume 3: DNA & RNA, ISBN 0-940030-31-4
Eds., Ramaswamy H. Sarma & Mukti H. Sarma, © Adenine Press 1990

Polymorphism and Isomorphism in DNA Crystals: The Effect of Crystal Packing, Hydration and Temperature on the DNA Double Helix

Zippora Shakked, Gali Guerstein-Guzikevich, Anat Zaytzev, Miriam Eisenstein, Felix Frolow and Dov Rabinovich
Department of Structural Chemistry
The Weizmann Institute of Science
P O Box 26, Rehovot 76100, Israel

Abstract

Polymorphism in DNA crystals has been investigated for the first time in the octamer d(GGGCGCCC). This oligomer crystallizes as an A-DNA duplex in two crystal forms (tetragonal and hexagonal). The structure of each form was analyzed at room temperature (293K) and low temperature (110K). This study demonstrates that several conformations may be adopted by the same molecule in the crystalline state depending on molecular packing, hydration and temperature. The global structure changes most from one crystal environment to the next whereas variations in the local structure are determined primarily by base-sequence and hydration effects. A comparison between several isomorphous crystal structures of the A-type and B-type helices shows that within the same crystalline environment, variability in the overall helical conformation is determined by the specific intermolecular interactions.

Introduction

Two factors play an important role in determining the structure of DNA in the crystal namely, the base sequence and the crystalline environment. Base-sequence effects may be estimated by studying isomorphous crystal structures, that is different oligomers in similar crystalline environments. The effects of the crystalline environment can be elucidated by studying polymorphic structures that is, the same molecules in various crystalline environments. Crystalline isomorphism has been observed in almost all DNA crystal structures reported so far. For example, A-type octamers were shown to adopt hexagonal (space group $P6_1$) or tetragonal (space group $P4_32_12$) crystal forms (1) and B-DNA dodecamers were shown to adopt a common orthorhombic crystal packing (space group $P2_12_12_1$) (2). These studies have shown that within the same crystal packing various DNA fragments exhibit different conformations which are related to the specific base sequence (1).

Polymorphism in DNA crystals has been reported only recently in the A-DNA octamer d(GGGCGCCC) (3). The detailed structural study of the different crystals reported here enables us to estimate for the first time the effects of crystal forces, hydration and temperature on the A-DNA double-helical structure. The structural results are compared with those of other A-type and B-type crystal structures.

Results and Discussion

(a) Global Conformations

The structure of the double-helical octamer d(GGGCGCCC) was analyzed in two crystal forms, tetragonal and hexagonal. Each form was studied at both room temperature (RT) and low temperature (LT). The experimental details were published in a preliminary report (3). Crystal data of the various structures of d(GGGCGCCC) are given in Table I.

The crystal structures (RT and LT) of the tetragonal form have been reported (4,5) showing that the double-helical structures at the two temperatures are very similar except for slight changes expected from the temperature change. Two hexagonal crystals differing slightly in cell dimensions were analyzed at room temperature. Another hexagonal crystal was determined at low temperature. As shown by the crystal data of Table I, the unit-cell volume of the hexagonal crystals is reduced by almost one fifth of its value upon cooling whereas the equivalent value for the tetragonal crystals is only 3%. The diffracting power of the hexagonal crystals is increased appreciably in this process. The observed differences between the RT and LT crystals indicate a phenomenon of phase transition, and hence the hexagonal LT structure represents a different crystal environment than the RT one. The structural analyses of these crystals demonstrate a large change in conformation between the RT and LT duplexes, as well as some significant variations between the two RT structures.

Table I
X-Ray Data of d(GGGCGCCC)[a]

	Tetragonal		Hexagonal		
	RT (293K)	LT (110K)	RT1 (293K)	RT2 (293K)	LT (110K)
Space Group	$P4_32_12$	$P4_32_12$	$P6_1$	$P6_1$	$P6_1$
a (Å)	43.28	42.74	46.96	46.54	43.62
b	43.28	42.74	46.96	46.54	43.62
c	24.66	24.57	44.31	43.98	41.49
V ($Å^3$)	46192	44882	84623	82497	68367
No. of oligomers/unit cell	8	8	12	12	12
Resolution (Å)	1.7	1.7	2.9	2.9	1.9

[a]Crystallization was done at 19°C using solutions containing 2 mM DNA, 5 mM $MgCl_2$, 0.15 mM spermine.4HCl, 5% MPD and 50 mM sodium cacodylate (pH 7.0), equilibrated against reservoir of concentrated MPD (2-methyl-2,4-pentanediol) solutions (30, 50%). Tetragonal crystals appeared predominantly at 30% MPD whereas hexagonal crystals appeared at 50% MPD when the drops almost dried out. The hexagonal crystals were transferred to a buffered solution containing 75% MPD before exposure to X-rays.

Table II
Average Helix Parameters of d(GGGCGCCC)[a]

	Tetragonal		Hexagonal		
	Ia	Ib	IIa	IIb	III
Helix twist (°)	32(4)	32(3)	31(4)	31(5)	32(2)
Rise/base-pair (Å)	3.3(0.1)	3.2(0.2)	2.9(0.3)	2.9(0.3)	2.9(0.3)
Base-pair inclination (°)	7(1)	7(1)	13(2)	12(2)	14(2)
Propeller twist (°)	−9(3)	−10(3)	−6(6)	−6(3)	−9(5)
Base-pair distance,dx (Å)	−3.8(0.2)	−3.4(0.1)	−4.9(0.3)	−4.6(0.3)	−3.5(0.2)
Helix diameter (Å)	19.5(0.9)	19.1(0.8)	19.7(0.8)	19.4(0.9)	18.1(0.4)
Major-groove width[b] (Å)	10.9(0.7)	9.6(0.5)	8.0(0.4)	7.5(0.3)	5.6(0.5)
Minor-groove width (Å)	9.4(0.3)	9.4(0.2)	9.7(0.6)	9.7(0.4)	10.3(0.5)

(Ia) Tetragonal RT (Ib) Tetragonal LT
(IIa) Hexagonal RT1 (IIb) Hexagonal RT2 (III) Hexagonal LT

[a]Helix diameter was estimated from the average distance of Phosphorus atoms from the helix axis. All other parameters were defined by Fratini *et al.* (11) and Dickerson *et al.* (12). All the values of Tables II and III were calculated by NEWHELIX computer program (version 1989) by R.E. Dickerson.
[b]The groove widths were estimated from averaging the shortest P-P distances across each groove of the continuous helices. The corresponding values of major-groove widths in the five structures derived from the distance between terminal 5′-phosphates are 10.1, 9.9, 8.2, 7.5 and 5.0 Å respectively.

The global parameters of each of the five structures are given in Table II. These values highlight the resemblance and differences between various helices. The two tetragonal structures (Ia, Ib) are very similar. They are characterized by a very small tilting of the base pairs with respect to the overall helix axis (7°), a large rise per base pair (3.3 Å) and a wide open major groove. They differ slightly in the depth of their major grooves as indicated by the average distance of the base pairs (dx) from the helix axis (−3.8, −3.4 Å), and also by the average helix diameter (19.5, 19.1 Å). Such changes are a consequence of a slight shrinkage (perpendicular to the helix axis) of Ib with respect to Ia. The two hexagonal RT structures (IIa,IIb) show medium values of base tilting (13, 12°) and rise (2.9 Å). Their major grooves are narrower and deeper than those of the previous structures. The two differ slightly in the width (8.2, 7.5 Å) and depth (−4.9, −4.6 Å) of their major grooves and also in their helix diameters (19.7, 19.4 Å). The hexagonal LT structure (III) displays the smallest diameter (18.1 Å) and the narrowest (5 Å) and shallowest major groove (−3.5 Å).

The five structures of d(GGGCGCCC) reveal three distinct conformations of the A-DNA double helix displayed by Ia, IIa and III in Figure 1. Continuous helices based on the three structures are displayed in Figure 2. These results show that the same oligomer can assume several conformations in the crystalline state.

(b) Local Conformations

The crystal structures of the various A- and B-type fragments determined so far have demonstrated a significant correlation between the local structure and the base sequence. The effect of the base sequence was reflected primarily by variations in base-stacking geometry and to a much lesser extent by changes in the sugar-phosphate backbone (1,6). Variations in the base-stacking geometry can be estimated

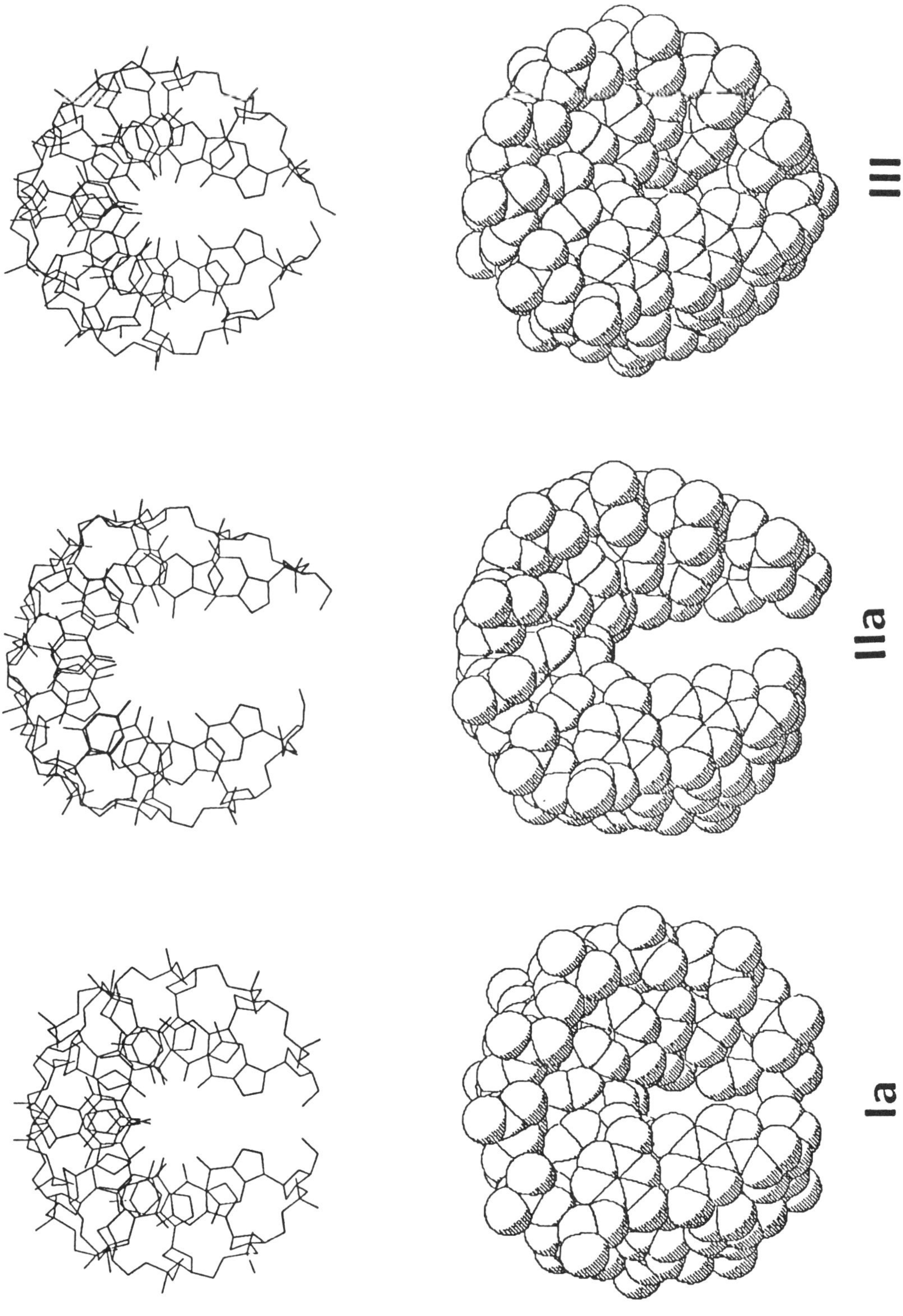

Figure 1: Stick-type and space-filling drawings of the double-helical octamers Ia, IIa, and III. The view is down the helix axis.

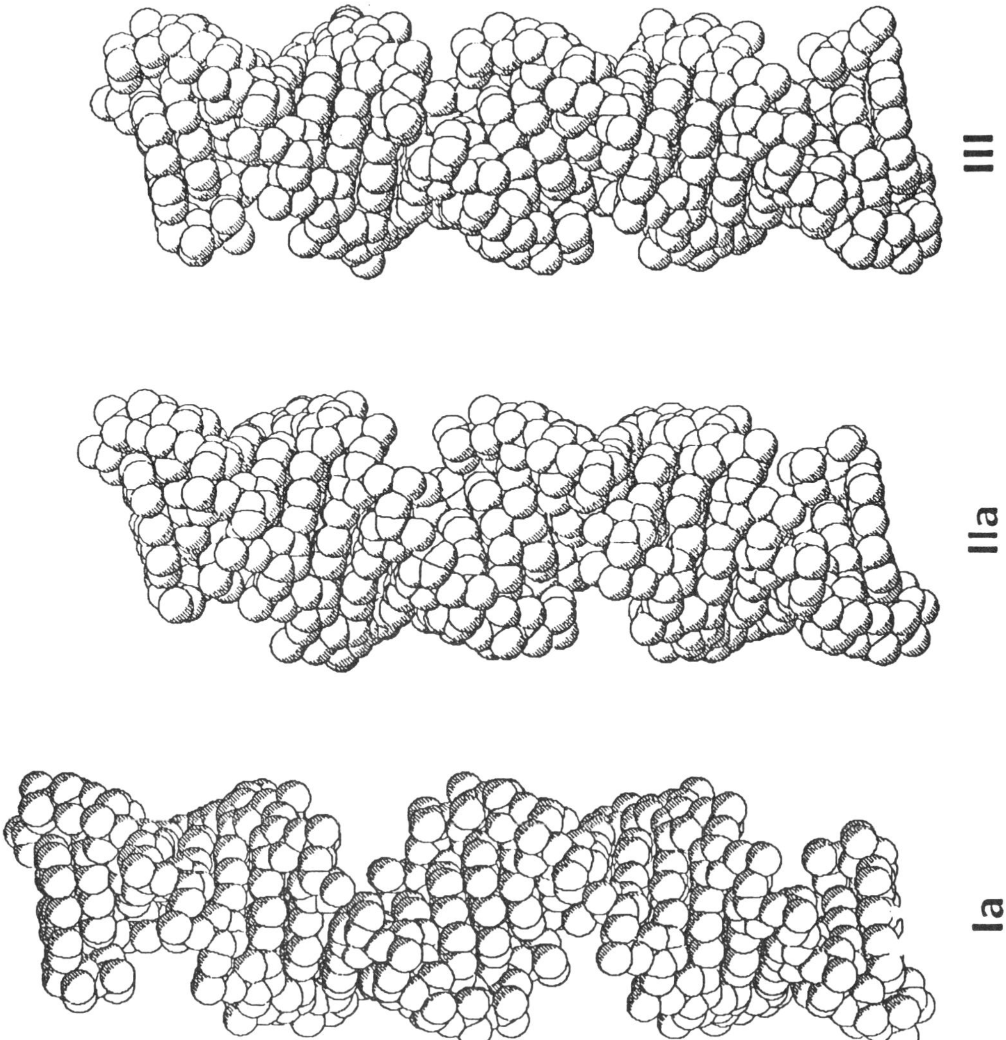

Figure 2: Continuous helices based on Ia, IIa, and III. Each helix (24 base pairs long) was generated by rotating and translating the corresponding double-helical octamer with respect to the overall helix axis, using the average values of helix twist and rise/base pair of Table II.

Table III
Local Stacking Parameters of d(GGGCGCCC)

Helical Step	Twist (°) (Ia)	(Ib)	(IIa)	(IIb)	(III)	Roll (°) (Ia)	(Ib)	(IIa)	(IIb)	(III)
G-G	32.3	32.5	29.4	27.8	32.0	7.2	10.3	1.2	3.2	3.7
G-G	31.2	32.0	28.9	33.2	36.0	6.4	5.9	13.2	2.4	5.5
G-C	34.7	34.9	35.5	33.4	32.6	3.7	3.8	2.0	13.8	7.1
C-G	24.0	25.1	23.7	24.8	29.0	3.5	8.3	8.9	4.6	10.0
G-C	34.7	34.9	37.3	36.2	32.0	3.7	3.8	3.5	5.2	6.1
C-C	31.2	32.0	30.0	32.8	33.4	6.4	5.9	10.4	4.9	7.5
C-C	32.3	32.5	30.1	28.0	30.8	7.2	10.3	11.1	14.4	6.9
Average	31.5	32.0	30.6	30.9	32.3	5.4	6.9	7.2	6.9	6.7
Helical Step	**Slide (Å) (Ia)**	**(Ib)**	**(IIa)**	**(IIb)**	**(III)**	**Rise (Å) (Ia)**	**(Ib)**	**(IIa)**	**(IIb)**	**(III)**
G-G	−1.4	−1.4	−2.2	−2.0	−1.6	3.4	3.3	2.9	3.0	2.9
G-G	−1.7	−1.6	−2.2	−1.9	−1.3	3.3	3.3	2.8	2.7	2.6
G-C	−1.3	−1.3	−1.6	−1.4	−0.7	3.1	3.0	2.6	2.7	2.9
C-G	−2.2	−1.9	−1.3	−1.7	−1.0	3.3	3.4	3.4	3.3	3.3
G-C	−1.3	−1.3	−2.0	−1.9	−0.8	3.1	3.0	2.3	2.6	3.0
C-C	−1.7	−1.6	−2.4	−2.2	−1.7	3.3	3.3	2.9	2.6	2.5
C-C	−1.4	−1.4	−1.5	−1.5	−1.5	3.4	3.3	3.0	3.1	2.9
Average	−1.6	−1.5	−1.9	−1.8	−1.2	3.3	3.2	2.9	2.8	2.9

from the relative rotations and translations of adjacent base pairs. Four of these (two rotations and two translations) are largely variable in the present structures: the local helical twist which is the relative rotation of two base pairs with respect to the helix axis; the roll angle which measures the opening of the base pairs towards the helical groove; the rise per base pair with respect to the helix axis and the slide, *i.e.*, the relative displacement of the two base pairs along their long axes. The values of the four parameters for each structure are given in Table III. The local features of the tetragonal structures are highly similar. However, they differ significantly from those of the hexagonal structures. Within the hexagonal series the two RT structures (IIa,IIb) are similar and differ from the LT one (III).

The central C-G step of the present sequence has been studied in several other A-type octamers: d(CCCCGGGG) (7) d(GGCCGGCC) (8) and d(GCCCGGGC) (9). In all these structures as well as the tetragonal form of d(GGGCGCCC), the C-G step adopts a unique stacking geometry with a small twist (av. 24°) and large negative slide (av. −2.1 Å) and rise (av. 3.3 Å). The corresponding averages calculated for all helical steps are 32°, −1.5 Å and 3.2 Å respectively (Table IV). In contrast to the three parameters which are almost invariant in this group, the roll angle and propeller twist display each a broad range of values indicating that both are relatively soft parameters and easily affected by environmental effects. All these oligomers are of the tetragonal space group and hence the central site incorporates a crystallographic 2-fold symmetry. The sugar-phosphate backbone of each of these sites

Table IV
Helical Parameters of C-G Doublets[a]

Sequence	Helical Twist	Roll	Slide	Rise	Propeller Twist
Tetragonal					
d(GGGCGCCC)	24.0(31.5)	3.5(5.4)	−2.2(−1.5)	3.3(3.3)	−8.0(−9.1)
d(GGCCGGCC)	24.9(32.7)	11.0(7.7)	−1.9(−1.3)	3.4(3.2)	−12.0(−12.0)
d(CCCCGGGG)	24.5(33.1)	0.0(3.6)	−2.0(−1.7)	3.1(3.1)	−1.4(−7.8)
d(GCCCGCCC)	23.2(31.3)	−0.1(3.8)	−2.3(−1.6)	3.2(3.2)	−6.0(−9.1)
average	24.1(32.1)	3.6(5.1)	−2.1(−1.5)	3.3(3.2)	−6.9(−9.5)
s.d.	0.7(0.9)	5.2(1.9)	0.2(0.2)	0.1(0.1)	4.4(1.8)

[a]The values in parentheses are the averages obtained from all other doublets. The references are given in Table V.

adopts an extended structure resulting from all *trans* conformation at the P-O5′-C5′-C4′ bonds.

The unique properties of C-G mentioned above are only partially retained in the hexagonal series. The two RT structures (IIa,IIb) display helix twist values (24, 25°) and rise (3.4, 3.3 Å) similar to those of Table IV. Slides are negatively smaller (−1.3, −1.7 Å). The values of the three parameters in the LT structure (III) are 29°, 3.3 Å and −1.0 Å. The roll angles of this step in the five structures vary from 3.5° to 10°. The individual propeller twist values of the central base pairs are −8° for Ia and Ib and −2, −7, −11° for IIa, IIb and III. In contrast to the extended backbone observed at C-G in all tetragonal structures, the backbone of this step in the hexagonal series displays the usual *gauche*(−), *trans*, *gauche*(+) conformation.

Hence, the rise of C-G is the only invariant parameter in this series. As the rise is measured with respect to the helix axis, it may be affected by the inclination of the base pairs and the slide. In a uniform A-structure the larger the inclination and sliding are, the smaller is the rise. For the tetragonal structures (Ia,Ib) where the bases are only slightly tilted, the rise is not dependent on either of the two parameters. It is rather constant along the helix (av. 3.3 Å). However, in the hexagonal duplexes the base-pair inclination is not negligible. Individual values of rise range from 2.3 to 3.4 Å. The largest values in each duplex are displayed by the C-G steps. These values cannot be accounted for by the slide values and thus indicating a significant increase in the vertical separation between the central base pairs compared to other steps.

The stacking geometry of the C-G doublet in each of the five structures is shown in Figure 3. The sliding motion is reflected by changes in the amount of overlapping or stacking between the central guanine bases. At high negative slide as for Ia and Ib, the six-membered rings of the two bases overlap extensively. The amount of overlapping diminishes gradually going from Ia to III. The decrease in interstrand stacking is associated by a simultaneous increase in intramolecular stacking between guanine and cytosine bases. The present study shows that this particular base-pair doublet

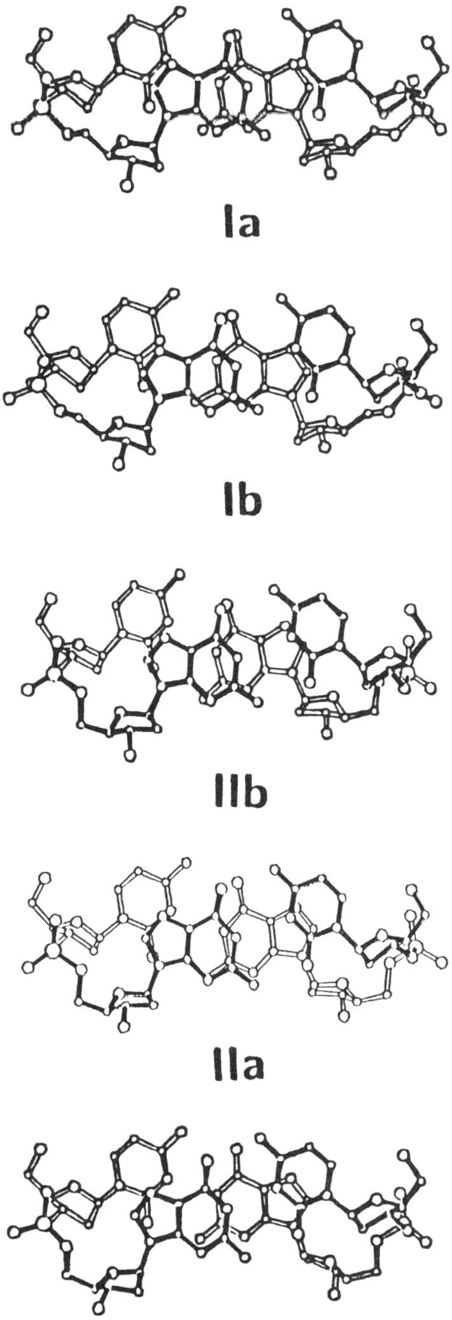

Figure 3: Stacking geometry of C-G doublets in Ia, Ib, IIb, IIa and III. The view is perpendicular to the upper base pair. It shows the gradual decrease in slide from top to bottom.

may adopt a continuous spectrum of stacking arrangements ranging from a purely A-type geometry with large negative slides through medium to very small ones approaching a B-type geometry.

The non-bonded stacking energies of the two helices which differ most in their local geometries (Ia,III) were calculated using a procedure described before (10). The energy is nearly constant along each helix (Figure 4). The central step of Ia is slightly destabilized compared to III. While the interstrand components of the energy are comparable, the intrastrand contribution of III is lower than that of Ia showing that an extensive overlapping of the guanines observed in several structures is not necessarily driven by stacking interactions as we discuss further on.

(c) Environmental Effects

Among the external factors that appear to affect helical conformation and molecular packing are hydration and temperature. Analysis of the water structure in the five duplexes shows that the level of hydration changes appreciably from one conformational type to the next. Ia and Ib are highly hydrated. III is fairly hydrated whereas IIa and IIb are poorly hydrated. It appears that during the phase transition of the hexagonal crystals the water structure undergoes a major rearrangement leading to an ordered network interacting with the double helix. The first hydration shell of each of the three unique structures (Ia, IIa, III) is shown in Figure 5. The major groove of Ia is extensively hydrated forming a pentagon-like network which was also observed in the structure of d(GGTATACC) (13,14). However, unlike d(GGTATACC), all the phosphate oxygens of Ia are individually hydrated in

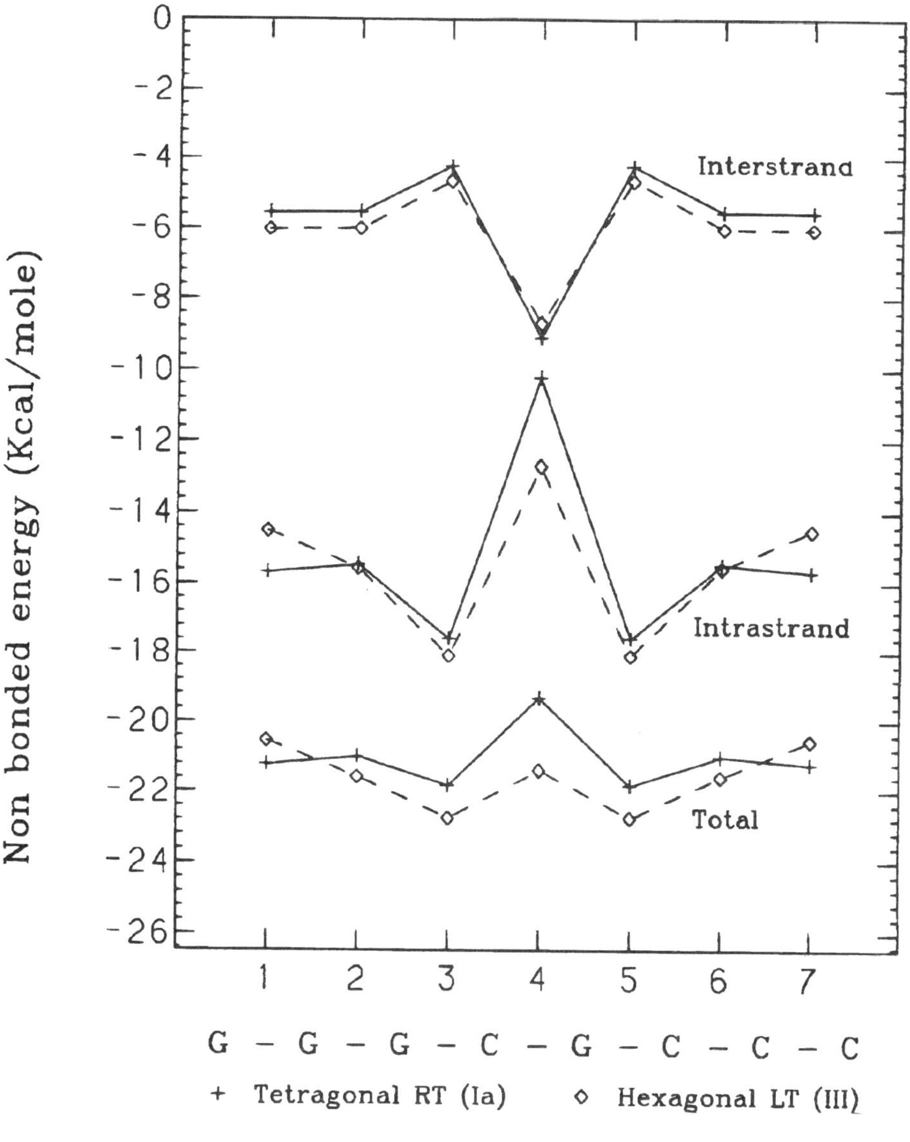

Figure 4: Non-bonding stacking energy variations along the double helix for Ia and III.

discord to the proposed principle of economy of hydration in A-DNA (15). The number of ordered water molecules interacting directly with the DNA atoms is 84. The major groove and the sugar-phosphate backbone of III are less hydrated than Ia incorporating 64 ordered waters. IIa is poorly hydrated with only 24 ordered waters bound to the DNA. The minor groove is scarcely hydrated in all three duplexes except for the central region of Ia discussed later on. We may therefore conclude that the tetragonal form is of high water activity and the hexagonal RT and LT forms are of low and intermediate water activity.

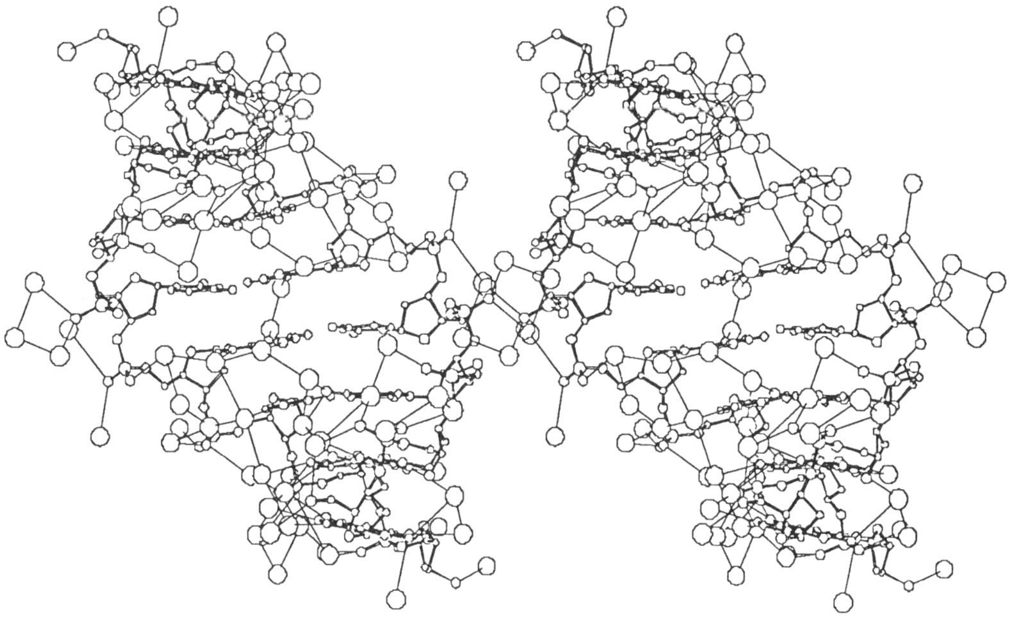

Ia

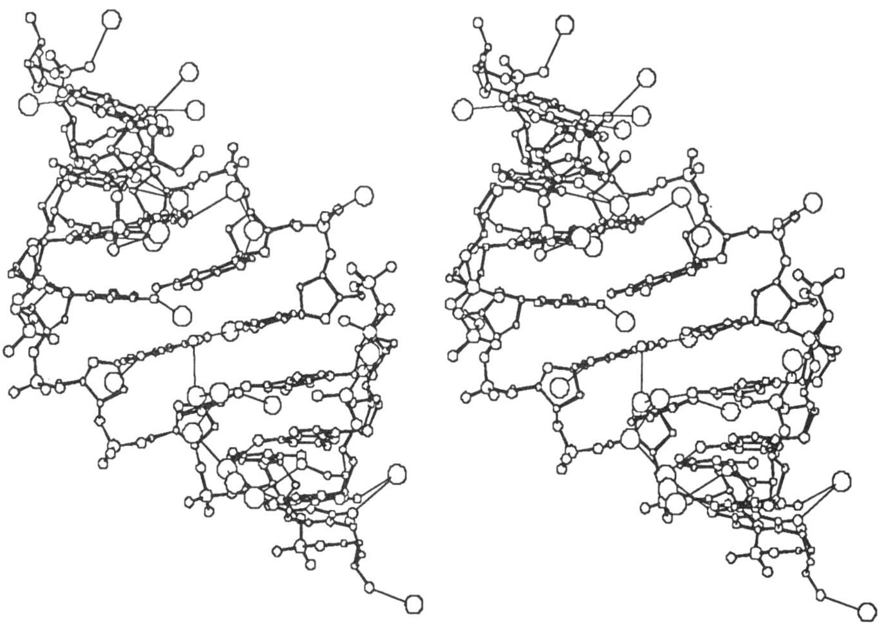

IIa

Figure 5: Stereoscopic drawings of Ia, IIa, and III showing mainly the first hydration shell. The view is down the major groove.

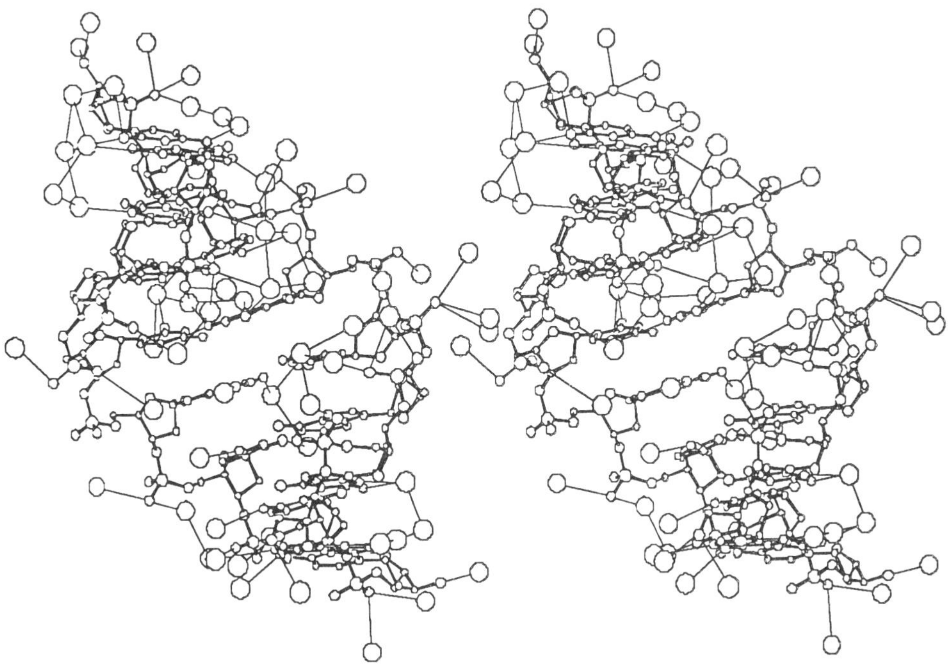

III

Figure 5: *continued*

Table V
Average Helix Parameters of A-DNA Octamers

Compound	Symmetry	Helix twist (°)	Rise/ base pair (Å)	Base Pair inclination (°)	Groove width Major (Å)	Groove width Minor (Å)	dx (Å)	Ref.
d(GGTATACC)	$P6_1$	31.9	2.9	13.2	6.3	10.2	−4.0	13
d(GGGGCCCC)	$P6_1$	31.6	2.9	12.6	6.8	10.2	−4.2	16
d(GGGTACCC)	$P6_1$	30.0	2.9	13.2	8.2	9.7	−4.6	17
d(GGGATCCC)	$P6_1$	30.0	2.9	12.9	8.7	9.4	−4.8	18
Mean		30.8	2.9	13.0	7.5	9.9	−4.4	
s.d.		1.0	0.0	0.3	1.1	0.4	0.4	
d(CCCCGGGG)	$P4_32_12$	33.1	3.1	9.0	8.6	9.4	−3.8	7
d(GGCCGGCC)	$P4_32_12$	32.7	3.2	11.4	7.7	9.8	−3.4	8b
d(GGGCGCCC)	$P4_32_12$	31.5	3.3	6.5	10.1	9.4	−3.8	4
d(GCCCGGGC)	$P4_32_12$	31.3	3.2	7.2	9.8	9.6	−4.0	9
Mean		32.1	3.2	8.5	9.1	9.6	−3.8	
s.d.		0.9	0.1	2.2	1.1	0.2	0.3	

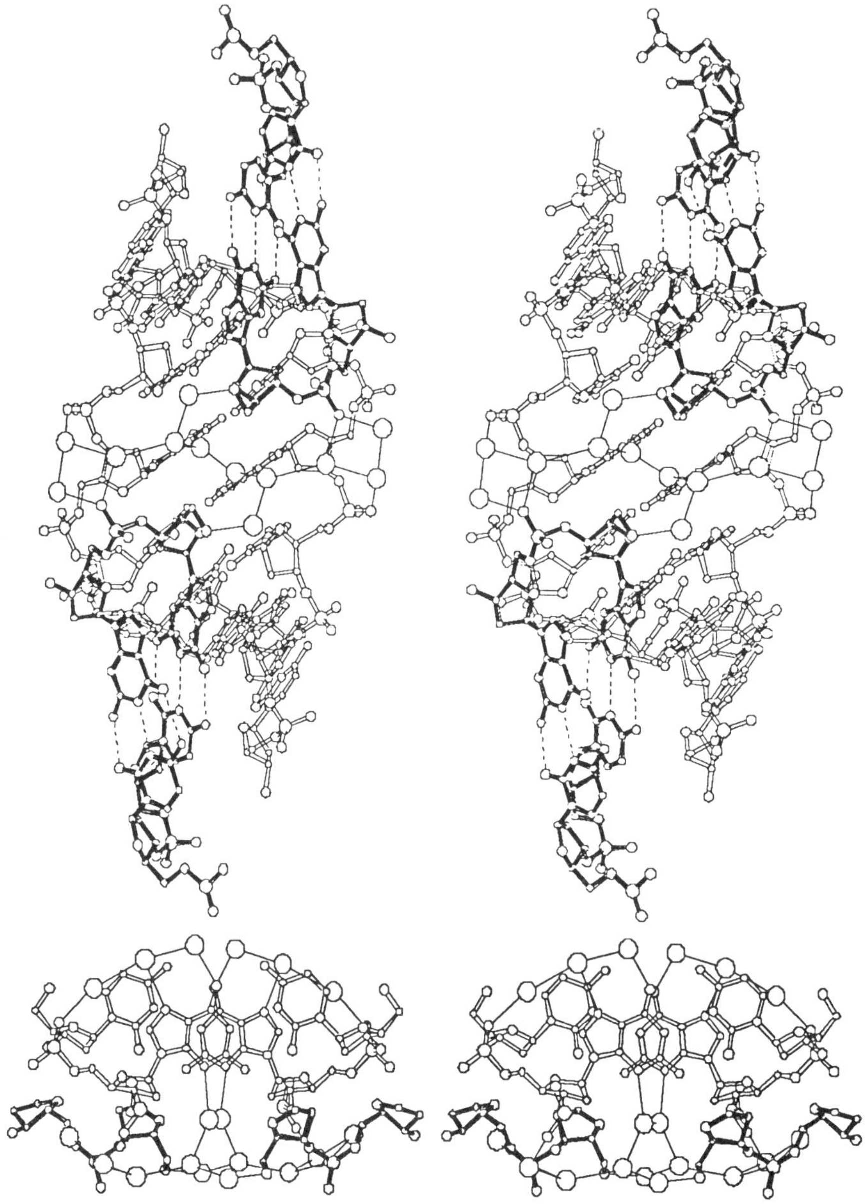

Figure 6: Stereoscopic drawings showing intermolecular contacts and hydration. (a) A view of Ia down the minor groove showing the hydration at the central C-G step. The hydration is held by hydrogen bonds to the guanine residues at the minor-groove side and to the sugar-phosphate backbone of two neighboring duplexes generated by the four-fold screw axes. Only the first two base pairs of each symmetry-related duplex (dark bonds) are shown. (b) The hydration at the minor and major grooves of C-G. The view is perpendicular to the upper base pair. Only part of the sugar-phosphate backbone of the symmetry-related molecules of the previous view is shown. (c) A view of IIa down the minor groove showing the intermolecular interactions with duplexes generated by the two-fold screw axis (top) and the six-fold screw axis (bottom). Only the first two base pairs of each duplex (dark bonds) are shown. (d) A view of III down the minor groove. The symmetry-related fragments are as in previous drawing. Water-mediated interduplex hydrogen bonds are shown as well. Note the significant changes in the positions of the symmetry-related duplexes in III with respect to those in IIa.

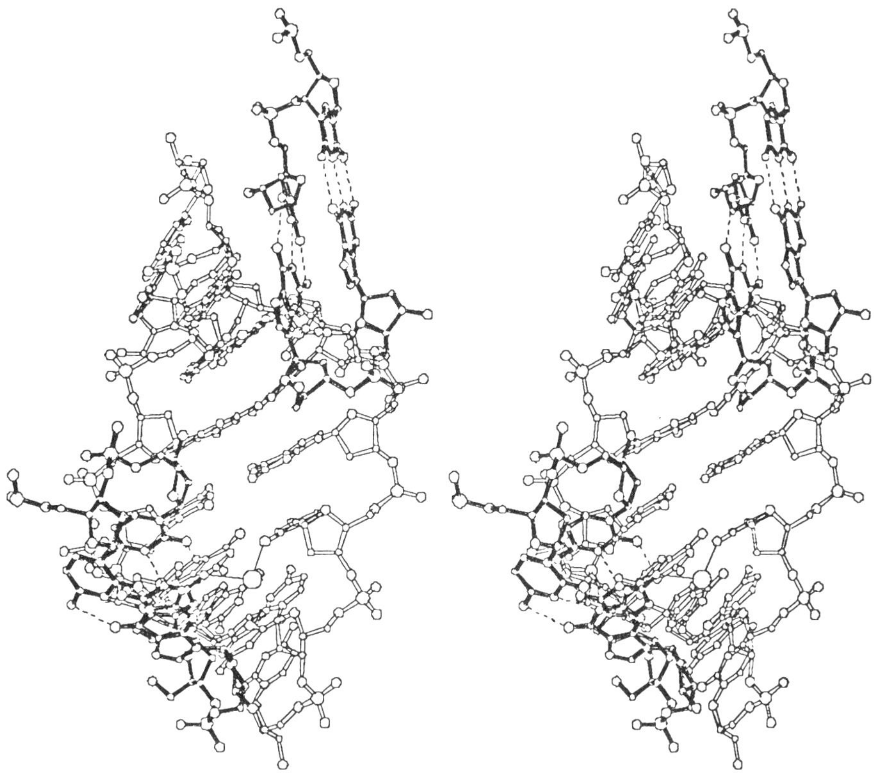

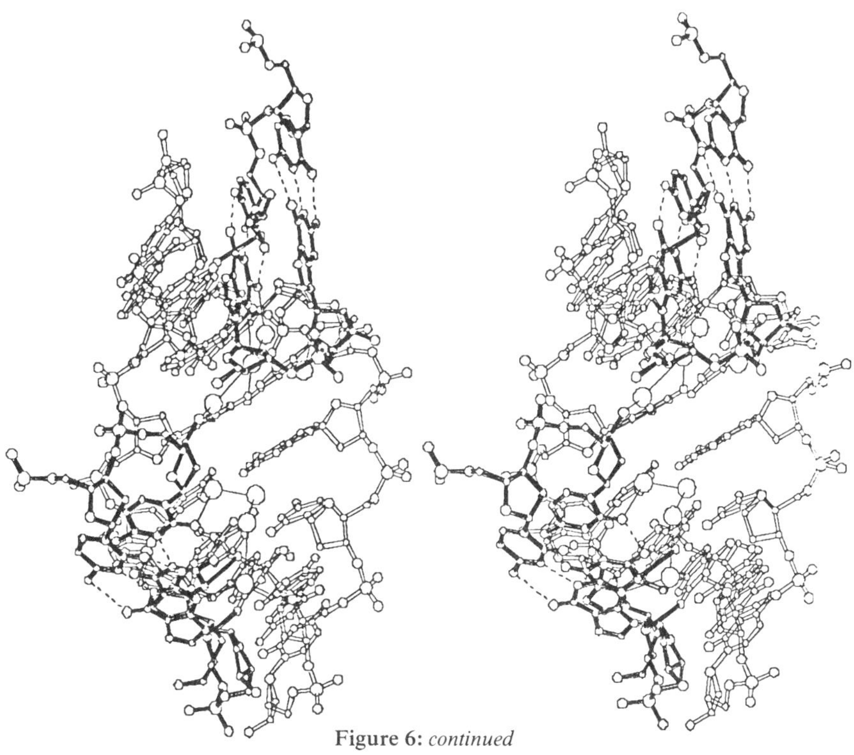

Figure 6: *continued*

Apart from hydration, intermolecular interactions may also play an important role in shaping the overall conformation of the double helix. As mentioned before all A-type octamers reported so far were crystallized in either the tetragonal or the hexagonal space groups. Table V gives the global helical paramcters of all octamers which were determined at room temperature, at reasonable resolution (< 2.5 Å) (excluding the ones with mismatched base pairs) and for which the required data was available. The eight structures can be classified into two distinct conformations. All the hexagonal structures adopt a common shape characterized by medium values of rise (2.9 Å) and inclination (av. 13°), and a deep major groove (av. −4.4 Å). All the tetragonal structures are characterized by a large rise (3.2 Å) and a small inclination of the base pairs (av. 8.5°). The major groove is wider and shallower than that of the hexagonal ones.

The intermolecular interactions observed in the A-octamer crystal structures were described in several papers (4,7,8,9,13,18). In each of these interactions a terminal base pair (C · G or G · C) of one duplex stacks at the flat minor groove of a crystallographic symmetry-related duplex. The specific location of the base pair at the minor groove varies depending on the symmetry axis involved (two-, four- or six-fold screw operation). These interaction modes are shown in Figure 6. In some cases the interaction is further stabilized by direct or water-mediated hydrogen bonds depending on the base sequence(17). We cannot correlate the global features of each of the two main conformations (Table V) with the difference in packing. It should be mentioned that the A-type double-helical tetramer d(^{I}CCGG) which simulates a double-helical octamer in the tetragonal-type of packing (23) displays the hexagonal-type global features such as a rise of 2.8 Å, base-pair inclination of 14° and a major-groove width of 5 Å. Hence the hexagonal conformational type can be accommodated in the tetragonal crystal packing. It is not clear however, if the other way around is feasible as well. It is also possible that water-mediated intermolecular contacts observed in several of these crystals (17) play a role in modulating the global helical conformation.

In view of these data it appears that either packing requirements control the overall helical shape or a particular conformation crystallizes in the appropriate crystal form. In other words, the global conformation and crystal packing are mutually dependent.

The variations in local structure from one crystalline environment to the next observed in the present study are not likely to be induced directly by crystal packing forces for the following reasons. Intermolecular interactions in the A-DNA crystals are relatively soft as described before. Also, the internal two-fold symmetry of the self-complementary helices is largely retained in the hexagonal structures which do not incorporate crystallographic two-fold symmetry axes. The RMS deviation between the two strands obtained by a best molecular fitting procedure in each of these fragments is around 0.5 Å. In other words, although the two molecular halves are subjected to different crystal forces their structures are similar. It is therefore likely that changes in local structure of the same molecule in different crystals are brought about by changes in hydration. This hypothesis is supported by the unique water structure observed for the C-G doublet of the tetragonal form (Figure 6a,b) and which is common to the other A-DNA octamers, d(CCCCGGGG), d(GGCCGGCC) and d(GCCCGGGC) sharing the same stacking geometry (19). The hydration at the minor groove leads to the water-mediated interstrand linkage of the guanine residues through the N3 atoms of the bases and the 3′-phosphate oxygens. The whole water structure is supported by the sugar-phosphate backbone of the first two residues of each of two symmetry-related duplexes generated by four-fold screw axes. Any sliding of the base pairs in a direction that decreases the overlap between the guanines would disrupt the hydration. At the major groove the strings of water molecules interacting with the guanines are stabilized by the formation of hydrogen bonds with the nearby 5′-phosphate oxygens. The later atoms are favorably oriented for such interactions as a result of the extended backbone conformation. Hence, the unique local conformation observed in all the tetragonal C-G sites, is induced by the particular water structure. Any similar hydration of the central C-G doublet in the hexagonal crystals is not feasible because of the interference caused by the backbone of a nearby molecule generated by the six-fold screw operation (shown partly at the bottom left of Figures 6c and 6d). Another duplex generated by the two-fold screw operation (part of it is displayed at the upper right of Figures 6c and 6d) is positioned in a similar manner to that generated by the four-fold screw axis of the tetragonal crystal (Figure 6a) as already discussed by us in a previous paper (4). The changes in hydration at the central minor-groove region of the present hexagonal-type duplexes lead to the observed variations in the stacking geometries of their C-G steps.

It is interesting to compare the degree of structural variability in the overall shape of isomorphous structures in the A- and B-DNA series. All B-DNA dodecamers of the general sequence CGCNNNNNNGCG crystallize isomorphously (2). We have chosen to compare two dodecamers which differ in sequence, crystallized under different conditions and determined at different temperatures. These are the original Drew/Dickerson dodecamer d(CGCGAATTCGCG) (20) and d(CGCGATATCGCG) recently analyzed in our laboratory (21). Crystal data and average helix parameters of the two duplexes are given in Table VI. The change in unit-cell volume from room temperature to low temperature is less than 5% and the global parameters of the two helices are practically identical. The RMS value between the two structures obtained by a best molecular fitting is 0.6 Å. A stereoscopic view of the superimposed duplexes is given in Figure 7. It demonstrates the remarkable resemblance of the two helices notwithstanding the great changes in the crystallization conditions and temperature. The specific features of the AT rich tract in d(CGCGAATTCGCG) such as the narrowing of the minor groove and the spine of hydration are also observed in d(CGCGATATCGCG). However, other local conformations are distinctly different at the central four base-pair regions. For example, the propeller twisting at ATAT is smaller than at AATT. The helix twist angles of ATAT alternate between low, high and low values as already predicted from energy calculations (10), whereas a reversed pattern is observed at AATT. The detailed description of the structure and hydration of d(CGCGATATCGCG) will be published elsewhere.

The overall conformations of the other B-dodecamers also resemble that of the Drew-Dickerson dodecamer whereas the local structure is sequence dependent. All

Table VI
Crystal Data of d(CGCGATATCGCG) and d(CGCGAATTCGCG)

Sequence	d(CGCGATATCGCG)[a]	d(CGCGAATTCGCG)[b]
Temperature	100K	293K
Space group	$P2_12_12_1$	$P2_12_12_1$
a (Å)	24.3	24.9
b	39.3	40.4
c	66.3	66.2
V (Å^3)	63411	66595
No. of oligomers/unit cell	8	8
Resolution (Å)	2.2	1.9
Average Helix Parameters		
Helix twist (°)	35(3)	36(4)
Rise/base-pair (Å)	3.3(0.4)	3.4(0.5)
Base-pair inclination (°)	1(6)	−1(6)
Propeller twist (°)	−11(5)	−12(6)
Base-pair distance, dx (Å)	0.1(1.2)	0.1(1.1)
Helix diameter (Å)	18.8(2.4)	18.7(2.0)
Major-groove width (Å)	12.0(0.5)	11.7(0.5)
Minor-groove width (Å)	5.4(2.4)	5.4(2.1)

[a]Crystallization was done at 4°C using solutions containing 0.6 mM DNA, 15 mM $MgCl_2$, 10 mM cacodylate buffer (pH = 7.0), 1.5 mM spermine.4HCl and 10% MPD equilibrated against 30% MPD solutions.

[b]Crystallization was done at room temperature using DNA solutions (pH = 7.5) with 2:1 molar excess of magnesium acetate and one spermine.4HCl per eight base pairs, by vapor diffusion from 20 to 30% MPD (22).

these helices are bent in a similar fashion as a consequence of the interlocking of the minor grooves of two duplexes related by the 2-fold screw axis operation. In this manner each terminal base pair of one duplex is stacked against the sugar-phosphate backbone of the other one. This type of intermolecular interface is stabilized by six hydrogen bonds involving guanine bases and free 3′-hydroxyls. As a result of the asymmetric deformation the RMS deviation between the two strands in all the isomorphous duplexes is close to 2 Å.

Unlike the specific intermolecular interactions of the B-dodecamer series, those of the A-series as mentioned earlier are non specific and soft. As a consequence, the variance in the global conformation observed within each of the isomorphous groups of the A-structures (Table V) is larger than that of the B-structures.

Based on this study the following conclusions may be drawn: The DNA double helix can adopt several conformations in the crystalline state. The molecular conformation and the molecular packing are mutually related. The global structure varies considerably between different crystal environments whereas the local structure is determined by both base-sequence and hydration effects. Within the same crystalline environment, the degree of conformational variability and flexibility are determined by the specific interactions between the molecules.

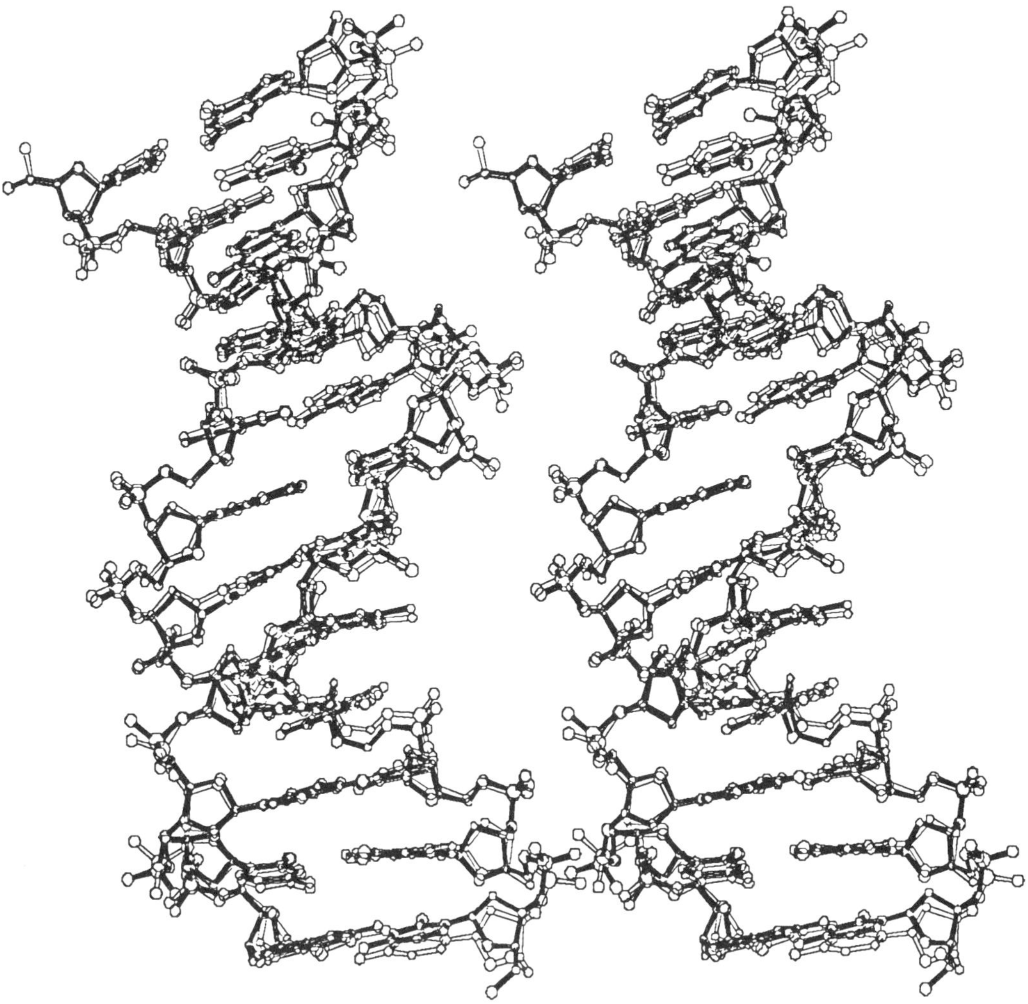

Figure 7: Stereoscopic drawing of the superposition of CGCGATATCGCG (dark bonds) and CGCGAATTCGCG (light bonds) derived by a best molecular fit procedure. The two central A · T and T · A base pairs (the first base is at the 5′-side) of the later were replaced by T · A and A · T pairs respectively to correspond to the base sequence of the former.

Acknowledgments

The work was supported by grants from the Minerva Foundation, Munich Germany, the United-States/Israel Binational Science Foundation and the Helen and Milton A. Kimmelman Center for Biomolecular Structure and Assembly. Z.S. holds the Helena Rubinstein Professorial Chair in Structural Biology.

References and Footnotes

1. Z. Shakked and D. Rabinovich, *Progr. Biophys. Mol. Biol. 47*, 159-195 (1986).
2. R.E. Dickerson in *Structure & Methods, Volume 3: DNA & RNA*, Eds., R.H. Sarma and M.H. Sarma, Adenine Press, p001-038 and references cited therein (1990).
3. Z. Shakked, G. Guerstein-Guzikevich, M. Eisenstein, F. Frolow and D. Rabinovich, *Nature*, in press (1990).
4. D. Rabinovich, T.E. Haran, M., Eisenstein and Z. Shakked, *J. Mol. Biol. 200*, 151-161 (1988).
5. M. Eisenstein, H. Hope, T.E. Haran, F. Frolow, Z. Shakked and D. Rabinovich, *Acta Crystallogr. Sect. B, 44*, 625-628 (1988).
6. T.E. Haran and Z. Shakked, *J. Mol. Struct. 179*, 367-391 (1988).
7. T.E. Haran, Z. Shakked, A.H.J. Wang and A. Rich, *J. Biomol. Struct. Dynam. 5*, 199-217 (1987).
8. (a) A.H.-J. Wang, S. Fujii, J.H. van Boom and A. Rich, *Proc. Natl. Acad Sci. USA 79*, 3968-3972 (1982). (b) T.E. Haran, Ph. D. thesis. The Feinberg Graduate School of the Weizmann Institute of Science (1986).
9. U. Heinemann, H. Lauble, R. Frank and H. Blocker, *Nucleic Acids Res. 18*, 9531-9550 (1987).
10. T.E. Haran, Z. Berkovich-Yellin and Z. Shakked, *J. Biomol. Struct. Dyn. 2*, 397-409 (1984).
11. A.V. Fratini, M.L. Kopka, H.R. Drew and R.E. Dickerson, *J. Biol. Chem. 257*, 14686-14707 (1982).
12. Dickerson, R.E., *et al., EMBO J. 8*, 1-4 (1989).
13. (a) Z. Shakked, D. Rabinovich, W.B.T. Cruse, E. Egert, O. Kennard, G. Sala, S.A. Salisbury and M.A. Viswamitra, *Proc. R. Soc. B 213*, 479-487 (1981). (b) Z. Shakked, D. Rabinovich, O. Kennard, W.B.T. Cruse, S.A. Salisbury and M.A. Viswamitra, *J. Mol. Biol. 200*, 151-161 (1988).
14. O. Kennard, W.B.T. Cruse, J. Nachman, T. Prange, Z. Shakked and D. Rabinovich, *J. Biomol. Struct. Dyn. 3*, 623-647 (1986).
15. W. Saenger, W.N. Hunter and O. Kennard, *Nature 324*, 385-388 (1986).
16. M. McCall, T. Brown and O. Kennard, *J. Mol. Biol. 183*, 385-396 (1985).
17. M. Eisenstein, F. Frolow, Z. Shakked and D. Rabinovich, *Nucleic Acids Res.*, submitted (1989).
18. H. Lauble, R. Frank, H. Blocker and U. Heinemann, *Nucleic Acids Res. 16*, 7799-7816 (1988).
19. Z. Shakked, M. Eisenstein, G. Guerstein-Guzikevich and D. Rabinovich, to be published (1989).
20. R.E. Dickerson and H.R. Drew, *J. Mol. Biol. 149*, 761-786 (1981).
21. A. Zaytzev, M. Sc. Thesis, The Feinberg Graduate School of the Weizmann Institute of Science (1989).
22. R. Wing, H.R. Drew, T. Takano, C. Broka, S. Tanaka, K. Itakura and R.E. Dickerson, *Nature 287*, 755-758 (1980).
23. B.N. Conner, C. Yoon, J.L. Dickerson and R.E. Dickerson, *J. Mol. Biol. 174*, 663-695 (1984).

Structure & Methods, ISBN 0-940030-32-2
Volume 3: DNA & RNA, ISBN 0-940030-31-4
Eds., Ramaswamy H. Sarma & Mukti H. Sarma, © Adenine Press 1990

Nucleic Acid Conformations Studied by Vibrational Spectroscopy

E. Taillandier
Laboratoire de Spectroscopie Biomoleculaire
UFR Biomedicale De Bobigby
74 Rue Marcel Cachin
93012 Bobigny Cedex, France

Abstract

The first FTIR spectra of oligonucleotide crystals are shown. Vibrational spectroscopy has given us the opportunity to study the conformation of the same oligonucleotide under different physical states: solution, hydrated film, crystal. Crystallization often but not always induces a change in the geometry of the studied oligodeoxyribonucleotides. In addition, the marker peaks of the different conformations have been used to detect mixtures of geometries in the same crystal. The coexistence of A and B form has been osberved in the case of the d(GGTATACC) crystal. In solution as in high or low hydrated films, A form spectra have been obtained in the case of $r(Au)_8$.

Vibrational spectroscopy is a technique well adapted to the study of nucleic acid conformations. Raman lines and IR bands characteristic of different nucleic acid structures permit the differentiation of A, B and Z backbone geometries, the identification of C3′ endo and C2′ endo families of nucleoside sugar puckers and of *syn* and *anti* glycosil bond orientations. One of the advantages of vibrational spectroscopy is to give the opportunity to study nucleic acids under a wide variety of physical states: solutions, gels, hydrated fibres or films, crystals. Thus A. Rich using Raman spectroscopy established the identity of the structures of the d(CGCGCG) Z form crystal and of poly d(G-C) in high salt solution (Thamann *et al.* 1981 (3)). Thanks to new developpements in microtechnology it is now possible to study nucleic acid crystals by microRaman spectroscopy and very recently by Fourier transform infrared spectroscopy using microscope attachments. We shall give a few examples of results obtained by the coupling of microscopes to Raman and Fourier transform infrared spectrophotometers.

The conformation of a given oligonucleotide is not necessarily the same in aqueous solution and in crystallized state and the results of vibrational spectroscopy can help in finding out the existing relationship between cristalline structures solved by

X-ray diffraction and solution structures proposed by NMR. Crystallization often induces a change in the geometry of the oligonucleotide, and this is the case for example for the d(CACGTG) sequence. The crystal has been found by X-ray diffuse scattering to belong to the Z family (Coll *et al.* 1988 (1)) and the microRaman spectrum of the crystal presents all the marker lines of the Z conformation concerning the phosphate backbone as well as the G-C and A-T base pairs. However the Raman spectrum of

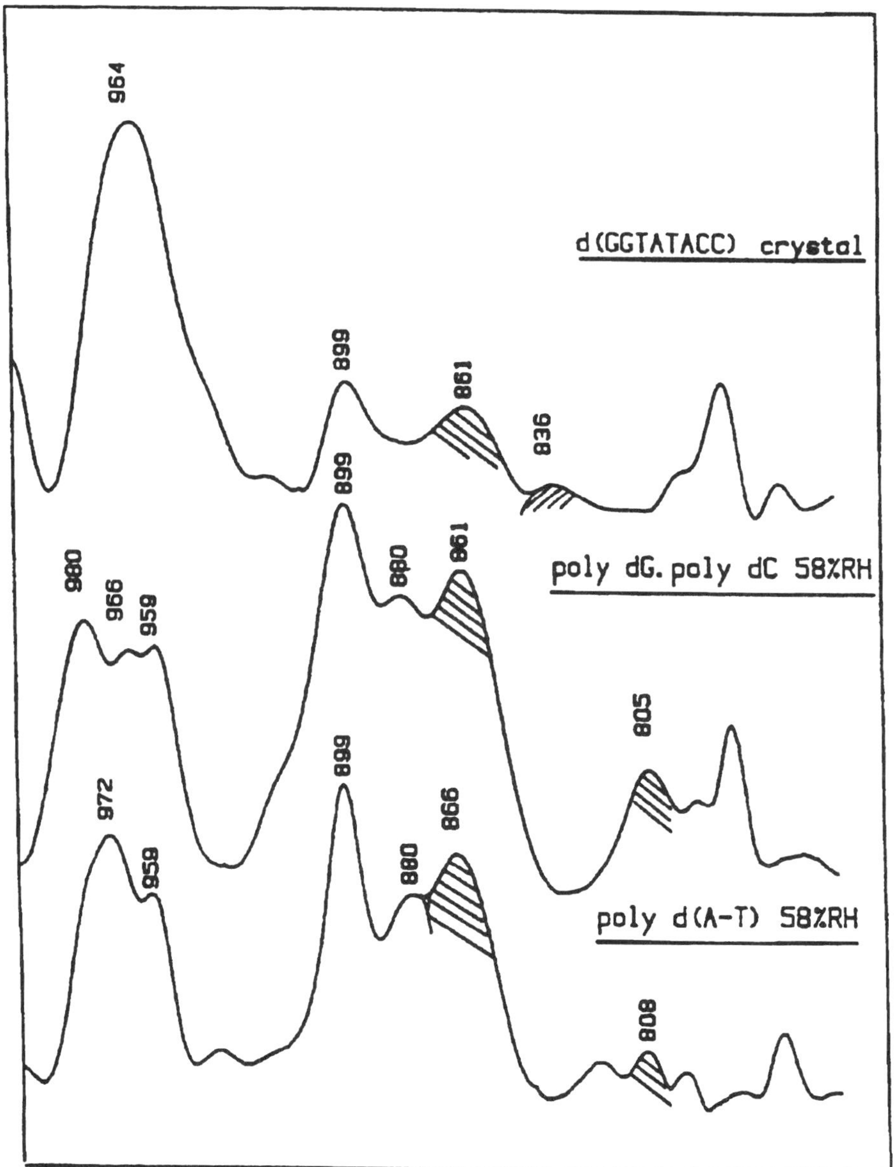

Figure 1: FTIR spectra of (top) d(GGTATACC) crystal (micro FTIR); (center) poly dG · poly dC film 58% relative humidity, A form \\\; (bottom) poly d(A-T) film 58% relative humdity, A form \\\.

d(CACGTG) in solution clearly shows that in these conditions the oligonucleotide is in a B geometry. We do not always observe a conformational transition occurring under the crystallization process. For example the microRaman spectrum of the d(GGCGCC) crystal reflects a B family conformation. The reverse 5′-3′ sequence d(CCGCGG) is more peculiar. The FTIR spectra of d(CCGCGG) hydrated films show that the decrease of relative humidity induces a B→Z transition of the oligonucleotide. This transition is also observed in solution induced in this case by an increase of the ionic strength. One would therefore expect that in the crystal the d(CCGCGG) sequence would adopt a Z type conformation. However the microRaman and microFTIR spectra clearly show that there is no Z geometry in the crystal. The

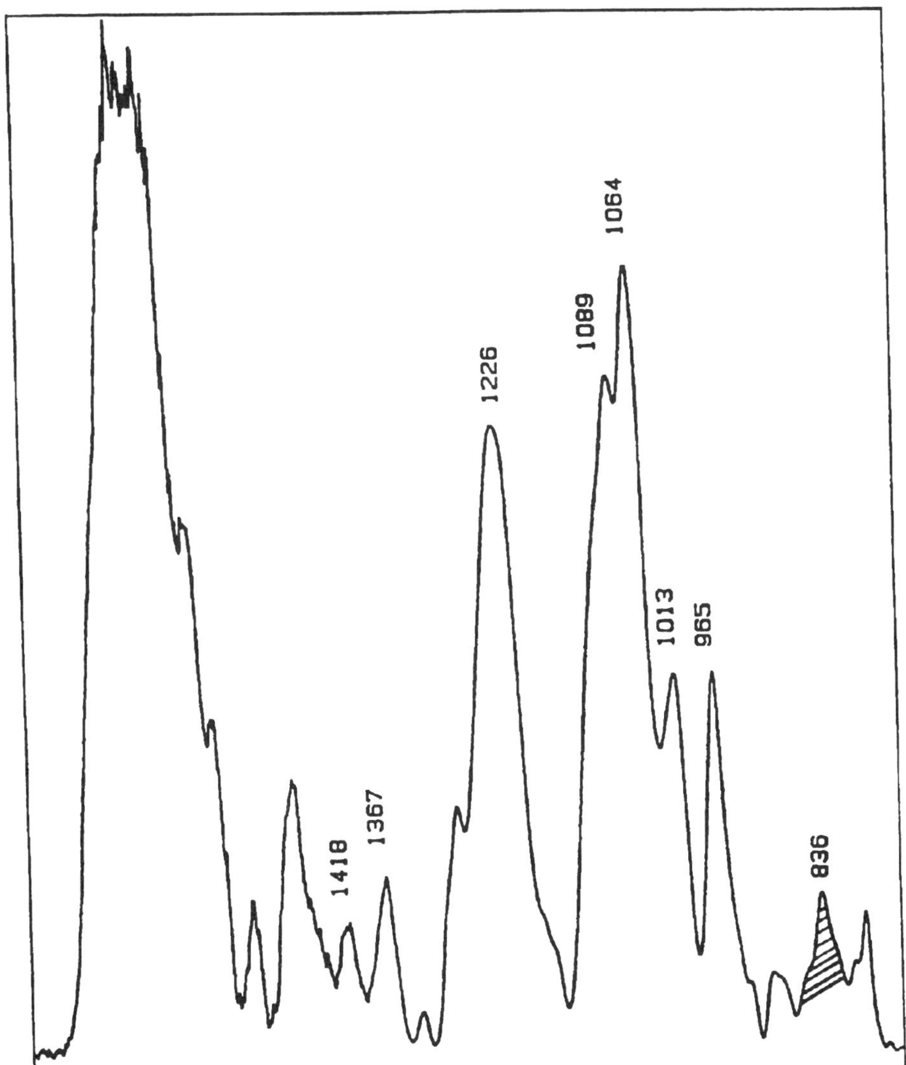

Figure 2: microFTIR spectrum of d(CGCGAATTCGCG) crystal, B form /ll/.

conformation is mainly rigth-handed with slight modifications when compared to a cannonical B form.

The marker peaks of the different conformations can be used to detect mixtures of geometries in different systems. Figure 1 top presents the microFTIR spectrum of the d(GGTATACC) crystal in the region where are observed in particular the phospodiester chain vibrations. The FTIR spectra shown in the center and at the bottom are those of films of poly dG.poly dC and poly d(A-T) recorded at 58% RH. In low relative humidity conditions the conformation adopted by both polynucleotides belongs to the A family. Characteristic bands of this helical geometry are observed around 861 and 805 cm^{-1}. We can observe on the d(GGTATACC) crystal microFTIR spectrum the signature of the A conformation. However the presence of an absorption

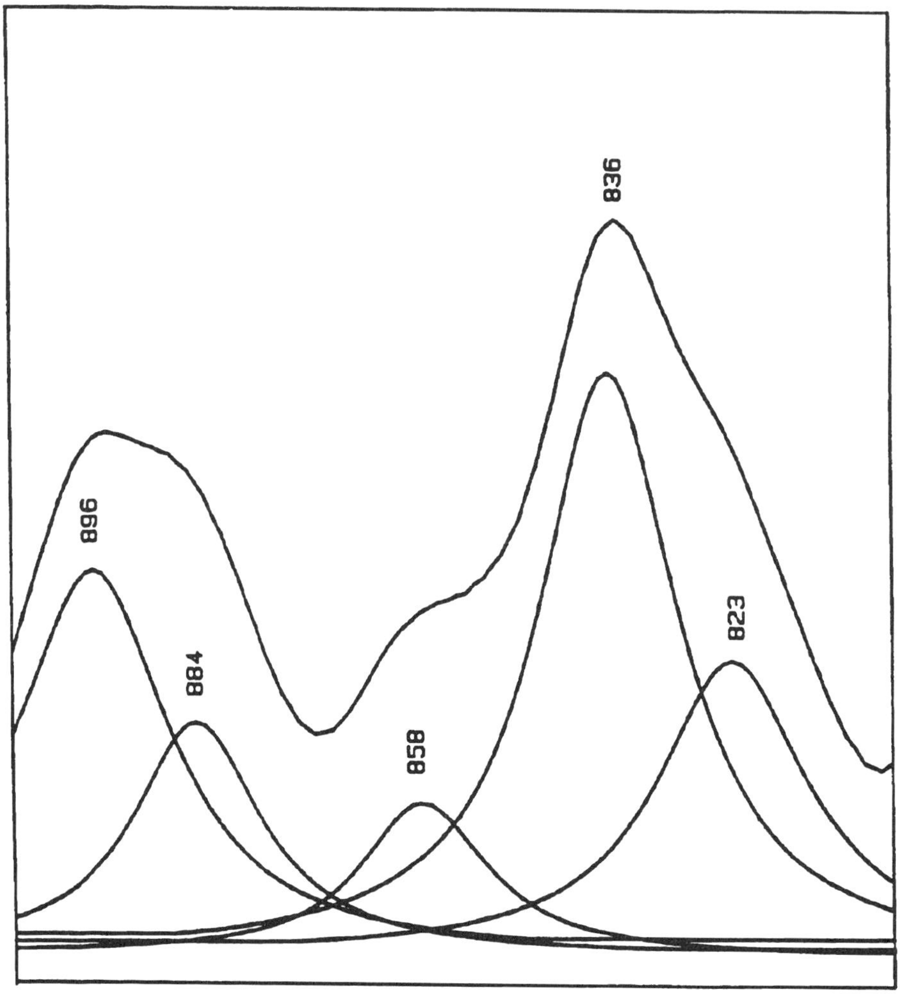

Figure 3: (Top) microFTIR spectrum of d(CGCGAATTCGCG) crystal; (bottom) curve fitting computation using Lorentzian contributions.

located at 836 cm^{-1} clearly indicates that a part of the molecules is in a B type geometry, in excellent agreement with recent X-ray diffraction results. This spectral region is very sensitive in particular to the geometry of the sugar. Figure 2 presents

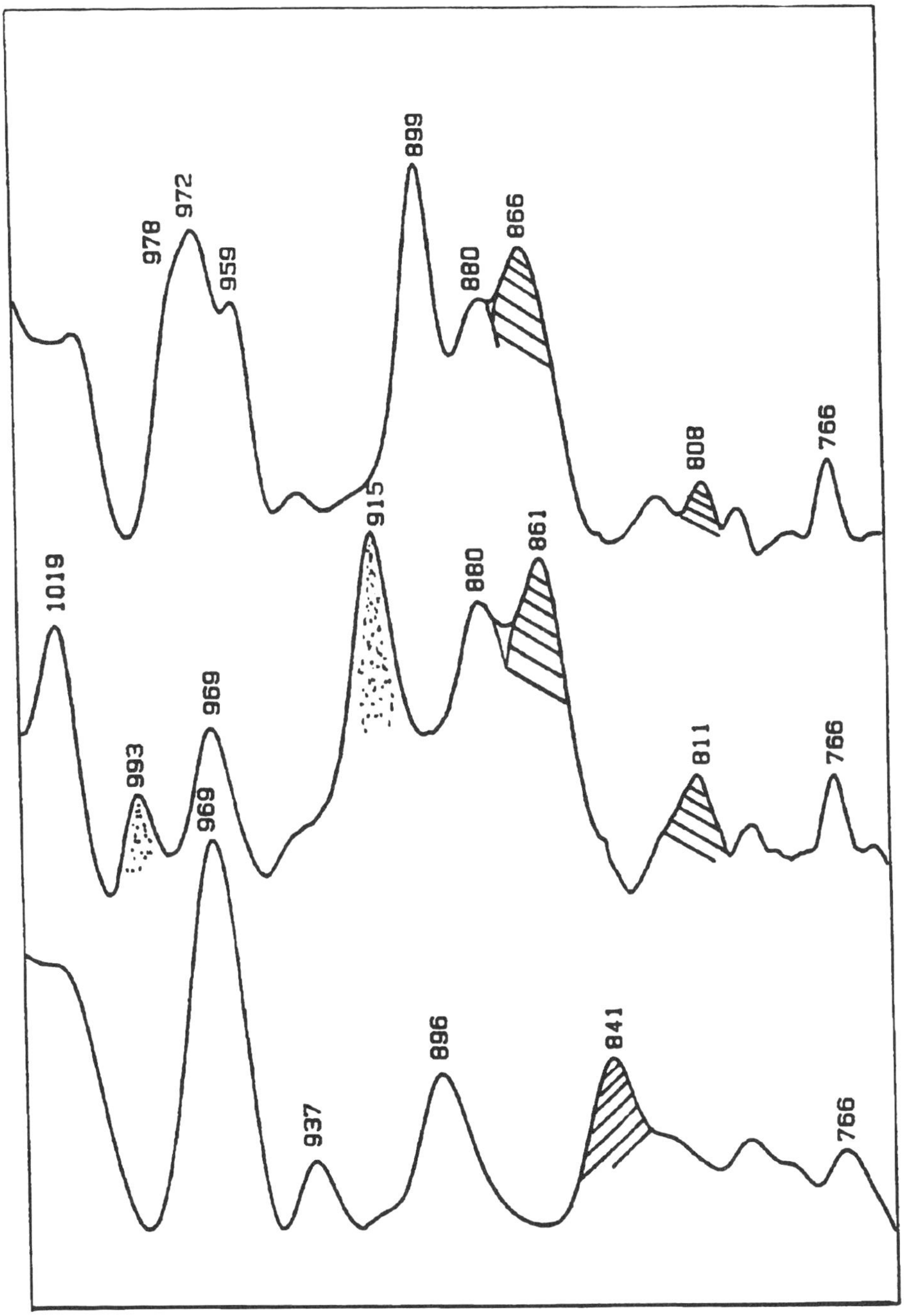

Figure 4: FTIR spectra of (top) poly d(A-T) A from \\\\; (center) r(A-U)$_8$; (bottom) polyd(A-T) B form ////.

the microFTIR spectrum of the d(CGCGAATTCGCG) crystal. The IR marker bands of a B geometry are detected on this spectrum. The low wavenumber region is shown with an expanded scale in Figure 3 top. At the bottom of Figure 3 is presented the result of a curve fitting computation. We observe that the broad band located around 836 cm^{-1} is complex and that three main components can be found. The X-ray diffraction study of this crystal (Dickerson and Drew 1981 (2)) has shown that the structure was B, but that important differences could be evidenced at the level of the deoxyribose geometries depending on the considered nucleotide. The large variability in the sugar conformations is reflected on the IR spectrum by the existence of several components in the absorption corresponding to this vibrational mode of the B form deoxyribose.

A family of nucleic acids has been up to now far less studied than DNAs: oligoribonucleotides. Preparation and handling problems may explain the very small amount of results published concerning conformations of these nucleic acids. We present here very recent results obtained by FTIR on a double stranded $r(A\text{-}U)_8$ sequence studied in solution and in hydrated films. Figure 4 center shows the FTIR spectrum of this sequence in solution in the region sensitive in particular to the backbone geometry. For comparison the spectra of A and B geometries of poly d(A-T) obtained in films at respetively 58% and 98% relative humidity are given above and below. We detect on the $r(A\text{-}U)_8$ spectrum the characteristic bands of the A geometry located at 861 and 811 cm^{-1} for this sequence. The presence of the ribose instead of the deoxyribose is detected by the existence on the FTIR spectrum in this region of two bands located at 915 and 993 cm^{-1}. The A conformation is adopted by the $r(A\text{-}U)_8$ sequence in solution and also in hydrated films. When the relative humidity is decreased from 100% to 58% no significative spectral modification is detected showing that the A geometry is conserved.

References and Footnotes

1. M. Coll, I. Fita, J. Lloveras, J.A. Subirana, F. Bardella, T. Huynh-Dinh and J. Igolen, *Nucleic Acids Res. 16*, 8695-8705 (1988).
2. R.E. Dickerson and H.R. Drew, *J. Mol. Biol. 149*, 761-786 (1981).
3. T.J. Thamann, R.C. Lord, A.H.-J.Wang and A. Rich, *Nucleic Acids Res. 9*, 5443-5447 (1981).

Structure & Methods, ISBN 0-940030-32-2
Volume 3: DNA & RNA, ISBN 0-940030-31-4
Eds., Ramaswamy H. Sarma & Mukti H. Sarma, © Adenine Press 1990

Dedicated to the memory of Professor Max Tishler, 1906-1989

Molecular Simulation Studies on the d(CGCGAATTCGCG) Duplex: Hydration, Ion Atmosphere, Structure and Dynamics

D.L. Beveridge, P. Subramanian, B. Jayaram, S. Swaminathan and G. Ravishanker
Chemistry Department, Hall-Atwater Laboratories
Wesleyan University
Middletown, CT 06457 USA

Abstract

This article reviews the results of a series of studies on the oligonucleotide dodecamer sequence d(CGCGAATTCGCG) based on molecular simulation. Monte Carlo methods were used to study the patterns of hydration in canonical B and A forms of the sequence, using two different choices of force field. AMBER/TIP4P and GROMOS/SPC. Monte Carlo calculations were also carried out to study the counterion atmosphere of the dodecamer, treating the mobile ions explicitly and the water as a dielectric continuum. Variations on the "primitive" model that incorporate dielectric saturation were explored. The dynamical structure of the dodecamer were studied via a molecular dynamics simulation based on the GROMOS force field, and the conformational and helicoidal dynamics was analyzed by a new procedure called Curves, Dials and Windows. The calculated results are compared with available experimental data to the fullest extent possible.

I. Introduction

The area of nucleic acid structure, dynamics and solvation presents an array of particularly interesting and challenging research problems, newly accessible to molecular simulation studies with the advent of present generation supercomputers and graphic workstations. This article reviews some of the recent studies involving Monte Carlo and molecular dynamics simulations carried out or currently in progress in this laboratory. We describe here descriptions of studies on the hydration, the ion atmosphere and the conformational and helicoidal dynamics of the dodecamer duplex d(CGCGAATTCGCG). Considerable structural information on this sequence is available from the crystallography and series of articles by Dickerson and coworkers (1-7), as well as diverse NMR investigations (8-10). The structure of the d(CGCGAATTCGCG) in canonical B, A (hypothetical) and the native crystallographic form are shown for reference in Figures 1-3.

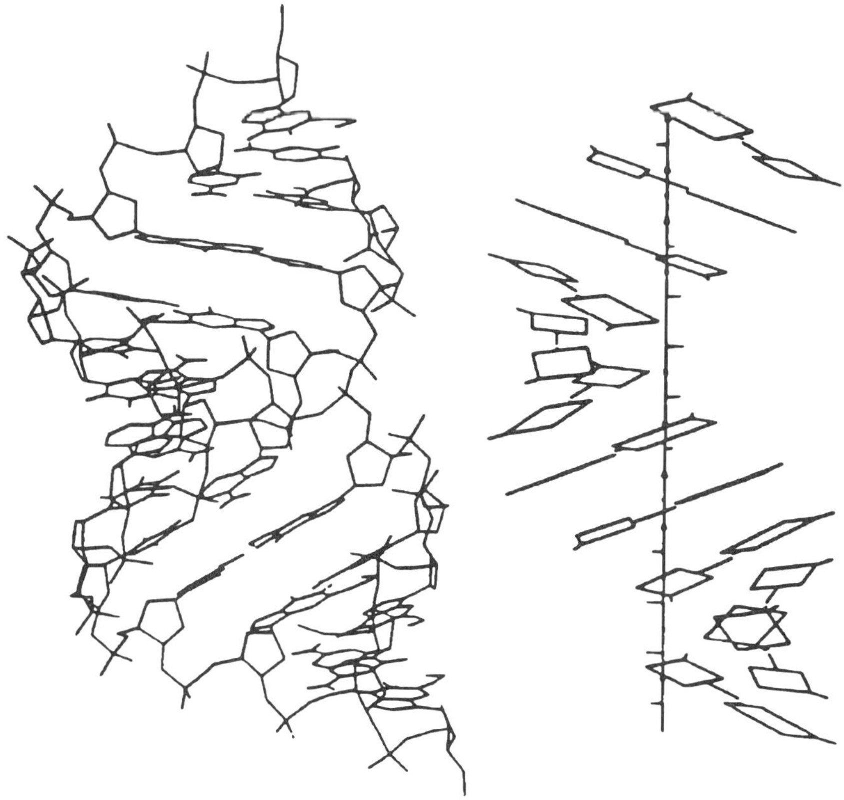

Figure 1: The canonical A structure of DNA (43): a) all-atom version (non-polar H's omitted); b) base-pair planes and helix axis representation from Curves analysis (39).

II. DNA Hydration: B and A Forms

The field of DNA hydration is the subject of a recent article in "Water Science Reviews" prepared by Westhof and Beveridge (11), which provides a comprehensive list of citations to the original literature. A series of studies on the hydration of A, B and Z DNA have been carried out at Wesleyan by P. Subramanian in the course of his dissertation research (12). These calculations consider the DNA with screened phosphate charges in an assumed structural form, canonical or crystallographic, together with a sufficient number of water molecules to provide in excess of two hydration shells. Molecular simulations were carried out on the water structure by Monte Carlo methods.

Simulations on the hydration of B-DNA (13-15) were performed on the dodecamer sequence d(CGCGAATTCGCG) in canonical B form together with 1777 water molecules, in a hexagonal prism cell under periodic boundary conditions. The prescription for energy functions was based on a combination AMBER 3.0 charge for the DNA atoms (16) and the TIP4P model for water (17). The analysis of results was carried out by means of the proximity criterion for assigning waters to substructures of the

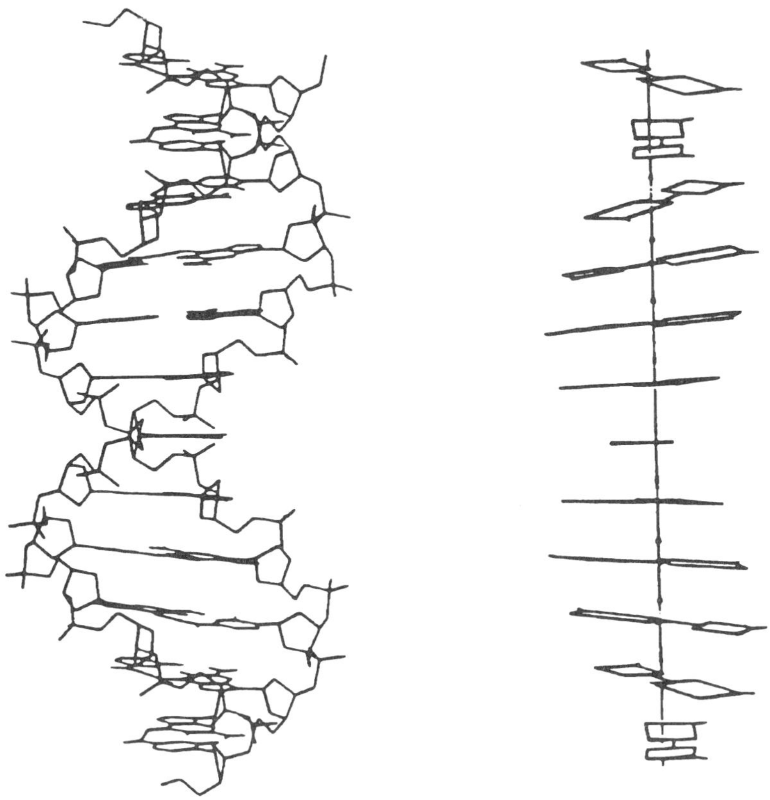

Figure 2: The canonical B structure of DNA (44): a) all-atom version (non-polar H's omitted); b) base-pair planes and helix axis representation from Curves analysis (39).

DNA. The calculated hydration density for the nucleic acid solute was depicted for presentation here as the linear superposition of points representing the centers-of-mass of solvent waters from a series of individual configurations taken at equally spaced intervals along the production (post-equilibration) segment of the Monte Carlo realization. An algorithm for the enumeration of water bridges between solute atoms, defined on the statistical state of the system as described by the simulation was also devised. Also, each potential bridge site intrinsic to the structure can be determined from the solute geometry, and thus the calculation of the probability of finding each of the water bridges in the simulation can be obtained. Hydration density distributions partitioned into contributions from the major groove side, the minor groove side and the sugar-phosphate backbone were examined, and the probabilities of occurence for one- and two-water bridges in the simulation were enumerated. The positions of a number of ordered water molecules have been located crystallographically (4).

The calculated total 1° coordination number of 10.4 waters/per nucleotide compares closely to the critical level of hydration inferred from spectroscopic studies (18) to be necessary for DNA stability, and further supports the idea that the experimental

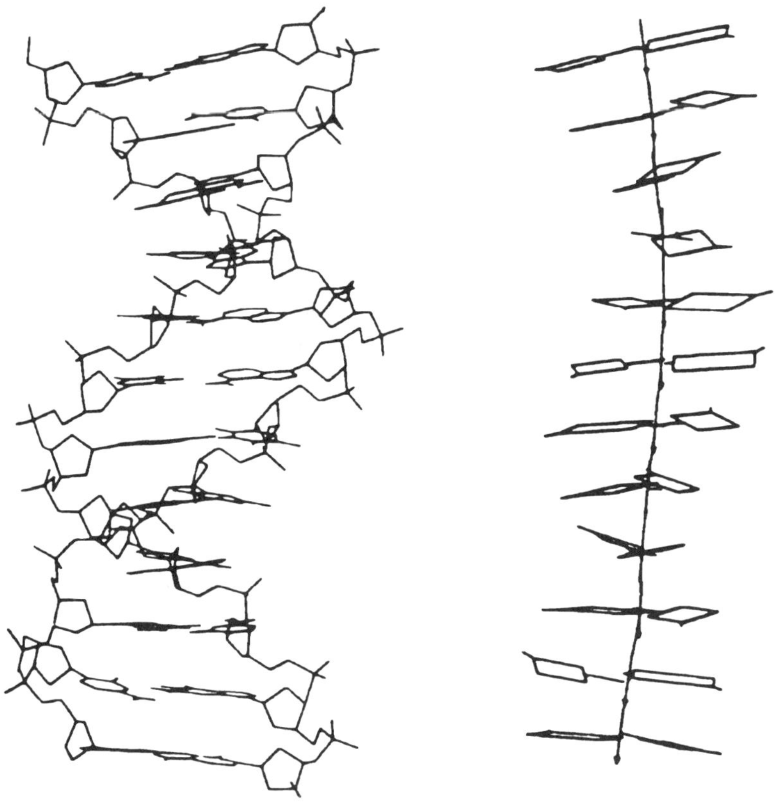

Figure 3: The structure of the 300° K, native dodecamer d(CGCGAATTCGCG) (1,2): a) all-atom version (non-polar H's omitted); b) base-pair planes and helix axis representation from Curves analysis (39).

number of 10 waters/nucleotide corresponds to an intact first hydration shell. The addition of the 2° coordination of the minor and major groove gives a total of 17.4 waters/nucleotide, reasonably close to the value of 20 indicated from the adsorption isotherm to be necessary for the stability of the B form. Considering that slightly in excess of first and second hydration shells would be required to completely fill the grooves of a B-DNA structure, the calculated results correspond closely to the estimates from solvent accessibility calculations by Alden and Kim (19).

The calculated hydration density for the minor groove of the canonical dodecamer is shown in Figure 4. The localization of hydration density occurs at A-N3 and G-N2 sites and describes essentially monodentate hydrogen bonding. The calculated hydration does not show much density at T-O2 sites, preferring instead successive A-N3 sites in the 1° coordination shell. The crystallographic sites are essentially limited to the AT tract, and indicate the existence of A-N3 ... W ... T-O2 bridges which comprise the 1° shell of the "spine of hydration." The results of a corresponding Monte Carlo calculation for the water structure of the native dodecamer from the crystallographic structure is shown in Figure 5 (15). In the latter, the inherently greater propeller twist in AT vs. GC base pairs orients the bases such that A-N3 and

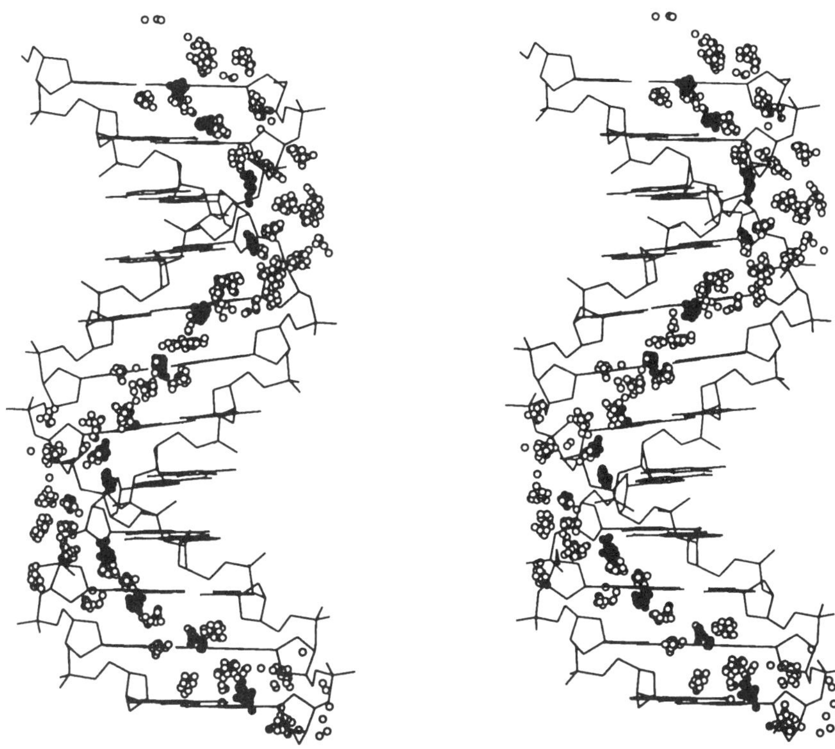

Figure 4: Calculated hydration density in the minor groove of canonical B73 d(CGCGAATTCGCG) based on AMBER 3.0 charges for nucleic acid atoms (16) and the TIP4P model for water (17), presented as a superposition of water oxygen positions from 16 snapshots of equally spaced intervals along the 1500 K Monte Carlo realization (13,14). Shaded circles: first hydration shell; open circles: second hydration shell.

T-O2 are 3.7 Å apart, a propitious distance for bridging by a single water molecule. In the canonical form, the corresponding distance is 4.4 Å, and in our calculation the T-O2 ... W ... A-N3 bridge is seen only ~18% of the time. The calculated regions of localized hydration density for the native dodecamer are still seen to be frameshifted slightly from the reported crystallographic sites.

Quite recently, we repeated the entire calculations using a different force field, using GROMOS charges for the DNA atoms (20) and the SPC model for water (21). The calculated hydration density at the floor of the minor groove, as shown in Figure 6, is seen to be in nearly perfect agreement with experiment (22). A full description of the hydration of DNA based on the GROMOS/SPC model for DNA is currently being prepared.

An intriguing result from the minor groove proximity analysis of the simulation is

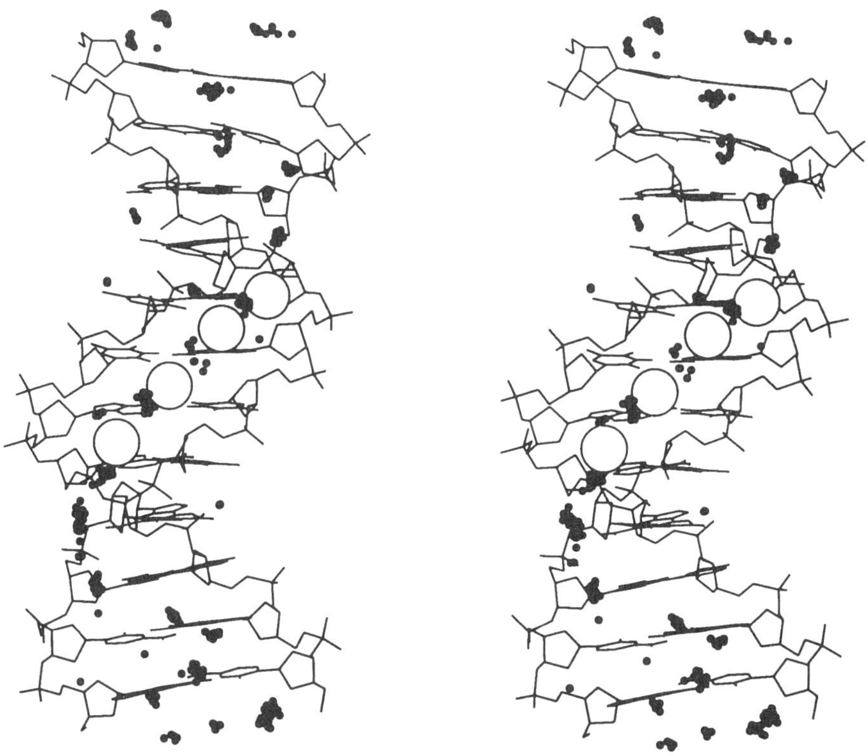

Figure 5: Calculated hydration density in the minor groove of the native crystallographic form of d(CGCGAATTCGCG) based on AMBER 3.0 charges for nucleic acid atoms and the TIP4P model for water, based on a superposition of 19 structures (22). See caption of Figure 4 for further details. Large open circles are the position of the crystallographic ordered water comprising the observed spine of hydration (4).

the extent to which the CG as well as the AT region can support an ordered water structure. The CG region, with the floor of the minor groove lined with N2 donor groups and cytosine O2 acceptor sites, appears to nucleate localized hydration density as readily as the AT region. The calculated ordered water network in the minor groove of our model dodecamer thus may extend completely from one end of the structure to the other in B-DNA, with the interface between the GC and AT regions dealt with readily by the geometric versatility of water-water hydrogen bonding. The penetration of water into the DNA is of course clearly greater for AT than for GC tracts, and this feature distinguishes the "spine of hydration" as defined by Dickerson and coworkers from the generic minor groove hydration pattern. Marky and Breslauer (23) recently reported a positive binding entropy of comparable magnitude to that of d(CGCGAATTCGCG) for the binding of netropsin to the poly [d(GC)] · poly[d(CG)] duplex. If the binding mechanism remains the same, this observation supports the existence of an ordered water network extending into the GC region.

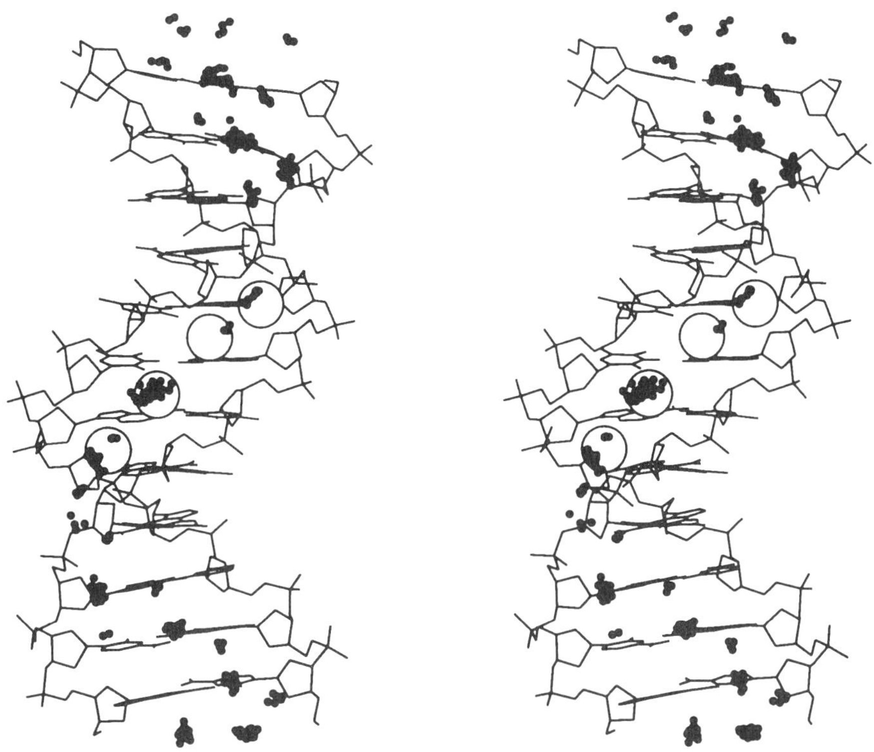

Figure 6: Calculated hydration density in the minor groove of d(CGCGAATTCGCG) based on GROMOS charges for the nucleic acid (20) and the SPC model for water (21), based on a superposition of 40 structures (22). See caption to Figure 4 for further details. Large open circles are the position of the crystallographic ordered water comprising the observed spine of hydration (4).

For the major groove (Figure 7), the calculated hydration density indicates saturation of hydrophilic binding sites with waters of hydration in the calculation corresponds closely to the crystallographic results reported by Dickerson and coworkers (4,6) and is calculated to be similar for canonical and crystallographic forms. The 16°K structure and the MPD7 structure show evidence for some various types of water bridges as well in the major groove region. At the phosphates, the calculated results (Figure 8) show the characteristic triad of waters in the "cone of hydration" motif at nearly every anionic oxygen. The phosphate hydration is observed to be disordered in the room temperature structure but extensive ordered solvent sites are found in the 16°K and MPD7 structures of the dodecamer. Examining the crystallographic results with the idea of cones of hydration in mind, the observed solvation sites can nearly all be interpreted in terms of fragments of this motif in which only one or two of the three waters has turned out to be ordered. Only rarely does one see a fully ordered triad of waters of a single cone in the crystal structure. The hydrophobic

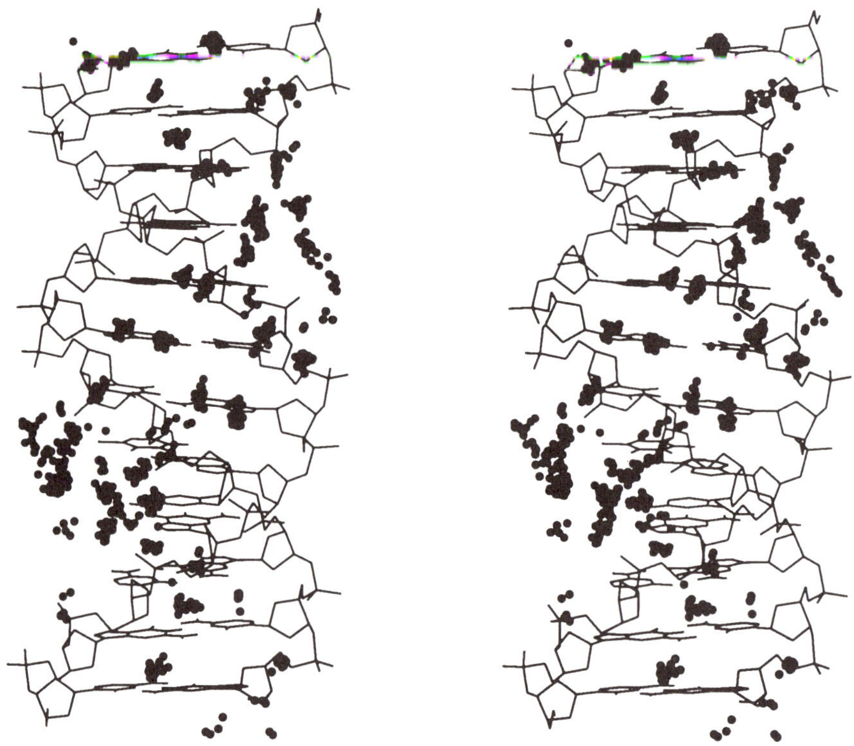

Figure 7: Calculated first shell hydration density for the major groove of d(CGCGAATTCGCG). Details analogous to those in Figure 1 (14).

hydration around the thymine methyl group and the nonpolar atoms of the furanose sugar ring is calculated to be diffuse and not observed to be ordered. The water 'wedged' between T-5CH_3 and a phosphate is clearly represented in the calculation as a water bridge occurring with a frequency of 51% (14).

A notable feature of the water bridge analysis of the simulation is that, with only a few exceptions, the calculated probabilities of occurrence are relatively low, i.e., < 50%. The reason for this appears to be as follows: water bridges are indeed an energetically favored structure for an individual water molecule, but also relatively ordered. For an assembly of water molecules at 300°K instead of absolute zero, entropy comes into the picture and destabilizes the ordered bridges with respect to forming sequential hydrogen bonds with different water molecules. This latter situation is more disordered than the water bridges and thus entropically favorable, with little loss of energy since the number of hydrogen bonds is essentially conserved. (One could even argue that two different water molecules could give a lower energy because they can individually optimize their orientations, whereas a bridged water has to compromise a little in both bonds.) The quantitative relationship of any of this to the free energy of the system has not yet been rigorously studied.

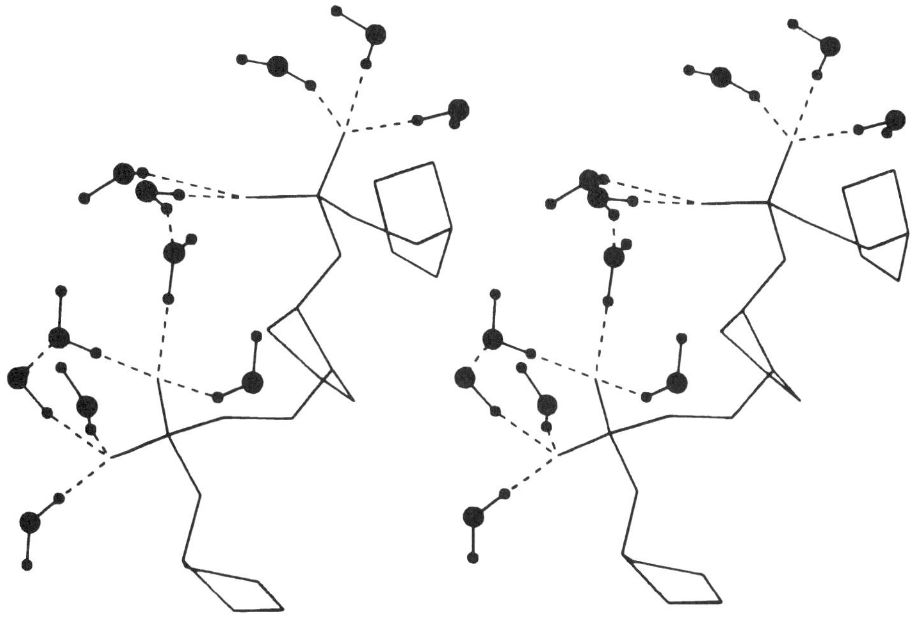

Figure 8: Molecular detail from a single configuration illustrating a representative phosphate hydration complex calculated for B-form d(CGCGAATTCGCG) (14).

The quantity in these Monte Carlo calculations which is most applicable to the subject of relative affinities is the solute-water binding energy. The proposed ordering, given with respect to decreasing affinity for water, places the anionic phosphate oxygens in first place, followed by the major and minor groove regions. The ester oxygens in phosphate and sugar groups have correspondingly lower average binding energies to water in the calculation. It is important to note that 'affinity' is really a free energy quantity and not directly addressed in these calculations.

Preliminary results have been obtained by Monte Carlo methods for the hydration density of the canonical A form of the dodecamer and the Z form of the hexamer d(CGCGCG) (24,25), in calculations which parallel those described in the preceding. The first and second shell hydration density in the minor groove of the A form is shown in Figure 9. The hydration structure here is somewhat more diffuse than that of the B form in this region (c.f. Figure 4). The calculations have been analyzed for the occurrence of water bridges betwen anionic oxygens of the phosphates which figures significantly in the "economics of phosphate" hydration hypothesis due to Saenger *et al.* (26). Such bridges are indeed found (Figure 10), but the calculated frequency of occurrence in this system (aqueous hydration, ~100% relative humidity) turns out to be relatively lower than expected, probably due to the entropic effects described earlier. The probability of occurrence of this bridge may increase with decreasing humidity.

III. The Counterion Atmosphere of B-DNA

Polyelectrolyte effects play an important role in many aspects of the structure and

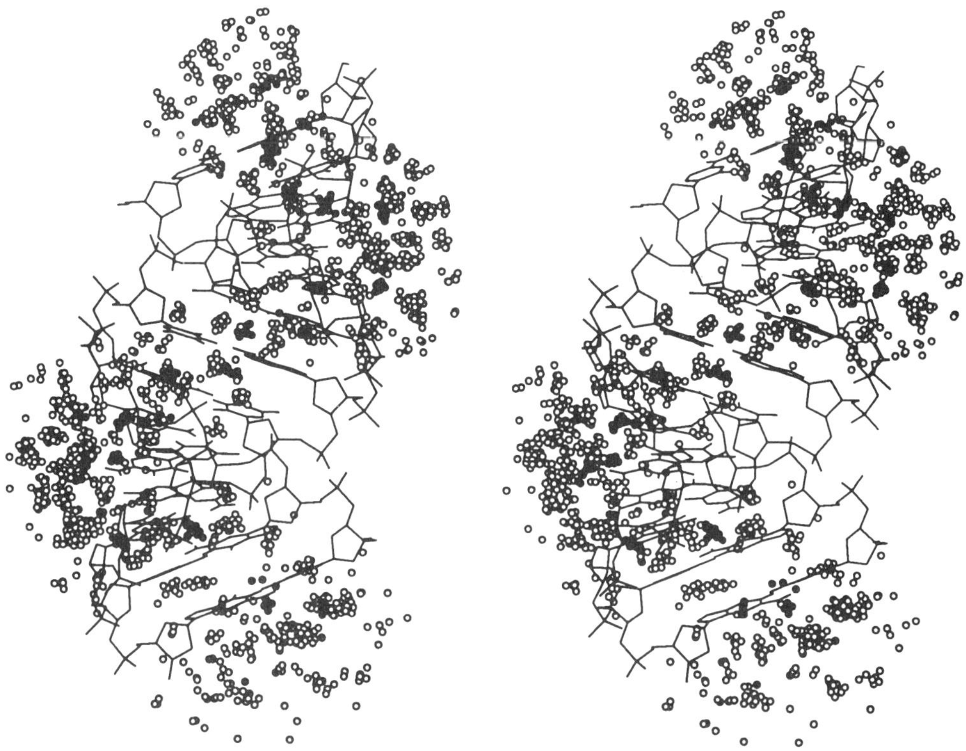

Figure 9: Calculated first and second shell hydration density for the minor groove of a hypothetical A72 d(CGCGAATTCGCG) determined from Monte Carlo simulation (15).

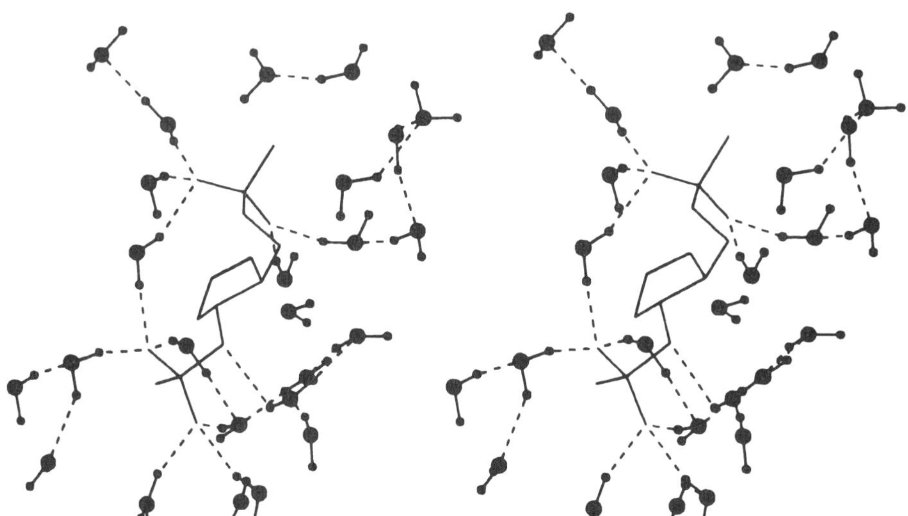

Figure 10: Calculated hydration complex for a segment of the backbone of A-form d(CGCGAATTCGCG) from Monte Carlo simulation (15), showing a water bridge between successive anionic oxygens. Note that the bridge here involves one of the "cone of hydration" waters.

function of nucleic acids (27,28). The counterion atmosphere of DNA neutralizes the charges of the anionic phosphates and imparts electrostatic stability to the system. The nature of this effect, "counterion condensation" (27), is unique in polyelectrolytes compared to simple electrolyte systems. Release of condensed counterions is considered to be an important thermodynamic component of ligand and protein binding to DNA (28). While the significance of counterion condensation is well-documented, relatively little is known at the molecular level about the structural details of the organization of counterions around the various forms of DNA, and the detailed nature of the electrostatic stabilization. We describe herein recent and current Monte Carlo studies of the counterion atmosphere of B-DNA, focussing particularly on issues of structure underlying counterion condensation as gleaned from presentations of counterion density analogous to those given previously for hydration density.

The role of dielectric saturation and the influence of the dielectric boundary between the DNA and solvent on the potential of mean force between the counterions and the anionic phosphates of duplex DNA are considered in our simulations via variations on the restricted primitive model. In the primitive model, ions are treated explicitly and water is represented as a dielectric continuum. This is clearly a serious approximation since the molecular nature of water as an associated liquid is neglected and its particular capacity for hydration, non-covalent bonding and solvation in different modes -- hydrophilic, hydrophobic and ionic -- is denied. Also, there is no way to accurately parametrize the heterogeneous qualities of the dielectric medium from experimental data. Thus we have taken up comparative simulations of the counterion distribution around DNA based on a series of models for the aqueous dielectric medium which hopefully bracket the true physical nature of the system. Subsequent comparisons of the results of the dielectric models with fully explicit simulation (DNA and water and counterions) studies are planned to ascertain further the relevance and applicability of the various simpler models considered here.

Statistical thermodynamic (T, V, N) ensemble Monte Carlo simulations were first carried out on dilute aqueous solutions of NaDNA at a temperature of 298°K, using Metropolis sampling procedures with multiple particle moves (29). The system for study consisted of two turns of DNA with 40 negatively charged phosphate groups, and 40 sodium counterions enclosed in a cylinder of radius 50 Å. The central cell of the simulated system thus corresponds to an electrically neutral solution of a 20 mer of NaDNA with the sequence of d(GCGAATTCGCGCGAATTCGC), fixed in the canonical B-form, 3 mM in DNA concentration and 120 mM in Na^+. The mole fractions $x_{Na^+} = x_{PO4^-}$, and we refer to this condition of minimum compensating sodium as "zero added salt".

The N-particle configurational energies of the system are calculated under the assumption of pairwise additivity in intermolecular interactions using (12,6,1) atom site potentials to describe both the sodium-phosphate and sodium-sodium interactions. The 12-6 parameters employed in this study are adapted from the GROMOS force field (20) and correspond to those of unhydrated sodium ion. Four prescriptions are examined in evaluating the electrostatic contribution to the sodium- phosphate interactions: a) Coulombic potential $(C_{ij}Q_iQ_j)/(\varepsilon r_{ij})$ with $C_{ij}=1$ and $\varepsilon=80$ (model DC), b) Modified coulombic potential incorporating the effects due to dielectric discontinuity using the data of Conrad *et al.* for C_{ij}'s (Table I of Ref. 30) with $\varepsilon=80$ (model DD), c) A modified Hingerty function (31) for the ε to include effects due to dielectric saturation with $\varepsilon=20$ at short distances, smoothly varying to $\varepsilon=80$, with the midpoint at 5 Å, and $C_{ij}=1$ (model DS), and d) a combination of models b and c, i.e., a modified ε as in DS model and C_{ij}'s as in model DD (model DS/DD). These are referred to as runs DC, DD, DS and DS/DD respectively.

The structure of our DNA is generated from the canonical B form of DNA with the sequence $d(GCGAATTCGC)_2$. A charge of -1 (in atomic units) is placed on the phosphate at the location of phosphorus atom, i.e., closest to the charge center of the phosphate group. Delocalization of the phosphate charge is not consistent with the model of Zimm and coworkers (30) and is not considered here. The solute in our simulations thus corresponds to simply a DNA-shaped molecule with charges on phosphates. Counterions are prevented from penetrating into the DNA interior by means of a repulsive step function added to the configurational energy.

Periodic boundary conditions along the helical axis and mass conserving diffusive boundary conditions in the radial direction are imposed on the system. The calculated radial dependence of the integrated counterionic charge/phosphate around DNA, denoted $q^+(R)$, is shown in Figure 11. The details seen in the curves below 10 Å are

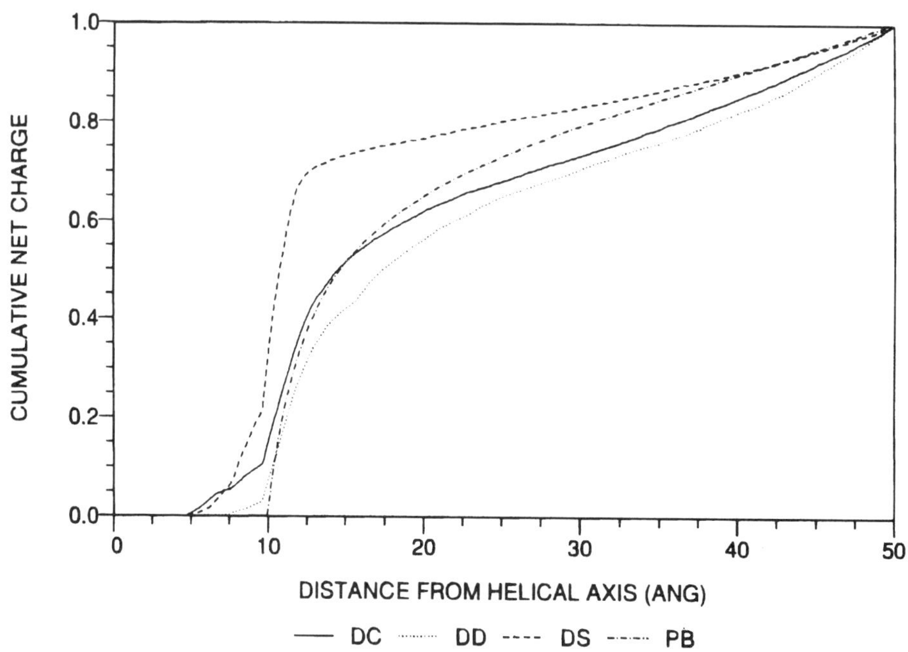

Figure 11: Cumulative counterionic charge per phosphate as a function of distance from the helical axis. (Solid line: DC model; dashed line: DS model; dotted line: DD model; and dash-dot refers to PB approach.)

due to the groove potentials manifested via the cylindrical grids for the C_{ij} data. These curves would be much smoother if a finer grid was used or in an all-atom treatment of DNA, which is under investigation. At least three distinct regions are noticeable in the behavior of $q^+(R)$: the groove region (below 10 Å), the backbone region ranging from 10 Å to 13 Å for the DS model, from 10 Å to 15 Å for the DC model and from 10 Å to 17 Å for the DD model, and a third region representative of the rest of the system, where the net charge increases monotonically with distance. The demarcations are particularly pronounced with the DS model. In the DS model, the Manning fraction of 0.76 for the counterions is achieved at a distance of ~17 Å, in reasonable accord with his analysis. Figure 11 and preliminary calculations with a larger cylinder of radius 100 Å, also show that the counterion distribution near DNA is not significantly influenced by the presence of the outer boundary at 50 Å.

The results from a PB treatment of the counterions are also shown in Figure 11, calculated by solving the non-linear Poisson-Boltzmann equation for a cylinder of radius 10 Å enclosed in an outer cylinder of radius 50 Å with $\varepsilon = 80$. The PB equation

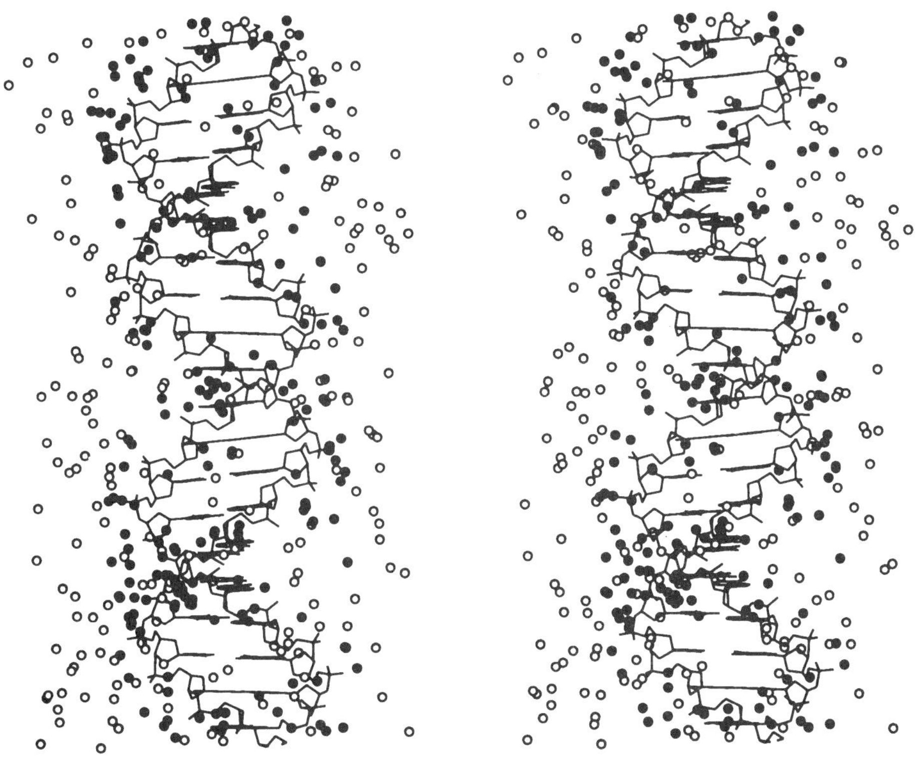

Figure 12: Stereo views of the counterion probability density around DNA (29). Full circles represent counterions in a cylinder of radius 12 Å enclosing the DNA. Open circles represent counterions in a coaxial cylinder from radius 12 Å to 20 Å around DNA. (a) DC model.

slightly underestimates the counterion concentrations compared with the DC model at distances below 15 Å from DNA, consistent with previous observations. The effect of inclusion of small ion correlations and finite size of the counterions are small. Finite ion size and ion-ion correlations have opposing effects on the distribution of counterions around DNA, which must partially account for the success of the simple continuum models.

The counterion probability densities are shown in Figures 12-14. This analysis scheme is analogous to that used for the description of hydration density around DNA reported earlier, and described in the preceding section. The calculated spatial distribution of the counterion density is depicted for presentation here as the linear superposition of points representing the counterions from a series of 20 configurations chosen at equally spaced intervals along the production segment of the Monte Carlo realization. Any individual point simply indicates that a counterion is present in one or another of the ion configurations contributing to the statistical state of the system. The important information conveyed by this figure is the clustering of points, indicating a concentration of counterion density in that region. The

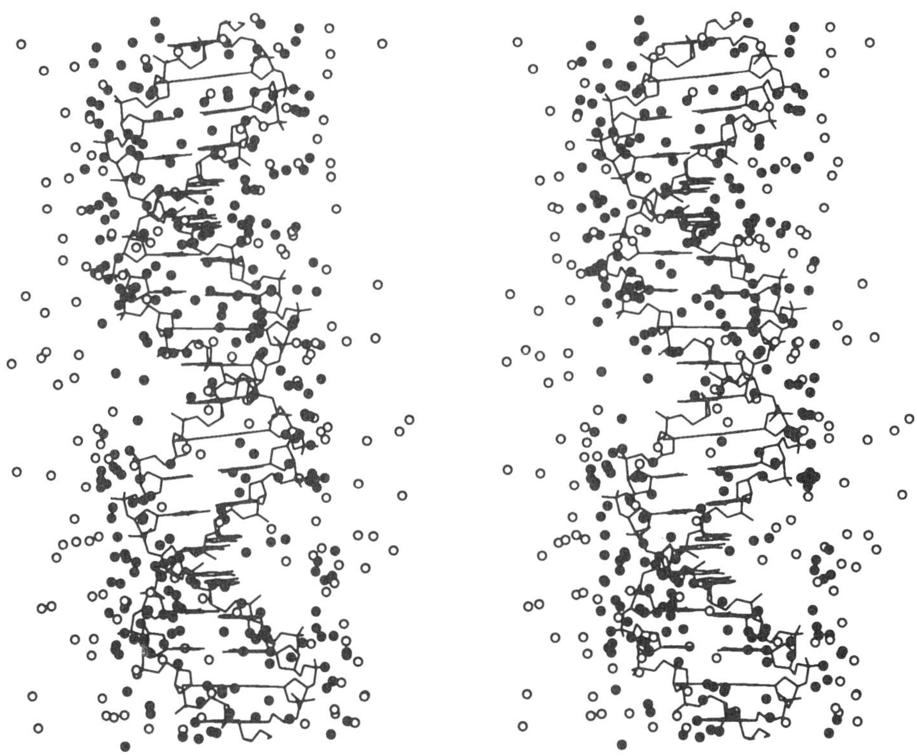

Figure 13: Stereo views of the counterion probability density around DNA. (b) DD model. See caption to Figure 12 for details.

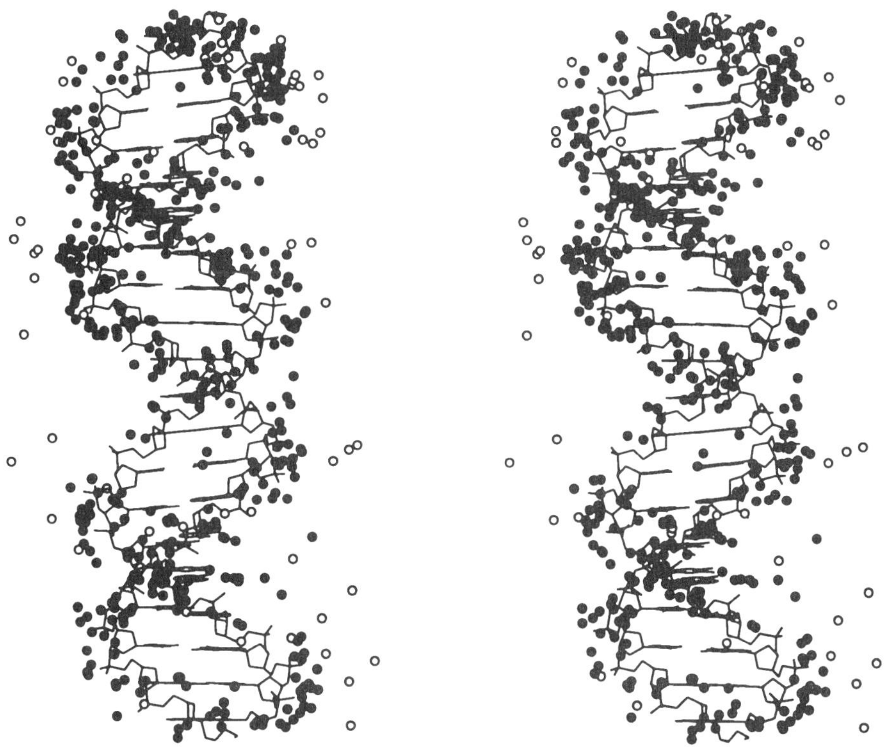

Figure 14: Stereo views of the counterion probability density around DNA. (c) DS model. See caption to Figure 12 for details.

shaded circles represent the counterions within 12 Å of the helical axis of the DNA and the open circles are ions from 12-20 Å. Note that the circles in Figures 12-14 represent about 62%, 56% and 77% of the counterions respectively in the system. Figures 12 (DC) and 13 (DD) show a more diffuse arrangement of the counterions along the length of DNA relative to Figure 14 (DS) where the counterions are densely populated along the backbone of DNA.

The simple coulombic model (DC model) gives a highly dispersed mobile ion density, with considerable groove as well as backbone populations. The net effect of incorporating dielectric discontinuity using the C_{ij} data is an overall decrease of the attraction of DNA for the counterions, particularly the groove regions. On introducing the dielectric saturation, the DNA and the groove regions in particular are found to be much more attractive to counterions.

We have also carried out Monte Carlo simulations on the three different dielectric models (DC, DD and DS) at 25 mM, 50 mM, 100 mM and 150 mM added salt (NaCl) concentrations. The salt dependence of the net counterionic charge within the

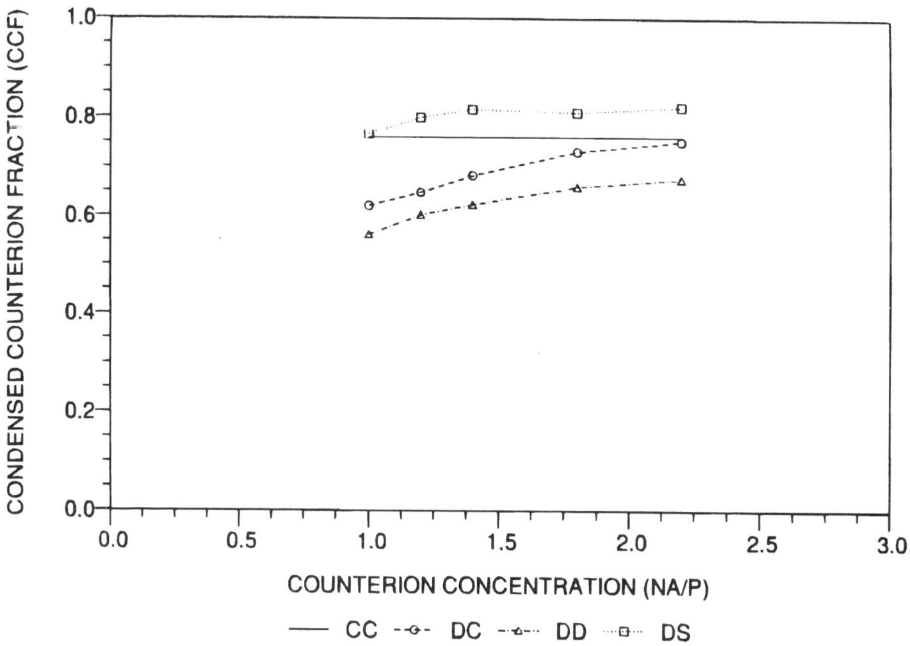

Figure 15: Net counterionic charge/phosphate integrated up to a distance of 20 Å from the helical axis versus added salt concentration shown as the ratio [Na]/[P]. [Na]/[P] = 1 refers to zero added salt condition (29).

vicinity of DNA is of interest in the light of ^{23}Na NMR experiments (32). The results for the net positive charge per phosphate in a cylindrical shell of 20 Å around DNA are shown in Figure 15 as a function of salt concentration. The added salt concentrations studied correspond to a sodium/phosphate ratio [Na/P] of 1.2, 1.4, 1.8 and 2.2 respectively. The salt independent estimate of 0.76 of the CC theory is shown as a continuous solid line. All the three models show a non-zero slope over the salt concentration range of 0 to 25 mM. As the salt concentration is increased further, the results from the DS model quickly stabilize to a salt independent value of 0.815 ± 0.005, while the results of the DC and DD models are still changing. A choice of a radius smaller than 20 Å would show even less dependence of the integrated net counterionic charge on the added salt for all the three models. The DS results seem to be the first observation of Manning-type salt independence of $q^+(R)$ in a primitive model system.

The results presented here cannot overall be construed as indicative of the superiority of any of the assumed models in describing the nucleic acid systems, but do serve to establish causal relationships between the various models and results as an aid to further understanding of the problem. A calibration of different models is currently being pursued in our laboratory via full-scale molecular dynamics simulations on DNA and counterions with water molecules treated explicitly which will provide a more rigorous theoretical reference point for comparing different simpler models. Our calculations could be extended to all atom treatment of the DNA-counterion interactions. In addition, effects of discontinuity in small ion interactions can also be considered. However, a limitation of the usage of C_{ij} data of Ref. 30 and the DD model is that any interpolation scheme is limited in accuracy and furthermore sequence specificities with an atomic level description of DNA cannot be readily treated. Incorporation of "DelPhi" potentials (33) however offers an alternative that is being pursued in collaboration with K. Sharp and B. Honig.

In summary we find in all cases a concentration of counterions near DNA (~10 Å) that is in excess of 1 M even in the absence of excess salt, consistent with counterion condensation theory and previous Monte Carlo and Poisson-Boltzmann studies on DNA-counterion systems (30,34). A comparison of the simulation results based on different dielectric models showed that the effects of saturation on the total energetics, the internal energies of counterion binding and the local counterion distributions are significant. Saturation favors increased counterion condensation relative to coulombic model, with DNA-counterion interactions dominating the small ion repulsions. The latter become significant only near the floor of the grooves where the available volume is small and at non-zero added salt concentrations. Also, saturation results in an essentially salt independent estimate of the net counterionic charge per phosphate around DNA that is consistent with the counterion condensation theory and the current ^{23}Na NMR experimental inferences (32).

IV. Structure and Dynamics

Nucleic acid polymers are systems of immense structural complexity, and even for an oligonucleotide the size of a dodecamer, hundeds of atoms, thousands of degrees of freedom, and many hours of time on a dedicated processor or supercomputer are involved in the simulation of O(100) psec of dynamics. Detailed analysis is required in methodological studies in order to fully comprehend the consequences of the various necessary assumptions made in setting up a calculation, such as choices for force field parameters and the treatment of solvent and electrostatics. Future applications will require increasingly high resolution information on the time evolution of structure, and information on complex issues such as the structural reorganization and adaptation of nucleic acids on interactions with drugs or regulatory proteins.

Analysis of structure and dynamics in the early papers on nucleic acid dynamics took several forms. Tidor *et al.* (35) displayed selected atomic correlation functions. In Levitt's study (36) on the dodecamer and and also a 24-mer duplex, omitting electrostatic terms in the force field, the display of structure as a function of time indicated fairly large amplitude bending and twisting in the molecule. This work together with a series of papers by Olson and coworkers (37) led to enhanced appreciation of the potential flexibility of DNA and the implications thereof.

The type of analysis involved in Levitt's paper can now be implemented on interactive graphics terminals and viewed in real time. This can indeed be very informative, but in a complex highly flexible system, we now recognize that simply watching a representation of the molecule move does not convey a comprehensive appreciation of the dynamics. Furthermore, in flexible systems like nucleic acids, an apparent conservation of structure over time may be the result of interesting compensatory conformational changes in the underlying molecular dynamics, such as crankshaft motions of the nucleic acid backbone. A system of analysis in which *all* the underlying changes are revealed as well as the overall evolution of structure with time is necessary for a comprehensive analysis of the MD of DNA.

Recently, in collaboration with Richard Lavery and Heinz Sklenar, we have been working on a method for a comprehensive, detailed analysis of an MD calculation on a DNA double helix (38). Lavery and Sklenar (39) had earlier reported the mathematics of a rigorously complete set of helicoidal coordinate parameters for single and double stranded nucleic acids, defined with respect to a unique global helical axis for a given system. Their procedure, "Curves", has been revised with respect to the Cambridge conventions (40). In this procedure, 6 parameters define uniquely the position of each base and 4 parameters define the position of the local helical axis. It is however useful to derive other parameters from this set in order to define the relative orientation of base pairs, the position of base pairs with respect to the local helical axis, the relative position of successive base pairs, and also to describe the junctions in the helical axis at each dinucleotide step . This leads to a total of 20 geometrically relevant parameters per base pair. The axis itself is obtained uniquely as optimum fit to the conformation in a generalized least squares sense.

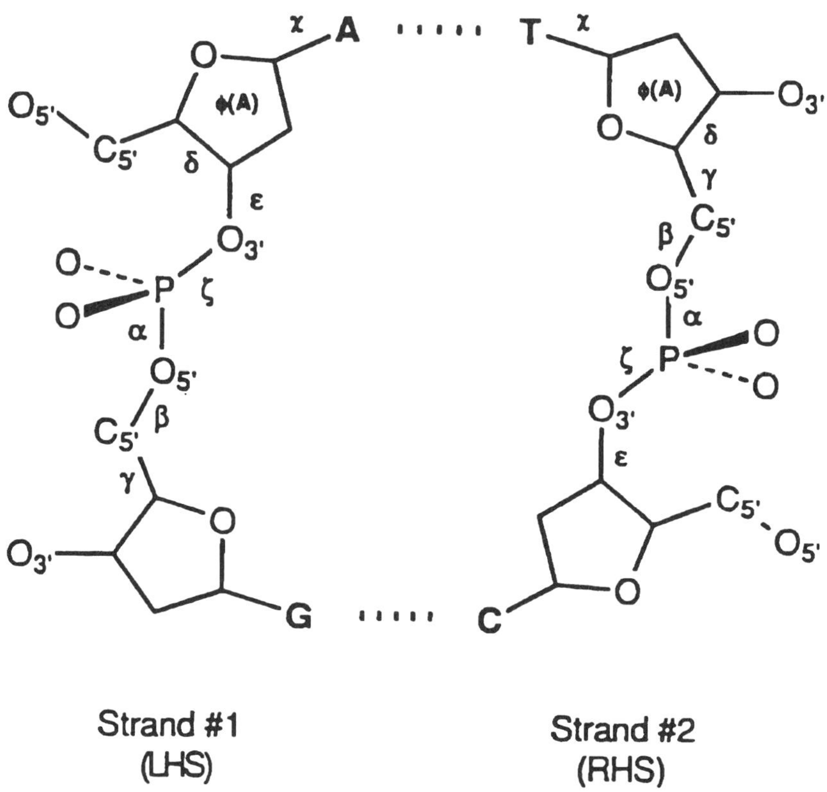

Figure 16: A base-pair step and designation of IUPAC conformational parameters (41) used in conformational dials analysis for nucleic acids.

We describe here the results of an investigation into the effective use of these parameters to analyze the ensemble of structures produced in an MD calculation on a DNA double helix, selecting d(CGCGAATTCGCG) as our demonstration case. The MD analysis depends heavily on computer graphics, and has been designed to convey the totality of structural and dynamical information on the system in as compact and rapidly accessible a form as possible. The task at hand was to reduce, using computer graphics, the complete analysis in this case of the time evolution of 206 conformational parameters and 230 helicoidal coordinates to a form that can be easily grasped, and for which patterns in the evolution of structure with time can be readily and accurately recognized. The result is a rigorous analysis of the dynamical evolution of structural parameters of a DNA double helix.

The conformational analysis is based on standard IUPAC conventions (41), as denoted in the structural schematic shown in Figure 16. The basic elements of our conformational analysis are 360° conformation wheels ("dials") for each of the backbone dihedral angles, α, β, γ, δ, ε and ζ, the exocyclic sugar base torsion χ, and the sugar pucker ϕ(A) where A is the amplitude. Following the usual convention, the vertical position, corresponding to "north" on a compass wheel, is taken as 0°. Furthermore, to facilitate cross reference, the layout of our dials in the graphic presentation was chosen to be isomorphic with the structure *per se*. On strand #1, the parameters δ, ϕ(A) and χ for the 5′ end as well as the succeeding ε, ζ, α, β and γ (moving 5′ to 3′) are assigned to the 5′ nucleotide base. On strand #2, the parameters δ, ϕ(A) and χ for the 3′ end as well as the succeeding γ, β, α, ζ and ε (moving 3′ to 5′) are assigned to the 3′ nucleotide base. Thus for a given sequence of n nucleotides, there will be n sets of dials for one strand (strand #1 or the "left-hand" strand) and n for the other (strand #2 or the "right-hand" strand). Here left and right are used only schematically, and refer to the arbitrary layout of the analysis on the page. The termini of the chain may have incomplete sets of dials, depending on which atoms are present. We begin our list with δ (instead of α) in the sequence in order to position the important phosphodiester torsion angles α and ζ of the backbone side-by-side, and centrally within the dial system for a given nucleotide. The phosphodiester (α,ζ) torsions for base pair steps on opposite strands are thus situated in corresponding interior positions in the respective sets of dials. In this article we use the terms *gauche* (*g*) and *trans* (*t*) to refer to broad regions of torsion angle space, and use Klyne-Prelog notation (synclinal, anticlinal, etc.) (42) when more specific designations are called for.

The helicoidal description of a nucleic acid involves a set of of 20 parameters, as shown in Figure 17. The 20 parameters are divided into four groups: axis-base pair (4 parameters), intra-base pair (6 parameters), inter-base pair (6 parameters) and axis junctions (4 parameters). The number of parameters in each group corresponds to the number necessary to rigorously define the relationship in space between the objects concerned. These parameters are said to be global in the sense that their definitions are made with respect to an overall helix axis for the system. The axis is obtained in Curves by minimizing a function which describes simultaneously the change in orientation between successive nucleotides and the non-linearity of the helical axis (39). The optimal helicoidal solution produces the overall helical axis that best fits the conformation considered, with structural irregularity distributed between changes in axis-base pair parameters and axis curvature.

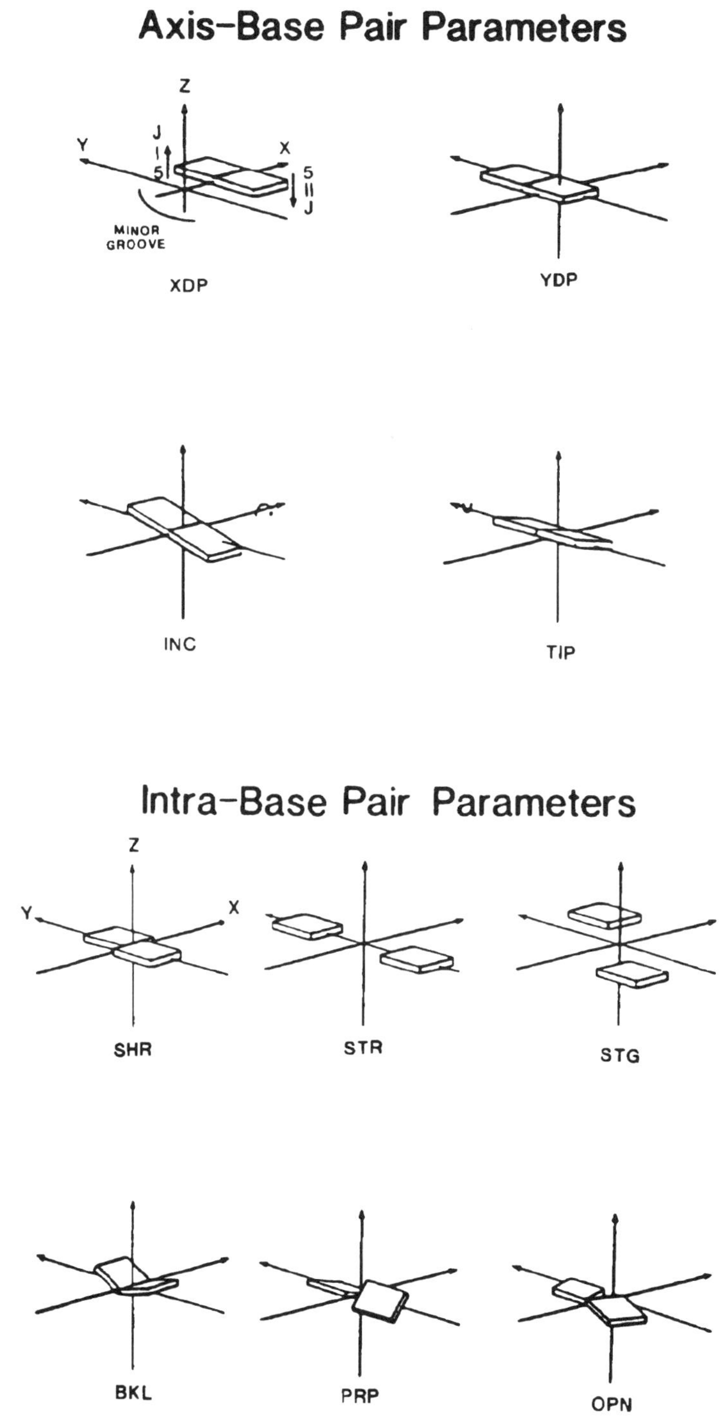

Figure 17: Helicoidal parameters for nucleic acids used in "Curves" analysis (39,40).

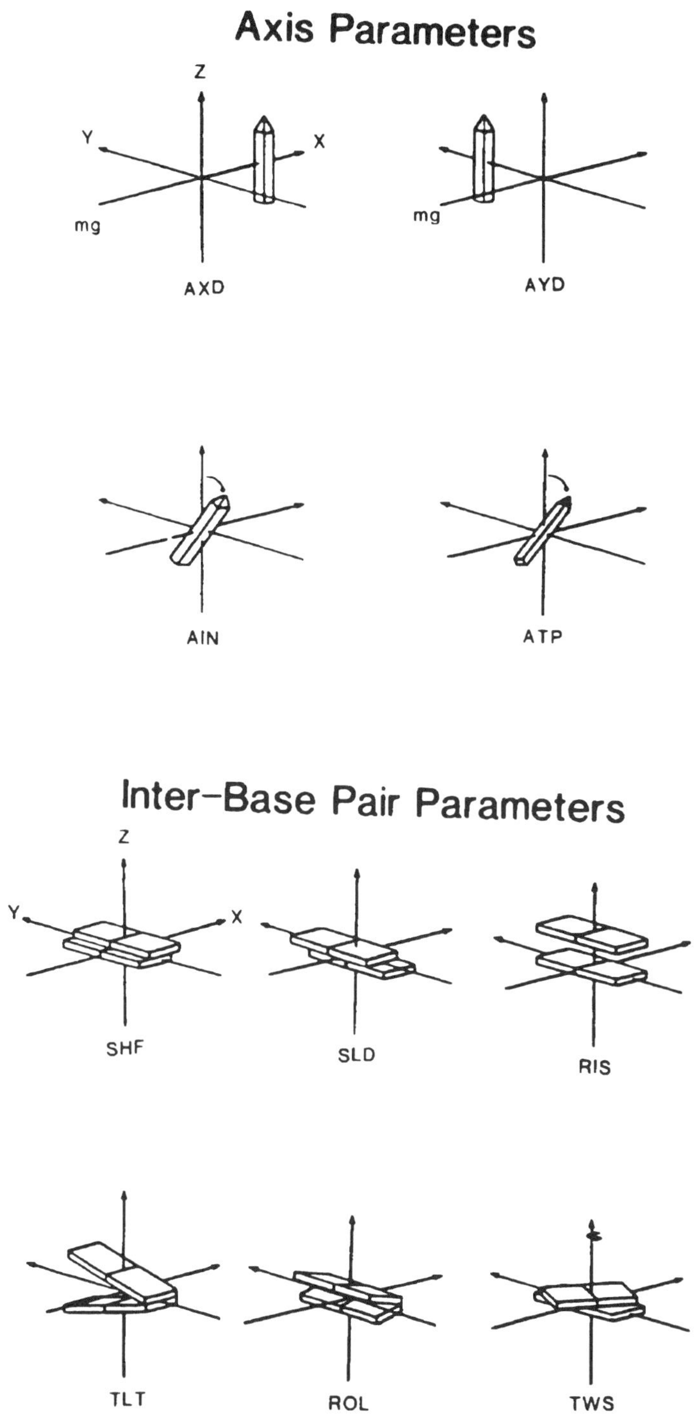

Figure 17 *continued*

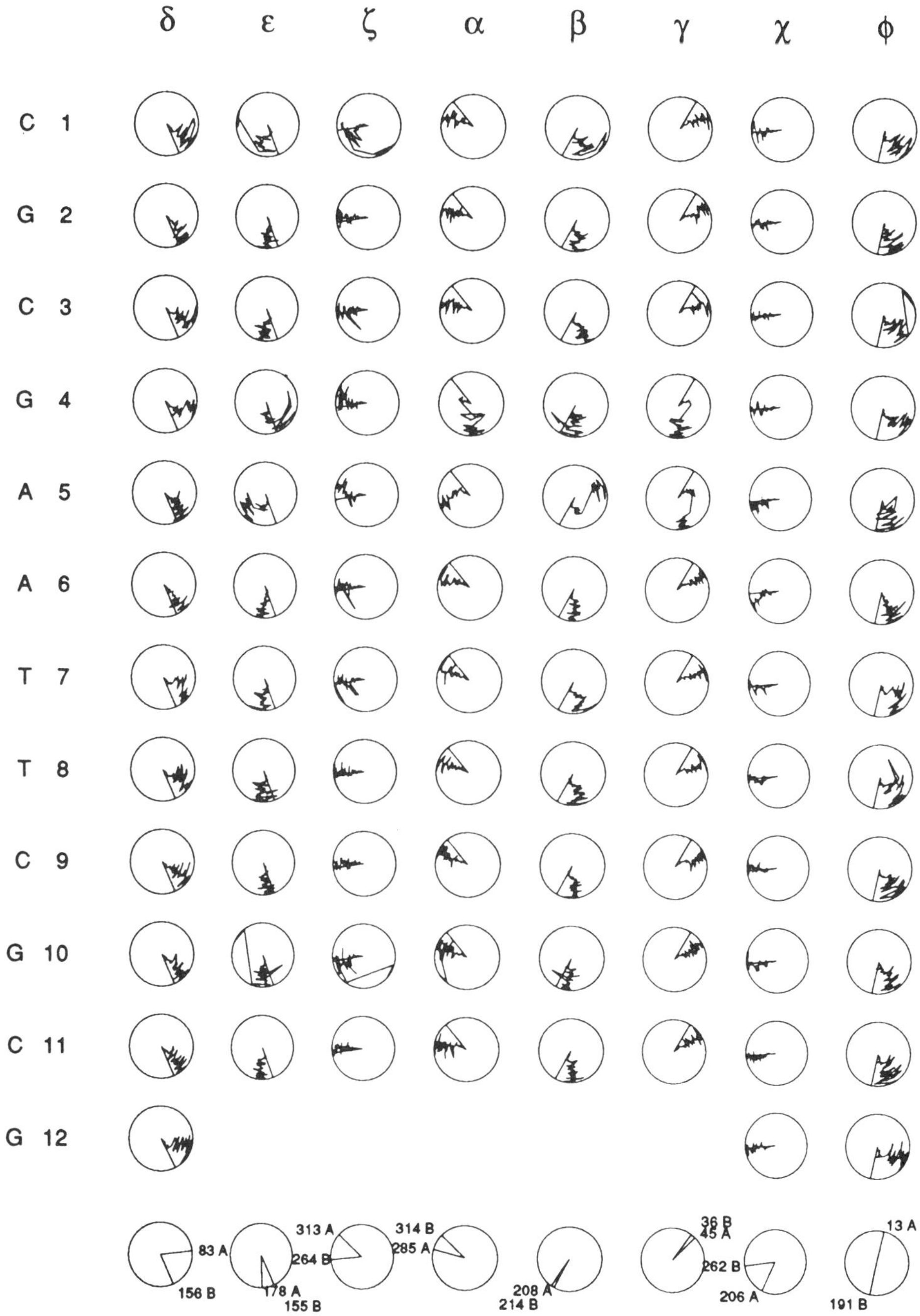

Figure 18: Conformational dials for the analysis of the dynamical behavior of strand #1 of d(CGCGAA-TTCGCG). The radial coordinate is the time axis, with t=0 at the center and t=30 at the circumference.

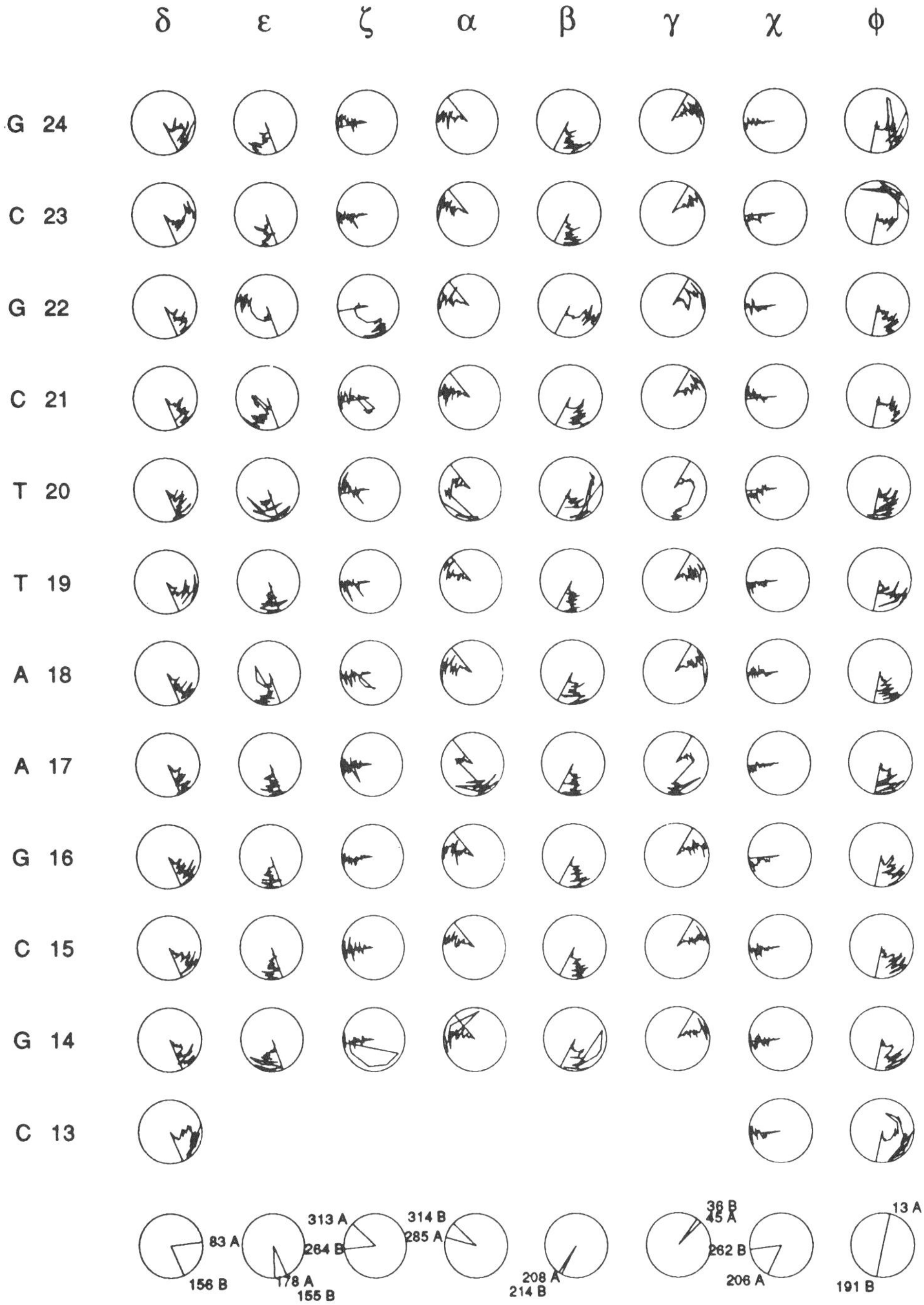

Figure 19: Conformational dials for the analysis of the dynamical behavior of strand #2 d(CGCGAA-TTCGCG). The radial coordinate is the time axis, with t=0 at the center and t=30 at the circumference.

The helicoidal parameters referenced to successive nucleotide base pairs are laid out in the graphics as "windows", defined on a suitable range of values for each parameter. Here 10 of the helicoidal parameters have units of distance and are grouped on the left hand side of the page and the other 10 are in angular units and are grouped together on the right hand side. As with the dials, the layout of windows is isomorphous with the structure being considered, viewed with the 5′→3′ polarity of the left hand strand running down the page and *vice versa* for the right hand strand.

The theoretical calculations carried out in conjunction with this project involve energy minimizations (EM) and MD simulations on the dodecamer duplex, d(CGCGAA-TTCGCG). In view of the approximations necessary in nucleic acid simulations and the still-evolving nature of the field with respect to force fields, hydration and electrostatic effects, the present calculations were set up as a demonstration project particularly to illustrate the analysis procedure involving Curves, dials and windows. This simulation is not claimed to be a definitive MD study on this system. In fact, one of our motivations in developing the analysis in this more elaborate form is to provide a means to examine critically the effect of various assumptions on the behavior of the simulation, and subsequently contribute to the further development of a well-characterized, reliable and credible protocol for MD on nucleic acids. These matters will be the subject of later studies, and the results described herein serve primarily to document and demonstrate the analysis procedure.

The system considered for simulation is the dodecamer duplex *in vacuo*. The calculations are all carried out using the "GROMOS" system of programs developed by van Gunsteren and Berendsen (20). The configurational energies and forces were computed using the GROMOS force field with the exception that charges on the phosphate were reduced from −1 to −0.25 in recognition of counterion condensation. At each phosphate, a solvaton of radius 2.6 Å and charge +0.25 was added for electrical neutrality. Switching functions were used to make the long range non-bonded interactions go smoothly to zero between 14.25 and 15.25 Å. In order to avoid artificially splitting dipoles, the switching function was applied on a "group by group" rather than atom by atom basis, where the "groups" correspond to sets of atoms comprising well-defined chemical subunits that, on the basis of structural chemistry, can be assumed to be electrically neutral.

The nature of this simulation was to probe via MD the energy surface in the immediate vicinity of the canonical B-DNA form of the dodecamer (43-45). Thus we first located the nearest local minimum in the neighborhood of this structure by EM and then performed MD beginning with this structure as an initial configuration. The EM was begun at the B73 structure (44) and subjected initially to conjugate gradient energy minimization, restrained via harmonic potentials to B73. The restraints were applied to all non-hydrogen atoms and the solvatons, using force constants of 25 kcal/mol/$Å^2$ in all cases. A nearby minimum was successfully located after 50 steps of conjugate gradient minimization characterized by an intrinsic temperature of 0.2°K, and deviating from B73 with an rms of 0.09 Å.

The next step was to prepare the simulation at 300°K by heating and equilibration, while remaining in the immediate vicinity of this minimum. The heating phase of the MD simulation was carried out under B73 restraints in steps of 50° in temperature over a time interval of 0.25 psec, reassigning the velocities based on a Gaussian approximation to a Maxwell-Boltzman distribution after each step. Then 4.5 psec of B73 restrained MD with Gaussian velocity adjustments was performed.

The B73 restraints were gently relaxed over the next 5 psec of MD by reducing the restraining force constants by 5 kcal/mol/$Å^2$ after each 0.5 psec. At this point, with the system prepared at T=300°K with a well-equilibrated structure in the vicinity of B73 form of DNA, 20 psec of free MD were performed. This calculation required 7.5 hours on the CRAY XMP/48 at the Pittsburgh Supercomputer Center. Energy was well conserved and stable over the course of the free dynamics. The temperature was seen to oscillate randomly about 300°K.

The behavior of the conformational parameters of the system with time is shown via dials in Figure 18 for strand #1 and Figure 19 for strand #2 of the dodecamer. The values of conformational parameters of B73, which collectively define the starting point of the initial energy minimization, are indicated on the dials as solid radial lines. For a description of the time evolution of the conformational parameters, the radial coordinate of the dial is treated as a time axis, defined on the 30 psec interval of the total calculation extending from t=0 at the center to t=30 psec at the circumference. The value of each parameter as a function of time is then displayed as an additional entry on each dial. Note in each case, near the origin, the conformational parameters stay close to the B73 values. This describes the behavior of the system during restrained heating and equilibration.

The results of the free conformational dynamics in the calculation in terms of the dials are as follows: The $C_{4'}$-$C_{3'}$ sugar torsion δ on both strands is quite stable and behaves in an oscillatory manner with respect to time. The conformational preference is essentially anticlinal throughout, a form intermediate between *t* and g^+ of canonical B and A values, respectively. The only minor deviation from this is found at C23, which as discussed below, is correlated with a sugar repuckering.

The $C_{3'}$-$O_{3'}$ torsion ε and the 3′ phosphodiester torsion ζ oscillate about trans and anticlinal (the high end of g^-), respectively, behaving in a manner quite consistent with a canonical B (i.e., B_I) structure. In two instances, however, interesting conformational transitions are seen. At C1 on strand 1, towards the end of the free MD, the parameter ε makes an abrupt change to g^-. Simultaneously ζ moves to *ca. t*. This is an example of a $B_I \rightarrow B_{II}$ transition. Another $B_I \rightarrow B_{II}$ transition is seen more or less at the outset of free dynamics at G22. The crystallographic dodecamer exhibits the B_{II} conformation at G10 on strand 1 and G23 on strand 2. Also A5, G14 and A18 show transitory $B_I \rightarrow B_{II} \rightarrow B_I$ behavior in the course of the simulation.

The parameters ζ and α comprise the 5′ phosphodiester torsion angles situated respectively on the 3′ and 5′ side of the phosphorus atom of the nucleotide chain. The α parameter is g^- in most cases, although tending more to the anticlinal side than B73 and ends up predominantly in an intermediate (relatively narrow in this case) range

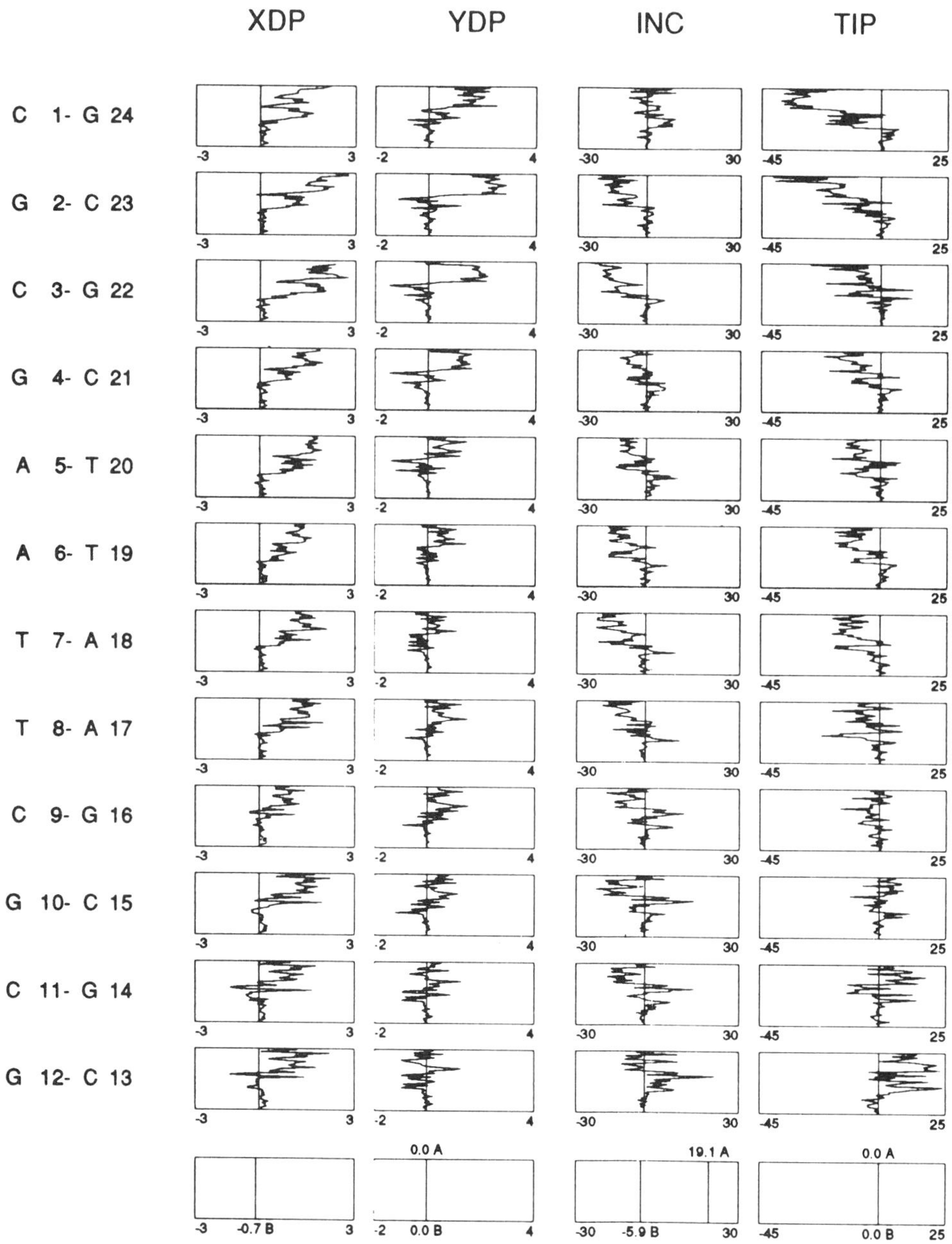

Figure 20: Helicoidal windows for the analysis of the dynamical behavior of axis-base pair parameters d(CGCGAATTCGCG). The vertical direction is the time axis, with t=0 at the bottom and t=30 at the top.

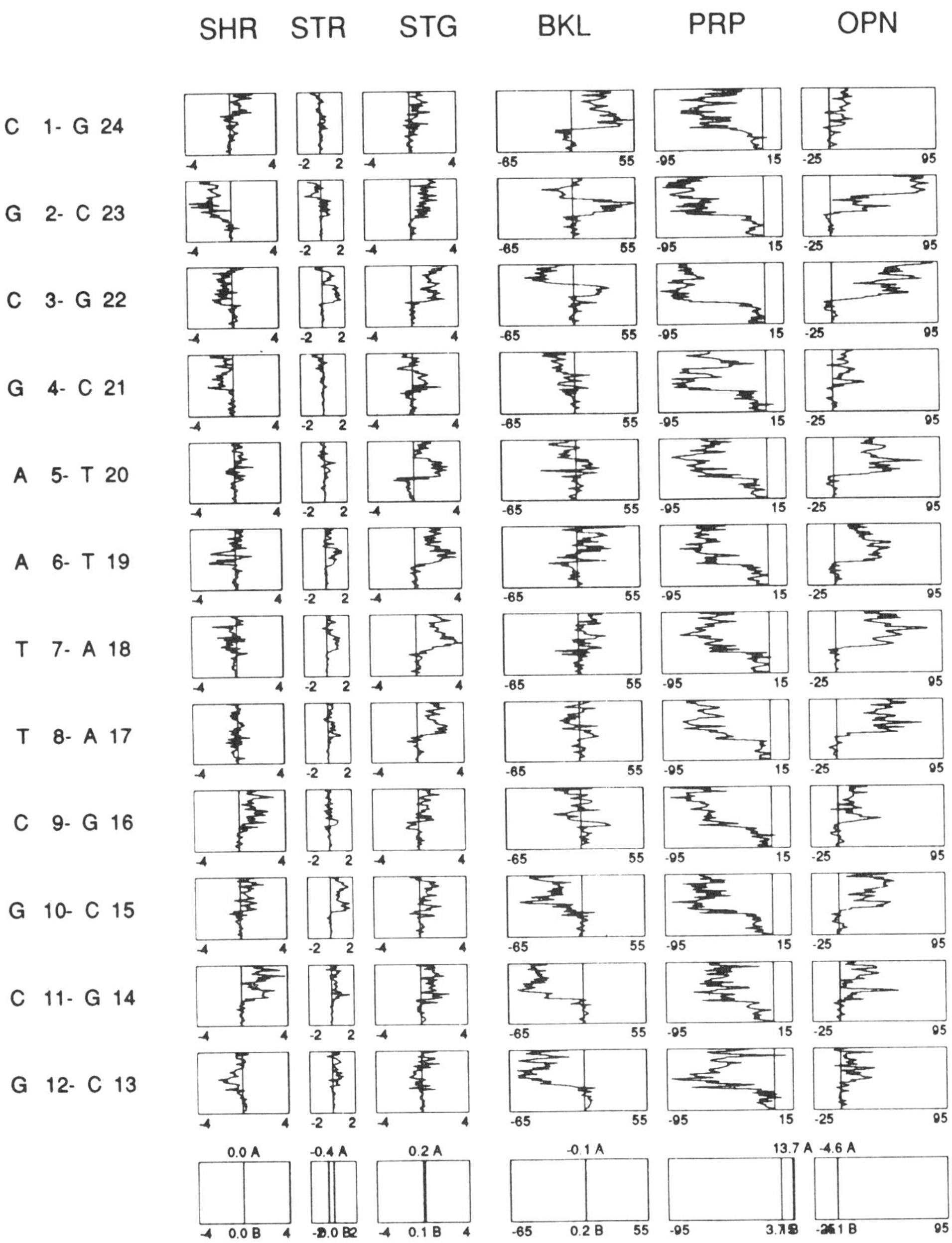

Figure 21: Helicoidal windows for the analysis of the dynamical behavior of intra-base pair parameters d(CGCGAATTCGCG). The vertical direction is the time axis, with t=0 at the bottom and t=30 at the top.

between A and B values for this parameter. Similar behavior is observed in the structure of the native dodecamer. Significant $g^{-} \rightarrow t$ conformational transitions for α are seen at G4 and A17. An incipient drift in a towards trans but only getting as far as anticlinal is seen at A5. Transitory $g^{-} \rightarrow t \rightarrow g^{-}$ behavior is seen in the free dynamics for T20. The changes in α are correlated with changes in both β and γ on the 5′ side of the nucleotide.

At G4, A17 and T20, $g^{-} \rightarrow t$ in α is accompanied by $g^{+} \rightarrow t$ in γ, a correlated motion known as a "crankshaft" transition. In this type of motion, compensating changes occur in two torsional parameters separated by one bond, and essentially no overall change in secondary structure takes place. At A5 α, β and γ change simultaneously from (g^{-}, t, g^{+}) to (t, g^{+}, t), and transitory $t \rightarrow g^{+} \rightarrow t \rightarrow g^{+}$ behavior is seen in β at T20. The 5′ side of the nucleotide is stable at (g^{-}, t, g^{+}) in the native dodecamer and similarly for both A and B forms of DNA.

The exocyclic χ parameter remains stable over the time course of the free MD. The sugar puckers are predominantly $C_{2'}$-endo. Repuckering to $C_{4'}$-exo is seen for the furanose ring at C3, and particularly at C23 and G24. Transitory $C_{2'}$-endo$\rightarrow$C3′-endo$\rightarrow C_{2'}$-endo changes are seen at T8 and C13 in the course of the 30 psec simulation.

The behavior of the helicoidal parameters of the system in time is described using "windows" defined in a manner analogous to the use of "dials" described above. For each of the helicoidal parameters, the time coordinate is defined with t=0 at the bottom, and the values of each parameter with respect to time are plotted on a vertical axis. The results for axis-base parameters are shown in Figure 20. The restrained heating and initial equilibration are clearly evident at the bottom of each window as the parameters do indeed stay close to that of B-DNA. At the onset of free dynamics, XDP is seen to drift to values slightly greater than B73 or B80, indicating a slight displacement of base pairs towards the major groove, but remains throughout the time course of the simulation in a distinctly B-form range with respect to XDP. The structure in fact is displaced slightly away rather than towards an A-DNA with respect to this key parameter. The parameter YDP oscillates in most cases around the initial B73 values which is also near A73 values for this parameter. The time evolution of INC and TIP are both reasonably stable and remain near canonical B values. INC, as with XDP, shows a slight but perceptible drift away from rather than towards A values.

The behavior of intra-base pair parameters with respect to time in the calculation is shown in Figure 21. The parameters SHR and STG remain near zero although end effects, particularly at the 5′ C1-G24 end, are evident. A positive STG of as much as ca. 1 Å is seen particularly in the AT region. There is fairly high amplitude buckling observed in the dynamics, oscillating around zero in the interior CAATTG tract but becoming systematic as the ends fray. There is large amplitude propeller twist evident from the onset of free dynamics as found in other MD studies of this and related systems, and in the native crystallographic dodecamer. The trend in PRP, AT ~ GC, is observed by the calculation, and generally PRP values in the GC sequence are larger than those seen in the crystal structure. Preferential base pair opening towards the major groove is seen consistently in the dynamics, with AT>GC in OPN consistent with trends observed in the crystal structure. However, OPN for GC is equivalent to that for AT at the G2 and G3 steps.

The inter-base pair parameters SHF, SLD and RIS, Figure 22, remain fairly stable in the calculation. Small compensatory changes in SHF are evident going up the chain. Interestingly, the oscillation in calculated values of RIS, also stable overall, encompasses the characteristic values of canonical A and B forms of DNA. TLT values are stable or compensatory, but ROL tends to increase in amplitude as the simulation progresses. As in the crystal, GpC>ApT in ROL. TWS is stable with respect to the B73 value of 36°, or else higher, except at the 5′ and 3′ termini where end effects are evident.

Finally, the dynamical behavior of the axis-junction parameters are shown in Figure 23. The interpretation of these results requires simultaneous consideration of a representation of the structure as well as the structural parameters. Thus a series of 8 snapshots of the structure at intervals along the time line of the calculation are shown in Figure 24. It is interesting to note that the bending of the helix axis occurs spontaneously in the vicinity of G3-G4 and G9-G10, at or near the position of the 1° hinge points! This result occured *ab initio* in the simulation, and thus supports further the idea set forth by Dickerson and coworkers of intrinsic, sequence specific hinge points in the structure (6). A full study of this point based on MD calculations is thus likely to be of considerable interest.

We illustrate further the analysis of DNA bending with considerations of the path length of the helix and the end-to-end length vs time. The bending in the time course of this simulation shows oscillation about a value slightly below the reference for a straight helix. The difference between these values for each structure is a useful higher resolution measure of bending. The difference plot is shown as a function of time in Figure 25. The time evolution of bending exhibits essentially normal mode behavior, with an effective vibrational frequency of ca. 10 cm^{-1}. The oscillatory bending/straightening of the helix axis in the calculation is clearly evident in the time sequence of structures displayed in Figure 24.

The rms deviation of the MD structures of the dodecamer from B73 *vs.* time is given in Figure 26. At the onset of the free dynamics, the structure transits to ca. 4 Å rms from B73, and oscillates in the range of 3-4 Å rms for the duration of the run. However, the dynamical analysis of the helicoidal parameters XDP, TIP and INC shows that, in spite of the large deviation from B73, The MD structures are seen to remain distinctly in the B-DNA family.

In summary, we have described in this section the use of the Curves algorithm and a presentation based on "Dials and Windows" to provide a comprehensive analysis of the structure and molecular dynamics of a DNA double helix, using the dodecamer d(CGCGAATTCGCG) as an example. The extent to which the structure maintains a B-DNA conformation is easily recognized, as is the pattern of structural irregularities

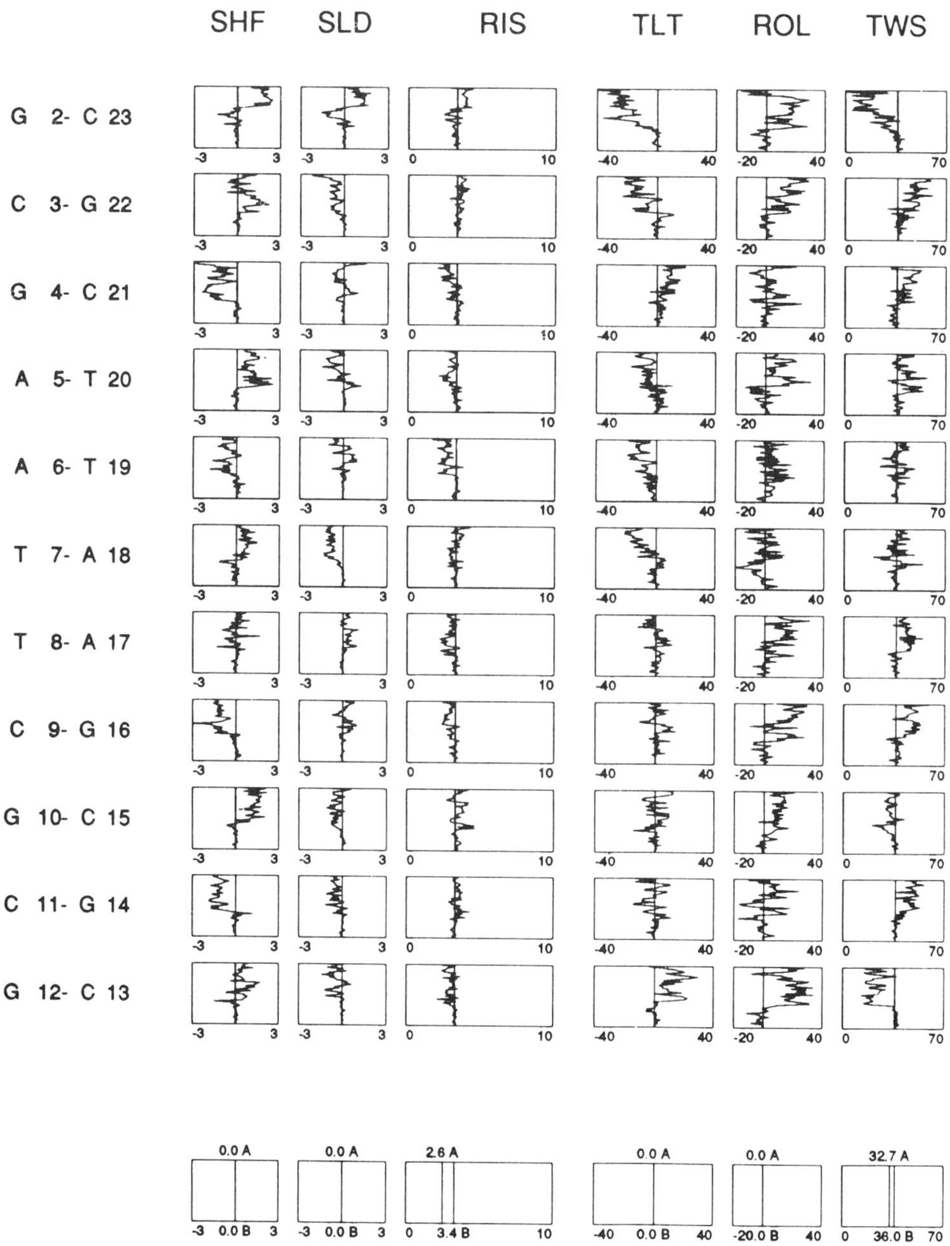

Figure 22: Helicoidal windows for the analysis of the dynamical behavior of inter-base pair parameters d(CGCGAATTCGCG). The vertical direction is the time axis, with t=0 at the bottom and t=30 at the top.

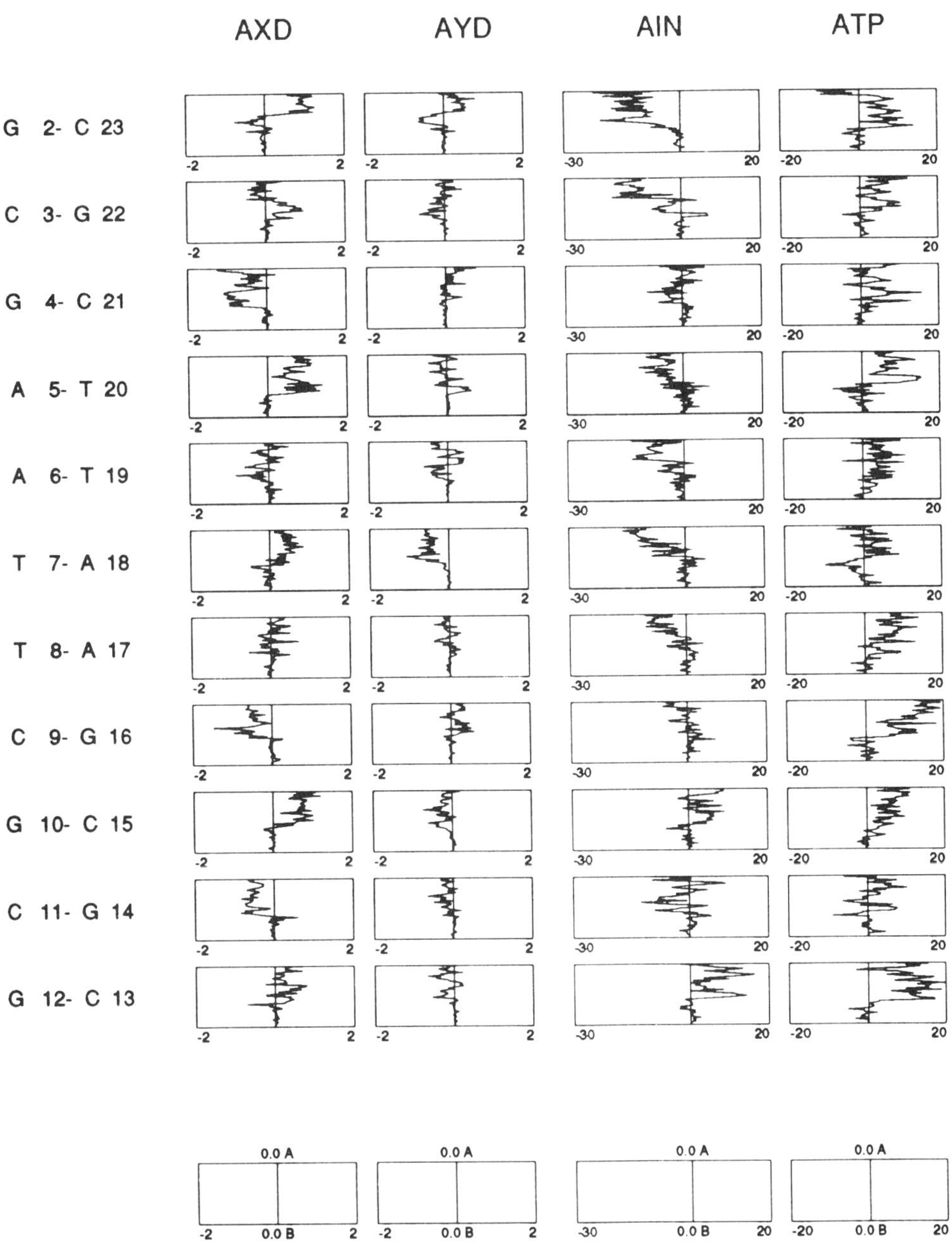

Figure 23: Helicoidal windows for the analysis of the dynamical behavior of the axis-junction parameters d(CGCGAATTCGCG). The vertical direction is the time axis, with t=0 at the bottom and t=30 at the top.

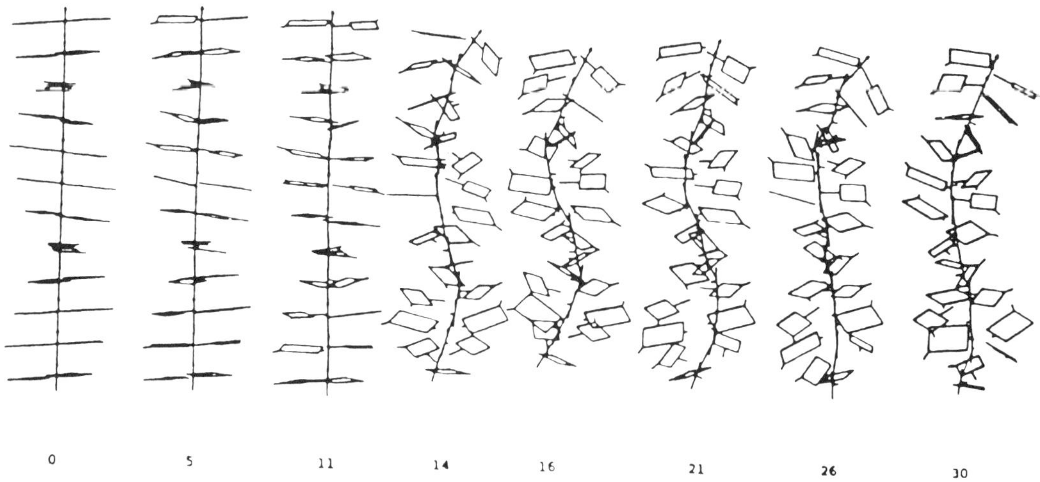

Figure 24: Time evolution of the base-pair orientations and helix axis for the dodecamer.

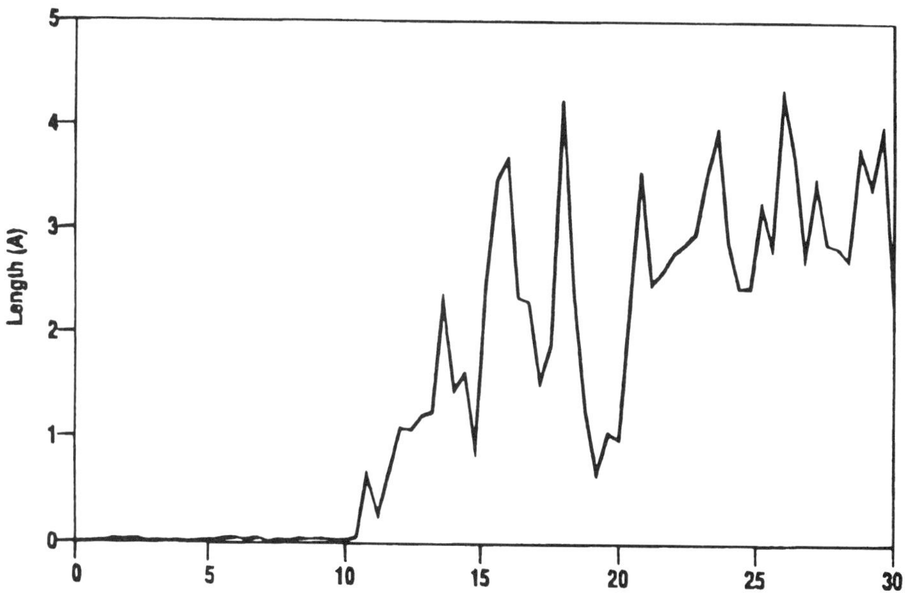

Figure 25: Calculated helix bending index, the difference of path length and end-to-end distance vs. time for the dodecamer.

in the native, crystallographic dodecamer. In the dynamical simulation, features such as crankshaft motions, B_I to B_{II} transitions, and sugar repuckering at selective points in the dodecamer sequence are readily perceived. The procedure also leads to a systematic analysis of dynamical bending of the helical axis in the native dodecamer

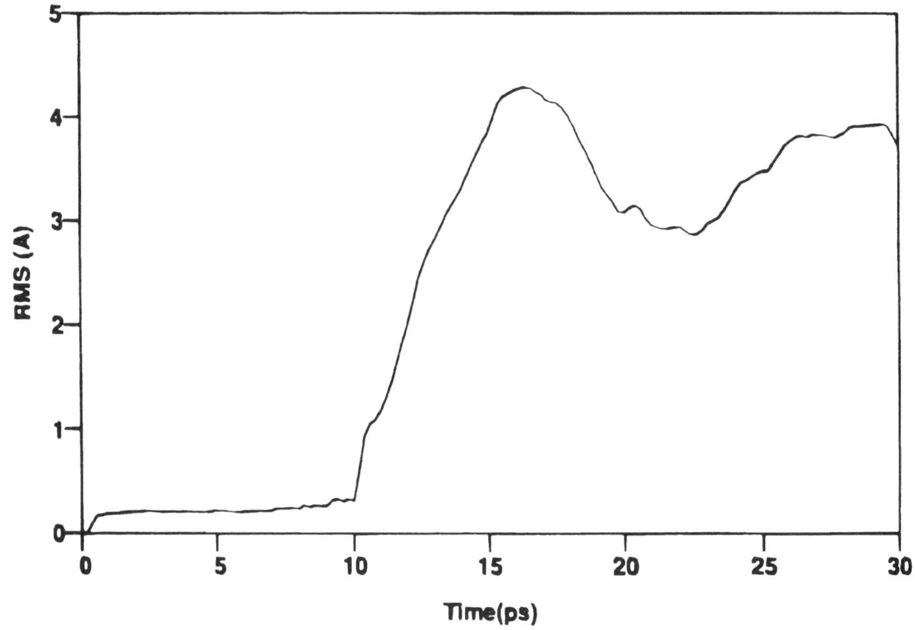

Figure 26: Calculated RMS deviation of the MD structures and B73 vs. time for the dodecamer.

that coincides with the proposed 1° and 2° hinge points in the crystallographic structure. The analysis introduced here, isomorphic with the structure *per se* for ease of cross reference, is expected to be useful in critical evaluation of the effect of force field parameters, hydration and models for electrostatic effects on DNA structure, and thus aid in the development of improved methodologies for nucleic acid simulations. Numerous direct applications in MD studies of nucleic acids are obvious, including monitoring the application of constraints in restrained MD calculations (46). In differential form, this method can yield an elegant systematic description of the molecular dynamics of the sequence dependent, structural adaptation of DNA on complexation with drugs and regulatory proteins.

Acknowledgements

We acknowledge particularly the contributions from our extramural collaborators R. Lavery, H. Sklenar, K. Sharp and B. Honig. This research was supported by grants from the National Institutes of Health (GM-37909) and the National Science Foundation (CHE-8696117), the Office of Naval Research (N-00014-87-K-0312), and the Bristol-Myers Corporation. Computer time on the CRAY XMP/48 was provided by the Pittsburgh Supercomputer Center.

References and Footnotes

1. R.M. Wing *et al., Nature 278*, 755 (1980).
2. H.R. Drew *et al., Proc. Natl. Acad. Sci. USA 78*, 2179 (1981).
3. R.E. Dickerson and H.R. Drew, *J. Mol. Biol. 149*, 761 (1981).
4. H.R. Drew and R.E. Dickerson, *J. Mol. Biol. 151*, 535 (1981).

5. H.R. Drew, S. Samson and R.E. Dickerson, *Proc. Natl. Acad. Sci. USA 79*, 4040 (1982).
6. A.V. Fantini, M.L. Kopka, H.R. Drew and R.E. Dickerson, *J. Biol. Chem. 257*, 14868 (1982).
7. M.L. Kopka, A.V. Fratini, H.R. Drew and R.E. Dickerson, *J. Mol. Biol. 163*, 129 (1983).
8. B. Reid, *Quart. Rev. Biophys. 20*, 1 (1987).
9. D.J. Patel, L. Shapiro and D. Hare, *Quart. Rev. Biophys. 20*, 35 (1987).
10. D.J. Patel, A. Pardi and K. Itakura, *Science 216*, 581 (1982).
11. E. Westhof and D.L. Beveridge, *Water Science Reviews*, in press (1989).
12. P. Subramanian, Ph.D. Thesis, Wesleyan University (1989).
13. P.S. Subramanian, G. Ravishanker and D.L. Beveridge, *Proc. Natl. Acad. Sci. 85*, 1836 (1988).
14. P. Subramanian and D.L. Beveridge, *J. Biomol. Str. Dyn.*, in press (1989).
15. P. Subramanian and D.L. Beveridge, MS in preparation.
16. S.J. Weiner *et al., J. Am. Chem. Soc. 106*, 765 (1984).
17. W.L. Jorgensen, J. Chandrasekar, J. Madura, R. Impey and M.L. Klein, *J. Chem. Phys. 79*, 926 (1983).
18. M. Falk, J.A. Hartman and R.C. Lord, *J. Am. Chem. Soc. 84*, 3843 (1962); ibid. 85, 387 (1963); *ibid. 85*, 391 (1963).
19. C.J. Alden and S.H. Kim, *J. Mol. Biol. 132*, 411 (1979).
20. W.F. van Gunsteren and H.J.C. Berendsen, GROMOS88: Groningen Molecular Simulation System, University of Groningen, The Netherlands (1988).
21. H.C. Berendsen, J.P.M. Postma, W.F. van Gunsteren and J. Hermans, in *Intermolecular Forces,* B. Pullman, ed., Reidel, Dodrect, 331, 1981.
22. P.S. Subramanian, S. Swaminathan and D.L. Beveridge, *J. Biomol. Str. Dyn.*, in press (1990).
23. L.A. Marky and K.S. Breslauer, *Proc. Natl. Acad. Sci. USA 82*, 6537 (1985).
24. P.S. Subramanian and D.L. Beveridge, MS in preparation.
25. P.S. Subramanian and D.L. Beveridge, MS in preparation.
26. W. Saenger, W.N. Hunter and O. Kennard, *Nature 324*, 385 (1986).
27. G.S. Manning, *Quart. Rev. Biophys. 11*, 179 (1978).
28. M.T. Record, C.F. Anderson and T. Lohman, *Quart. Rev. Biophys. 11*, 1203 (1979).
29. B. Jayaram, S. Swaminathan, K. Sharp, D.L. Beveridge and B. Honig, *Macromolecules*, in press (1990).
30. J. Conrad, M. Troll and B.H. Zimm, *Biopolymers 27*, 1711 (1988).
31. B.E. Hingerty, R.H. Ritchie, T.L. Ferrell and J.E. Turner, *Biopolymers 24*, 427 (1985).
32. M.L. Bleam, C.F. Anderson and M.T. Record, Jr., *Biochemistry 22*, 5418 (1983).
33. B. Jayaram, K. Sharp and B. Honig, *Biopolymers 28*, 975 (1989).
34. C.F. Anderson and M.T. Record, *Ann. Rev. Phys. Chem. 33*, 191 (1982).
35. B. Tidor, K.K. Irikura, B.R. Brooks and M. Karplus, *J. Biomol. Str. Dyn. 1*, 231 (1983).
36. M. Levitt, *Cold Spring Harbor Symp. Quant. Biol. 47*, 251 (1983).
37. W.K. Olson in *Topics in Nucleic Acid Structure*, Part II, S. Neidle, ed., MacMillan Press, London (1982).
38. G. Ravishanker, S. Swaminathan, D.L. Beveridge, R. Lavery and H. Sklenar, *J. Biomol. Str. Dyn. 6*, 669 (1989).
39. R. Lavery and H. Sklenar, *J. Biomol. Str. Dyn. 6*, 63 (1988).
40. R. Lavery and H. Sklenar, *J. Biomol. Str. Dyn. 6*, 655 (1989).
41. IUPAC-IUB Joint Commission on Biochemical Nomenclature, *Eur. J. Biochem. 131*, 9 (1983).
42. W. Saenger, *Principles of Nucleic Acid Structure,* Springer Verlag, New York (1983).
43. S. Arnott and D.W.L. Hukins, *Biochem. Biophys. Res. Comm. 47*, 1504 (1972).
44. S. Arnott and D.W.L. Hukins, *J. Mol. Biol. 81*, 93 (1973).
45. S. Arnott, R. Chandrasekaran, D.L. Birdsall, A.G.W. Leslie and R.L. Ratliffe, *Nature 283*, 743 (1980).
46. J. Withka, P.H. Bolton and D.L. Beveridge, MS in preparation.

Structure & Methods, ISBN 0-940030-32-2
Volume 3: DNA & RNA, ISBN 0-940030-31-4
Eds., Ramaswamy H. Sarma & Mukti H. Sarma, © Adenine Press 1990

Applications of Imino Proton Exchange to Nucleic Acid Kinetics and Structures

M. Guéron, E. Charretier, J. Hagerhorst, M. Kochoyan, J.L. Leroy and A. Moraillon
Groupe de Biophysique
Ecole Polytechnique
91128 Palaiseau, France

Abstract

Imino proton exchange in duplexes is commonly limited by the chemical exchange step. Hence it may be catalysed by proton acceptors. In the limit of infinite catalyst concentration, the exchange time is equal to the lifetime of the closed state. The efficiency of the catalyst at moderate concentrations provides a value for the base-pair dissociation constant. With appropriate methods for the suppression of the solvent signal, exchange times between 1 ms and 1 s can be measured by NMR of imino protons. Those longer than 1 minute are accessible to direct measurement in D_2O. Furthermore, NMR can measure exchange of individual, assigned protons.

Using such methods, we have shown that base pairs open one at a time. In B-DNA, the lifetime is in the range of milliseconds at room temperature, and the influence of neighbors is not large. In oligodeoxyduplexes containing tracts of A · T base pairs, the lifetimes are anomalously long if the tract contains four consecutive A · T base pairs, possibly including a 5′-AT step but not a 5′-TA step. This strongly suggests that, in such tracts, a conformation distinct from standard B-DNA is formed cooperatively. The lifetime anomaly occurs in all A · T tracts known to generate curved DNA, suggesting that the structure responsible for the long lifetimes is involved in the curvature of DNA. In the Z form, the lifetime is 100 times longer than in B-DNA.

The base-pair dissociation constant is obtained by comparison with exchange from mononucleosides, under a specific assumption, whose plausibility rests on the relative efficiency of a large variety of catalysts. The dissociation constants of B-DNA base pairs at 25°C are in the range of 10^{-5} and 10^{-6} for A · T and G · C respectively.

We discuss the possibility of other disruptions of the Watson-Crick pairs, beside the one characterized by imino proton exchange. Processes with equilibrium constants as large as 10^{-2} have been proposed in the past, and have always been disproved.

But the possibility exists. A sample is provided by the formation of G · CH^+ Hoogsteen base pairs, which is demonstrated at low pH, and must exist as a minority species at neutral pH.

Introduction

It has long been considered that internal motions could play a role in the structural and functional properties of nucleic acids. Among these motions, base-pair opening has been the subject of numerous studies. Probing the imino groups of guanosine, thymidine or uridine, one compares their reactivity in the polymer with that of an isolated and fully accessible monomer. In favorable circumstances, such studies may provide extensive information on base-pair lifetimes, base-pair dissociation constants, accessibility of the open base pair, structural features of the internal motion, etc.

Chemical probes such as mercury (1) and formaldehyde (2) or isotopic probes such as tritium (3,4,5) and deuterium (6,7) were used in early investigations. More recently, proton-proton and proton-deuterium exchange has been studied by proton magnetic resonance. This technique provides precise identification of the exchanging group (8).

The exchange of imino protons of synthetic RNA (9), transfer RNA (10), 5s RNA (11) and DNA (8,12) is catalyzed by proton acceptors such as tris, imidazole or ammonia. This demonstrates that in usual buffer conditions, exchange is limited by a chemical step and does not occur at each base-pair opening event. The base-pair lifetimes are obtained by extrapolation of the imino proton exchange time to infinite catalyst concentration. They are in the range of milliseconds for RNA and B-DNA duplexes.

Base pair lifetimes are fairly easy to measure, and they provide interesting probes of nucleic acid structures. When the DNA sequence is random, chemically speaking, so that the structure is probably close to standard B-DNA, the lifetimes are insensitive to sequence, and in particular to the nature of the nearest base-pairs. But stretches of A display anomalously long base-pair lifetimes, which may be related to the so-called B′or P structure (13,14). This is also the case for GC stretches in the Z form.

The dissociation constant of a base pair may be evaluated by comparison of the exchange rate at moderate catalyst concentration with that of the mononucleoside. Imino protons exchange even in the absence of added catalyst, due to exchange catalysis in the open state by the acceptor group of the opposite base, a process taking place through a bridging water molecule (15). Whether opening is to the minor or major groove remains unknown.

Future applications of proton exchange may include renewed studies of tRNA and studies of other RNAs, studies of triple helices and investigations of complexes of nucleic acids with drugs, proteins or other molecules. Some of these are presently under investigation.

In a recent review (16), NMR methods for the investigation of proton exchange and base-pair opening were presented. Structural applications, in particular to DNA curvature, and some properties of the base-pair dissociation constant were discussed.

In the present work, we propose standard samples and methods for the evaluation of solvent signal suppression, a procedure required for the NMR study of exchangeable protons. Among structural aspects we include further developments on Z-DNA. We present and discuss the reference data for the determination of base-pair dissociation constants, namely catalyst efficiencies for exchange from mononucleosides. Finally, we discuss the uniqueness of the mode of base-pair opening, and consider acid-catalysed exchange and the formation of Hoogsteen base-pairs in that context.

2. *Materials and Methods: Solvent Signal Suppression*

Most of the chemical and NMR methods used in the work presented or reviewed here have been described (8), and further information is given in the text, as necessary. However, we wish to make some remarks on the suppression of the solvent signal, which is an important requirement for the observation of imino proton spectra.

Numerous methods for solvent signal suppression (SSS) have been proposed. Their characterization and comparison involves many properties, including (i) sensivity for the protons of interest, (ii) sensivity in the vicinity of the solvent peak and (iii) phase-shift and base-line distorsions. These problems will be discussed in detail elsewhere (17). Here we propose two practical tests for the comparison of SSS methods and for evaluation of probe sensivity. We use two samples containing thymidine at a concentration of 10 mM, in D_2O and H_2O (90%) respectively. Spectrum (a) in Figure 1 is from the D_2O sample after a 90° pulse. Spectrum (b) is from the H_2O sample, using the JR sequence for SSS. The same phase correction is applied to both spectra. The line broadening (3 Hz) ensures that the spectrum is not sensitive to field homogeneity. The signal-to-noise ratio in spectrum (a) provides a global test of spectrometer sensivity. Spectrum (b) shows that the JR method produces SSS without phase shift. For chemical shifts close to the sensivity maxima, chosen here at ± 4.54 ppm from water, the signal-to-noise ratio is nearly as high as in spectrum (a). The sensivity remains fair even close to the solvent chemical shift, and the H'_3 peak is clearly visible 0.3 ppm upfield from water. The solvent suppression factor (about 300 in this case) is quite dependent on field homogeneity, and is not the most important criterion of SSS.

The intense water resonance provides a simple and absolute test of the probe sensivity (18). In Figure 2 are shown two spectra of a water sample. Spectrum (a) is obtained after a 30° pulse. It is broadened by radiation damping. The narrower spectrum is obtained in the same way except that the magnetization is reduced by 80% prior to the 30° pulse, so that it is only slightly affected by radiation damping, whose rate is proportional to the magnetization. In the case of equilibrium magnetization, the broadening by radiation damping Δ is given by:

$$\Delta = (Q\eta)\, B_0/5.8 \qquad [1]$$

where Q is the coil quality factor, η the filling factor and B_0 is the magnetic field, 8.46 T. Thus one obtains $Q\eta$, the factor which characterizes probe sensivity for the given sample. In the present case, $\Delta = 2.9$ Hz, hence $Q\eta = 2.0$.

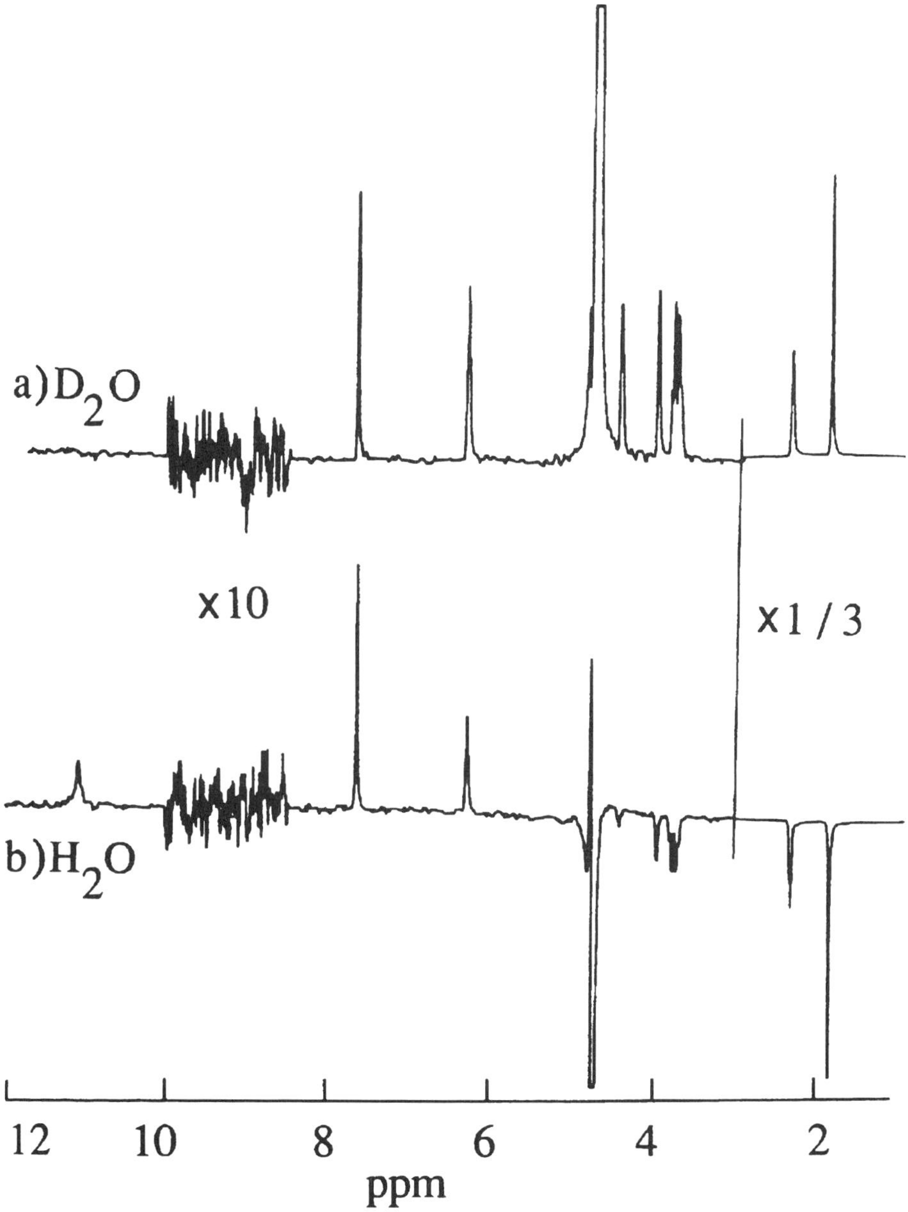

Figure 1: Proposed test for signal solvent suppression. a) Proton NMR spectrum in D_2O, with excitation by a 90° pulse. The sample is a solution of thymidine, 10 mM, with NaCl, 100 mM, pH 4.5, T = 25°C. Proton frequency, 360 MHz; one acquisition; 3 Hz line broadening. b) Same sample and conditions as above, except that the solvent is 90% H2O, 10% D_2O. Excitation is by a JR sequence, consisting of two 90° pulses at the water frequency, separated by 153 μs, corresponding to maximum sensivity at 9.34 and 0.26 ppm. The sensitivity in these regions is the same as in (a): compare for example the H6 peak at 7.7 ppm; the imino proton peak at 11 ppm, broadened by exchange, is also detected with good sensitivity. Even lines which are rather close to the solvent line remain detectable (e.g., the H_3' line, 0.3 ppm upfield from water), and there is no base line artifact.

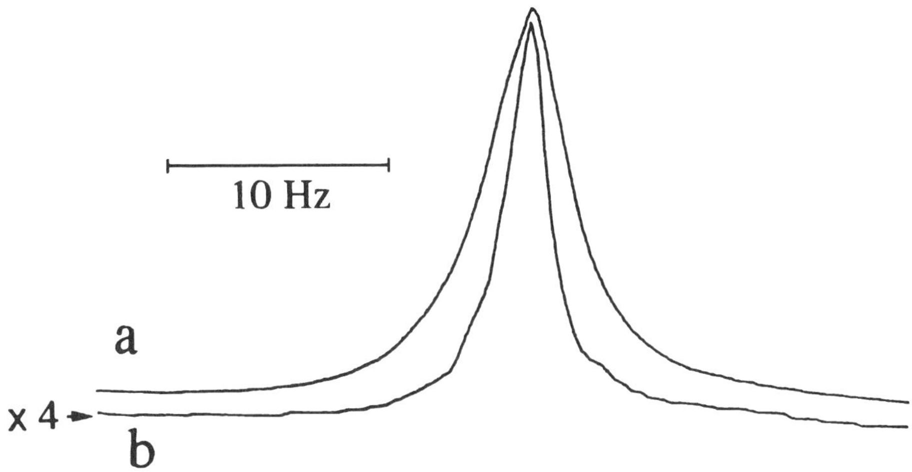

Figure 2: Proposed probe sensivity test, based on line broadening by radiation damping. Spectra of a 270 μl water sample in a 5 mm tube; 30° excitation pulse. (a) Starting from equilibrium; (b) after 80% saturation.

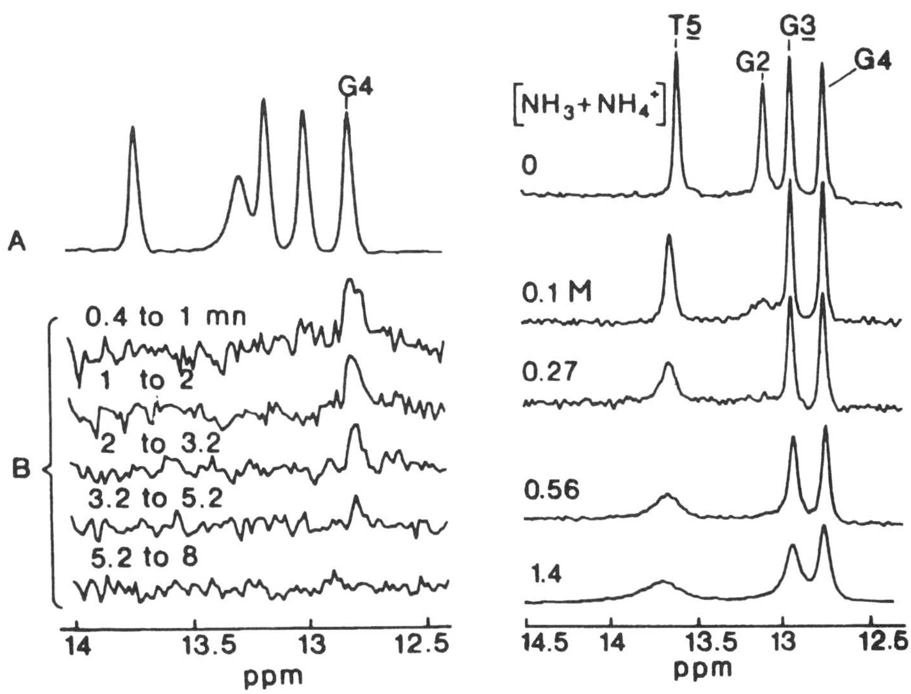

Figure 3: Imino proton exchange experiments on the d(CGCGATCGCG)$_2$ duplex (T5 means T opposite to A5). *On the left side*: real-time solvent exchange at pH 7.2, O°C, in the absence of added catalyst. (A) reference spectrum in 90% H_2O. (B) difference spectra between the spectra obtained at various times after dilution of the protonated sample in D_2O, and the final spectrum at 30 mn. The exchange time of the G4 imino proton is 3 minutes. *On the right side*: Exchange broadening of the imino protons for increasing concentrations of ammonia; pH 8.8; T = 15°C.

3. *Base-Pair Lifetimes*

Base-pair lifetimes are obtained as the limit of imino proton exchange times for infinite concentration of exchange catalyst. The measurements are straightforward and require very little interpretation. In this section, we summarize observations corresponding to three different structural situations. The reference is provided by sequences which presumably have a standard B structure. We also consider sequences containing adenine tracts, and lastly turn to Z-DNA.

3.1 B-DNA

We have studied the kinetic and exchange properties of a number of self-complementary duplexes (8), in particular the 10-mer 5′-d$(CGCGATCGCG)_2$,as shown in Figure 3. Here and below, all sequences are written in the direction from 5′ to 3′.

In all cases where the B-form is expected, the lifetimes of A · T pairs are in the range of 1 to 7 ms at 15°C, and 7 to 40 ms for GC pairs. The lifetime is determined mainly by the *nature of the base-pair.* It is not sensitive to the nature of neighboring base-pairs.

The lifetimes of neighboring base pairs are different. Coupled with the small dissociation constant, 10^{-5} to 10^{-6} (see below), this shows that *base pairs open one at a time.*

The activation enthalpies range from 40 to 65 kJ/M, with no clearcut difference between A · T and G · C pairs. This is the same range as that of the enthalpies for adding a base pair to a double-stranded RNA (19).

3.2. Adenine Tracts and their Relation to DNA Curvature

The curvature of DNA which includes tracts of A · T base pairs has been studied by the anomalous electrophoretic mobility of duplexes built on repeating decamer sequences (20,21). Does this involve a specific structure of A · T base pairs or of A · T tracts?

Consider for example the two self-complementary decamers d$(CCT_3A_3GG)_2$ and d$(GGA_3T_3CC)_2$, which give rise by repetition to straight and curved duplexes respectively (22). The difference could result from the geometrical combination of dinucleotide steps, among which CT, TA and AG in the first polymer differ from GA, AT and TC in the second (23). Alternatively, the structures of the A_3 (and/or T_3) stretches could differ in the two sequences.

We have found large anomalies in the base-pair kinetics of adenine tracts, in striking correlation with DNA curvature. For instance the lifetimes of the second and third A · T base pairs in the DNA-curving duplex d$(CGCA_5GCG)$ · d$(CGCT_5GCG)$ are extraordinarily long (Figure 4), more than ten times longer than the values for B-DNA given above. This is also the case for d$(GGA_3T_3CC)_2$. By contrast, the lifetimes

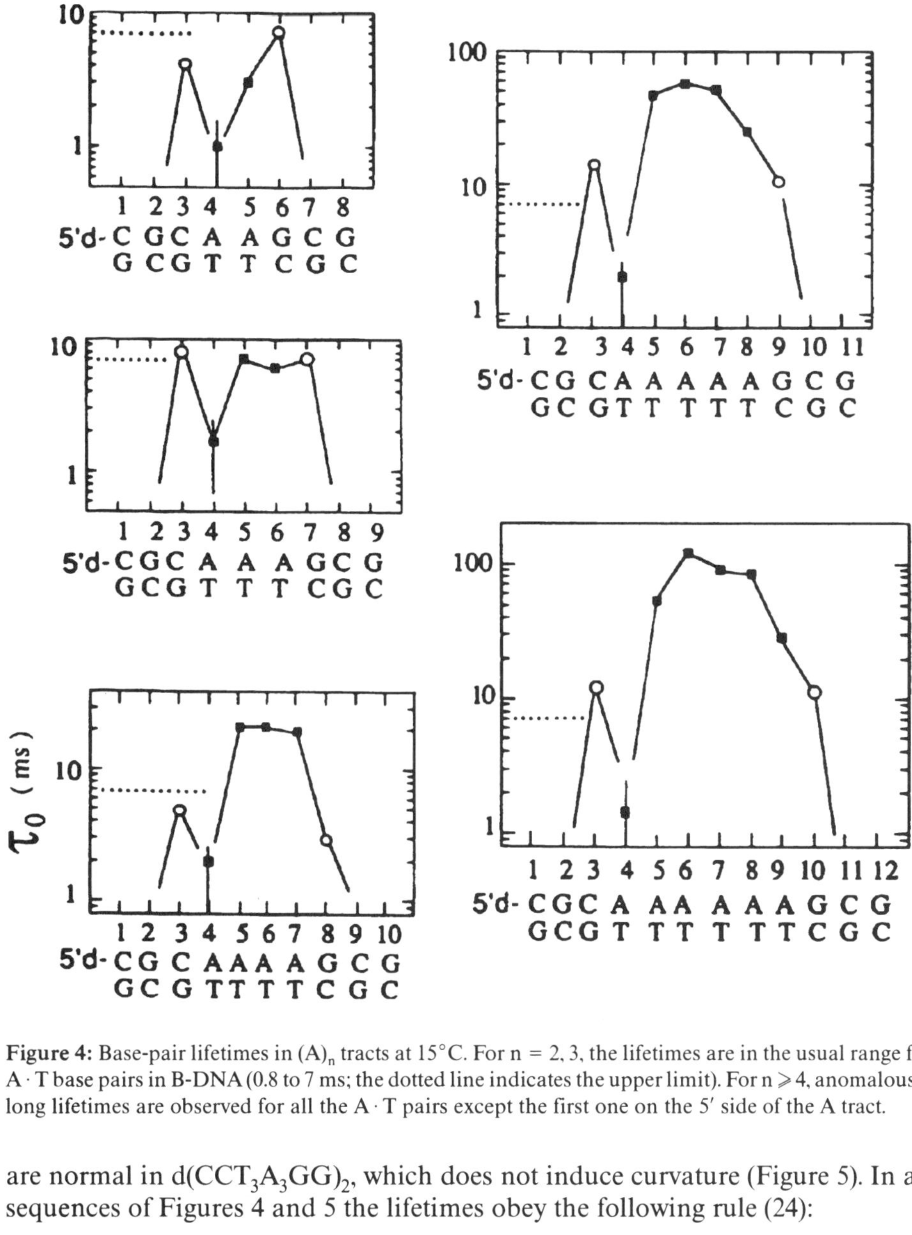

Figure 4: Base-pair lifetimes in $(A)_n$ tracts at 15°C. For n = 2, 3, the lifetimes are in the usual range for A · T base pairs in B-DNA (0.8 to 7 ms; the dotted line indicates the upper limit). For n ≥ 4, anomalously long lifetimes are observed for all the A · T pairs except the first one on the 5′ side of the A tract.

are normal in $d(CCT_3A_3GG)_2$, which does not induce curvature (Figure 5). In all sequences of Figures 4 and 5 the lifetimes obey the following rule (24):

Anomalously long base-pair lifetimes are found in DNA tracts of contiguous A · T base pairs. The tract must have a length of at least four (four is marginal), which may include a 5′-AT step, but not a 5′-TA step. The A · T base pair at the 5′-A end of the tract is not anomalously long. No G · C pair is part of the tract.

This simple rule is obeyed without exception by the 16 sequences in which we have measured base-pair lifetimes.

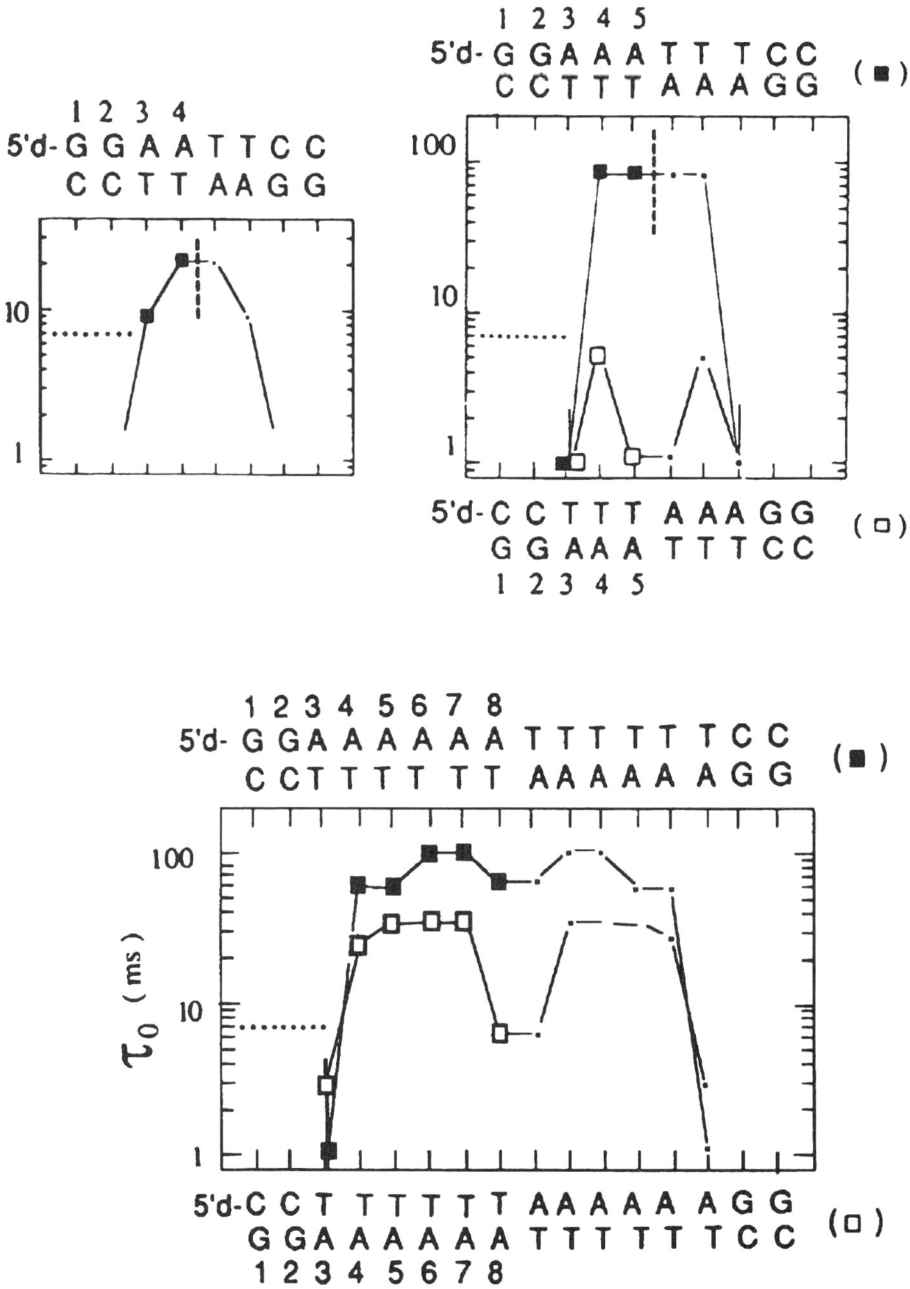

Figure 5: Effect of AT and TA steps on base-pair lifetimes. These five symmetrical sequences provide examples of the general rule that long lifetimes are found for tracts of 4 or more A · T base pairs, including possibly one 5′-AT step, but not a 5′-TA step. The sequences are closed by only two G · C pairs. This may affect the lifetime of the contiguous A · T base pair.

The same rule was proposed previously by Chuprina (42) on the basis of energy computations which include a spine of hydration in the minor groove, and by consideration of the observed sequence dependence of sensitivity to DNAse I, and of DNA bending.

We have also studied the effect of inserting a G · C or I · C base pair in an A · T tract, for example at the third position in an $(A)_5$ tract (24). Long lifetimes are found for the $(A)_5$ sequence (Figure 4) and for A_2IA_2 but not for A_2GA_2. The I · C base-pair lifetime itself is long, 33 ms, compared to the lifetimes in $d(CGCI_6GCG) \cdot d(GCGC_6GCG)$ (2 ms) and in the duplex $d(CGC(IC)_3GCG)_2$ (0.8 ms).

Structural implications. The kinetic anomaly is strong evidence for a structure which deviates from B-DNA. The structure forms cooperatively, requiring at least four A · T base pairs, as described by the proposed rule. According to the lifetimes (Figures 4 and 5), the first base pair at the 5′ side of the A tract seems to play a special role. Its lifetime is not long, either because its structure is not abnormal, or because it is at the interface with B-DNA. It is flanked by G · C pairs whose lifetime is normal for B-DNA. All the other A · T base pairs, including the last one, participate in the anomalous structure.

Another observation is that the maximum lifetime increases with the length n of the A · T tract, suggesting that the structure which forms cooperatively for $n \geqslant 4$ presents some variations according to n.

The lifetime measurements give indications on some properties of the anomalous structure. These may be considered with reference to the crystal structures of duplexes containing A · T tracts (13,14,26), in which A · T base pairs have a large propeller twist, neighboring base pairs are connected by a bifurcated hydrogen bond, the bases are well stacked and the minor groove is narrow, a feature which is also suggested by reduced susceptibility to chemical cleavage (27).

The possibility of incorporating an I · C but not a G · C pair in the anomalous structure also suggests that the minor groove is narrow, since a G · C pair cannot fit in a narrow minor groove. Similarly, a narrow minor groove is compatible with a 5′-AT step but not with a 5′-TA step, which is indeed disruptive according to the rule and to Figure 5. Another point is that an I · C pair cannot accept or donate the bifurcated hydrogen bond. Its compatibility with the abnormal structure suggests that this bond is not energetically important. Lastly, we shall see below (section 5, Figure 11) that the base-pair dissociation constant is much reduced for all base pairs of the anomalous structure, including the last one but excluding the first. The stabilization could be due to enhanced stacking. At the junction of the normal and abnormal structures, the bases of the first pair may be unable to stack well on all of their four neighbors.

Other NMR data provide further evidence for an altered structure (25). In particular, the chemical shifts of the T imino protons vary monotonically according to the location in the A tract. Nadeau and Crothers suggest that the shifts originate in a

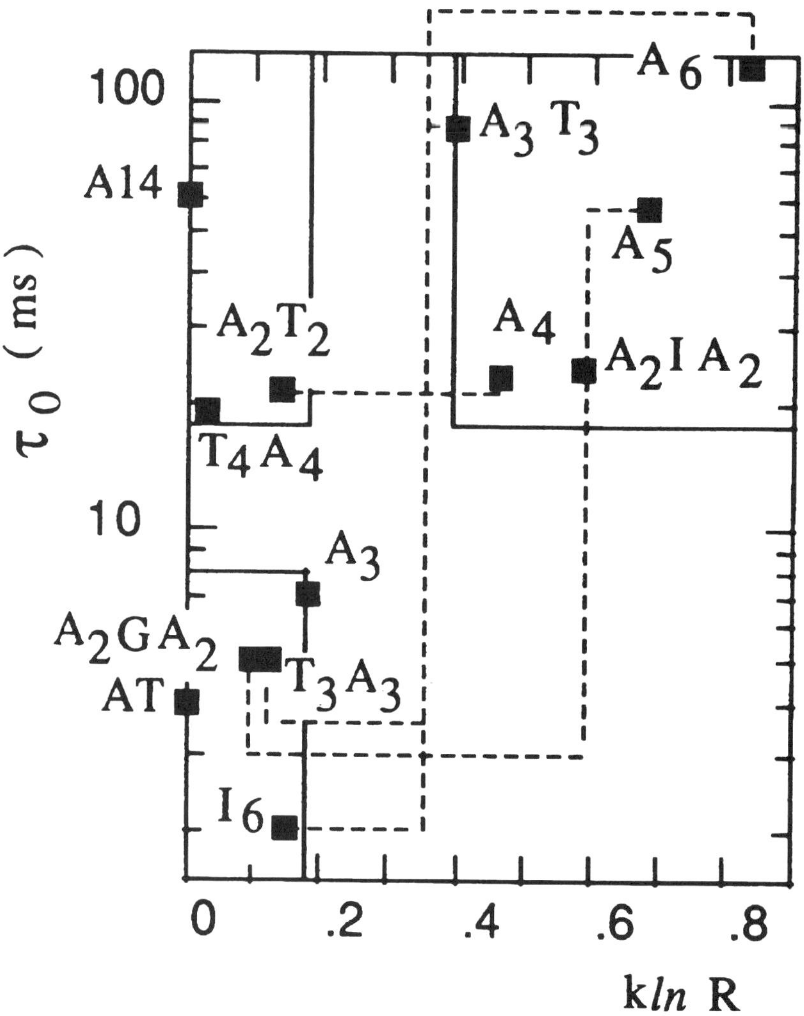

Figure 6: Correlation plot of the room temperature electrophoretic mobility anomaly of different decamer repeats, with the longest base-pair lifetime of its potential DNA-curving tract, measured at 15°C (24). Each decamer is labelled by the sequence of one strand of the tract. The electrophoretic mobility anomaly is characterized by k ln R, where R is the ratio of the length of a random sequence to the length of the decamer repeat having the same mobility, and k is a correction factor for gel composition (23). The five curving sequences all include long-lived base pairs. The gap in electrophoretic mobility anomaly between 0.18 and 0.39 provides a distinction between straight and bent DNA. Points corresponding to adenine tracts of identical length are connected by a dashed line.

shortening of the H-bond. They also observed H2-H1′ NOEs indicative of a narrow minor groove.

Connection with DNA curvature. Figure 6 correlates the electrophoretic mobility anomaly R of the repeated 10-mer with the longest A · T base-pair lifetime of the tract, in all thirteen cases where the data are available. The correspondance is striking.

First, all the tracts with short (⩽ 7 ms) lifetimes, namely A_3, A_2GA_2, AT, T_2A_3 and I_6 have normal mobility (k ln R ⩽ 0.18). The corresponding points fall in the box at the lower left of the plot.

Second, most of the tracts with long lifetimes have a large mobility anomaly (k ln R ⩾ 0.39), indicative of curvature. This is the case for A_4, A_2IA_2, A_5, A_6 and A_3T_3; the corresponding points fall in the box at the upper right of the plot.

Third, the lower right-hand area of Figure 6 is empty: all polydecamers known to be curved are based on sequences displaying long lifetimes. The correlation suggests that the structure causing anomalous base-pair lifetimes is involved in DNA-curving. If so, one understands why T_3A_3 is non-curving whereas A_3T_3 and A_6 do induce curvature, and why A_3 is non-curving, in contrast to A_4, since both T_3A_3 and A_3 have base-pair lifetimes indicative of B-DNA.

The comparison of A_3T_3 and T_3A_3 shows that base-pair lifetimes and, by extension, DNA conformation, are dependent on a neighborhood extending beyond first neighbors: *DNA structure cannot be described solely by a universal set of dinucleotide geometries.*

The three sequences which fall in the upper left-hand corner of Figure 6 correspond to long lifetimes but no curvature. In both A_2T_2 and T_4A_4, the length of the anomalous tract is only 4, which is marginal, and there could be compensation of curvature in the polydecamers (22).

The case of A_{14}, representative of poly(dA) · poly(dT), shows that in the absence of junctions to B-DNA, the abnormal structure does not generate curvature. One must conclude that the *curvature due to A tracts in the abnormal structure does not originate inside the tract, but at the junctions (21) of the A tract with B-DNA.*

3.3. Proton Exchange and Base-Pair Lifetime in Z-DNA

Consensus has not yet been reached regarding the interpretation of proton exchange in Z-DNA. As was the case for B-DNA, the data to be reconciled come on one hand from techniques in which the assignment of exchanging protons is obtained indirectly (tritium exchange (28,29), deuterium exchange monitored by IR (30) or Raman spectrometry (31)), and on the other hand from proton NMR (32,16). Comparison is made difficult by the different experimental conditions and methods of sample preparation.

We have investigated proton exchange and base-pair kinetics of Z-DNA in the duplexes of $d(CG)_6$, $d(CG)_{12}$, $d(CGm^5CGCG)$ and $d(CBr^8GCGCBr^8G)$. Compounds of different lengths were chosen so that end effects could be detected, if present. The imino proton resonance was observed at all temperatures. The C amino protons were identified by their NOE to H5 of cytidine. An exchangeable resonance at 7.05 ppm, corresponding to two protons, was observed above 50°C and assigned to the G amino protons (Figure 7). This resonance became very broad at all temperatures below 45°C.

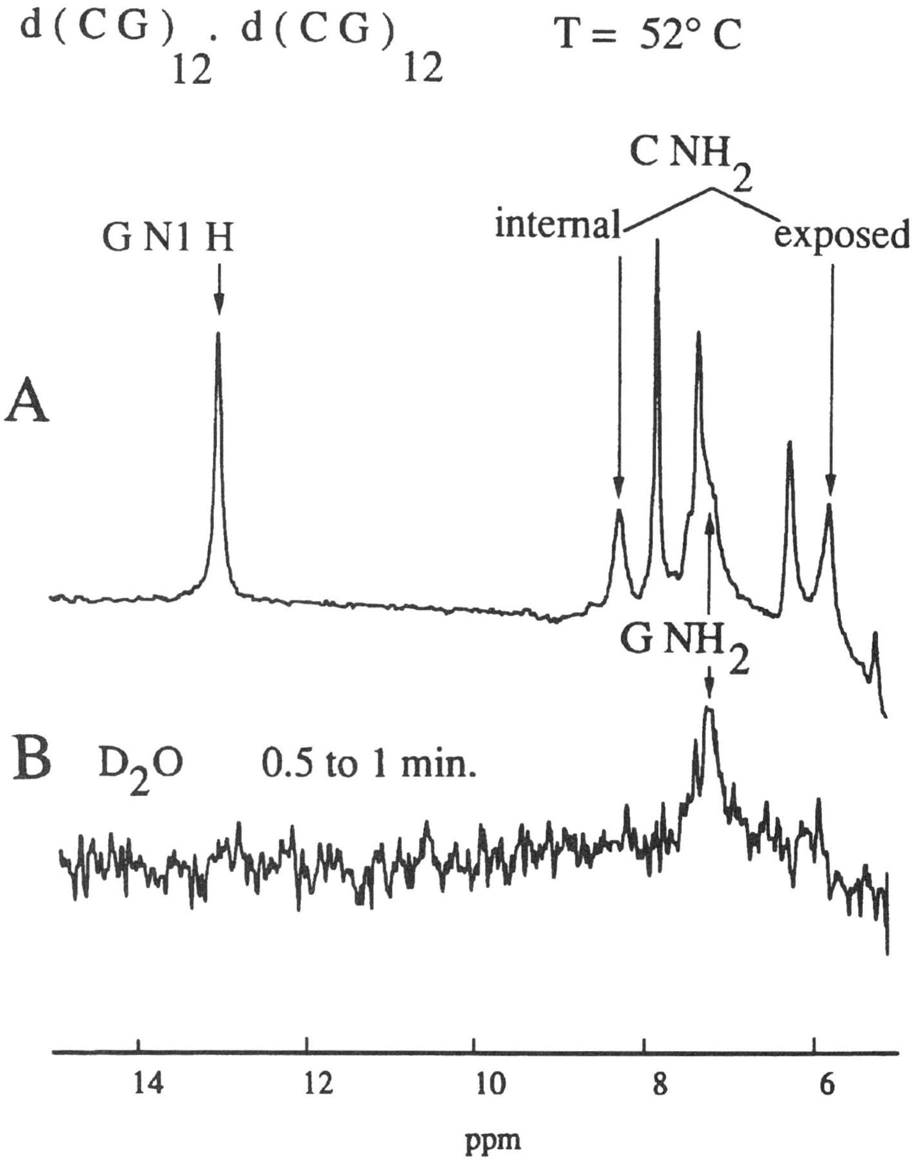

Figure 7: Real-time exchange experiment on the 5′-d(CG)$_{12}$ in the Z-form. (A) Reference spectrum in a 90% H_2O solution. Solution conditions: $NaClO_4$, 3.5 M; pH 7, T = 52°C. (B) Difference between two spectra obtained after dilution of a concentrated H_2O solution into D_2O. The data for the first spectrum were obtained between 0.5 and 1 minute after the solvent change. The second spectrum was accumulated between 20 and 25 minutes after the solvent change. At 0.5 minutes, the exchange of the G imino and C amino protons is complete. The G amino protons exchange more slowly, with an exchange time of 1.5 minutes.

Imino proton exchange was found to be catalysed by proton acceptors. Base-pair lifetimes ranged from milliseconds at 80°C to 120 ms at 35°C (Figure 8), they were the same for the d(CG) 12-mer and for the 24-mer. Extrapolation from the high-temperature values gives a lifetime of 800 ms at 15°C, vs 7 ms for the B-form of the same duplex. At 5°C, the extrapolated value is 3 s and measurement provides an upper limit of 20 s.

The exchange of amino protons has some interesting properties. In the absence of added catalyst and at neutral pH, the C amino and G imino protons exchange in comparable times, as already observed by Mirau and Kearns (32). Both are acid-catalysed, a process which is also observed in B-DNA, and which is discussed in the next section.

We compared the common exchange time of these three protons to the exchange time of the G amino protons. The experiment could be carried out only above 50°C (see above). At 52°C, the G amino protons exchanged much more slowly than the other protons: at least three times according to the experiment of Figure 7, and about 40 times according to the interpolation of Figure 8.

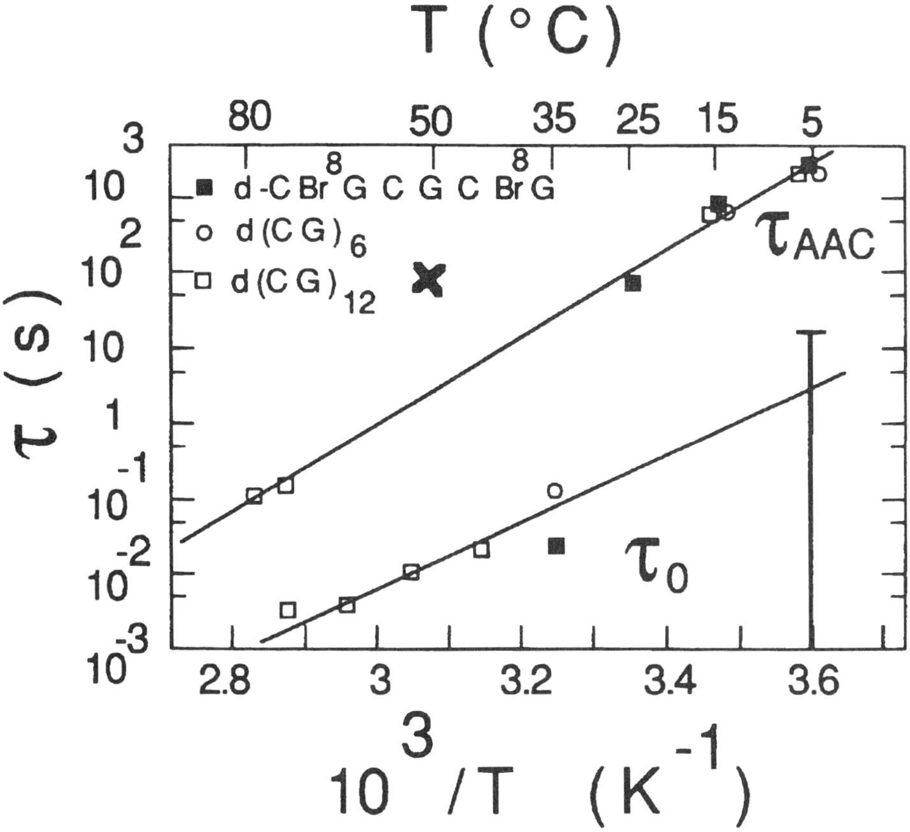

Figure 8: Imino proton exchange times in the absence of added catalyst, τ_{AAC}, and base-pair lifetimes, τ_0, for internal G · C pairs of duplexes in the Z form, versus the inverse of the temperature. The salt conditions were: NaCl, 100 mM, for d(CBr^{8}GCGCBr^{8}G)$_2$, and either $NaClO_4$, 3.5 M, or NaCl, 4 M, for the duplexes of d(CG)$_6$ and d(CG)$_{12}$. The base-pair lifetimes were obtained using ammonia as a catalyst. At 5°C, imino proton exchange occurred in less than 20 s at high catalyst concentrations. This is the experimental upper limit for the base-pair lifetime. The "X" symbol denotes τ_{AAC} of the G amino protons, as measured in Figure 7.

In the tritium and deuterium exchange measurements (28-30), no effect of catalyst was detected, and therefore no catalyst was used in general. Two classes of exchange times were found. The fast one, corresponding to three protons, was assigned to the three protons of guanosine. The slow one, corresponding to two protons, was assigned to the cytidine amino protons. The two times are roughly in the ratio of 1 to 100. The shortest one falls fairly well on the line traced through our τ_{AAC} measurements. We suggest that the slow exchange time corresponds to the two guanosine amino protons, that the fast exchange time corresponds to the guanosine imino and to the two cytidine amino protons and that neither is related to the base-pair lifetime.

4. Dissociation Constant of Base Pairs

The dissociation constant is an important parameter of the opening process. The larger it is, the greater the possibility that the opening process affects various properties, such as polymer flexibility, chemical reactivity or specific interactions with structural or functional proteins. In contrast to the base-pair lifetime, the dissociation constant is not obtained directly, but requires the measurement of proton exchange in monomers, and an assumption regarding the relative efficiency of catalysts in monomers and duplexes.

4.1. Theory of Proton Exchange

The theory of exchange of imino protons from a double helix has been presented (33). The exchange time τ_{ex} is given by:

$$\tau_{ex} = \tau_0 (1 + k_{cl}/k_{tr}) \qquad [2]$$

where τ_0 is the base-pair lifetime, k_{tr} is the rate for proton transfer from the open state, and k_{cl} is the closing rate. Different mechanisms may contribute to exchange, e.g., catalysis by an added catalyst or by an intrinsic catalyst. When the former dominates, k_{tr} is proportional to the catalyst concentration. Extrapolation of τ_{ex} to infinite catalyst concentration yields the base-pair lifetime, but at moderate concentrations, we have:

$$\tau_{ex} \approx \tau_0\, k_{cl}/k_{tr} = 1/(K\, k_{tr}) = 1/(\alpha\, K\, k_i) \qquad [3]$$

where K is the dissociation constant of the base pair. We have introduced a factor α by $k_{tr} = \alpha\, k_i$, where k_i is the proton transfer rate from the isolated monomer at the same catalyst concentration.

Exchange is slowed down because the base pair is open only a fraction of the time (K), and it is altered if the exchange rate is not the same in the nucleoside (k_i) and in the open state of the base pair, in which case α differs from one.

In practice, very different concentrations of catalyst (C_m and C_d) are used for studies on the monomer and duplex, because K, and therefore the catalyst efficiency for exchange from the duplex, are very small. If the exchange times $\tau_i \equiv 1/k_i$ and τ_{ex} are measured with catalyst concentrations C_m and C_d respectively, αK is given by:

$$\alpha K = \tau_i C_m/(\tau_{ex} C_d). \quad [4]$$

Differences in exchange from duplex and from monomer could be caused by the electric interaction between a charged catalyst and the highly charged duplex (a polyelectrolyte), or by limited access of a bulky catalyst to the open state. A slight difference is that the collision rate between two reactants is proportional to the sum of the diffusion coefficients (each is proportional to (molecular mass)$^{-1/3}$), so that the collision rate of a catalyst with a monomer, k_{coll}, is larger than with an oligomer.

If the monomer were immobile, the collision rate would be:

$$k'_{coll} = k_{coll}/(1 + (M_C/M_N)^{1/3}) \quad [5]$$

where M_C and M_N are the molecular masses of catalyst and monomer respectively, and the exchange rate k'_i would be reduced in the same ratio with respect to k_i. Due to its large mass, the duplex may be considered immobile, so that its k_{coll} is equal to the k'_{coll} of the nucleoside. We therefore define a factor α' by:

$$\alpha' K = \tau_i' C_m/(\tau_{ex} C_d) \quad [6]$$

such that $\alpha' = 1$ if catalysis operates identically in the monomer and the open state except for the mass effect.

The exchange rate from the monomer is given by:

$$k_i = k_{coll}[C]/(1 + 10^{(pK_N - pK_C)}) \quad [7]$$

where pK_N and pK_C are the pKs of the nucleoside (respectively 9.7, 9.5 and 9.2 for thymidine, uridine and guanosine at 25°C) and of the catalyst. The concentration of the base catalyst [C] is related to the total concentration of buffer [B] by:

$$[C] = [B]/(1 + 10^{(pK_C - pH)}) \quad [8]$$

4.2. Exchange Times in Mononucleosides

Imino proton exchange in monomers was measured by the line broadening induced by addition of proton exchange catalysts. The pH of the nucleoside solution (10 to 15 mM) was in the range where exchange catalysis by water and its component ions is minimum and pH-independent, i.e., pH 4 for deoxythymidine and for uridine (34), and pH 5 for guanosine 2′:3′-cyclic monophosphate (35). The exchange catalyst was added as small aliquots (2 to 20 μl), and its concentration was computed according to the pH value and to the total concentration of proton donor and acceptor (e.g., NH_4^+ and NH_3). The catalyst is the latter, and this was proved by the effect of pH for a constant total concentration. Solutions were passed through a Chelex 100 column before use. The exchange time is:

$$\tau_i \equiv 1/k_i = 1/(\pi\Delta) \quad [9]$$

Table I

Imino proton exchange rates of guanosine 2′:3′-cyclic monophosphate, thymidine, uridine and poly(rU). The values given are $k_i/[C]$, where [C] is the catalyst concentration. They are derived from the line broadening by $k_i = \pi\Delta$

Catalyst	pK	G	T	U	poly(rU)
adenosine	3.7		5.4 10^3		
cytidine	4.3	1.9 10^4			
$HPO4^{2-}$	6.8		0.77 10^6	2.7 10^6	
imidazole	6.95	8.8 10^6	8.4 10^6	8.1 10^6	16 10^6
4-methyl I*	7.52			38 10^6	
triethanolamine	7.72	3.5 10^6	7.4 10^6	10.4 10^6	6.2 10^6
2-methyl I*	7.8	4.4 10^7	3.9 10^7	5.7 10^7	
Tris	8.08	3.5 10^7	3.4 10^7	4.6 10^7	2.9 10^7
2,4-dimethyl I*	8.35	5.6 10^7	6.4 10^7	6.8 10^7	
$borate^-$	9.23			1.4 10^7	
NH3	9.25	2.1 10^8	2.0 10^8	3.4 10^8	4.8 10^8
$glycine^-$	9.78	3.3 10^8	2.8 10^8	3.0 10^8	
piperidine	11.12			4.3 10^8	
OH^-	15.7	110 10^8	85 10^8	71 10^8	60 10^8

*Imidazole

where Δ is the line broadening. In all cases, Δ was proportional to the catalyst concentration.

The results are presented in Table I and in Figure 9. The table gives the values of $k_i/[C]$ derived from Equation [9]. In the figure we have plotted $k'_i/[C]$, the exchange rate expected if the nucleoside were immobile, as a function of the pK of the catalyst. The theoretical curves give $k'_i/[C]$ according to Equations [5] and [7] for the stated value of k'_{coll}.

The values of $k'_i/[C]$ for poly(rU) are generally close to those for uridine. Indeed, we expect good access to the imino proton of the single-stranded polymer, and there is no significant difference in pK between monomer and polymer in our salt conditions (36).

4.3 Results

The comparison of exchange times of the imino proton on the nucleoside and in a base pair gives the product α′K (Equation [6]). If catalysts operated differently on the open state and on the mononucleoside, α′ K could vary strongly according to the catalyst. In the opposite case, α′ would be equal to 1, so that α′ K would be catalyst-independent.

Figure 10 gives the values of α′ K for poly(rA) · poly(rU) and for individual base pairs of the decamer duplex $d(CGCGATCGCG)_2$. The first observation is that most

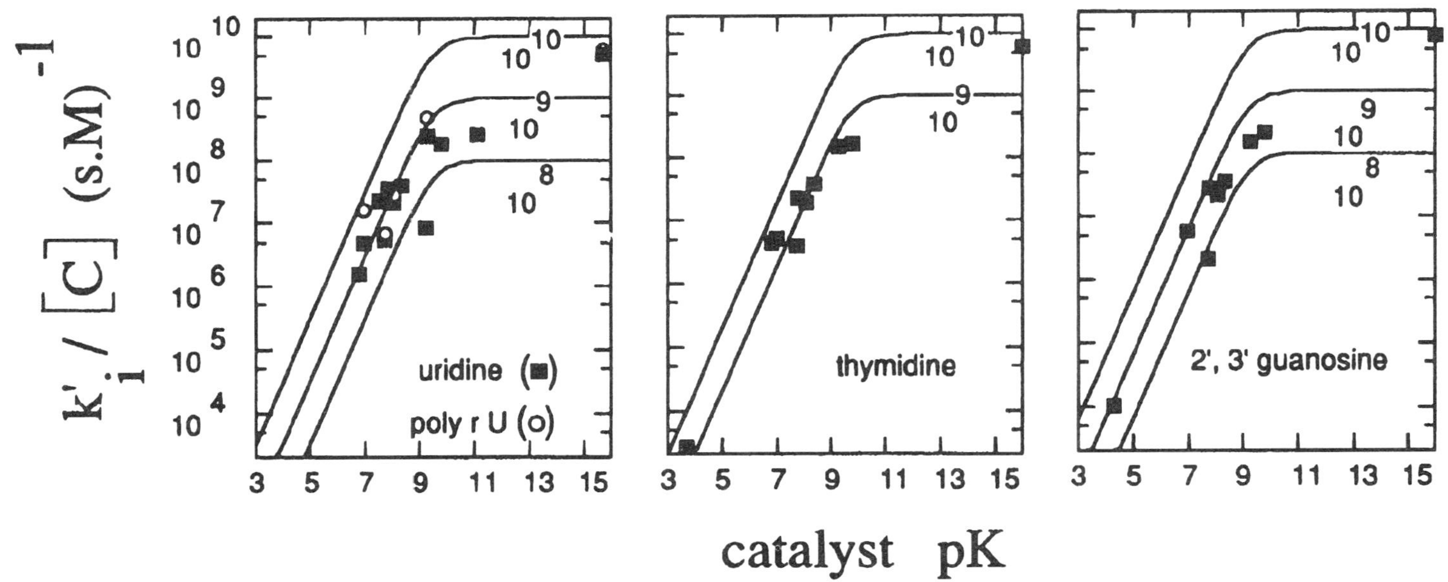

Figure 9: Imino proton exchange in ribouridine, deoxyribothymidine, 2′-3′guanosine and poly(rU) at 25°C. Exchange rates k_i were proportional to the catalyst concentration. The relation between k_i and k'_i is explained in the text. The curves are computed according to Equations [5] and [7], and are labelled according to the value of k'_{coll}; see also Table I.

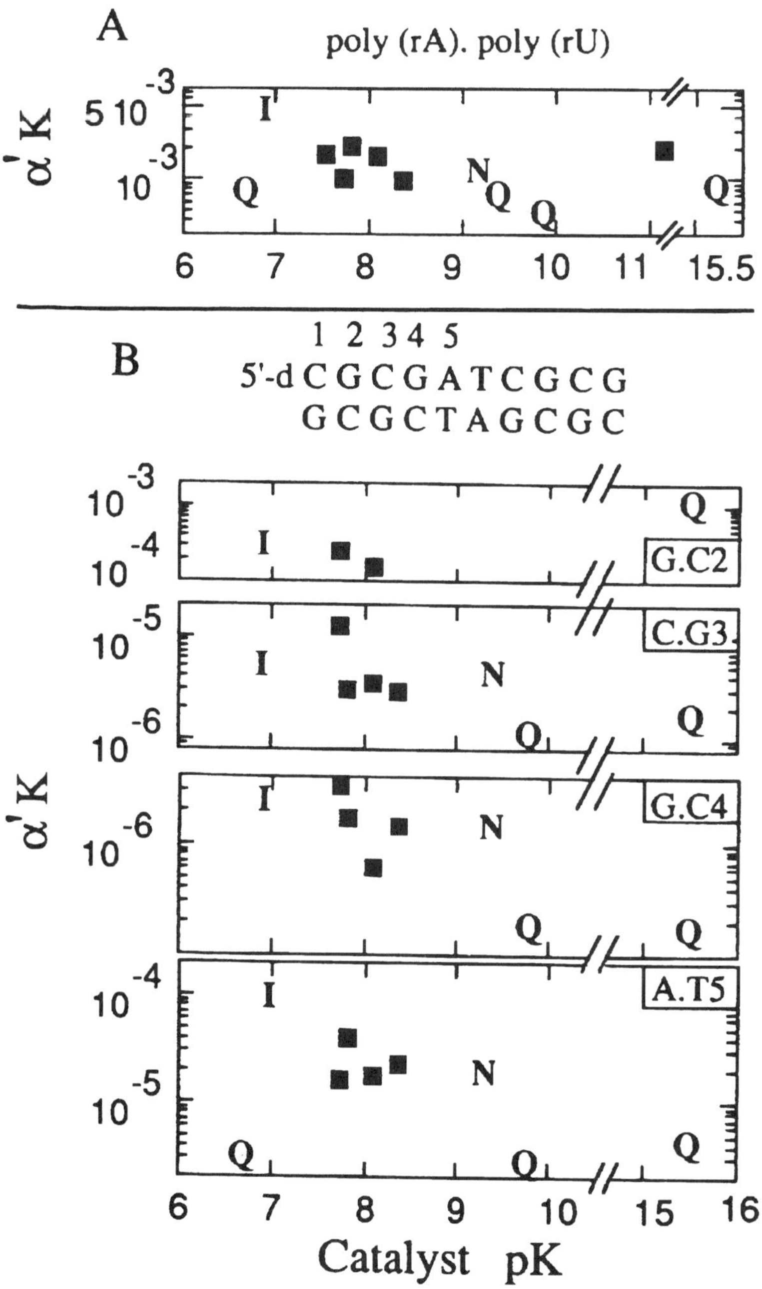

Figure 10: (A) Apparent base-pair dissociation constant (αK) of poly(rA) · poly(rU) derived from imino proton exchange catalysis by the same proton acceptors as in Table I. Charged catalysts are symbolized by Q, imidazole by I and ammonia by N. Temperature: 25°C. The values of α'K are well clustered around 1×10^{-3} except for those corresponding to the charged acceptors glycine^{-} (pK = 9.8) and phosphate^{2-} (pK = 6.8), and to imidazole. (B) Apparent dissociation constant α'K for individual base pairs of $d(GCGCATCGCG)_2$. Same conditions and symbols as in Figure 10A.

values of α'K fall approximatively within a factor of three, a rather narrow range if one takes note that the ratio of rates is as small as 10^{-6}. In some cases, lower values are found for negatively charged catalysts. Larger ones are found for positive catalysts such as spermidine (not shown), and for imidazole. An effect of charge would be expected, due to the local concentration or rarefaction of charged catalyst near the polyelectrolytic nucleic acid. The particular efficiency of imidazole, which is also observed for poly(rU), may be due to groove-binding or stacking.

Bulky catalysts such as triethanolamine seem to be as efficient as smaller ones: there is no indication of a structural barrier. But this does not imply that the two bases swing wide apart in the open state, for proton transfer may occur efficiently through one or more water molecules (37,15).

For most catalysts, the range of values of α'K, and therefore of α', is narrow, showing that they distinguish in the same way, or not at all, between monomer and open state. Considering the differences between the catalysts, we favor the second option. This means that the values of α' are equal to one, or more conservatively, to a value between 0.1 and 10 for this group of catalysts. Henceforth, we assume that $\alpha' = 1$ for the ammonia catalyst, which is small, uncharged, and whose α'K value falls in the middle of the clustered values.

With this interpretation, one finds a dissociation constant of 10^{-3} at 25°C for the base pairs of poly(rA) · poly(rU) (Figure 10 A). The values for B-DNA (Figure 10 B) are much smaller, in the range of 10^{-5} and 10^{-6} for A · T and G · C base pairs respectively (except for end effects, e.g., in the case of G.C2). The lifetimes of the open state, $K\tau_0$, are all in the range of 30 to 300 ns. These values are representative of those found in other B-DNA duplexes.

In tracts of A · T base pairs, the dissociation constants (Figure 11) are much smaller than for A · T base pairs of B-DNA, except for the first base pair, as mentioned in section 3.2. The open-state lifetime is not much altered.

5. One or More Modes of Base-Pair Opening?

5.1 One Mode in Standard Conditions?

In section 4.1, we described a theory of proton exchange from base pairs subject to a single opening mode. We have shown previously (15) that our measurements and those of others can be interpreted by such a model.

Referring to Figure 12, this opening mode gives a curve such as (a) for the exchange time vs. the inverse of the catalyst concentration. There are three regions: (i) at high catalyst concentrations, $\tau_{ex} = \tau_0$; (ii) at moderate catalyst concentration, $\tau_{ex} - \tau_0$ is inversely proportional to catalyst concentration; (iii) at low catalyst concentration, τ_{ex} become independent of the concentration of added catalyst. It is controlled by intrinsic catalysis. This explanation is supported in particular by cases, such as in Figure 13, where exchange from a base-paired nucleoside is faster than from a non-paired neighbor.

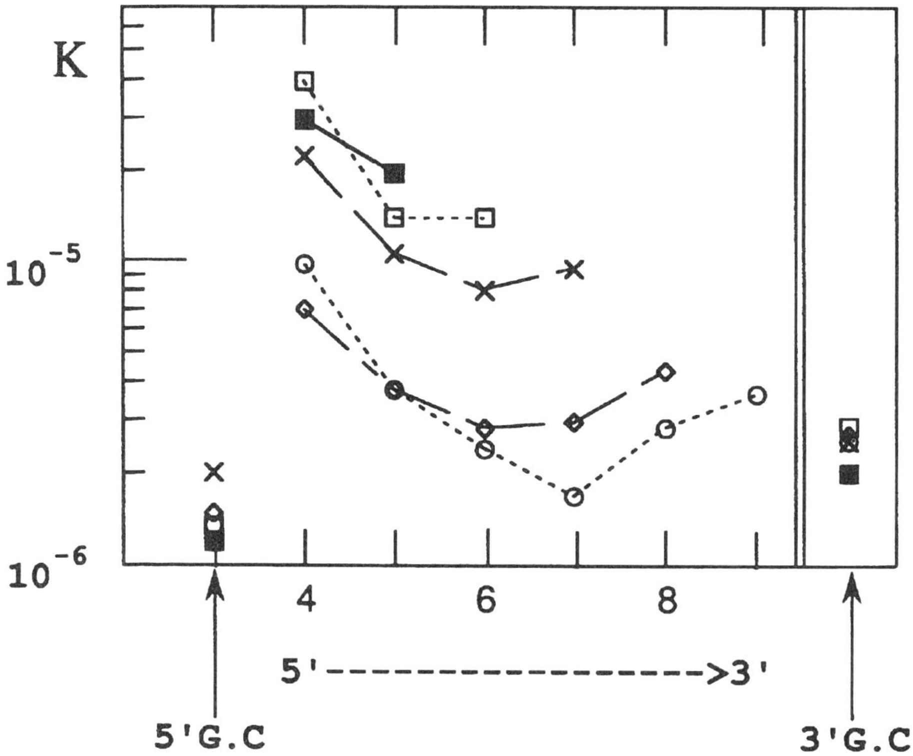

Figure 11: The dissociation constant of individual base pairs in d(CGC(A)$_n$GCG) · d(CGC(T)$_n$GCG) duplexes for n = 2 to 6. In each case, the first A · T base pair on the 5′ side of the A tract has the largest dissociation constant; K of the second base pair is much smaller, for all n ≥ 3. The trends for 1/K are similar to those for τ_0 (Figures 4 and 5). In particular, K is anomalously small for n = 5,6. The K values for the immediately flanking G · C pairs are normal.

The observations rule out the existence of other opening modes which would be more efficient for imino proton exchange. For instance, an opening process with a shorter lifetime, such as (b), would be dominant for exchange at high catalyst concentration. A process with a longer base-pair lifetime but with a large dissociation constant, such as (c), would give the faster exchange rate at intermediate catalyst concentrations. Both could therefore be detected by their effect on imino proton exchange.

But process (d), despite its large dissociation constant (inversely proportional to the slope) would go undetected at all catalyst concentrations, because its base-pair lifetime is larger than the exchange time corresponding to intrinsic catalysis in process (a). Hence, the imino proton exchange data do not rule out the existence of opening processes which involve a much larger base-pair dissociation constant.

Such processes have been proposed in the past, but they have always been disproved. Thus, a base-pair dissociation constant in the range of 10^{-2} was derived on the basis of denaturation kinetics of DNA by formaldehyde (2). However it was later argued that the data are compatible with $K \leqslant 10^{-4}$ (38). Early studies of proton

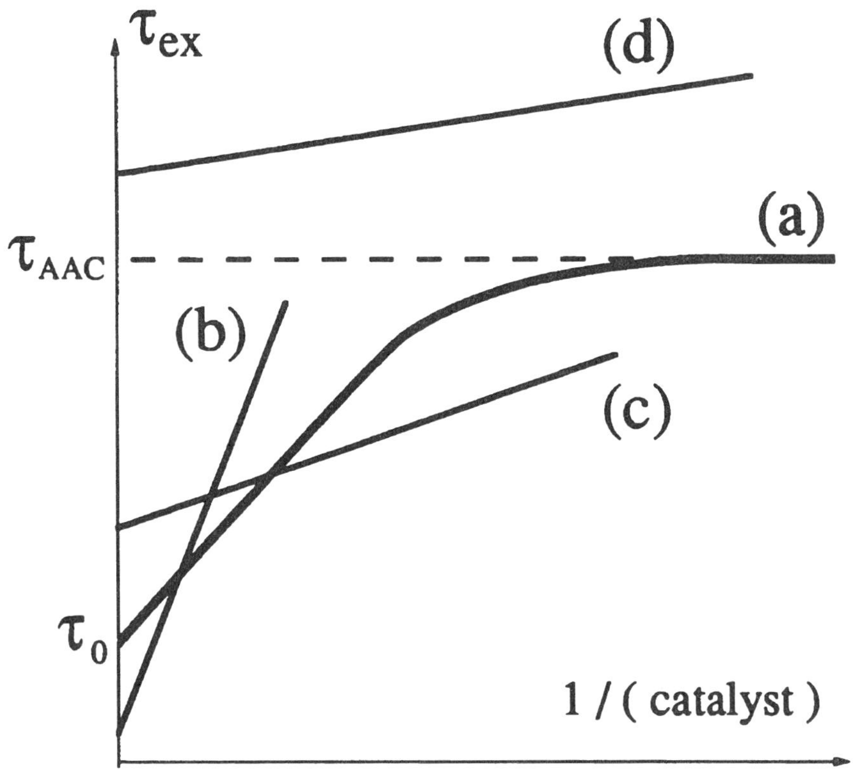

Figure 12: Exchange time vs. 1/[catalyst] for various opening modes. It is assumed that the experimental data correspond to mode (a), with its base-pair lifetime τ_0, its time for intrinsically catalyzed exchange τ_{AAC} and its dissociation constant which is inversely proportional to the slope at intermediate catalyst concentrations. If so, processes such as (b) or (c) cannot be operating concurrently with (a) since mode (b) would have been detected by its smaller value of τ_0 and mode (c) by smaller exchange times at intermediate catalyst concentrations. But mode (d), whose base-pair lifetime is longer than the τ_{AAC} of mode (a) would be undetected by the exchange data, even though its dissociation constant is very large.

exchange lead to large values of K and of τ_0 as well; but the observations were later explained by intrinsic catalysis (9,15), so that they do not provide information on K or τ_0. The variation of the persistence length of DNA with temperature also implies $K \leqslant 10^{-4}$ (39). The situation is similar regarding ribonucleic acids. Large values of K were derived from early proton exchange studies, but the analysis ignored intrinsic catalysis of imino proton exchange and of amino proton exchange from closed base pairs (9). By contrast, the dissociation constants derived from the kinetics of reaction with Hg ions (1) and from thermodynamical data (40) agree with the value given here for poly(rA) · poly(rU).

In summary, the single mode of base-pair opening with small K and τ_0 explains all data on imino proton exchange. *It is presently the only mode which is proven and well characterized.* The exchange data also exclude concurrent opening modes such as (b) or (c).

As for a mode like (d), with a large dissociation constant, it is excluded by the chemical

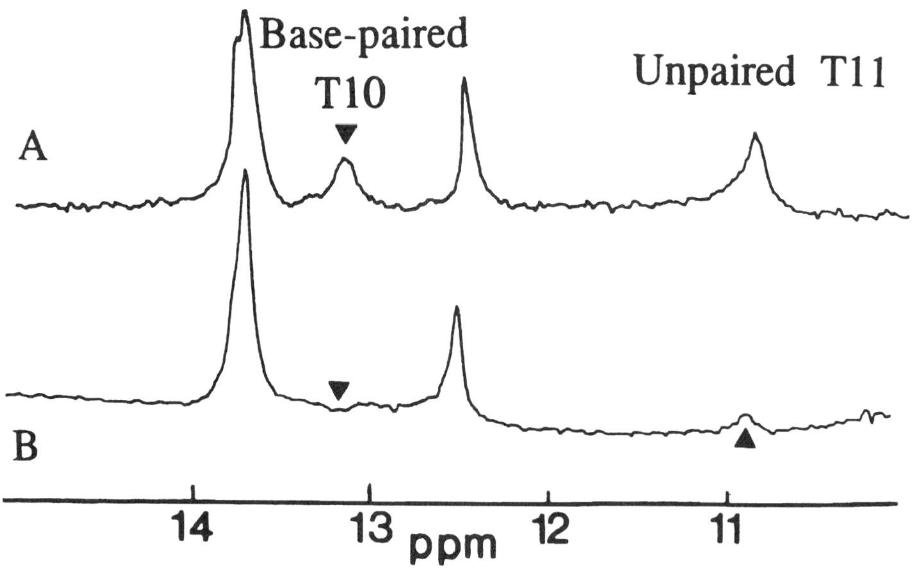

Figure 13: Comparison of the exchange times of the imino protons of base-paired T10 and of unpaired T11, in the d-$(AATTGCAATTT)_2$ undecanucleotide dimer. (a) Reference spectrum. (b) Spectrum obtained 12 ms after selective inversion of water. The magnetization of the imino proton of base-paired T10 is already negative whereas that of unpaired T11 is still positive. The exchange time of the paired imino proton (9 ms) is *shorter* than that of the unpaired one (30 ms)! Magnetization is also transferred to the G5 resonance, at 12.5 ppm, due to acid-catalyzed exchange. Duplex concentration, 0.5 mM; NaCl 100 mM; EDTA 1 mM; pH 4.8; T = 15°C.

modification data, but only if the dissociation constant is larger than 10^{-4}. This upper limit is larger than the dissociation constants (10^{-5}, 10^{-6}) of the mode responsible for imino proton exchange.

Concurrent opening modes are a real possibility. For instance, besides the single base-pair opening that has been demonstrated, strand separation is bound to occur at high enough temperature. Another example concerns the formation of Hoogsteen base pairs at acid pH, and perhaps even at neutral pH.

5.2. A Second Mode at Acid pH? Hoogsteen Base Pairs in DNA Duplexes

We have found that the exchange of G imino protons is acid-catalysed. The rate is proportional to 10^{-pH} and it is remarkably fast: at pH 4 and 25°C, the exchange time is 20 ms, compared to 10 ms for the acid-catalyzed exchange from isolated guanosine, which occurs via protonation at N7 (35). This phenomenon has been observed in all the B-DNA duplexes examined so far: G2, G3 and G4 of $d(CGCGATCGCG)_2$, G3 of $d(CGm5CGCG)_2$ in the B form, G5 of $d(AATTGCAATT)_2$ and G5 of d(AATTGC-$AATTT)_2$. In the latter case, Figure 13 displays the transfer of magnetization to the G5 resonance at 12.5 ppm.

Explanations involving protonation of guanosine at N7 (pK = 2.1) should be considered. This lowers the pK of the imino proton by roughly 3 units. Exchange catalysis by the intrinsic catalyst (N3 of cytidine) would be enhanced correspondingly. The computation of this exchange process requires a better knowledge of the lowering of the imino proton pK. It seems that the computed exchange rate may be lower than the observed rate by a factor of 10.

The exchange rate of the C amino protons is also acid-catalyzed, both in B- and in Z-DNA. In the Z-DNA duplex, d(CBr^{8}GCGCBr^{8}G)$_2$, the exchange time at 5°C and pH 5.7 was 5 minutes for the G4 imino and for the C amino protons. It is extremely difficult to explain the fast exchange of the C amino protons unless exchange occurs from protonated cytidine, a condition in which the amino proton pK falls to values between 7 and 9 (35). This immediately suggests the possibility of G · CH$^+$ Hoogsteen pairs in which the guanosine N1 is exposed to the solvent.

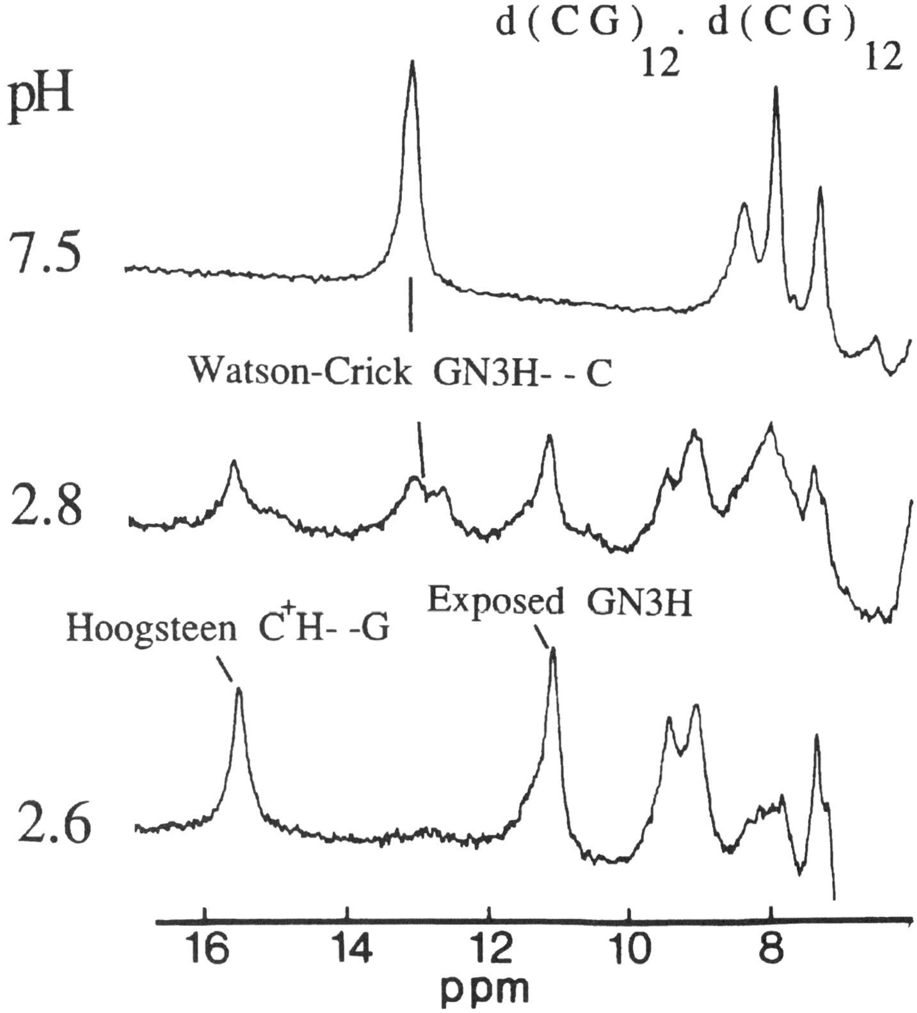

Figure 14: Proton NMR spectra of d(CG)$_{12}$ · d(CG)$_{12}$ vs. pH. Experimental conditions: T = 0°C, 100 mM NaClO$_4$, 10% D$_2$O.

This species has indeed been detected and characterized in the NMR spectrum of the duplex $d(CG)_{12} \cdot d(CG)_{12}$ in the B form. As the pH is lowered, a resonance appears at 15.5 ppm. It is first detected around pH 3.2 and its intensity increases, while that of the G imino proton of the Watson-Crick base pair at 13 ppm decreases. At pH 2.6, it corresponds to 70% of the base pairs (Figure 14).

The 15.5 ppm resonance is assigned to the imino proton of CH^+ in a Hoogsteen base pair by its NOE to the H8 of guanosine. Furthermore, it cannot be due to a non-paired protonated cytidine whose N3 proton would be expected to exchange with water in one microsecond. Together with this resonance, another one grows at 11 ppm, the position expected for the G imino proton exposed in the Hoogsteen base pair.

The pH 2.8 spectrum shows imino protons from both Hoogsteen and Watson-Crick base pairs. The splittings may be due to a distribution of Hoogsteen and Watson-Crick neighbors.

The Hoogsteen to Watson-Crick equilibrium constant should vary as 10^{-pH}, leading to a value ca. 10^{-4} at pH 7, one hundred times larger than the dissociation constant of the base-pair opening mode considered previously.

These observations provide strong evidence for the existence of $CH^+ \cdot G$ Hoogsteen pairs in DNA, in agreement with an earlier proposition (41), and even at neutral pH as a minor species. One should also consider whether A · T Hoogsteen pairs might exist in DNA. Besides the open state characterized by imino proton exchange, another minority species has now appeared.

References and Footnotes

1. M.N. Williams and D.M. Crothers, *Biochemistry 14*, 1944 (1975).
2. J.D. McGhee and P.H. von Hippel, *Biochemistry 16*, 3276 (1977).
3. M.P. Printz and P.H. von Hippel, *Proc. Nat. Acad. Sci. USA 53*, 363 (1965).
4. H. Teitelbaum and S.W. Englander, *J. Mol. Biol. 92*, 55 (1975).
5. H. Teitelbaum and S.W. Englander, *J. Mol. Biol. 92*, 79 (1975).
6. N. Nakanishi, Y. Mitane and M. Tsuboi, *Biochim. Biophys. Acta 798*, 46 (1984).
7. B. Hartmann, M. Leng and J. Ramstein, *Biochemistry 25*, 3073 (1986).
8. J.L. Leroy, M. Kochoyan, T. Huynh-Dinh and M. Guéron, *J. Mol. Biol. 200*, 223 (1988).
9. J.L. Leroy, D. Broseta and M. Guéron, *J. Mol. Biol. 184*, 165 (1985).
10. J.L. Leroy, N. Bolo, N. Figueroa, P. Plateau and M. Guéron, *J. Biomol. Struct. Dynam. 2*, 915 (1985).
11. N.B. Leontis and P.B. Moore, *Biochemistry 25*, 5736 (1986).
12. P. Bendel, *Biopolymers 26*, 573 (1987).
13. H.C.M. Nelson, J.T. Finch, B.F. Luisi and A. Klug, *Nature 330*, 221 (1987).
14. M. Coll, C.A. Frederick, A.H.-J. Wang and A. Rich, *Proc. Nat. Acad. Sci. USA 84*, 8385 (1987).
15. M. Guéron, M. Kochoyan and J.L. Leroy, *Nature 382*, 89 (1987).
16. M. Guéron, E. Charretier, M. Kochoyan, and J.L. Leroy, in *Frontiers of NMR in Molecular Biology, UCLA Symposia on Molecular and Cellular Biology, New Series, Vol. 109*, (D. Live, I. Armitage and D. Patel, Eds.) Alan R. Liss, Inc., New York, NY (1989).
17. M. Guéron, P. Plateau and M. Decorps, in preparation.
18. M. Guéron and J.L. Leroy, *J. Mag. Res.*, in press (1989).
19. P.N. Borer, B. Dengler and I. Tinoco Jr., *J. Mol. Biol. 86*, 843 (1974).

20. H.M. Wu and D.M. Crothers, *Nature 308*, 509 (1984).
21. H.S. Koo, H.M. Wu and D.M. Crothers, *Nature 320*, 501 (1986).
22. P.J. Hagerman, in *Unusual DNA Structures*, (R.D. Wells and S.C. Harvey, Eds.) Springer-Verlag, New York, p.225 (1988).
23. C.R. Calladine, H.R. Drew, and M.J. McCall, *J. Mol. Biol. 201*, 907 (1988).
24. J.L. Leroy, E. Charretier, M. Kochoyan and M. Guéron, *Biochemistry 27*, 8894 (1988).
25. J.G. Nadeau and D.M. Crothers, *Proc. Nat. Acad. Sci. USA 86*, 2622 (1989).
26. A.D. DiGabriele, M.R. Sanderson and T.A. Steitz, *Proc. Nat. Acad. Sci. USA 86*, 1816 (1989).
27. A.M. Burkhoff and T.D. Tullius, *Nature (London) 331*, 455 (1988).
28. J. Ramstein and M. Leng, *Nature (London) 288*, 413 (1980).
29. J. Ramstein, N. Vogt and M. Leng, *Biochemistry 24*, 3603 (1985).
30. B. Hartmann, J. Pilet, M. Ptak, J. Ramstein, B. Malfoy and M. Leng, *Nucleic Acids Res. 10*, 3261 (1982).
31. A. Laigle, L. Chinsky, P.Y. Turpin and B. Jollés, *Nucleic Acids Res. 17*, 2493 (1989).
32. P.A. Mirau and D.R. Kearns, *Proc. Nat. Acad. Sci. USA 82*, 1594 (1985).
33. M. Kochoyan, J.L. Leroy and M. Guéron, *J. Mol. Biol. 196*, 599 (1987).
34. H. Fritzsche, L.S. Kan and P.O.P. Ts'O, *Biochemistry 20*, 6118 (1981).
35. B. McConnell, *Biochemistry 17*, 3168 (1978).
36. N.N. Aylward, *J. Chem. Soc. B.*, 401 (1967).
37. E. Grunwald, A. Lowenstein and S.J. Meiboom, *J. Chem Phys. 27*, 630 (1957).
38. M.D. Frank-Kamenetskii, in *Structure and Motion: Membranes, Nucleic Acids and Proteins*, (E. Clementi, G. Corongiu, M.H. Sarma and H. Sarma, Eds.) Adenine Press, N.Y., p.417 (1985).
39. J. Wilcoxon and J.M. Schurr, *Biopolymers 22*, 2273 (1983).
40. J. Gralla and D.M. Crothers, *J. Mol. Biol. 78*, 301 (1973).
41. Y. Courtois, P. Fromageot and W. Guschlbauer, *Biochemistry 6*, 493 (1968).
42. V.P. Chuprina, *Nucleic Acids Res. 15*, 293 (1987).

Structure & Methods, *ISBN 0-940030-32-2*
Volume 3: DNA & RNA, *ISBN 0-940030-31-4*
Eds., Ramaswamy H. Sarma & Mukti H. Sarma, *© Adenine Press 1990*

Real and Apparent Curvature in Oligonucleotides

Manju Bansal and Dhananjay Bhattacharyya
Molecular Biophysics Unit
Indian Institute of Science
Bangalore 560012, India

Abstract

Base-pair and helical parameters have been calculated for the available crystal structures of oligonucleotides, using an algorithm developed in our laboratory. A comparison with the values reported earlier using the HELIB algorithm, of Dickerson and co-workers, shows that all the local parameters are quite similar in both cases while the global parameters show differences depending on the choice of global helix axis.

A quantitative estimate has also been made of axial curvature in oligonucleotide structures using several different methods. It is found that none of the methods, except those making use only of the first and last base-pair orientations (and hence similar to the procedure followed in HELIB) give curvature values as reported earlier. The well known methods, such as fitting of a plane curve or sphere to the local helix origins, give small and very similar radii of curvature for all the structures. An alternative estimate is made from an examination of the path traced by the local helix axes, as well as the local helix origins at each step. The angle between the first and last helix axes is quite small for all the crystal structures, indicating that there is no significant curvature in any of the structures. Thus a perturbation in the base-pair orientation in an oligonucleotide does not necessarily lead to the molecule being really curved, though it may appear curved.

The above procedures using local helix axes or origins can be applied to a DNA sequence of any length. Their application to polymeric structures, with different stretches of oligo As in the middle of a decamer repeat, give values identical to those obtained from the decamer repeats, thus proving the general validity of these methods.

Introduction

The observed anomalies in the mobility of some DNA sequences in polyacrylamide gels have been attributed to the intrinsic curvature of these polymeric molecules(1-6). The possibility of this inherent curvature being important in the biological function of DNA has also been suggested (7,8). Hence a rigorous, and physically meaningful description of curvature in DNA molecules is necessary to quantify this property and to compare the results obtained from different physicochemical studies. At the moment there is no commonality between the description of curvature in small oligonucleotides, studied by x-ray crystallography, nmr etc.(9-13) and the polymeric molecules investigated by gel migration and cyclization studies (1-6,14). While a rigorous analysis of curvature in a solid cylindrical molecule like DNA should treat the problem as one of surface curvature, for the sake of simplicity the bending or curving of DNA has generally been defined in terms of the curvature of its long cylinder axis. This axis is easy to define for a reasonably long and uniformly curved fragment of DNA and the orientation of the various nucleotides in space can be exactly defined by a combination of terms describing their orientation about this axis and the superhelical path of the axis itself. The most notable example of this description is the approximation of the DNA duplex in the nucleosome as a uniform superhelix wound on a cylindrical surface (15-17). A similar superhelical approximation has recently been used for describing the structures of the polymers showing retardation in their gel mobility (18), while the original workers have explained their data in terms of simple bending of the molecule in a plane(2,6). The former model is successful in explaining the reported values of 'N', the number of nucleotides (or polymer length) at which the gel mobility reaches a steady state for a given sequence, while the latter model fits better to the gel mobility retardation data in the pre-steady state condition.

The divergent models outlined above clearly highlight the need for a generalized procedure to describe all possible types of DNA bending -- plane curves, solenoids, coiled-coils, as well kinked or junction bending models. In order to devise such a procedure we first need to choose a suitable reference point (or vector) associated with each basic unit, such that the path traced by this reference point (or vector) in space corresponds to the axial curvature of the molecule. An obvious first choice in the case of double-stranded nucleic acids is the center of the base-pair (or normal to the base-pair mean-plane) and these have been used to describe DNA bending in crystal structures of oligonucleotides (9,12). However, this description is applicable only when the DNA fragment comprises more than one turn of the helix and is close to the B-DNA form (*viz* the base-pair is oriented almost perpendicular to the molecular axis). Even then this procedure gives only a qualitative idea of the molecular bending if the structure is non-uniform. We have therefore estimated the bending of DNA in both oligo and polynucleotide structures using several different theoretical methods and conclude that the spatial path of a reference point associated with a base-pair doublet, rather than the base-pair center, generally gives a more correct picture of the molecular bending in DNA of all sizes and forms. It turns out that the relative bending ascribed to the various structures with the dodecamer sequence d(CGCGAATTCGCG), on the basis of the orientation of the 1st and 11th base-pair normals (9,12), is not apparent from any of the quantitative procedures used by us. In nearly all cases the central region of the molecule appears to be almost straight (9,12) while the base-pairs at the two ends have random variations in their orientations. The various procedures used to estimate the molecular curvature, along with the results obtained for both short and long DNA fragments are described in this paper. The possible reasons for the discrepancies between the results obtained by using the different methods are also discussed.

Method and Results

In order to calculate the curvature of nucleic acid fragments, we first calculated the

Table I
The Values of Wedge Parameters as Reported in Ref. 6 and the Recalculated Values for our Method

Sequence of Bases	Reported			Recalculated		
	Tilt	Roll	Twist	Tilt	Roll	Twist
B - A_n	−9.6	−5.8	36.0	−7.707	8.915	38.118
A_n - B	12.0	0.0	36.0	11.995	−3.899	37.890
B - T_n	9.6	0.0	36.0	−11.995	3.899	37.885
T_n - B	−12.0	−5.8	36.0	11.451	2.655	37.184
A_n - T_n	0.0	0.0	36.0	0.000	0.000	36.000
T_n - A_n	0.0	−11.6	36.0	3.757	11.594	37.766

various local and global parameters for each base-pair and doublet step, as the case may be. These parameters were calculated using an algorithm developed in our laboratory (19,20) and based on the nomenclature and definitions suggested at the EMBO Workshop at Cambridge, U.K. (21). A uniformly curved polymer fragment of DNA, with a 4° wedge angle at every base-pair was generated, as also junction bending models for the junction parameters given by Koo and Crothers (6). Since these wedge parameters have been defined keeping one of the base-pairs at the origin and using its base-pair normal as the Z-axis (22), while our definition is with respect to a mean plane lying between the two base-pairs constituting the wedge (20), the absolute values of local roll, tilt and twist are different in our definition. The parameter values for the Crothers' type of junction, but using our definition, are listed in Table I. Decamer as well as polymer fragments were generated, with planar base-pairs and no local translations except the Z-rise along the helical axis, for decamer sequence repeats containing oligo $(A)_n$ runs (n varying from 3 to 9). Line diagrams of the base-pairs in the $N_2A_4N_4$ decamer fragments, generated using both the sets of parameters given in Table I, are shown in Figure 1, along with the vectors representing the local helix axes and the path traced by the local helix origins. The 34-mer fragments, for the same decamer repeat were also generated, to illustrate the smoothly bent nature of the longer fragments, even though the bending occurs at localized junctions. The base-pairs in the fragment generated using the symmetric wedge procedure (20) are shown in Figure 2.

The molecular curvature for the various fragments has been estimated in the following ways:

(i) The mean angle between successive local axes is a good indicator of curvature and is related to the angle between the local helix axes at the ends of the decamer repeats. In the ideal, uniformly curved models, this angle is exactly the same as that between the base-pair normals and is the sum of the angles between the successive helix axes in the fragment (Figure 3a).

(ii) The angle between the local helix origins in successive decamer repeats.

(iii) The sum of the angles between three linear segments in the decamer repeat. The dihedral angle (ϕ) between the three segments should be close to 0° or 180° if the molecule curves in a plane (Figure 3b).

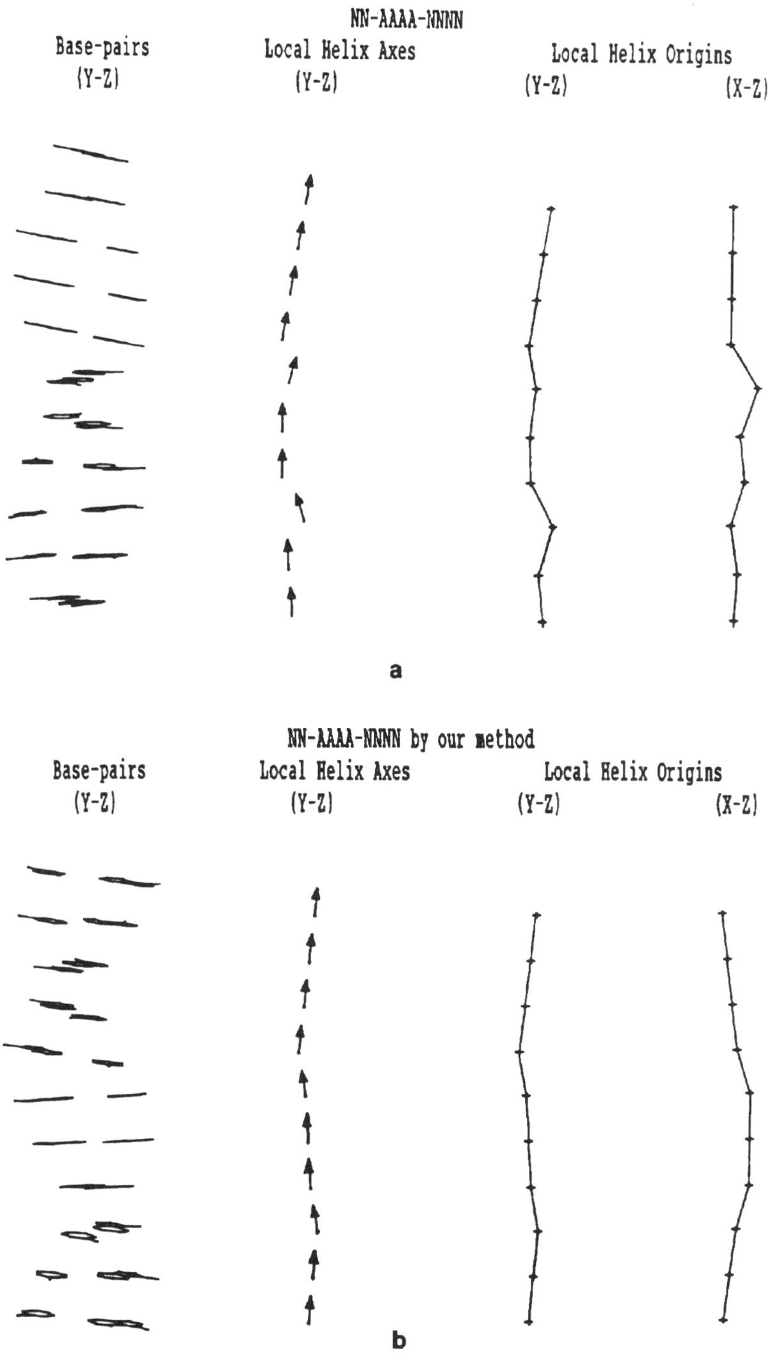

Figure 1: The base-pairs in a decamer fragment with the sequence $N_2A_4N_4$ and bends at the B - A_n and A_n - B junctions (as in Table I). The structure was generated using (a) the Levene and Crothers procedure (22) and (b) our symmetric wedge procedure (20). The local helix axis at each step, as well as the local helix origins (both X-Z and Y-Z projections) are also shown. The discontinuity at the junctions is clearly seen as also the angle between the two terminal helix axes. The local helix origins follow a smoother path in (b).

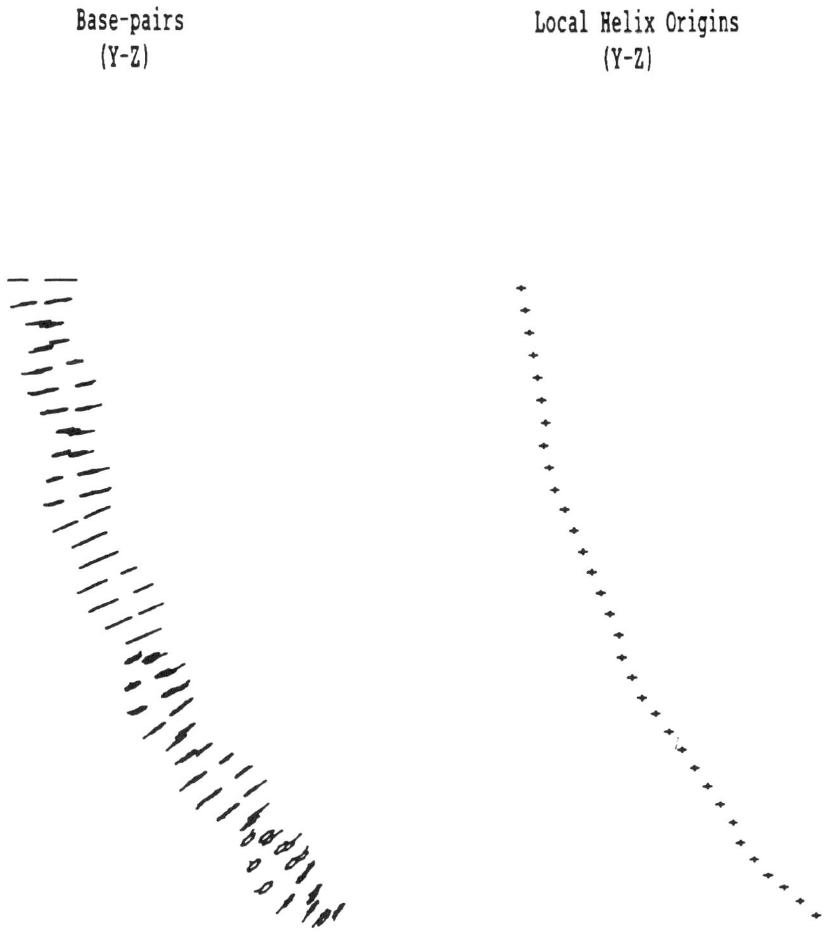

Figure 2: A 34-mer fragment with a $N_2A_4N_4$ decamer repeat, generated using our wedge procedure (20). This long fragment appears smoothly bent for both the models shown in Figure 1 and the value of R calculated using the curve fitting procedures are almost identical in both the cases.

(iv) Curve-fitting in three dimensional space, *viz.* best sphere fit was carried out using the the local helix origins (or the base-pair centers) in the decamer as well as longer fragments.

(v) The ratio of the end-to-end distance to the actual path length traced by the local helix origins.

(vi) Generation of a long polymeric (N = 500) molecule, projecting it down the normal to the plane curve described by it and directly reading off the radius of curvature and spiral rise, if any, from the graphical plots.

The various structural parameters which have been calculated to give an estimate of the curvature are listed in Table II for the decamer as well as the polymeric fragments.

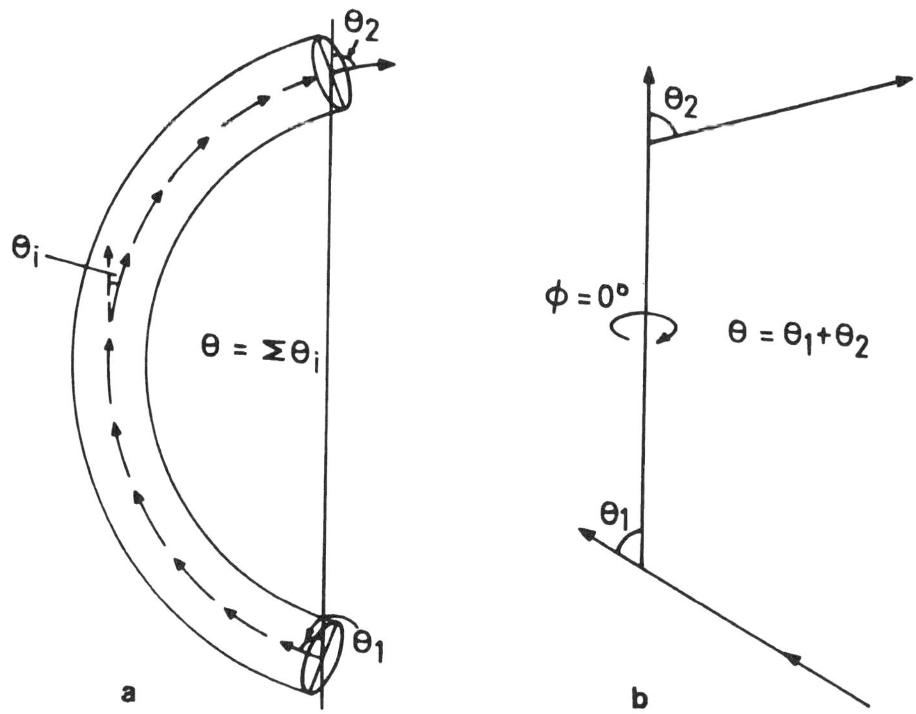

Figure 3: A schematic diagram showing the (a) smooth bending and (b) kinked or junction bending in a plane. In both cases the total bending angle corresponds to the difference in inclinations between the helix axis vectors at the two ends. However if $\phi \neq 0°$, in case (b), then the total bending is not the sum of the bending at the two junctions.

Table II
Curvature Values Obtained for the Structures Containing Runs of Oligo A's and Bends at the Junctions

An (R)[a]	Angle between Local Helix Axes 1&11[b] (R)	Angle between line segments (1&2)	(2&3)	Radius (for 60-mers) end to end distance	from sphere fit[c]	Superhelix (500-mers) Radius	Rise
A3 (234)	7.9 (246)	12.6	6.7	200	230 (80)	243	46
A4 (134)	14.2 (137)	16.2	9.4	128	132 (60)	134	0
A5 (100)	19.1 (101)	14.8	11.3	99	100 (58)	100	16
A6 (87)	22.1 (88)	11.2	11.9	87	87 (67)	86	28
A7 (84)	23.1 (84)	11.1	12.7	84	85 (98)	85	40
A8 (89)	21.6 (90)	11.1	9.3	89	91 (134)	89	36
A9 (106)	18.0 (108)	11.7	9.4	106	108 (170)	107	24

[a]The models are identified by the number of A's in the decamer repeat and the corresponding radii of curvature obtained, from the circle size reported in ref. 6, are given in parenthesis.
[b]Almost identical values are obtained for the angle between the local helix origins in successive decamer repeats (e.g., origins at steps 1, 11 and 21).
[c]The values obtained for the 11-mer fragments are given in parenthesis.

It is seen from Table II that all these methods give values for the radius of curvature which are similar to those reported by Koo and Crothers (6). However, it is also seen that the curve-fitting procedures give reliable estimates only for the longer fragments. This is to be expected since these methods assume a smooth curvature in the molecule while the actual bending in these models is concentrated at the B - A_n and A_n - B junctions. The angle between the three linear segments also gives curvature values similar to those obtained by the other methods.

An excellent fit is also obtained, using all the methods, in the case of the uniform model with 4° wedge angle and in-plane curvature (R = 51 Å), as well as for the uniform spiral, as in the nucleosome. The values of curvature obtained from the methods (i) and (ii) are identical to those given by the curve-fitting procedures.

We therefore, decided to quantify the curvature or bending of oligonucleotides, as seen in the crystal structures, using the above procedures. The reported set of atomic co-ordinates for the dodecamer d(CGCGAATTCGCG) was an obvious test case, since five of the reported structures have been interpreted (12) as exhibiting axial bends ranging from 3° (in the MPD7 structure) to 22° (in the 16K structure). Since the various procedures make use of both local and global base-pair parameters, we first recalculated these parameters using our algorithm, for all the oligonucleotide crystal structures available in the Brookhaven Data Bank and compared them with the values obtained using the HELIB Program (12). As already reported (20), for most of the parameters, the values obtained by our procedure are similar to those obtained from HELIB, with small differences arising due to the choice of local base-pair doublet axes for defining the roll (ρ), tilt (τ), local twist (Ω_1), slide (dy), slip (dx)

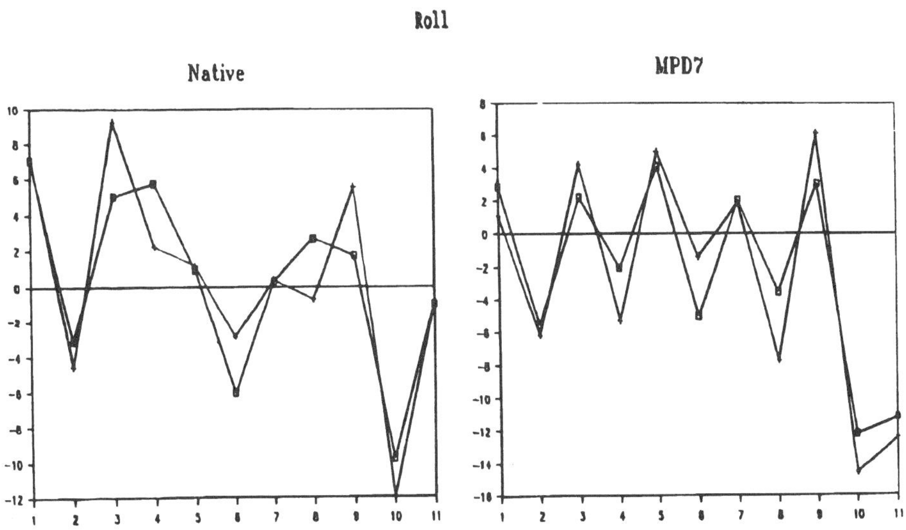

Figure 4: The values of wedge roll (ρ) calculated using our algorithm (+) are plotted for the Native and MPD7 structures for the dodecamer d(CGCGAATTCGCG), along with the values reported earlier (12) using the HELIB program (□). Even though our method uses only the ring atoms to define the base-pair normal and the definition of local roll is also different from that used in HELIB, the overall trends in the values of ρ are quite similar in both the structures.

and rise (dz), in our algorithm. The values of local wedge roll are shown in Figure 4, for the Native and MPD7 structures, as representative examples of the two sets of calculations, while the recalculated values of the important local and global parameters for the Native structure are given in Table III. The local base-pair doublet parameters can also be defined in terms of a set of local helix axes (20) and any non-uniformity in the molecule will be reflected in the relative orientations of these axes. The mean angle between successive helix axes generally has small values for A-DNA crystal structures, indicating that they are nearly straight (23-25). The five B-DNA structures

Table III

Structural Parameters for the Native Dodecamer d(CGCGAATTCGCG) (12)

(a) Base-pair parameters (propeller twist and buckle) along with the local doublet parameters (calculated with respect to the mean Z-axis) are listed here.

	Tilt	Roll	Twist	dx	dy	dz	Prop. Twist	Buckle
C:G	2.42	7.63	37.01	−.38	.26	3.19	−14.31	2.08
G:C	−.46	−4.01	38.70	.45	.47	3.42	−10.86	−4.41
C:G	−1.61	8.14	26.34	−.32	.66	3.74	−3.90	−6.56
G:C	1.76	2.99	36.97	−.07	.04	3.17	−10.75	8.94
A:T	.48	1.10	37.38	.01	−.40	3.25	−16.21	5.57
A:T	−1.74	−2.75	33.09	.25	−.62	3.20	−18.16	3.50
T:A	−2.25	.62	35.54	−0.4	−.31	3.23	−17.68	1.27
T:A	−.86	−.42	40.47	.04	−.10	3.00	−17.71	−.96
C:G	1.62	4.31	28.62	.34	.81	3.75	−17.30	−10.23
G:C	2.56	−11.03	41.58	−1.16	.65	3.42	−5.28	1.74
C:G	−.76	−1.59	35.65	.73	.18	3.70	−18.10	−3.92
G:C	-	-	-	-	-	-	1.65	6.68
Avg.	.11	.45	35.58	−.01	.15	3.37	−12.38	.27
Std. Dev.	1.66	5.22	4.44	.48	.45	.25	6.39	5.51

b) Base-pair parameters calculated with respect to the global helix axis, obtained as the best line fitted to the local helix origins[a]

	Inclin.	Tip	Twist	Displacement dX	Displacement dY	Rise dZ
C:G	−15.36	.60	38.17	−.08	1.02	3.15
G:C	−12.69	−1.30	39.13	−.14	.35	3.47
C:G	−8.21	−12.59	26.38	−.27	−.00	3.67
G:C	−5.04	−7.65	36.52	.68	.33	3.14
A:T	1.25	−5.94	37.28	.81	.74	3.26
A:T	4.69	−2.83	33.25	.51	.95	3.25
T:A	4.63	−2.80	35.66	−.08	.72	3.24
T:A	3.18	.32	40.49	−.35	.50	3.01
C:G	1.58	1.66	28.66	−.69	.15	3.70
G:C	1.08	6.65	41.66	−1.50	.52	3.44
C:G	2.29	−3.10	35.69	−.76	.47	3.72
G:C	3.44	−2.84	-	−1.51	.13	-
Avg.	−1.60	−2.49	35.72	−.28	.49	3.37
Std. Dev.	6.68	4.66	4.49	.72	.31	.24

[a]The molecule was rotated about vector (.93560 −.35305, 0.00) by 12.255° and translated by 14.087Å and 18.959Å along X and Y axes to make the global helix axis coincide with the Z-axis.

Table IV
(a) Curvature Values for the Crystal Structures of d(CGCGAATTCGCG)

	Angle between (1&11) B.P. normals HELIB (R)	Ours	Angle between (1&11) Local Helix axes (a)[a]	(b)[b]	Angle between line segments (1&2)	(2&3)	Radius from sphere fit (Rms. Dev.)
Native	17.4 (111)	18.0	4.2(11.8)	18.3	10.1	17.4	85(0.4)
16K	21.7 (89)	21.9	6.1(15.3)	21.9	20.3	19.4	79(0.4)
MPD20	14.7 (132)	14.5	4.6(14.2)	14.6	15.0	18.3	91(0.5)
MPD7	7.8 (250)	8.1	19.7(13.9)	7.9	15.1	37.0	91(1.0)
Cisplatin	16.2 (120)	17.5	6.6(13.2)	17.5	3.0	33.3	79(0.5)

[a]These are the values corresponding to the actual crystal data. The mean angle for the 11 steps is given in parenthesis.
[b]These values are obtained if the 11th step in the crystal is replaced by the 1st step, so that there is an exact decamer repeat.

(b) Curvature Values for the Polymers Generated Using the Local Parameters for Steps 1 to 10 of the Crystal Structures

	Angle between Helix origins (1,11&21)	Radius from sphere fit: B.P. centres	Radius from sphere fit: Helix origins	Superhelix Radius	Superhelix Rise
Native	18.2	111	107	105	21
16K	21.9	97	94	85	21
MPD20	14.6	135	131	132	5
MPD7	7.9	252	343	244	58
Cisplatin	17.5	111	109	108	10

for d(CGCGAATTCGCG), give comparatively larger values for this parameter, mainly due to large fluctuations at the two ends (Table IV).

After considerable trial and error we have arrived at a uniformly reasonable choice of global helix axis, as being the best line through the local helix origins. If the oligonucleotide comprises nearly a full turn of the helix, then the base-pair centres can also be used to define the global helix axis. We routinely did a best line fit through the origins, rather than the best line-fit to the local helix axes as reported in our earlier paper (20), since this procedure gives a more uniform distribution of the base-pair displacements (dX and dY), while the earlier procedure gave a more symmetric distribution of the base-pair inclination (η) and tip (Θ) with respect to the global axis (as seen from the Table III given here and Table I of Ref. 20). Whichever procedure is used to calculate the best global axis, the base-pair inclinations show a trend similar to that reported by Dickerson *et al.* (12) for the five structures. This has been interpreted by them as being indicative of axial bend, *viz* the difference between the base-pair inclinations of the 1st and 11th base-pairs follow the trend 16K [22°] > Native [18°] > cisPt [17°] > MPD20 [14°] > MPD7 [3°] (as seen in Figure 5a). A similar trend is seen in the values for the wedge roll at steps 4 and 8 (shown in Figure 5b). If polar plots of the base-pair normals are drawn, a drift similar to that shown in Figure 41 of Dickerson *et al.* (12) is seen. However, an estimate of the oligonucleotide

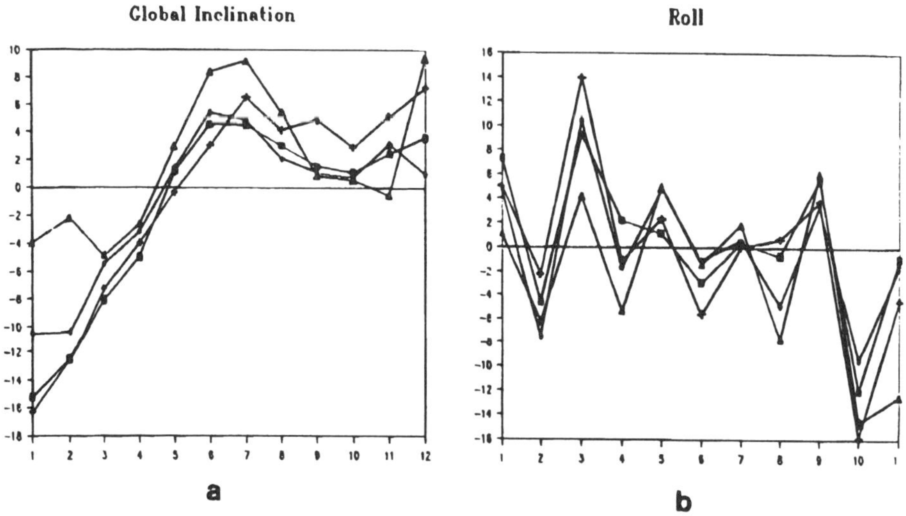

Figure 5: (a) The base-pair inclinations w.r.t the global helix axis and (b) the wedge rolls calculated using our algorithm are plotted for the Native (■), 16K (+), MPD20 (♦) and MPD7 (Δ) structures of d(CGCGAA-TTCGCG). The global axis is defined in an identical manner for all the structures and is the best line through the local helix origins (the base-pair centers can also be used in this case and give similar values). The difference in inclinations between the terminal base-pairs is clearly seen in all the structures. The values of wedge roll at steps 3 and 8 also show a trend similar to that reported earlier, using HELIB (12). However the alternation in the signs of the rolls is seen for all the structures in the present calculations, while HELIB showed this feature only for the MPD7 structure.

curvature, following the procedures described in the previous section, shows marked discrepancies between these axial bend values and the other quantitative definitions. The values obtained for the curvature in the five related dodecamer structures, are listed in Table IV(a). As mentioned above the definitions based on the orientations of the 1st and 11th base-pair normals agree well with the reported values of Dickerson *et al.* (12). The other definitions in terms of the angle between 1st and 11th helix axes, sphere-fit to the local helix origins or base-pair centres, linear-fitting to three straight line segments, all give conflicting values. The extremely low values obtained by the curve fitting to the local helix origins, or the base-pair centres, in these small molecules is indicative of random variations in base-pair orientations or kinked rather than smooth bending. In an analogous description of α-helix bending in proteins, a radius of curvature (R) < 45 Å has been taken to indicate an irregular or kinked helical fragment (26).

Since the large deviations in the curve fitting procedures might be attributed to the small number of data points and also to see if the molecule has sharp bends/kinks joining linear fragments, a line segment fitting was also tried as in the case of Crothers' type of junction models. This type of fitting clearly shows an almost straight central fragment consisting of a run of 3 purines followed by 3 pyrimidines (GAATTC) flanked by base-pairs that are randomly oriented. The angles between the lines fitted to the terminal three residues on either side of this central portion do not show any well defined trend nor do the values for the angle between the 1st and 3rd fragment correspond to the sum of the angles at the two junctions. In addition

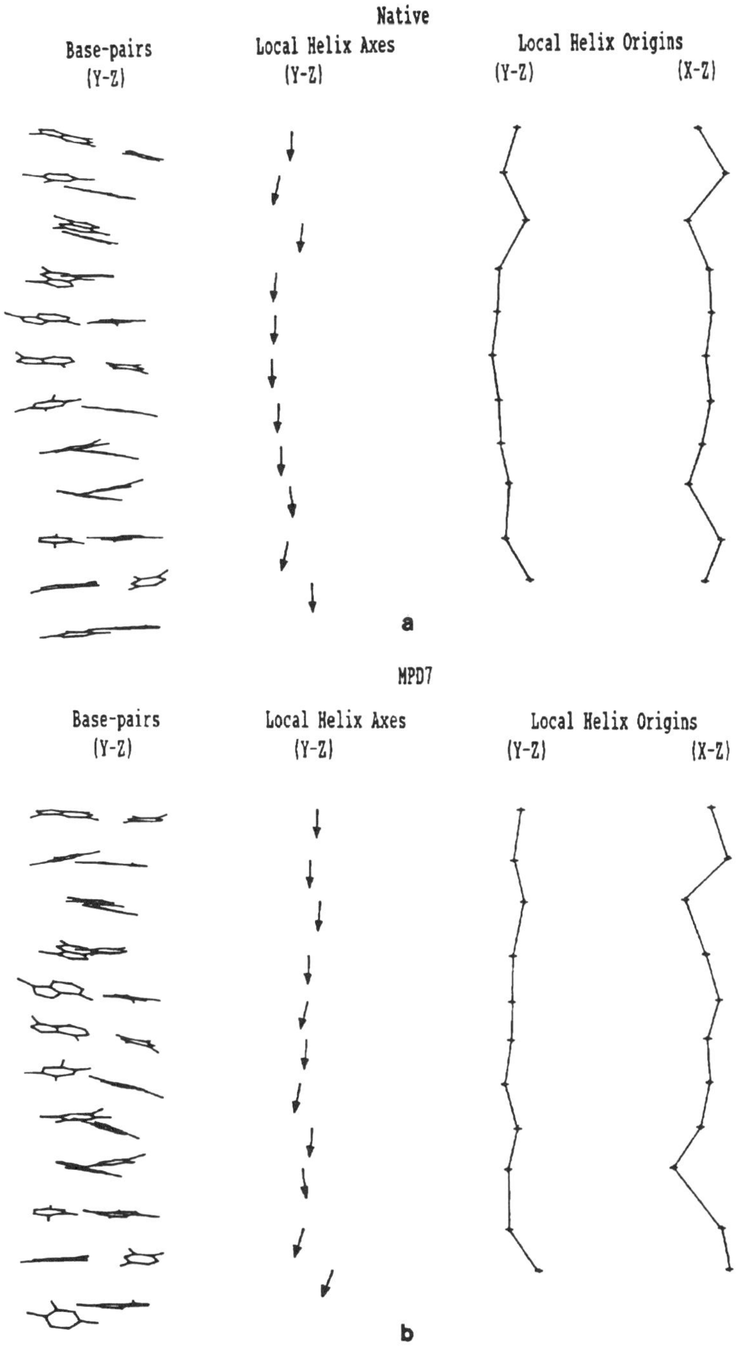

Figure 6: The base-pairs in the (a) Native and (b) MPD7 structures are shown along with the local helix axes positioned at the local helix origins. The almost random variations in the local helix axes and origins, for the terminal C-G-C-G regions, are clearly seen in the various projections. There are noticeable discontinuities at steps 1-3 and 8-11, while the central four or five steps (corresponding to the G-A-A-T-T-C region) are relatively uniform in all the structures.

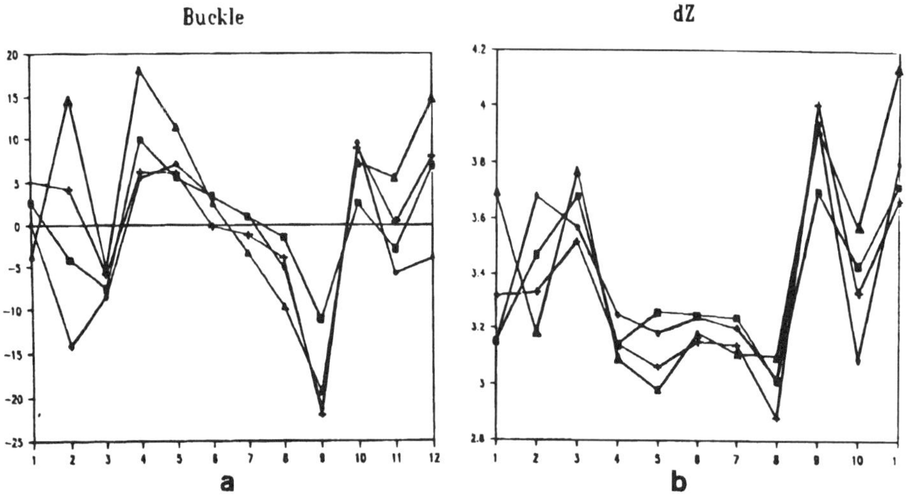

Figure 7: (a) The buckle between the bases in the four dodecamer structures (same as in Figure 5) and (b) the helical rise (dZ) along the global axis are plotted. Large deviations from the mean dZ values are associated with steps where two constituent base-pairs buckle in opposite directions. (The deviations in dZ are reduced if the center of mass is taken to be the base-pair center rather than the mid-point of C6--C8.) The large base-pair buckling in the C-G-C-G region is mainly responsible for giving the large values of inclinations for these base-pairs (as seen in Figure 5). The unusually large buckle at base-pairs 2,4,11 and 12, in the MPD7 structure makes the difference between the terminal inclinations less than that in the other structures.

the dihedral angle between the three segments has a wide range of values. The straight central portion and randomly varying terminal regions can be seen in Figure 6, where the base-pairs, as well as the local helix axes and origins are shown for the Native and the MPD7 structures.

Thus, none of the methods used to calculate the intrinsic bending in the dodecamer crystal structures show any well-defined trend for the molecule progressively unbending from the 16K structure to the MPD7 structure. We therefore decided to examine the reasons as well as implications of the undoubted differences in base-pair inclinations with respect to the global base-pair axes, in the five structures. The reason for the differences in the base-pair inclinations becomes apparent if the intra base-pair parameters are examined. While the central base-pairs have large propeller twists and small buckles, there is a large buckling of the base-pairs at steps 3-4 and 9-10 (see Figure 7a). This leads to a correspondingly large change, both in the wedge roll (ρ), as well as the rise (dZ) along the helix axis (shown in Figure 7b) at doublet steps 3 and 9. However, the terminal base-pairs, do not uniformly follow the trend set by base-pairs 3-4 and 9-10, but instead exhibit random variations (probably due to crystal packing). Hence there is a large difference between the inclinations of the base-pairs related by a full turn of the helix *viz* 1 and 11, as well as 2 and 12. However, if the molecule is really curved, then the base-pair centres of the 1st and 11 base-pairs should also show a translation relative to those in the middle of the molecule, in a direction perpendicular to the global helix axis. While a small amount of translation is in fact observed, the values do not correlate with the trends shown by base-pair inclinations, nor do the angles between the terminal local helix axes or helix origins show a matching trend (Table IVa). If however we replace the 3′-terminal C-G doublet (11th step) with a step identical to the first C-G doublet (1st step), then the consequences of the non-parallel nature of base-pairs 1 and 11 are immediately apparent (Figure 8). The helix axes at the two ends now show a trend similar to that seen for the base-pair normals (Table IVa). If a long polymeric structure is generated, using only these first ten steps, then the curve fitting procedure as well as the graphical projection down the super-helix axis, give the radii of curvature values similar to those obtained from the inclinations of the 1st and 11th base-pair normals (Table IVb).

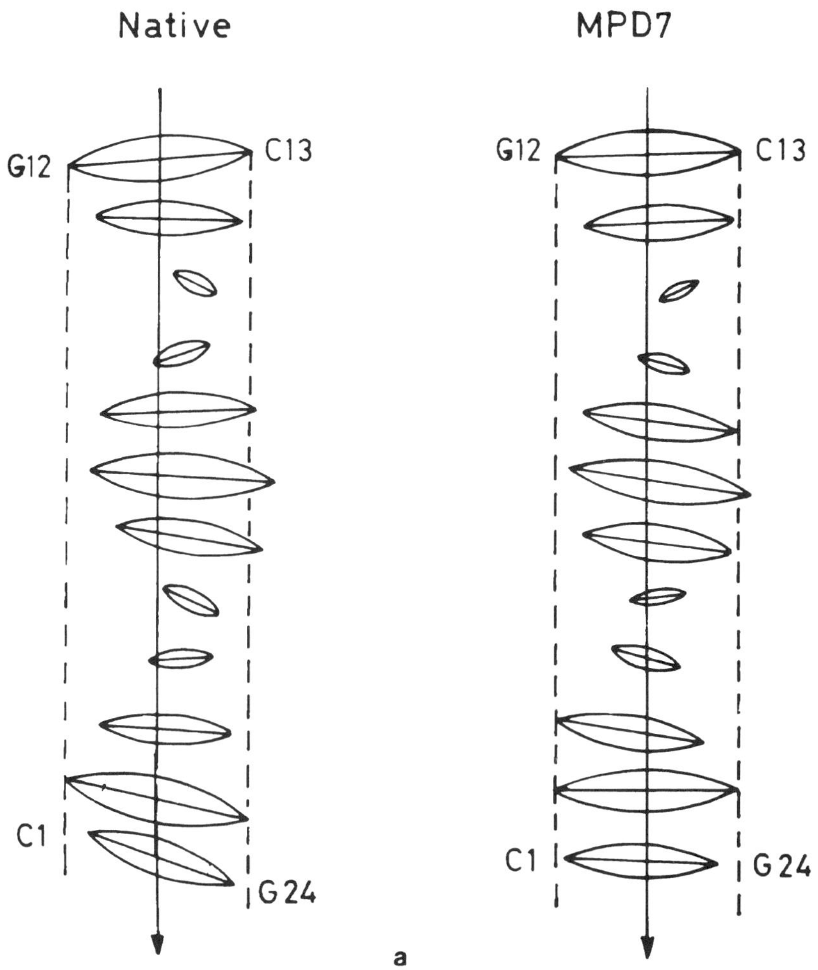

Figure 8: (a) A schematic diagram showing the C6--C8 vectors in the Native and MPD7 structures with imaginary cylinders fitted around the 1st and 11th base-pairs. The cylinders encompass almost all the base-pairs and the overall dimensions of the cylinders are similar for both structures. The only obvious difference between the two structures is non-parallelism of the two end faces of the cylinder in the case of Native structure due to the differences in the terminal base-pair inclinations. (b) Two similar cylinders, as shown in (a), are placed head-to-tail to highlight the fact that nearly straight DNA fragments with small bends at the junctions can lead to a curved polymeric structure.

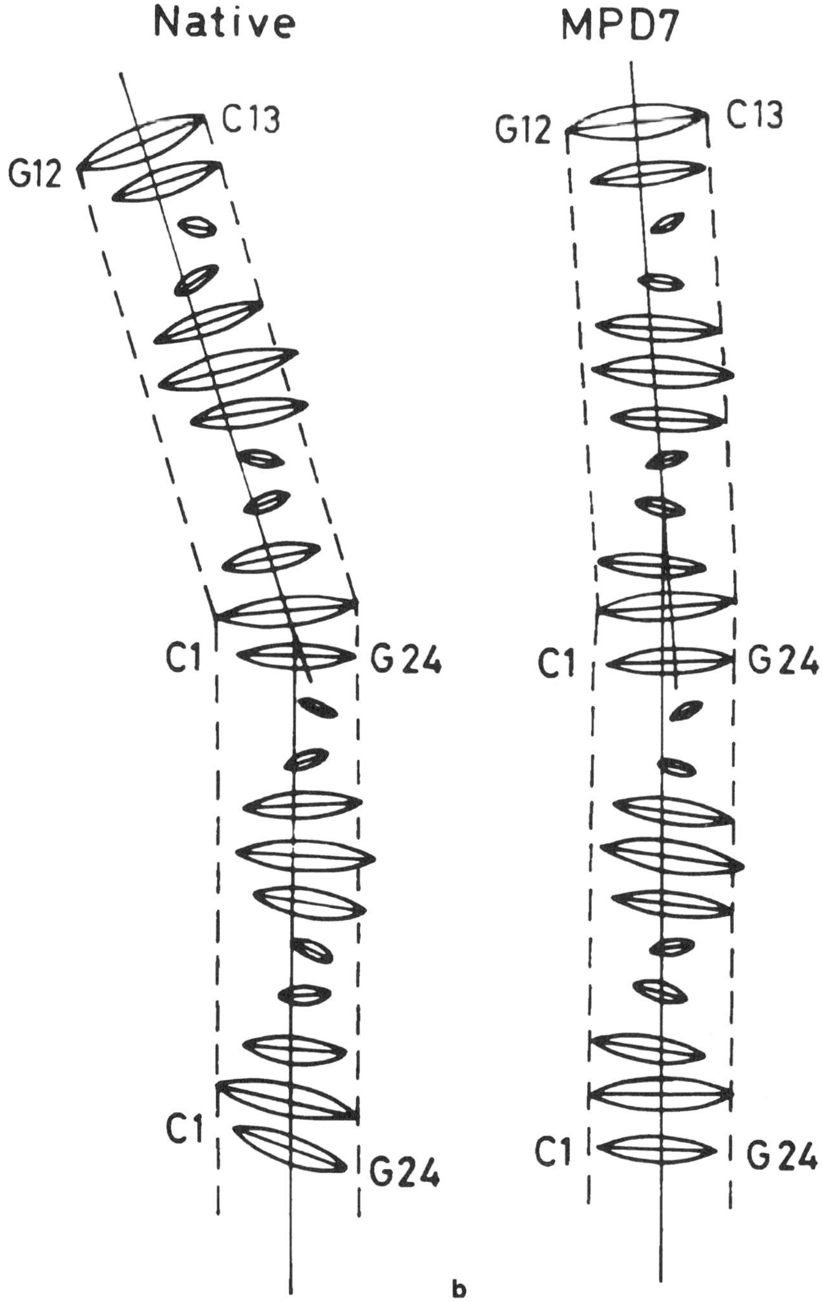

Figure 8 *continued*

This is clearly a consequence of stacking the (10-mer repeat) cylinders on top of each other. Hence even though the cylinder axis itself is nearly straight (for the decamer), the mutual inclination between the two end-faces of the cylinder, leads to the polymer generated using this cylinder as a repeating unit to follow a curved path (as shown in Figure 8b). This need not always be true, as is seen by the fact that if the 5′-terminal step (1st step) is removed, and the 11th step repeated, then this feature of curvature in the polymeric structure is not observed, indicating that it is not the base-pair inclination alone, but the total geometry of the doublet step that is crucial in determining the local helix axis direction.

We therefore conclude that a change in base-pair inclinations does not necessarily lead to molecular bending, though the molecule may appear curved. However, if a molecule is really bent, then the base-pair inclinations with respect to a linear helix axis must necessarily change. Using several different quantitative criteria, the various B-form dodecamer structures cannot be assigned any well defined bending as reported earlier.

Acknowledgments

D.B. thanks CSIR, India for a fellowship.

References and Footnotes

1. H.-M. Wu and D.M. Crothers, *Nature 308*, 509 (1984).
2. H.-S. Koo, H.-M. Wu and D.M. Crothers, *Nature 320*, 501 (1986).
3. P.J. Hagerman, *Nature 321*, 449 (1986).
4. S. Diekmann, E. von Kitzing, L. McLaughlin, J. Ott and F. Eckstein, *Proc. Natl. Acad. Sci. USA 84*, 8257 (1987).
5. L. Ulanovsky and E.N. Trifonov, *Nature 326*, 720 (1987).
6. H.-S. Koo and D.M. Crothers, *Proc. Natl. Acad. Sci. USA 85*, 1763 (1988).
7. E.N. Trifonov, in *CRC Crit. Rev. Biochem 19*, 89 (1985).
8. E.N. Trifonov and G. Mengeritsky, in *Structure and Expression, Vol. 3: DNA Bending & Curvature* (Eds., W.K.Olson, M.H.Sarma and M. Sundaralingam) 159 (1987).
9. A.V. Fratini, M.L. Kopka, H.R. Drew and R.E. Dickerson, *J. Biol. Chem 257*, 14686 (1982).
10. Z. Shakked and O. Kennard, in *Biological Macromolecules & Assemblies, Vol. 2: Nucleic Acids & Interactive Proteins* (Eds., F.A. Jurnak and A. McPherson), 1 (1985).
11. Z. Shakked and D. Rabinovich, in *Prog. Biophys. Molec. Biol. 47*, 159 (1986).
12. R.E. Dickerson, M.L. Kopka and P. Pjura, in *Biological Macromolecules & Assemblies, Vol. 2: Nucleic Acids & Interactive Proteins* (Eds., F.A. Jurnak and A. McPherson), 37 (1985).
13. J.-L. Leroy, E. Charretier, M. Kochoyan and M. Gueron, *Biochemistry 27*, 8894 (1988).
14. L. Ulanovsky, M. Bodner, E.N. Trifonov and M. Choder, *Proc. Natl. Acad. Sci. USA 83*, 862 (1986).
15. F.H.C. Crick, *Proc. Natl. Acad. Sci. USA 73*, 2639 (1976).
16. F.B. Fuller, *Proc. Natl. Acad. Sci. USA 75*, 3357 (1978).
17. A. Klug and A.A. Travers, *Cell 56*, 9 (1989).
18. C.R. Calladine and H.R. Drew, *J. Mol. Biol. 192*, 907 (1986).
19. D. Bhattacharyya and M. Bansal, *Curr. Sci. 57*, 1159 (1988).
20. D. Bhattacharyya and M. Bansal, *J. Biomol. Struct. Dynam 6*, 635 (1989).
21. Definition and Nomenclature of Nucleic Acid Structure Parameters, *J. Mol. Biol. 205*, 787 (1989).
22. S.D. Levene and D.M. Crothers, *J. Biomol. Struct. Dynam. 1*, 429 (1983).
23. U. Heinemann, L. Lauble, R. Frank and H. Blocker *Nucl. Acids Res. 15*, 9531 (1987).
24. Z. Shakked, D. Rabinovich, O.Kennard, W.B.T. Cruse, S.A. Salisbury and M.A. Viswamitra, *J. Mol. Biol. 166*, 183 (1983).
25. M. McCall, T. Brown and O. Kennard, *J. Mol. Biol. 183*, 385 (1985).
26. D.J. Barlow and J.M. Thornton, *J. Mol. Biol. 201*, 601 (1988).

Structure & Methods, ISBN 0-940030-32-2
Volume 3: DNA & RNA, ISBN 0-940030-31-4
Eds., Ramaswamy H. Sarma & Mukti H. Sarma, © Adenine Press 1990

Parallel Stranded DNA

Thomas M. Jovin, Karsten Rippe, Niels B. Ramsing, Reinhard Klement, Wim Elhorst and Marie Vojtišková
Department of Molecular Biology
Max Planck Institute for Biophysical Chemistry
Postfach 2841, D-3400 Göttingen, FRG

Abstract

Two DNA oligonucleotides consisting of dA and dT residues in sequences with complementarity in a parallel orientation can hybridize spontaneously, forming a duplex structure distinctly different from that of the conventional antiparallel B-DNA helix. The helical stability and other features of this parallel stranded DNA conformation (ps-DNA) have been determined with a series of linear duplexes 15 to 25-nt in length as well as with specially designed hairpin molecules. Ps-DNA is characterized by the following properties: (i) *Spectra.* The UV absorption is blue shifted relative to that of B-DNA (aps-DNA) such that the difference spectra (ps -aps) in the native state show a positive peak (~ 250 nm) in the region of 235-265 nm, an isosbestic point at 267 nm, and a negative peak (~ 280 nm) in the range 270-300 nm. The CD and the ^{31}P-NMR spectra of the native ps duplexes also differ significantly from those of their aps counterparts. (ii) *Helical stability.* The van't Hoff transition enthalpies ΔH_{vH} determined from temperature resolved UV absorption spectra are found to be independent of salt concentration, and are similar in magnitude for all related sets of molecules when expressed per nearest neighbor interaction (N.N. ≡ $(n - 1)$ where n is the chain length). That is, ΔH_{vH}/N.N. = 20 ± 2 kJ mol^{-1} for ps-DNA and 25 ± 2 kJ mol^{-1} for aps-DNA in NaCl. The melting temperatures are 13-19° lower for the ps compared to the aps duplexes (10° in the case of the hairpins), but the T_m values of all molecules show essentially the same dependence upon salt concentration. (iii) *Drug binding.* The intercalating drug ethidium bromide binds better to ps- than to aps-DNA, but the opposite is true of the minor groove specific drugs bis-benzimidazole H-33258 (BBI-258) and 4′, 6-diamidine-2-phenylindol (DAPI). (iv) *Substrate specificities.* The spectrum of reactivity of ps duplexes as substrates for DNA specific enzymes and chemical reagents is broad, ranging from a total lack of reaction to greater susceptibility relative to that of the corresponding aps molecules. (v) *Influence of dG · dC base pairs.* The substitution of four dA · dT base pairs with dG · dC base pairs in a 25-nt duplex destabilizes but does not abolish the ps conformation. (vi) *Model calculations.* Force field calculations yield models for the ps-DNA helix and the constituent *trans* base pairs.

Introduction

In 1986, N. Pattabiraman (1) reported force field calculations predicting a stable homopolymeric duplex $d(A)_6 \cdot d(T)_6$ with the two strands oriented in the same 5′-3′ direction. The secondary structure of the proposed parallel stranded helix was characterized by *reverse* Watson-Crick base pairing; i.e., a *trans* orientation of the glycosidic bonds of the dA and dT hydrogen bonded residues, denoted here as *trans*-Crick-Watson base pairs. Furthermore, the predicted helical stability was comparable to that of the corresponding antiparallel B-DNA structure.

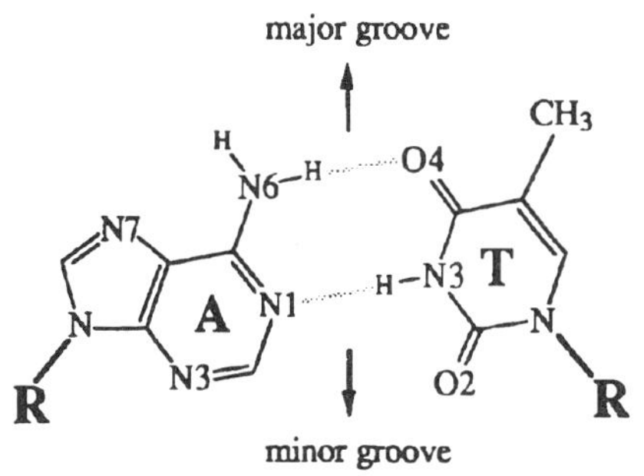

cis-Watson-Crick base pair

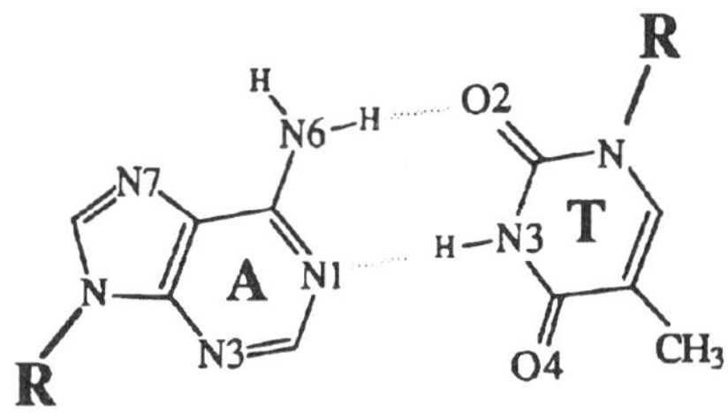

trans-Crick-Watson base pair

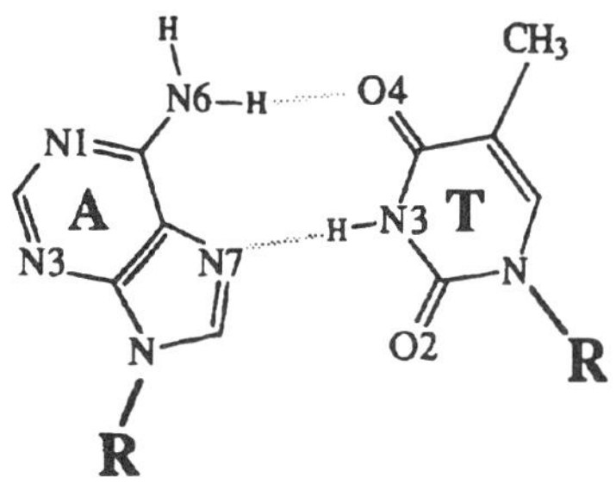

Hoogsteen base pair

The first experimental demonstration of parallel stranded DNA (ps-DNA) was with a series of hairpin molecules (Figure 1A) in which 3′-p-3′ and 5′-p-5′ phosphodiester bonds were introduced in the loops consisting of four dC nucleotides (hairpin ps-C10) or four dG nucleotides (hairpin ps-G10), thereby forcing the strands of $d(A)_{10} \cdot d(T)_{10}$ stems into a parallel orientation (2). Studies of these molecules demonstrated that (i) the ps hairpins are only slightly less stable than reference aps molecules, and that (ii) they exhibit characteristic differences in absorption and CD spectra, electrophoretic mobilities, enzyme substrate specificities, and drug-binding properties (2). The existence of Hoogsteen base pairing (see above) observed with other DNA structures involving parallel stranded interactions was excluded on the basis of the chemical methylation pattern obtained with dimethyl sulfate (2).

The findings with ps hairpins stimulated further studies with linear duplexes of oligonucleotides. The construction of ps linear duplexes requires selection of sequences for which the parallel orientation with perfect complementarity is greatly favored over alternative antiparallel secondary structures. A set of three 21-nt deoxyoligonucleotides ("C-series," see Figure 1B) was devised according to these criteria and provided the first evidence for a ps-DNA duplex arising from the spontaneous hybridization of two strands (3); a somewhat different approach was reported by Germann *et al.* (4). The selection rules discriminating against competitive antiparallel structures were refined and led to the design and synthesis of four 25-nt deoxyoligonucleotides ("D-series," see Figure 1C) (5). The ps duplexes in both the C- and the D-series showed a 1:1 strand stoichiometry and exhibited spectroscopic, thermodynamic, electrophoretic, and ligand binding properties (3,5,6) different from the aps references but comparable to those obtained previously with the hairpin molecules.

More recently, other studies have been carried out with the D-series duplexes. They have been evaluated as substrates for a number of DNA dependent enzymes and chemical nucleases (7) and ^{31}P-NMR spectra have been obtained (K. Rippe, N.B. Ramsing, F. Eckstein and T.M. Jovin, in preparation). In addition, we have constructed variants of the D-series in which four dA residues in one strand and the dT residues in the complementary strand have been replaced with dG and dC, respectively (see Figure 1C, oligonucleotides D5 and D6). These molecules still adopt the ps conformation (8). In this study we summarize the characteristic features of the ps molecules we have examined to date.

Materials and Methods

Oligonucleotide Synthesis and Characterization. Oligonucleotides ps-C8, ps-C10, ps-G10, aps-C8, aps-C10, and aps-G10 (Figure 1A) were synthesized by modifications of standard phosphoramidite chemistry and purified as described elsewhere (2). The oligonucleotides constituting the linear duplexes were prepared according to Refs. 3 and 5. All solutions contained a standard buffer, 10 mM Na-cacodylate, pH 7.2, in addition to the specified salts (NaCl, $MgCl_2$). The molar extinction coefficients of the oligonucleotides (Table I) were determined by spectral and phosphate analysis (2,3,5). The DNA duplexes were prepared for measurements by mixing the appropriate oligonucleotides in the desired salt solutions, heating to 50-60°C for 5 minutes, and cooling slowly to room temperature. DNA concentrations are given in nucleotide + terminal nucleoside units.

An amino group was introduced at the the 5′ end of the F-series oligonucleotides (Figure 1D) by an extra cycle of phosphoramidite synthesis with Aminolink-1 (4-dimethylamino-pyridine, Applied Biosystems). The presence of the 5′-amino group in fractions obtained during oligonucleotide purification was demonstrated by a spot test with fluorescamine (Sigma).

Spectroscopy. Ultraviolet absorption measurements were made with a Uvikon 820 spectrophotometer equipped with computer-controlled thermostated cuvette holders and data acquisition. Spectra were recorded in steps of 2 nm from 220 to 320 nm in 4° intervals for both heating and cooling cycles in the range from 2 to 96°C. The data sets were corrected, analyzed and plotted as described elsewhere (6). Circular dichroism (CD) spectra were acquired on a Jobin Yvon Model IV Dichrograph with a resolution of 1 nm. ^{31}P-NMR spectra were measured with a Bruker AM 360L spec-

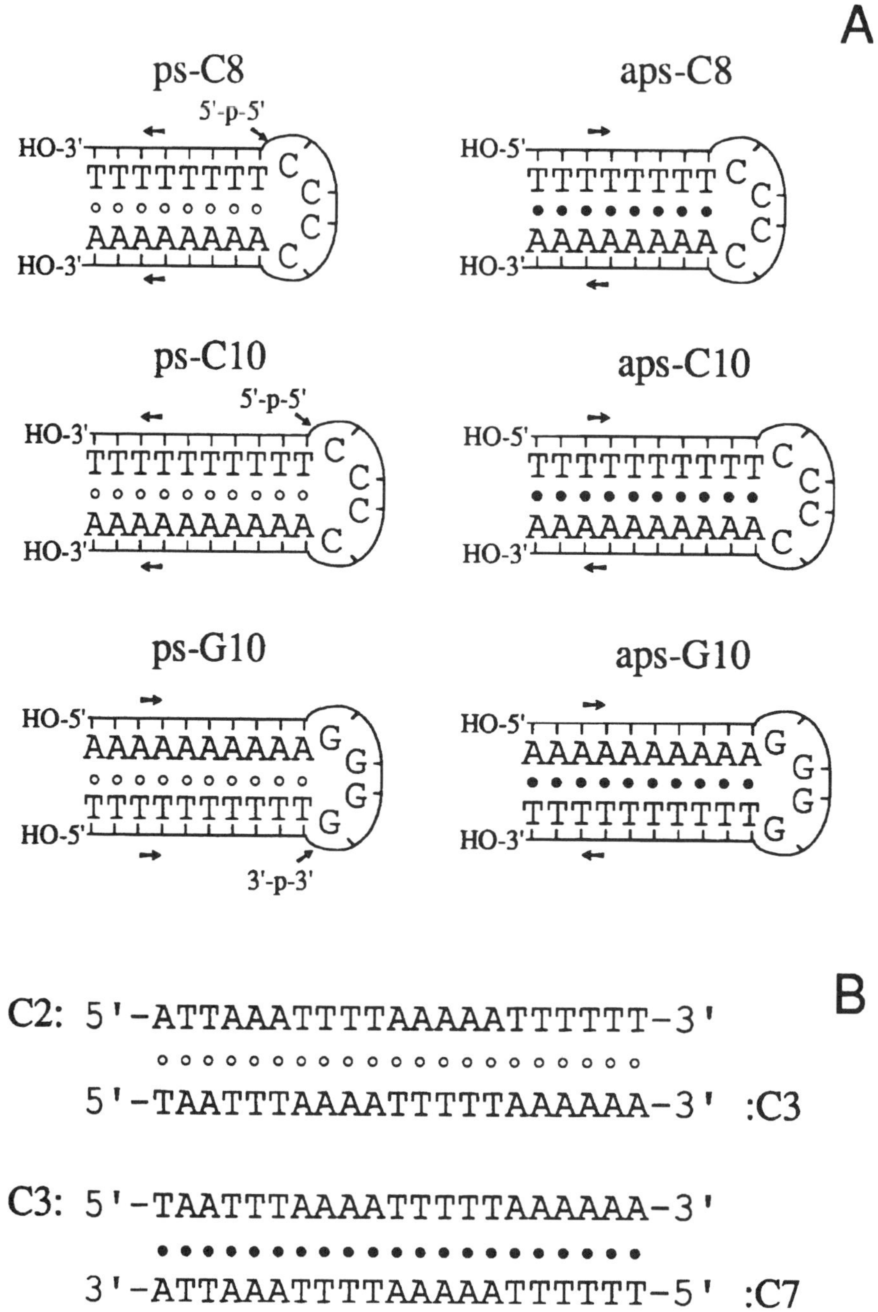

Figure 1: *Oligonucleotide hairpins and linear duplexes in the ps and aps conformations.* The Watson-Crick conventional *cis*-base pairs of the antiparallel stem regions are shown by the symbol (●) and the *trans*-Watson-Crick base pairs of the parallel stranded duplex by the symbols (○) for the dA · dT and (□) for the dG · dC base pairs. (A) Hairpin structures (2). The unusual phosphodiester bonds (5′-p-5′ and 3′-p-3′) in the ps hairpins are indicated. (B) C-series duplexes (3).

C

```
D1: 5'-AAAAAAAAAATAATTTTAAATATTT-3'
       ooooooooooooooooooooooooo
    5'-TTTTTTTTTTATTAAAATTTATAAA-3' :D2

D3: 5'-AAATATTTAAAATTATTTTTTTTTT-3'
       ooooooooooooooooooooooooo
    5'-TTTATAAATTTTAATAAAAAAAAAA-3' :D4

D5: 5'-AAAAAGAAAGTAGTTTTAAGTATTT-3'
       ooooo□ooo□oo□oooooo□ooooo
    5'-TTTTTCTTTCATCAAAATTCATAAA-3' :D6


D1: 5'-AAAAAAAAAATAATTTTAAATATTT-3'
       •••••••••••••••••••••••••
    3'-TTTTTTTTTTATTAAAATTTATAAA-5' :D3

D2: 5'-TTTTTTTTTTATTAAAATTTATAAA-3'
       •••••••••••••••••••••••••
    3'-AAAAAAAAAATAATTTTAAATATTT-5' :D4
```

D

```
F1: 5'-NH2-TTTTTATTAAATATA-3'
           ooooooooooooooo
    5'-NH2-AAAAATAATTTATAT-3'  :F2

F1: 5'-NH2-TTTTTATTAAATATA-3'
           •••••••••••••••
        3'-AAAAATAATTTATAT-NH2-5' :F4
```

Figure 1 *continued*

(C) D-series duplexes (5,8). (D) F-series duplexes. Oligonucleotides F1, F2, F3 and F4 were synthesized with an amino group at the 5′ end. In all cases, the formation of base paired structures was established electrophoretically as well as by other means (2,3,5,8, this study).

Table I
Ultraviolet Absorption of ps and aps Duplexes[a]

DNA duplex	Extinction coefficients[b] in 0.1 M NaCl, 20°C			Absorbance ratios in 0.1 M NaCl, 20°C			$\frac{A_{250}}{A_{284}}$ in 0.1 M NaCl	
	λ_{max}	ε_{max}	ε_{260}	$\frac{A_{250}}{A_{260}}$	$\frac{A_{280}}{A_{260}}$	$\frac{A_{290}}{A_{260}}$	20°C	80°C
Parallel Stranded Duplexes								
ps-C8	258	7.9	7.9	0.83	0.49	0.13	2.4	2.2
ps-C10	259	7.9	7.8	0.85	0.48	0.12	2.5	2.3
ps-G10	257	8.7	8.4	0.92	0.43	0.13	3.0	2.6
ps-F1 · F2[c]	260	7.2	7.2	0.81	0.43	0.09	3.3	2.8
ps-C2 · C3	258	7.0	6.9	0.85	0.42	0.09	3.1	2.7
ps-D1 · D2	258	7.0	7.0	0.84	0.41	0.08	3.2	2.7
ps-D3 · D4	258	7.1	7.0	0.84	0.40	0.08	3.3	2.7
ps-D5 · D6[c]	258	6.9	6.9	0.86	0.44	0.12	2.9	2.5
Antiparallel Stranded Duplexes								
aps-C8	260	7.1	7.1	0.82	0.62	0.20	1.8	2.3
aps-C10	261	6.9	6.9	0.80	0.62	0.20	1.8	2.2
aps-G10	258	7.6	7.6	0.89	0.56	0.19	2.1	2.6
aps-F1 · F4[c]	260	6.8	6.8	0.77	0.51	0.14	2.2	2.7
aps-C3 · C7	260	6.1	6.1	0.79	0.55	0.16	2.0	2.7
aps-D1 · D3	260	6.0	6.0	0.77	0.56	0.16	2.0	2.8
aps-D2 · D4	260	6.1	6.1	0.78	0.54	0.16	2.0	2.7

[a]The subscripts refer to wavelengths in nm. All values were measured in 10 mM Na-cacodylate, pH 7.2. The Na^+ concentration including the buffer contribution was 0.11 M. Data in part from Ref. 6.
[b]λ_{max} is the wavelength in nm with the highest extinction coefficient; ε_{max} and ε_{260} are in units of $mM^{-1}cm^{-1}$.

trometer at the Max Planck Institute for Experimental Medicine, Göttingen, FRG, operating at 145.785 Hz with ^1H broad-band decoupling. Chemical shifts refer to 80% phosphoric acid as an external standard.

Enzymatic Reactions. The oligonucleotides were end-labeled with [^{32}P] to a specific activity of 10^5 cpm $nmol^{-1}$ with T4 polynucleotide kinase (New England Biolabs). Nuclease studies were carried out in the following buffers: (i) DNase I (Cooper Biomedicals): 40 mM Tris-HCl, pH 7.5, 3.3 mM $MgCl_2$, 0.2 mM $CaCl_2$. (ii) *Escherichia coli* exonuclease III (New England Biolabs): 50 mM Tris-HCl, pH 8.0, 5 mM $MgCl_2$, 10 mM 2-mercaptoethanol. The products of the enzymatic degradation were examined by polyacrylamide gel electrophoresis under denaturing conditions: 20% polyacrylamide (5% crosslinking), 8 M urea, 90 mM Tris-borate, 2 mM Na-EDTA, pH 8.0, 70°C.

Drug Binding and Energy Transfer. Fluorescence measurements were made with an SLM 8000 photon counting spectrofluorimeter. DNA additions were made with a 25 µl Hamilton microsyringe dispenser unit maintained at a temperature not higher than that of the thermostated cuvette. The emission spectra were corrected by internal standards and smoothed with Chebyshev polynomials after background subtraction.

Preparation of Fluorescently Labeled Amino-Oligonucleotides. Fluorescein-5′-isothiocyanate (FITC, Molecular Probes) was dissolved in dimethylformamide to a concentration of 10 mg/ml. Twenty μl of the reagent were added to 1.0 optical density unit (ODU) of oligonucleotides F1 or F3 in a total volume of 100 μl of 0.3 M Na-carbonate buffer, pH 9.5, and incubated 4 hours in the dark at room temperature. The reaction was quenched by addition of glycine to a final concentration of 10 mM. Labelling of oligonucleotides F2 and F4 with tetramethylrhodamine-5′-isothiocyonate (TRITC; Molecular Probes) was carried out by the same procedure, but in 0.2 M carbonate buffer pH 9.5 and with addition of 3 μl of an 80 mg/ml solution of the reagent in methylsulfoxide. The reacted oligonucleotides were purified by (i) spin-column gel filtration with Sephadex G25-Superfine (Pharmacia), and (ii) reverse phase FPLC (Pharmacia).

Model Force Field Calculations. To construct the different ps and aps structures a modified version of the AMBER package (Refs. 2 and 3 and citations therein) was used in conjunction with the INSIGHT (Biosym Tech.) molecular modelling package and a PS390 Evans and Sutherland graphics workstation.

Results and Discussion

Spectroscopic Properties

An overview of the spectroscopic properties of ps-D1 · D2 compared to aps-D1 · D3 is given in Figure 2. The results are representative for the other ps molecules examined to date (Table I) with the exception of the ^{31}P-NMR spectra which have only been recorded with the indicated duplexes. The UV spectra of the native ps molecules show a blue shift relative to the aps references, whereas the spectra in the denatured state are nearly identical. The distinctive absorption spectrum of native ps-DNA presumably reflects particular features of the electronic structure and stacking geometry. A plot of the ratio of the absorbances in the denatured and native states versus wavelength emphasizes the characteristic differences between ps-DNA and aps-DNA in a manner independent of concentration (Figure 2B1,B2). By judicious choice of wavelengths, absorbance ratios can be derived which emphasize the qualitative differences in the spectra and melting temperature of ps- and aps-DNAs (Figure 2B3, Table I). Thus the A_{250}/A_{284} ratio decreases in the case of ps-DNA but increases upon denaturation of aps-DNA. The CD spectra confirm the existence of a native duplex structure with both the ps and aps pairs of oligonucleotides but the differences in circular dichroism between 260 and 290 nm indicate that the conformations are not the same (Figure 2C).

^{31}P-NMR spectra of ps-D1 · D2 and aps-D1 · D3 have been measured in the native and denatured states (K. Rippe, N.B. Ramsing, F. Eckstein, T.M. Jovin, in preparation). It is evident from Figures 2D1,D2 that the backbone structures of ps-D1 · D2 and aps-D1 · D3 are dissimilar. The distinctions (broader, downfield shifted spectrum

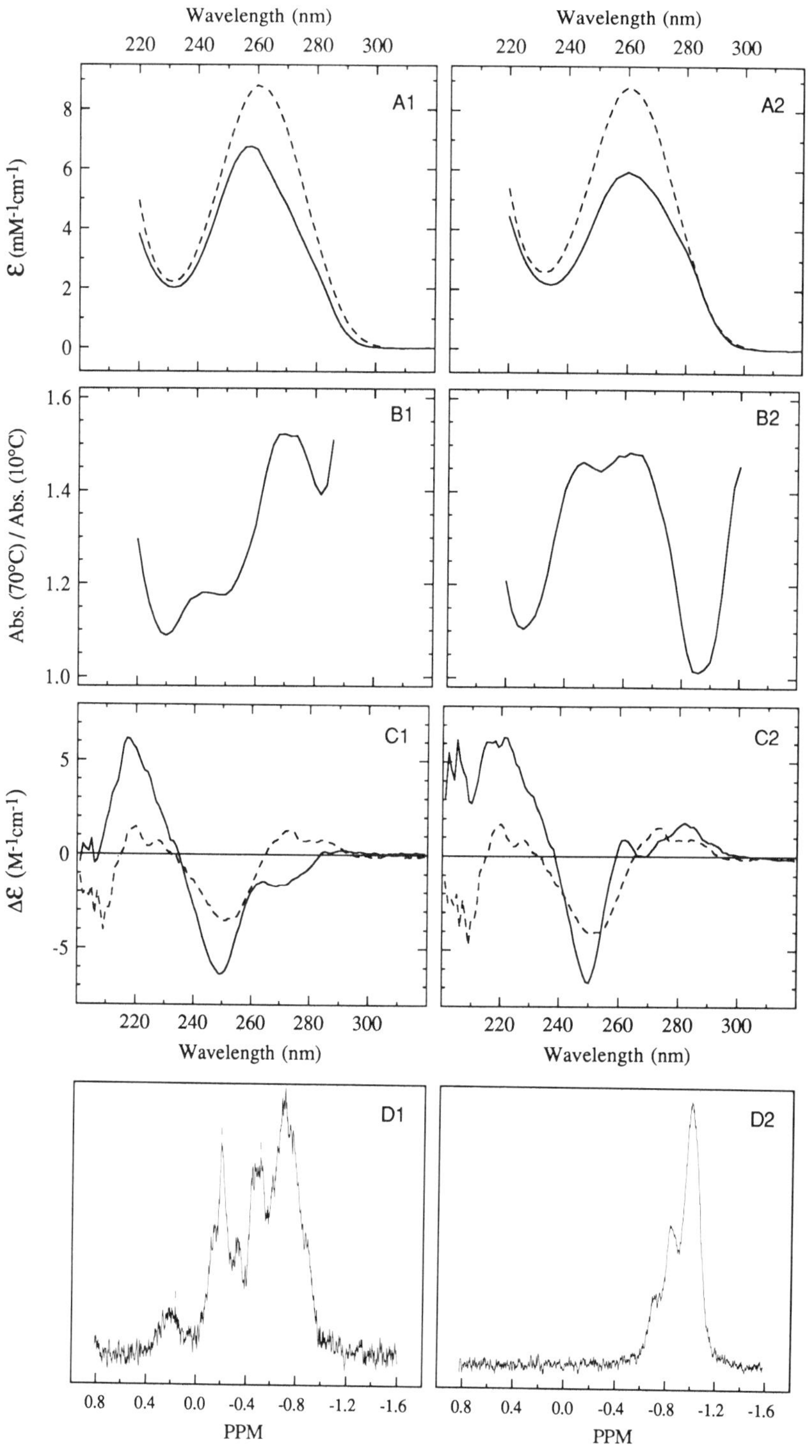
Wavelength (nm)
220 240 260 280 300
A1
A2
B1
B2
C1
C2
D1
D2
ε (mM-1cm-1)
Abs. (70°C) / Abs. (10°C)
Δε (M-1cm-1)
PPM
0.8 0.4 0.0 -0.4 -0.8 -1.2 -1.6

Figure 2

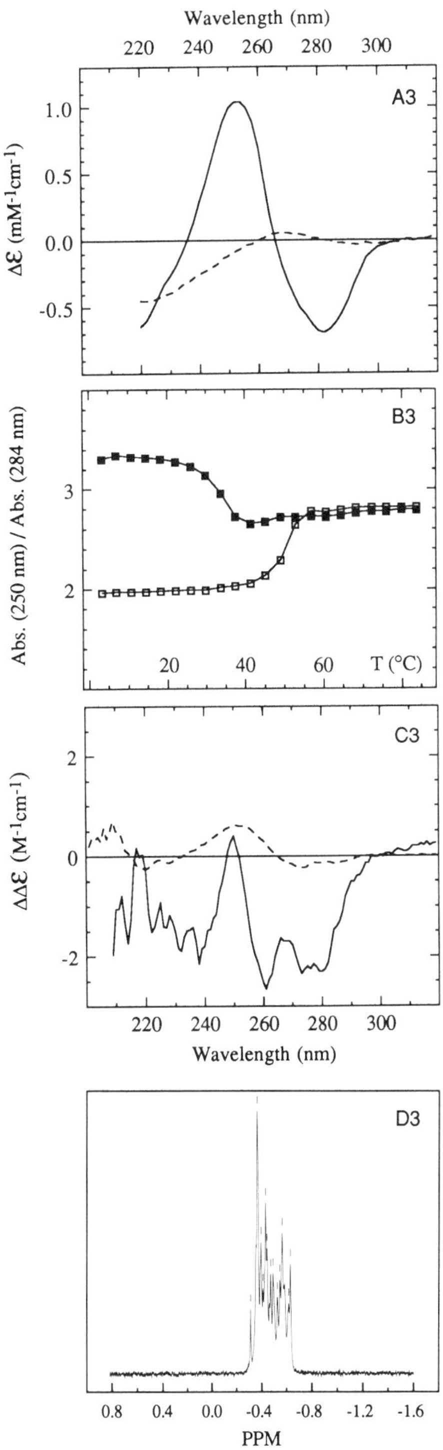

Figure 2: *Spectroscopic properties of ps-D1 · D2 and aps-D1 · D3 duplexes.* (A1, B1, C1, D1) ps-D1 · D2. (A2, B2, C2, D2) aps-D1 · D3. (A1, A2) UV-spectra at 10°C (—) and at 70°C (----). (A3) UV difference spectra (ps − aps) at 10°C (—) and at 70°C (----). (B1, B2) Hyperchromicity spectra expressed as the ratio of absorbances at 70°C and 10°C. (B3) Wavelength dependent melting curve of ps-D1 · D2 (■) and aps-D1 · D3 (□). The ratio of UV absorbances at 250 nm and 284 nm is plotted versus temperature. (C1, C2) CD spectra at 10°C (—) and at 70°C (----). Δε is the difference in the molar extinction coefficients for right and left polarized light. (C3) CD difference spectra (ps − aps) at 10°C (—) and at 70°C (----). ΔΔε is the difference between the Δε values for the ps and aps structures. (D1, D2) ^{31}P-NMR spectra at 20°C. (D3) ^{31}P-NMR spectra of ps-D1 · D2 at 55°C. All spectra in 2 mM $MgCl_2$ and 10 mM Na-cacodylate, pH 7.2, except for the ^{31}P-NMR (see D) data that were recorded in 50 mM NaCl, 25 mM Na-cacodylate, pH 6.8, 25 mM EDTA, and 50% D_2O.

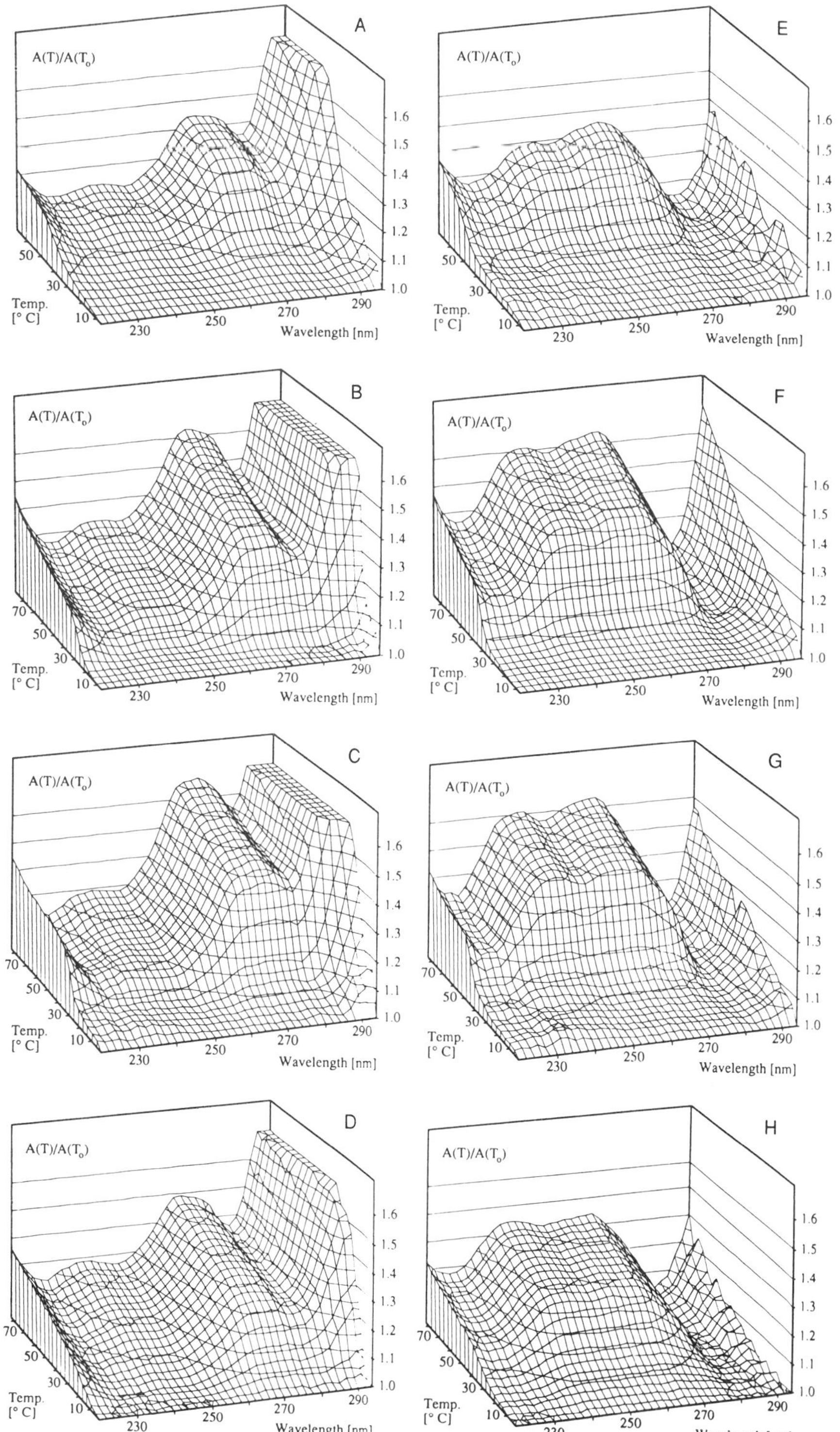

Figure 3: *Thermally-resolved ultraviolet absorption spectra of ps and aps helices.* The ratio of $A_\lambda(T)/A_\lambda(T_o)$, where T_o is the initial temperature is plotted versus temperature. Left column: parallel stranded DNAs: (A) ps-C10; (B) ps-C2 · C3; (C) ps-D3 · D4; (D) ps-F1 · F2. Right column: antiparallel stranded DNAs: (E) aps-C10; (F) aps-C3 · C7; (G) aps-D2 · D4; (H) aps-F1 · F4. All spectra in 0.1 M NaCl, 10 mM Na-cacodylate, pH 7.1, except for (D) and (H) that were measured in 0.4 M NaCl.

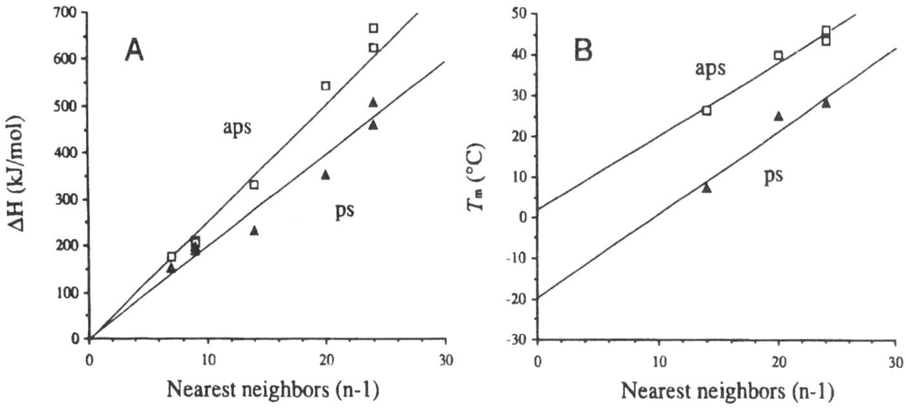

Figure 4: *Length dependence of the van'Hoff enthalpy of melting ΔH_{vH} and melting temperature T_m.* The ps duplexes are shown by the symbol (Δ) and the aps duplexes by (□). (A) Dependence of ΔH_{vH} upon number of nearest neighbor interactions N.N. = $(n-1)$, where n is the length of the base paired region. The slope of the regression line the mean value of ΔH_{vH} per nearest neighbor (ΔH_{vH}/N.N.), which for the ps molecules is $\Delta h = 19.9$ kJ mol^{-1} and for aps molecules $\Delta h = 25.3$ kJ mol^{-1}. (B) Dependence of T_m on $(n-1)$. The hairpins are not shown because their T_m is independent of concentration and is higher. The T_m values of the linear duplexes were scaled to a concentration of 2 μM strands. The solid lines are linear regressions with slopes of 1.8°C/N.N. for the aps and 2.1°C/N.N. for the ps duplexes.

Table II

Thermodynamic Data for Helix-Coil Transitions of ps-DNA and aps DNA[a]

DNA duplex	ΔH_{vH}[b] (kJ/mol) NaCl (0.1-1.0 M)	ΔH_{vH}[b] (kJ/mol) $MgCl_2$ (0.5-8 mM)	$T\Delta S$[c] (kJ/mol, 25°C) NaCl (0.1 M)	$T\Delta S$[c] (kJ/mol, 25°C) $MgCl_2$ (2 mM)	ΔG[d] (kJ/mol, 25°C) NaCl (0.1 M)	ΔG[d] (kJ/mol, 25°C) $MgCl_2$ (2 mM)
ps-C8	152 $_{8}$	160 $_{6}$	147 $_{8}$	152 $_{7}$	5 $_{8}$	8 $_{8}$
ps-C10	198 $_{2}$	-	188 $_{2}$	-	10 $_{2}$	-
ps-G10	190 $_{8}$	-	180 $_{8}$	-	10 $_{8}$	-
ps-F1 · F2	231*	-	210*	-	22*	-
ps-C2 · C3	353 $_{13}$	400 $_{15}$	317 $_{15}$	353 $_{15}$	36 $_{2}$	47 $_{8}$
ps-D1 · D2	459 $_{3}$	507 $_{2}$	418 $_{3}$	453 $_{2}$	41 $_{<1}$	54 $_{<1}$
ps-D3 · D4	507 $_{2}$	542 $_{2}$	466 $_{2}$	484 $_{2}$	42 $_{<1}$	58 $_{<1}$
ps-D5 · D6	372 $_{2}$	451 $_{1}$	414 $_{2}$	349 $_{1}$	23 $_{<1}$	37 $_{<1}$
aps-C8	177 $_{6}$	192 $_{4}$	166 $_{6}$	177 $_{4}$	11 $_{6}$	15 $_{4}$
aps-C10	212 $_{3}$	-	195 $_{3}$	-	17 $_{3}$	-
aps-G10	206 $_{6}$	-	189 $_{6}$	-	16 $_{6}$	-
aps-F1 · F4	334*	-	296*	-	38*	-
aps-C3 · C7	546 $_{6}$	610*	484 $_{6}$	532*	62 $_{3}$	78*
aps-D1 · D3	670 $_{4}$	736 $_{3}$	590 $_{4}$	641 $_{4}$	80 $_{2}$	95 $_{2}$
aps-D2 · D4	628 $_{2}$	669 $_{2}$	555 $_{2}$	581 $_{2}$	73 $_{1}$	88 $_{1}$

[a]The listed parameters are average values obtained from numerous experiments with 0.1-1.0 M NaCl or 0.5-8 mM $MgCl_2$, and 10 mM Na-cacodylate, pH 7.2. Analysis of both the increasing and decreasing temperature slopes are included. The small number beside each entry is the relative magnitude of the 95% confidence limits in %. For example, 152 $_{8}$, signifies an average value of 152 with a 95% confidence limit of 8%, that is, ±12. Data in part from Refs. 6 and 8.

[b]ΔH_{vH} is the average van't Hoff enthalpy of melting. No correlation with salt concentration in the range 0.1-1.0 M NaCl or 0.5-8 mM $MgCl_2$ is observed.

[c]$T\Delta S$ is the product of the temperature, T (298.1 K) and entropy of melting, ΔS, at 25°C in 0.1 M NaCl (the Na^+ concentration including the buffer contribution was 0.11 M). The entropy was calculated by using the average ΔH_{vH} and the T_m in 0.1 M NaCl and 2 mM $MgCl_2$ calculated from linear regressions (Table III).

[d]ΔG is the average Gibbs free energy of transition, calculated by using the average ΔH_{vH} and the estimate of $T\Delta S$.

*Indicates that too few measurements were made to calculate 95% confidence limits.

of ps-DNA) disappear upon thermal denaturation (Figure 2D3), as in the case of the other spectroscopic techniques. Such data yield information about the structure of the sugar-phosphate backbone, inasmuch as the chemical shifts are influenced primarily by the P-O torsion angles and O-P-O bond angles (9). Although we are not able as yet to assign peaks to particular phosphate residues in the sequences, we interpret the broadening of the spectrum of the native ps duplex as indicative of greater flexibility of the sugar-phosphate constituents of the backbone (Figure 2D1).

Helical Stability

The systematic comparison of the ps-DNA constructs with the reference aps duplexes is particularly advantageous in studies of relative thermodynamic stability. For

Table III
Salt Dependence of Melting Temperatures[a]

	T_m[b]		$\frac{1}{T_m} = \alpha + \beta \cdot \log_{10}(c)$[c]				$\frac{\partial T_m}{\partial \log_{10}(C)}$[d]	
	NaCl	$MgCl_2$	NaCl (M)		$MgCl_2$ (mM)		NaCl	$MgCl_2$
DNA			$\alpha \cdot 10^3$	$\beta \cdot 10^3$	$\alpha \cdot 10^3$	$\beta \cdot 10^3$		
duplex	(°C, 0.1 M)	(°C, 2 mM)	($K^{-1} \cdot 10^3$)	($K^{-1} \cdot 10^3$)	($K^{-1} \cdot 10^3$)	($K^{-1} \cdot 10^3$)	(°C)	(°C)
Parallel stranded duplex								
ps-C8	33.5 2	41.0*	3.10 <1	−0.17 8	-	-	16 9	-
ps-C10	39.4 1	-	3.01 <1	−0.19 7	-	-	19 8	-
ps-G10	40.6 1	-	3.01 <1	−0.18 5	-	-	18 6	-
ps-F1 · F2	7.5*	-	-	-	-	-	-	-
ps-C2 · C3	25.1 4	33.8*	3.19 <1	−0.17 13	-	-	15 12	-
ps-D1 · D2	28.5 4	35.7*	3.11 <1	−0.21 12	-	-	17 10	7[†]
ps-D3 · D4	28.4 5	37.4 2	3.11 <1	−0.22 17	3.26 <1	−0.10 12	19 14	10 11
ps-D5 · D6	15.1 1	25.6 1	3.26 <1	−0.21 4	3.38 <1	−0.11 6	18 5	10 5
Antiparallel stranded duplexes								
aps-C8	44.7 2	49.7*	3.00 <1	−0.15 17	-	-	15 8	-
aps-C10	50.4 1	-	2.93 <1	−0.16 11	-	-	17 11	-
aps-G10	50.5 2	-	2.93 <1	−0.16 19	-	-	17 17	-
aps-F1 · F2	26.5*	-	-	-	-	-	-	-
aps-C3 · C7	40.0 2	46.8*	3.04 <1	−0.16 11	-	-	16 9	-
aps-D1 · D3	46.0 2	50.8*	2.97 <1	−0.17 10	-	-	16 8	5[†]
aps-D2 · D4	43.5 1	50.3 2	2.99 <1	−0.17 7	3.12 <1	−0.09 11	17 6	8 9

[a]The listed parameters are obtained from a linear regression of $1/T_m$ and T_m versus log(c), where c is the concentration of NaCl (0.05-0.5 M) or $MgCl_2$ (0.12-2 mM), with 10 mM Na-cacodylate, pH 7.2, throughout. The experimental T_m values from measurements with linear duplexes were adjusted to a total strand concentration of 2 μM (6). Only results derived from data for increasing temperatures were included in the regressions. The small number beside each entry is the relative magnitude of the 95% confidence limits in %. For example, 33.5 2 signifies an average of 33.5 with a 95% confidence limits of 2%, that is, ±0.7. Data in part from Ref. 6.

[b]T_m is the melting temperature in 0.1 M NaCl (the Na^+ concentration including the buffer contribution was 0.11 M) and 2 mM $MgCl_2$ with a total strand concentration of 2 μM. It was calculated from the linear regression of $1/T_m$ versus $\log_{10}(c)$.

[c]Linear regression coefficients for $1/T_m$ as a function of $\log_{10}(c)$. α is the intercept and β the slope of the regression line.

[d]The slope of linear regression of T_m versus $\log_{10}(c)$.

*Indicates that too few measurements were made to calculate the 95% confidence limits.

example, in the case of the D-series of molecules (Figure 1C), each oligonucleotide was examined in both the ps and the aps conformation. The thermally induced helix-coil transitions measured by UV absorption spectroscopy are best visualized by normalizing the absorbances at each temperature T and wavelength to the values at the initial (low) temperature T_0. The resultant three-dimensional plots (Figure 3) reveal for all members of the ps and aps groups, respectively, the characteristic differences alluded to earlier (3,5,6) The results from the analysis of the thermal transition are summarized in Figure 4 and in Tables II and III.

The important findings are: (i) All species demonstrate reversible thermal transitions in $MgCl_2$ (0.5-8 mM) and NaCl (0.05-1.6 M). (ii) Very good fits to a concerted two state transition model are achieved, the primary parameters of which are the melting temperature T_m and van't Hoff melting enthalpy ΔH_{vH}. (iii) The T_m increases with salt concentration in a classical manner ($\partial T_m/\partial \log_{10}[NaCl] = 17 \pm 2°$), but is lower by ~10° and 15°, respectively, for the hairpins and duplexes in the ps relative to the aps conformation (Table III). (iv) The divalent cation Mg^{2+}, even at low concentrations ⩽2 mM, strongly stabilizes ps-DNA, as reflected in the increased T_m as well as in the magnitude of both ΔH_{vH} and ΔG (Table II). (vi) ΔH_{vH} appears independent of the salt concentration and is ~20% lower in the case of the ps-DNAs. (vi) The data for the various DNA species can be normalized to the number of nearest neighbor interactions (N.N. ≡ chain length $- 1 = n - 1$), thereby revealing a rather consistent picture (Figure 4). Average enthalpy changes per mole of nearest neighbor interaction, Δh, obtained from the slopes of the lines in Figure 4A, are 20 kJ mol^{-1} for ps-DNA and 25 kJ mol^{-1} for aps-DNA in NaCl; the values in Mg^{2+} are ~7-17% higher. The values for individual oligonucleotides show systematic deviations in both Na^+ and Mg^{2+}, which we attribute to differences in nearest neighbor frequencies and nucleation probabilities. The T_m for aps and ps duplexes varies with chain length by ~1.8° and 2.1° per residue, respectively (Figure 4B).

Drug Binding

The interactions of the DNA specific dyes bis-benzimidazole H-33258 (BBI-258), 4′, 6-diamidine-2-phenylindol (DAPI), and ethidium bromide are characterized by a significant enhancement of fluorescence upon binding with B-DNA, i.e., the aps constructs (Figure 5). However, in the case of ps-DNA, only the intercalator ethidium binds to a significant degree and with an affinity actually higher than that for aps-DNA (Figure 5C) (2,3). Both BBI-258 and DAPI have been shown to bind within the minor groove of A-T rich regions in B-DNA (10-12). Thus, the reduced fluorescence with the ps molecules probably reflects differences in the pattern of hydrogen bonding sites and other stereochemical features of the grooves of the ps helix compared to the minor groove of B-DNA (Figures 8 and 9).The facilitation of intercalation may be related to the somewhat greater helical rise of the ps duplex estimated from model calculations (see below).

Conformational transitions of macromolecules can be almost invariably coupled to changes in ligand binding, as exemplified in the case of DNA by the highly cooperative B-Z isomerization (13,14). Numerous small molecules with binding

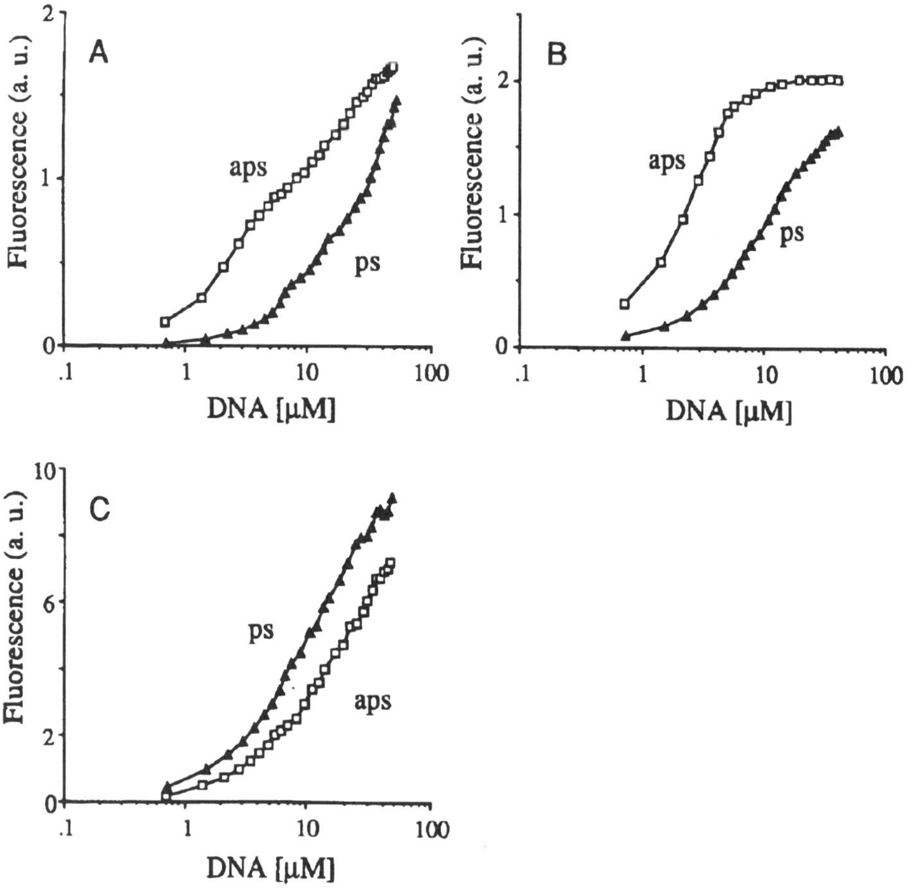

Figure 5: *Drug binding to ps-D3 · D4 and aps-D2 · D4 duplexes.* Titration of different fluorescent dyes with ps-D3 · D4 (Δ) and aps-D2 · D4 (□). (A) 0.5 μM BBI-258 in 2 mM $MgCl_2$ at 5°C. λ_{ex} = 355 nm, λ_{em} = 465 nm. (B) 0.5 μM DAPI in 0.1 M NaCl at 5°C. λ_{ex} = 368 nm, λ_{em} = 446 nm. (C) 0.5 μM ethidium bromide in 0.1 M NaCl at 5°C. λ_{ex} = 520 nm, λ_{em} = 610 nm.

specificity for one of the two conformations exist, one of them being ethidium, the addition of which to the high salt left-handed Z form of poly[d(G-C)] induces the reverse transition to the B conformation (15). In view of the apparent facilitation of ethidium intercalation in ps-DNA, it was important to establish whether similar processes are involved. To this end, we synthesized DNA oligonucleotides end-labeled with fluorescent probes suitable for fluorescence resonance energy transfer (FRET) determinations. FRET provides a sensitive "spectroscopic ruler" (16) with a resolution in the range of 10 nm, and has been applied recently to other proximity studies of DNA (17,18). The photophysical basis of the method is the transfer of excitation energy between a donor and an acceptor chosen such that the absorption spectrum of the latter overlaps the emission spectrum of the former. The transfer efficiency depends upon the 6th power of the separation distance as well as on the relative orientations of the donor and acceptor. For the donor-acceptor pair we employed fluorescein (*fl*) and tetratmethylrhodamine (*tmRh*), for which the critical

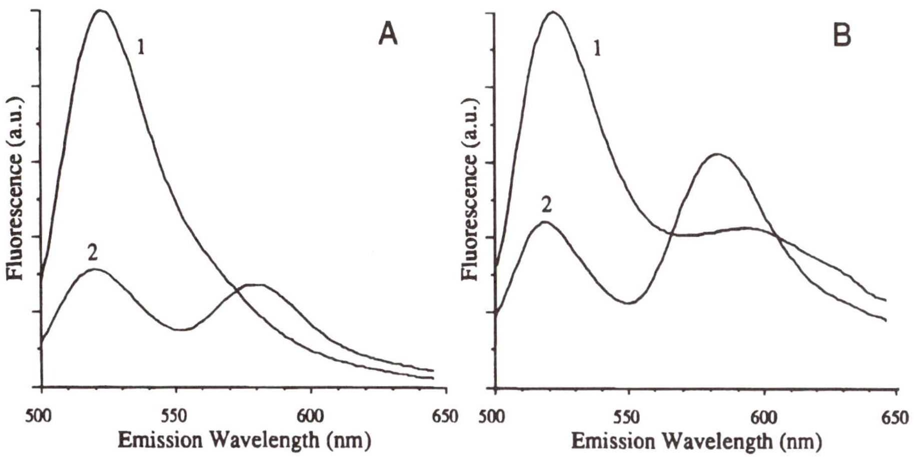

Figure 6: *Fluorescence emission spectra of dye labeled ps-F1 · F2 duplexes.* Curve 1 represents the donor emission of a duplex of with fluorescein labeled F1 and unlabeled F2, ps-[*fl*-F1 · F2]. Curve 2 corresponds to a duplex of F1 and F2 labeled at the 5′ end with fluorescein and tetramethylrhodamine, respectively, ps-[*fl*-F1 · *tmRh*-F2]. (A) Emission spectra in 1 mM $MgCl_2$ at 4°C, A_{260} = 0.1, λ_{ex} 490 nm. (B) Same conditions as (A) but with the addition of 2 μM ethidium bromide.

distance for 50% transfer (R_o) is ~5 nm (19). Fluorescein is also a good donor for the intercalation complex of ethidium. We exploited the potential for dual FRET to demonstrate (i) the formation of a ps duplex with two oligonucleotides labeled at the 5′ termini with donor and acceptor chromophores (FRET *a*); and (ii) intercalation to the ps duplex as evidenced by transfer from the fluorescein donor to intercalated ethidium bromide (FRET *b*). The results of such an experiment are shown by a set of emission spectra in Figure 6. The 15-nt oligonucleotides F1 and F2 (Figure 1D) were labeled with fluorescein and tetramethylrhodamine, respectively. In the case of the ps-[*fl*-F1 · F2] duplex, an unperturbed donor emission is observed with its characteristic peak at ~520 nm (Figure 6A, 1). With the dual labeled ps-[*fl*-F1 · *tmRh*-F2] combination, however, the donor is quenched significantly and the sensitized acceptor (rhodamine) emission appears with a peak at ~580 nm (Figure 6A, 2). A similar effect is observed in the presence of ethidium bromide (Figure 6B) except that both FRET *a* and *b* processes are superposed. That is, transfer from *fl*-F1 to ethidium is evident from the emission shoulder at the dye peak of ~610 nm (Figure 6B, 1). With the dual labeled DNA, the rhodamine acceptor is sensitized at the expense of the alternative ethidium acceptor, the emission of which is consequently diminished (Figure 6B, 2). No FRET is observed at temperatures above the T_m of ps-F1 · F2. Together with other emission and excitation spectra, these results confirm the formation of and intercalation to the ps-F1 · F2 duplex. Further experiments with longer oligonucleotides are in progress in order to establish that the 5′ termini are at the same end of the double helix, the fundamental structural feature of ps-DNA.

Substrate Specificities. Ps-DNA shows different substrate properties than B-DNA (Table IV). As an example, the results of digestion with pancreatic DNase I and *E. coli* exonuclease III are shown in Figure 7. Both enzymes exhibit nuclease activity specific for double-stranded structures. DNase I introduces single strand breaks

Table IV
Summary of Substrate Properties[a]

Enzyme activity[b]	ps-DNA	aps-DNA	ss-DNA[c]
Restriction enzymes			
*Dra*I	–	+++	++
*Mse*I	–	+++	–
*Ssp*I	–	+	–
DNA nucleases			
DNase I	–	+++	+++
Exonuclease III[d]	–	++	+++
Bal 31 nuclease	+[e]	+[e]	++
S 1 nuclease	++	+	+++
Micrococcal nuclease	++	+	+++
λ-exonuclease	+	++	+++
DNA pol. I, large fragment[f]	+++	++	+++
DNA polymerase I			
3′→5′ activity	+++	++	+++
5′→3′ activity	–	+	+
Chemical reagents			
Phenanthroline-Copper	+[e]	+[e]	+
Iron (II)-EDTA	+	+	+
Other DNA processing enzymes			
T4 DNA ligase, blunt end ligation	–	+++	+++
T4 DNA kinase[g]	+++	+++	+++

[a]Data from Ref. 7.
[b]Relative enzyme activities: +++, very high; ++, high; +, moderate; –, none or very low.
[c]The ss-DNA apparently also formed aps secondary structures such as aps homoduplexes with mismatches.
[d]Similar results were found also with the ps and aps hairpins (2).
[e]Bal 31 and the phenanthroline-copper complex degrade ps-DNA and aps-DNA at approximately the same rate but show preferred cutting sites only with aps-DNA.
[f]No polymerase activity with ps-DNA (4).
[g]Determined with the ps and aps hairpins (2).

into the B-DNA helix (20) with Mg^{2+} and Ca^{2+} as cofactors whereas exonuclease III from *E. coli* degrades the substrate processively by removing nucleotides from both 3′ ends (21).

DNase I and exonuclease III show a very low level of activity with ps-D1* · D2* compared to aps-D1* · D3* and aps-D2*-D4* (Figure 7A lanes 2-5, Figure 7C lanes 2-7). The experiment with DNase I was also performed at 37°C (Figure 7B). At this temperature, the ps duplex should be melted and, as expected, the activity of DNase I with both the ps and the aps substrates is similar. It follows that the difference in cleavage rate observed at 23°C (Figure 7A) reflects the fundamental distinctions in the helical conformations. The observed susceptibility of the single-stranded substrate to both nucleases (Figure 7A, lanes 6 and 7; Figure 7C, lanes 8-10) may be due to a transient aps secondary structure. It has been shown by X-ray studies of the crystallized complex between DNase I and B-DNA that an exposed loop of the enzyme binds in the minor groove of the DNA (22), a finding consistent with the fact that confor-

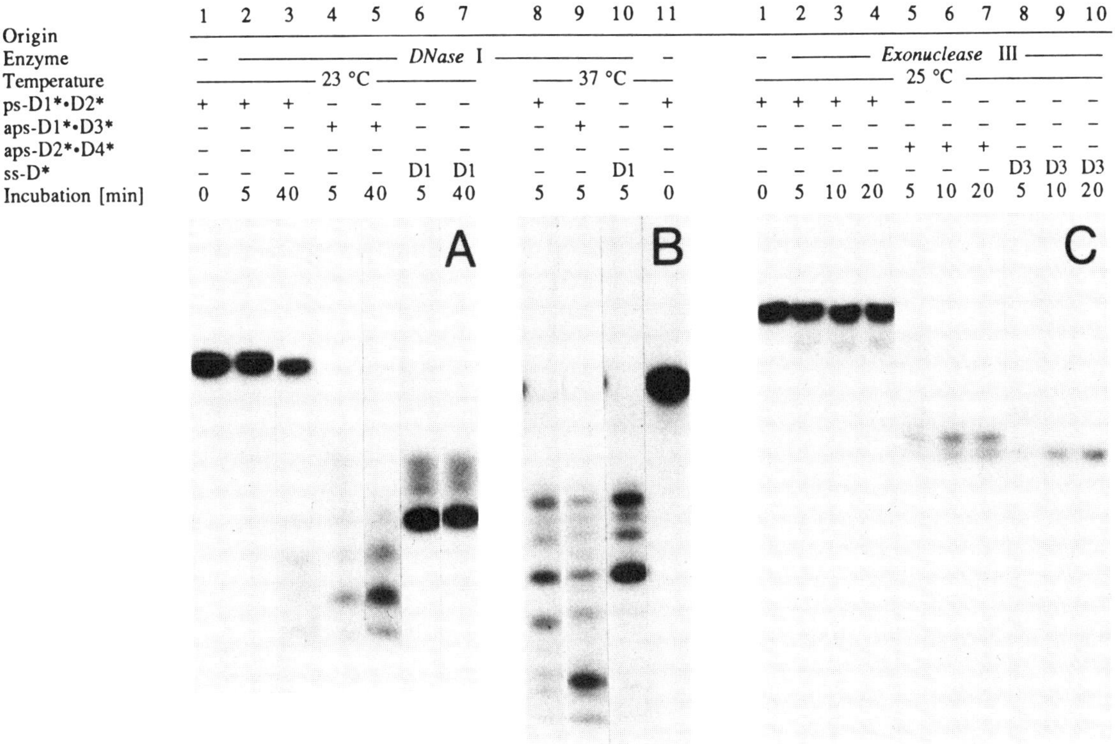

Figure 7: *DNase I and exonuclease III digest of ps-D3 · D4 and aps-D1 · D2.* Data from Ref. 7. (A) DNase I: Incubation of 8 U DNase I/nmol nucleotide and 10 μM DNA in 90 μl restriction buffer at 23°C for given time intervals. 14 μl of each sample were run on a denaturing gel. (B) DNase I: Incubation of 8 U DNase I/nmole nucleotide and 10 μM DNA in 90 μl restriction buffer at 37°C for 5 minutes. 14 μl of each sample were run on a denaturing gel. (C) Exonuclease III: 1.3 U/nmole nucleotide, 10 μM DNA in 100 μl restriction buffer at 25°C for given time intervals. 10 μl of each sample were run on a denaturing gel.

mational changes of the minor groove lower the cleavage rate (23). Thus, the reduced activity of DNase I with ps-DNA could be due to the different groove geometry and disposition of functional groups in the ps helix (Figure 8).

Influence of dG-dC Base Pairs

In order to determine if dG and dC residues could be incorporated into the parallel stranded helix, we synthesized two 25-nt variants of the D-series oligonucleotides designated as D5 and D6, in which 4 dA (D5) or 4 dT (D6) bases were replaced by dG and dC, respectively (Figure 1C). A ps-D5 · D6 duplex forms with characteristic UV absorption and CD contributions that can be ascribed to the dG · dC *trans*-base pair (8). The van't Hoff enthalpy difference ΔH_{vH} for the helix-coil transition of ps-D5 · D6 is reduced by 20% (in NaCl) and 10% (in $MgCl_2$) compared to that of ps-D1 · D2. We calculated that each dG · dC/dA · dT step makes a positive enthalpic contribution to the helical stability of ps DNA that is about half (0.42 in NaCl, 0.66 in $MgCl_2$) that of the dA · dT/dA · dT step.

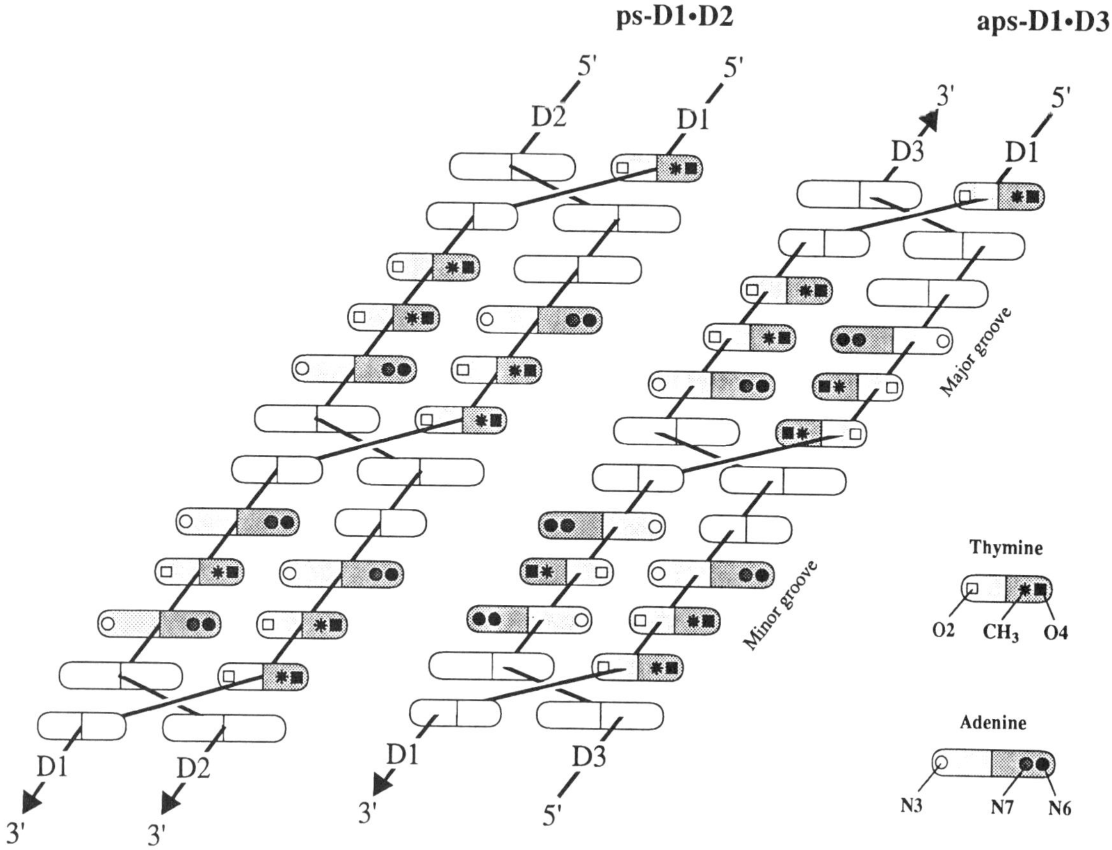

Figure 8: *Schematic view of the last 12 bp at the 3' end of ps-D1 · D2 and aps-D1 · D3 laid out in a cylindrical projection.* The sugar-phosphate backbone is shown as a continouous line with the given polarity. The empty base symbols indicate that the nucleotides in those positions are oriented more or less perpendicular to the image plane. Note that the two grooves of ps-DNA cannot be distinguished a priori. That is, the functional groups of both bases project equally into both grooves. The ps helix is also slightly more extended according to model calculations. Adapted from Ref. 7.

Base Pairing and Model Structure. The model ps-C2 · C3 and aps-C3 · C7 duplexes in Figure 9 were constructed from the stems of the hairpin structures as described in Refs. 2,3. The characteristic features of ps-DNA perceived in Figure 9 are: (i) parallel polarity of the two strands, (ii) equivalence of the grooves, and (iii) *trans*-Crick-Watson (*reverse* Watson-Crick) base-pairing. The helical twist is comparable to that of the aps helix, but the helical rise is approximately 3% greater. Models for ps-DNA incorporating dG · dC base pairs are presented elsewhere (8).

Concluding Remarks

Next to B-DNA, ps-DNA is the most stable double helical DNA conformation described to date and can exist readily under physiological conditions, given an appropriate sequence complementarity. We note, however, a fundamental distinction between the equilibria characteristic of isomerization reactions, such as in the B-Z transition (13,14) and those which would involve ps-DNA. One would presume that the latter structure would arise most readily in the course of recombination or exchange reactions; i.e., involving interactions between *separated* segments of DNA (or RNA). For example, the model duplexes discussed in this report (Figure 1C) can formally exchange according to the reaction

$$\text{aps-D1} \cdot \text{D3} + \text{aps-D2} \cdot \text{D4} \leftrightarrow \text{ps-D1} \cdot \text{D2} + \text{ps-D3} \cdot \text{D4}.$$

As discussed in the section on drug binding, environmental conditions (salt, temperature) and the presence of selective ligands would determine the distribution of species. The demonstration that dG · dC base pairs are also compatible with the ps helix (8) extends the potential for this alternative conformation in the case of natural sequences. We have identified elsewhere (3) four canonical situations in which the sequence relationships would comply with the requirements for ps-DNA, the simplest of which involves circularization of single stranded DNA or RNA. Although experimental data for RNA constructs are not yet available, model calculations indicate no obvious stereochemical hindrances. Clearly, secondary and tertiary interactions in rRNA, tRNA, transcripts, and in viruses with a single stranded genome are suitable circumstances in which the parallel stranded helical orientation could provide additional stabilization or specificity, particularly if proteins intervene. In fact, single *trans* base pairs are observed in tRNA crystal structures (24,25).

Acknowledgments

We thank Gudrun Heim for technical assistance. One of us (T. M. J.) is indebted to N. Pattabiraman for drawing his attention to ps-DNA in 1985.

References and Footnotes

1. Pattabiraman, N., *Biopolymers 25*, 1603-1606 (1986).
2. van de Sande, J.H., Ramsing, N.B., Germann, M.W., Elhorst, W., Kalisch, B.W., von Kitzing, E., Pon, R.T., Clegg, R.M. and Jovin, T.M., *Science 241*, 551-557 (1988).
3. Ramsing, N.B. and Jovin, T.M., *Nucleic Acids Res. 16*, 6659-6676 (1988).
4. Germann, M.W., Kalish B.W. and van de Sande, J.H., *Biochemistry 27*, 8302-8306 (1988).
5. Rippe, K., Ramsing, N.B. and Jovin, T.M., *Biochemistry*, in press (1989).
6. Ramsing, N.B., Rippe, K. and Jovin, T.M., *Biochemistry*, in press (1989).
7. Rippe, K. and Jovin, T.M., *Biochemistry*, in press (1989).
8. Rippe, K., Ramsing, N.B., Klement, R. and Jovin, T.M., submitted (1989).
9. Gorenstein, D.G., Schroeder, S.A., Fu, J.M., Metz, J.T., Roongta, V. and Jones, C.R., *Biochemistry 27*, 7223-7237 (1988).
10. Teng, M., Usman, N., Frederick, C.A. and Wang, A.H.-J., *Nucleic Acids Res. 16*, 2671-2690 (1988).
11. Pjura, P.E., Grzeskowiak, K. and Dickerson, R.E., *J. Mol. Biol. 197*, 257- 271 (1987).
12. Larsen,T.A., Goodsell, D.S., Cascio, D., Grzeskowiak, K. and Dickerson, R.E., in *J. Biomol. Struct. Dyn. 7*, 477-491 (1989).
13. Jovin, T.M., McIntosh, L.P., Arndt -Jovin, D.J., Zarling, D.A., Robert-Nicoud, M., van de Sande, J.H., Jorgensen, K.F. and Eckstein, F., *J. Biomol. Struct Dynam. 1*, 21-57.
14. Jovin, T.M., Soumpasis, D.M. and McIntosh, L.P., *Ann. Rev. Phys. Chem. 38*, 521-560 (1987).
15. Pohl, F.M., Jovin, T.M., Baehr, W. and Holbrook, J.J., *Proc. Natl. Acad. Sci. USA 69*, 3805-3809 (1972).
16. Stryer, A., *Ann. Rev. Biochem. 47*, 819-846 (1978).

17. Cardullo, R.A., Agrawal, S., Flores, C., Zamecnik, P.C. and Wolf, D.E., *Proc. Natl. Acad. Sci. USA 85*, 8790-8794 (1988).
18. Duckett, D.R., Murchie, A.I.H., Clegg, R.M., von Kitzing, E., Diekmann, S. and Lilley, D.M.J., *Structure & Methods, Volume 1: Human Genome Initiative & DNA Recombination*, (Eds., R.H. Sarma and M.H. Sarma) Adenine Press (1990).
19. Chan, S.S., Arndt-Jovin, D.J. and Jovin, T.M., *J. Histochem Cytochem. 27*, 56-54 (1979).
20. Campbell, V.W. and Jackson, D.A., *J. Biol. Chem. 255*, 3726-3735 (1980).
21. Wu, C., *Nature 317*, 84-87 (1985).
22. Suck, D., Lahm, A. and Oefner, C., *Nature 332*, 464-468 (1988).
23. Drew, H.R. and Travers, A.A., *Nucleic Acids Res. 13*, 4445-4467 (1985).
24. Kim, S.H., Sussman, J.L., Suddath, F.L., Quigley, G.J., McPherson, A., Wang, A.H.J., Seeman, N.C. and Rich, A., *Proc. Natl. Acad. Sci. USA 71*, 4970-4974 (1974).
25. Westhof, E. Dumas, P. and Moras, D., *J. Mol. Biol. 184*, 119-145 (1985).
26. Klement, R., Soumpasis, D.M. and Jovin, T.M., *Biopolymers*, in press.

Structure & Methods, ISBN 0-940030-32-2
Volume 3: DNA & RNA, ISBN 0-940030-31-4
Eds., Ramaswamy H. Sarma & Mukti H. Sarma, © *Adenine Press 1990*

Telomeric Sequence Under Superhelical Stress and Low pH: a Novel DNA Structure with Non-Watson-Crick Pairing

V.I. Lyamichev[1], S.M. Mirkin[1], O.N. Danilevskaya[1], O.N. Voloshin[2], S.V. Balatskaya[2], V.N. Dobrynin[2], S.A. Filippov[2] and M.D. Frank-Kamenetskii[1]

[1]Institute of Molecular Genetics
USSR Academy of Sciences
Moscow 123182, USSR

[2]M.M. Shemyakin Institute of Bioorganic Chemistry
USSR Academy of Sciences
Moscow, USSR

Abstract

We have inserted into a plasmid the *Tetrahymena* telomeric motif $(G_4T_2) \cdot (A_2C_4)$ and probed it by two-dimensional gel electrophoresis, chemical modification and oligonucleotide binding. Our data indicate that the insert adopts, under superhelical stress and low pH, a novel DNA conformation, the (C,A)-hairpin. In this structure the two strands form independent hairpins stabilized primarily by non-Watson-Crick protonated base pairs $C \cdot C^+$ and $A \cdot A^+$.

Introduction

The functioning of DNA inside the cell involves supercoiling. This has become especially clear after the recent discovery by Wang and co-workers of trancriptional waves of supercoiling (1-3) which create very high local superhelicity, both positive and negative. These findings indicate that any DNA structure formed under superhelical stress may prove to be physiologically significant.

During the past decade three types of non-canonical (other than the Watson-Crick B form) structures were shown to be induced by negative supercoiling. They are the cruciform, the left-handed Z form and the triplex H form. In contrast with the B form which is adopted by an arbitrary DNA sequence, all alternative structures exhibit a sequence preference. Thus, cruciforms are formed in invertedly repreated sequences (4-6), the Z form is adopted preferentially by alternating purine-pyrimidine sequences (7) and the H form is inherent in homopurine-homopyrimidine palindromic sequences (8-11).

Telomeric sequences have been attracting a great deal of attention as potential sites for an unusual DNA structure. They consist of the (G_nT_m) (or (G_nAT_m)) motif $(n \geqslant m)$ and, in the single-stranded state, were shown to form hairpins stabilized by the non-canonical $G \cdot G$ pairs (12). In the duplex state, they show S1 hypersensitivity under superhelical stress (13). This may suggest the formation of an unusual structure, as is the case for the homopurine-homopyrimidine sequences (14-16). To check whether the telomerica sequences actually form an unusual structure, we have inserted into a plasmid the *Tetrahymena* telomeric motif $({}_4T_2) \cdot (A_2C_4)$ and probed it by two-dimensional gel electrophoresis, chemical modification and oligonucleotide binding. Our data demonstrate that the insert adopts under superhelical stress and low pH a novel DNA conformation. We have concluded that in this structure the two strands form independent hairpins stabilized, though not to the same extent, by non-Watson-Crick base pairs $C \cdot C^+$, $T \cdot T$, $G \cdot G$ and $A \cdot A^+$. We term this new DNA structure the (C,A)-hairpin.

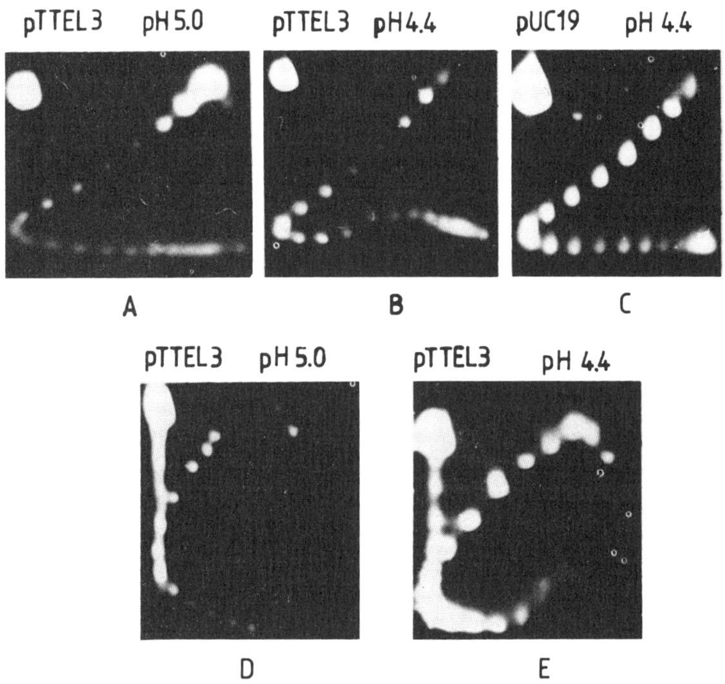

Figure 1: 2-D agarose gel electrophoresis of the PTTEL3 plasmid (A,B,D,E) carrying the insert 5'-$G_3(T_2G_4)_7G_3(T_2G_4)_9$ and the vector pUC19 plasmid (C). Separation in the first direction (top to bottom) was in a sodium citrate buffer (40 mM sodium), pH 5.0 (A and D) or 4.4 (B,C and E), electric field strength 1.5 V/cm, gel temperature 10°C (A,B,C) or 30°C (D,E), 24 hours. In the second direction (from left to right) the TAE buffer (40 mM Tris-acetate, pH 8.0, 1 mM EDTA) was used and 1.7 µg of chloroquine was added to relax superhelical stress. Note that although the patterns at 10 and 30° qualitatively agree with each other, there is a distinct and reproducible difference between them. Namely, for an unclear reason, the pattern at 10° exhibits a plateau after the mobility drop, which is not observed at 30°.

2-D Gel Electrophoresis

Figure 1 shows the 2-D gel electorphoresis patterns for our plasmid pTTEL3, carrying the insert 5′-$G_3(T_2G_4))_7G_3(T_2G_4)_9$. One can see at pH 4.4 a characteristic discontinuity, which indicates that a structural transition takes place in the plasmid carrying the insert whereas the vector plasmid without the insert shows no such thing. The total superhelical release we observe is about 9 superhelical turns, which indicates that almost the whole 102 bp-long insert forms an unusual structure and that in this structure the two complementary strands are not interwound. This conclusion is additionally confirmed by chemical modification experiments (see below). The transition is strongly pH-dependent. Figure 1 shows that, while the formation of an alternative structure is clearly seen at pH 4.4, no transition is observed at pH 5.0.

Thus, the insert under study exhibits a strongly pH-dependent structural transition, which is similar to the transition inherent in homopurine-homopyrimidine palindromes (8,9,16,17). Does this mean that the alternative structure we observe in our pTTEL3 plasmid is the triplex H form? It is doubtful because the sequence under study deviates too much from the homopurine-homopyrimidine pattern, and even isolated nucleotide substitutions are known to seriously inhibit the formation of the triplex H form (9).

Chemical Probing

The most convincing evidence of the triplex H form in homopurine-homopyrimidine palindromes has been obtained by chemical probing (10,11,18-22). Therefore we applied this method to our pTTEL3 plasmid. To this end we used diethyl pyrocarbonate (DEP), dimethylsulphate (DMS), osmium tetroxide (OT) and potassium permanganate (PP). The results are shown in Figure 2. The pattern of modification here is significantly different from that of the triplex H form. Indeed, in contrast to the case of the H form (10,11,18-22), in the present case all chemical probes show symmetrical modfification patterns (within the insert) for both strands. However, the two strands are modified quite differently. The modification of the G-rich strand is almost uniform throughout the insert. At pH 4.2 all the thymines in the insert are accessible to reactions with both OT and PP, and there is no protection of quanines against the reaction with DMS. These data indicate that the bases of the G-rich strand are virtually unpaired within the structure under study.

By contrast, only the central part of the C-rich strand of the insert is heavily modified at pH 4.2. In addition to the central part, a distinct modification of the 3′-end-flanking region of the C-rich strand is also observed. Our chemical probing data confirm that the structure under study is stabilized by low pH (see Figure 2).

The Model

Thus, our data do not fit the triplex H form, though they do unambiguously indicate that the new structure is also stabilized by protons. What is it? We believe that our data are most consistent with the structure in which the two strands form independent

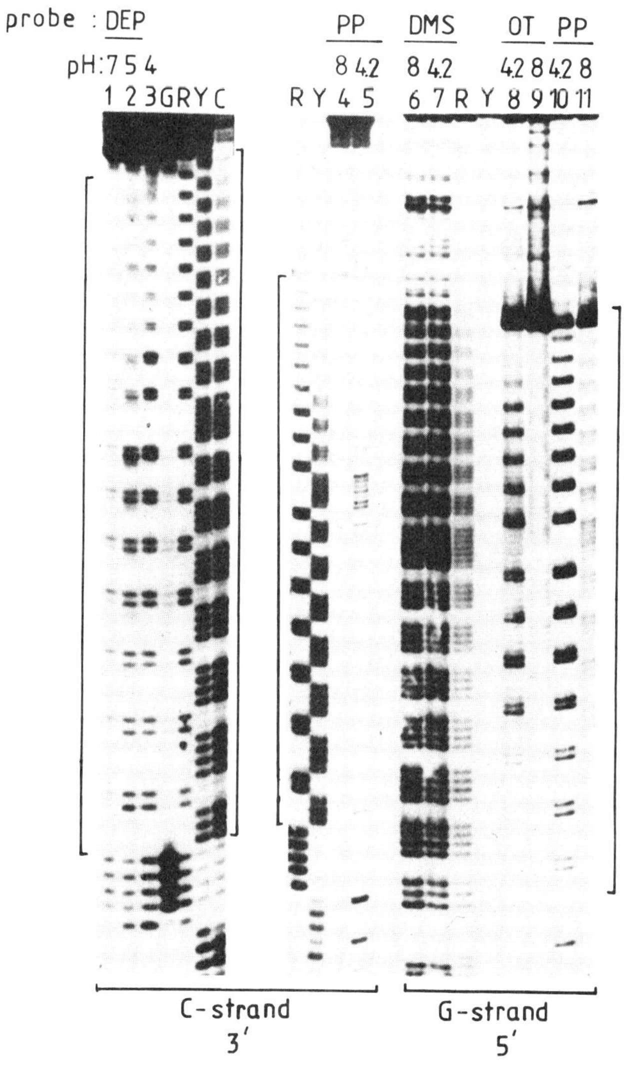

Figure 2: The chemical probing of the $G_3(T_2G_4)_7G_3(T_2G_4)_9$ insert (indicated by brackets) within the pTTEL3 plasmid. For the C-strand the 5′-end is at the top, whereas for the G-strand it is at the bottom. Lanes R, Y, C and G are strandard Maxiam-Gilbert probes for purines, pyrimidines, cytosines and guanines respectively. Lanes 1, 2 and 3 show results for diethyl pyrocarbonate (DEP) at pH 7.0, 5.0 and 4.0 respectively. Lanes 4, 5, 10 and 11 show results for potassium permanganate (PP) at pH 4.2 (lanes 5, 10) and 8.0 (lanes 4, 11). Lanes 6 and 7 show results for dimethylsulphate (DMS) at pH 8.0 and 4.2. Lanes 8 and 9 show results for osmium tetroxide (OT) at pH 4.2 and 8.0.

hairpins with non-canonical base pairing. Specifically, the C-rich hairpin is stabilized by the protonated $C \cdot C^+$ base pairs and this explains why the structure is strongly pH-dependent. We term our structure the (C,A)-hairpin (Figure 3).

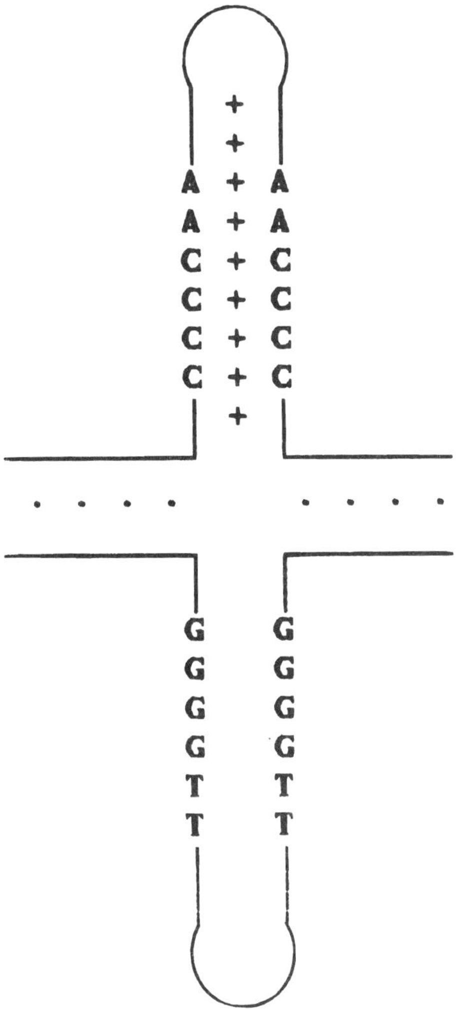

Figure 3: The proposed model of the (C,A)-hairpin. The structure is stabilized by the $C \cdot C^+$ and $A \cdot A^+$ base pairs (see Figure 4). Our data indicate that the G-rich strand is virtually unstructured.

Note that this model is strikingly similar to our original model for the structure of homopurine-homopyrimidine sequences (16). However, we found it inadequate for homopurine-homopyrimidine sequences and arrived at the triplex H model (8), which was shown to be inherent in homopurine-homopyrimidine palindromes (H-palindromes) under superhelical stress and acid pH (9-11,17-22).

Non-Watson-Crick Base Pairing

The (C,A)-hairpin is stabilized primarily by the $C \cdot C^+$ base pairs. Such pairs may be formed between both parallel and antiparallel strands (Figure 4) under acid conditions (23). The results of modification by DEP also suggest the formation of $A \cdot A$ base pairs. Although several protonated pairing schemes of $A \cdot A^+$ base pairs were proposed (see 24), we could not find in the literature an $A \cdot A^+$ pair isomorphous to the $C \cdot C^+$ pair. Such an isomorphous $A \cdot A$ pair proposed by us is shown in Figure 4. We assume that protonation of the N1 site, which is not involved in the hydrogen bonding, in one adenine would stabilize the pair by favouring the formation of a hydrogen bond between C8 of the same adenine and N1 of the other one.

The detailed pairing scheme for the C-rich strand, which is consistent with our chemical modification data and 2-D gel electrophoresis, is as follows:

$$\begin{array}{ll} & \text{A-A-}(C_4A_2)_7\text{-C-5}' \\ \text{C} & \quad\;\; + + \quad + \\ & \text{C-C-}(C_4A_2)_7\text{-}C_3\text{-3}' \end{array}$$

The three cental A_2 sites are the most DEP-accessible in the structure (Figure 2, lane 3). All other A_2 sites are also reactive. This agrees with the pairing scheme for $A \cdot A^+$ shown in Figure 4, in which one of the two N7 positions in the pair may be accessible to modification. Indeed, it is known that, in contrast with B-DNA, in Z-DNA the

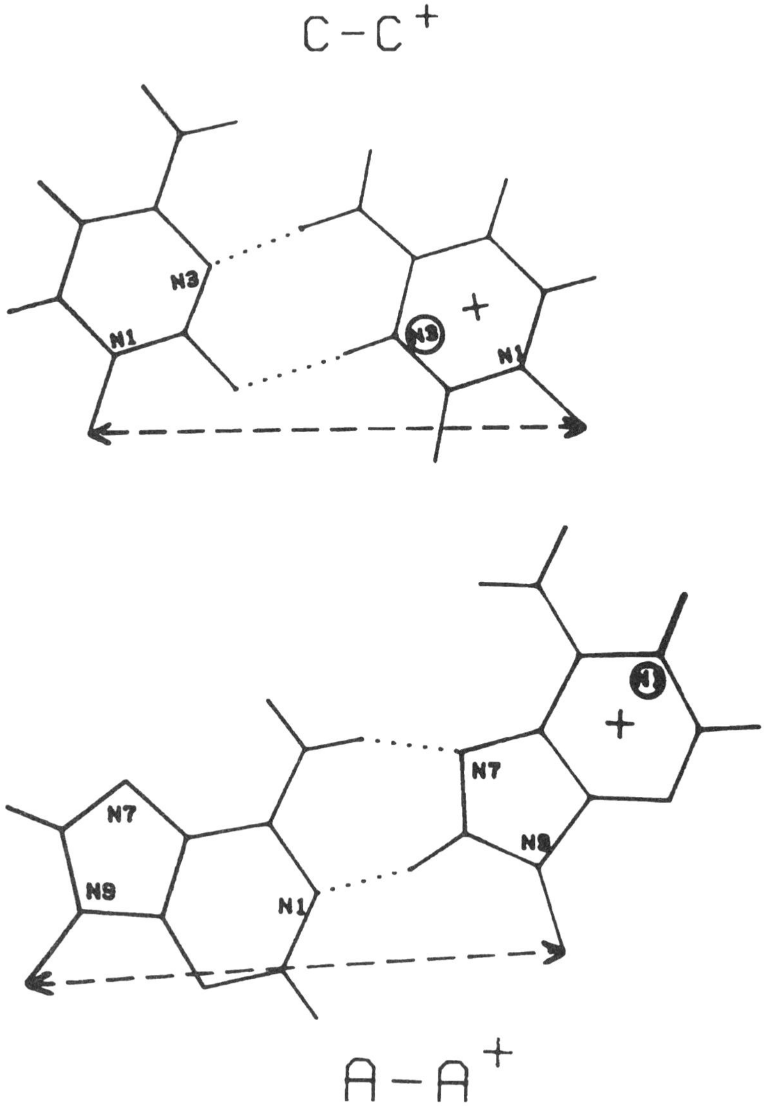

Figure 4: Protonated C · C$^+$ and A · A$^+$ base pairs. The protonation sites are encircled. The hydrogen bond is assumed between C8 of protonated adenine and N1 of unprotonated one. The distances between glycosyl bonds (shown by arrows) in the two pairs are almost equal.

adenine N7 position is accessible to DEP (25-27). One can see in Figure 2, lane 3, that four guanines and one adenine in the 3′-flanking region are also modified by DEP. This may be explained in terms of stable or transient unwinding of the duplex from its open end under superhelical stress. A similar effect is observed in the case of chemical modification by DEP of the H form (10,19,21,22).

Chemical probing did not reveal any structure in the G-rich strand. This is unexpected since Henderson *et al.* (12) demonstrated the formation of antiparallel G · G base pairs in single-stranded telomeric sequences. One explanation for this disagreement is the the G · G base pairs are destabilized under mildly acid conditions.

Oligonucleotide Binding

The asymmetry of the two strands in the (C,A)-hairpin was additionally tested in a series of experiments on the compiexing of the $C_3A_2C_4A_2C$ (C-rich) and $(G_4T_2)_2$ (G-rich) oligonucleotides with our plasmid pTTEL3 DNA. If our model in Figure 3 is correct, we should observe the uptake of the oligonucleotide that is complementary to the G-rich strand ($C_3A_2C_4A_2C$) but not to the C-rich strnad ($(G_4T_2)_2$). Figure 5

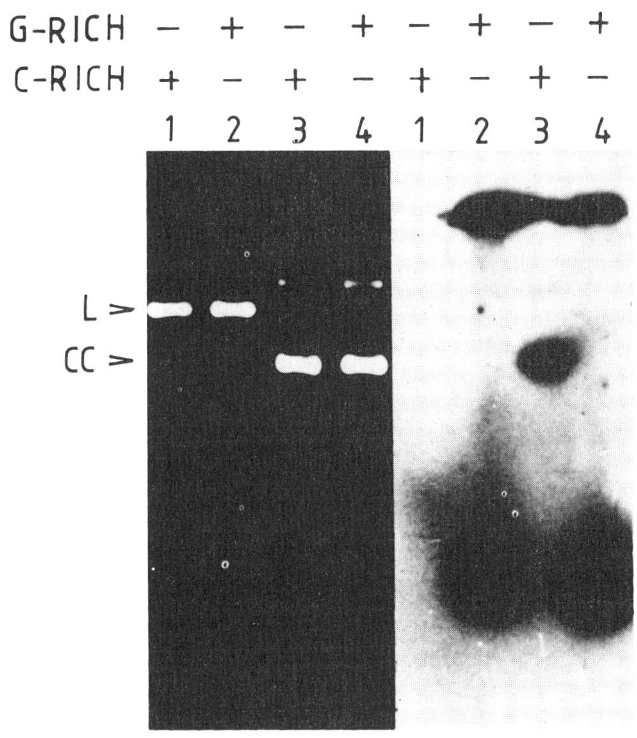

Figure 5: Agarose gel electrophoresis of linear (lanes 1,2) and supercoiled (lanes 3,4) plasmid pTTEL3 DNA. The samples were preincubated for 6 hours in the Na-citrate buffer (100 mM of Na^+, pH 4.5) with deoxyoligonucleotides 5′-CCCAACCCCAAC (C-rich, lanes 1,3) and 5′-GGGGTTGGGGTT (G-rich, lanes 2,4), γ-^{32}P-ATP-labelled by polynucleotidekinase of phage T4. The C-rich oligonucleotide concentration was about 0.5 μg/ml, DNa was in an approximately equimolar concentration. The G-rich oligonucleotide concentration was several times larger. Electrophoresis was performed in 2% agarose gel, 100 mM of Na-citrate buffer (100 mM of Na^+, pH 4.5), electric field strength 1.2 V/cm, gel temperature 10°C, 15 hours. Linear and closed circular DNA are labelled L and CC respectively. Panel A, ethidium stained gel. Panel B, autoradiograph of the gel in panel A. The upper hand in lanes 3,4 in panel A most probably contains closed circular dimers of the pTTEL3 plasmid.

shows the results. Neither oligonucleotide binds to non-superhelical DNA. However, $C_3A_2C_4A_2C$ forms a complex with superhelical DNA at low pH, revealed as a strong band in lane 3 in Figure 5B. This band was not observed at pH 8 (Figure 6). In the case of $(G_4T_2)_2$ no trace of radioactivity was observed to move with DNA at either pH 4.5 or pH 8 (Figure 5B, lane 4, Figure 6B, lane 4), even though there was an excess of the G-rich oligonucleotide as compared with the C-rich oligonucleotide (compare lanes 1 and 2 in Figure 5B). These data strongly support our model ofthe (C,A)-hairpin with a stable C-rich strand and a virtually unstructured G-rich strand.

The data in Figure 5 are quite different from the behaviour we observed when complexing homopurine and homopyrimidine oligonucleotides with a plasmid that carried the homopurine-homopyrimidine insert (28). Complexing with the single-stranded part of the H form was masked by a strong binding of the pyrimidine oligonucleotide to the double helix, which was interpreted as triplex formation. In

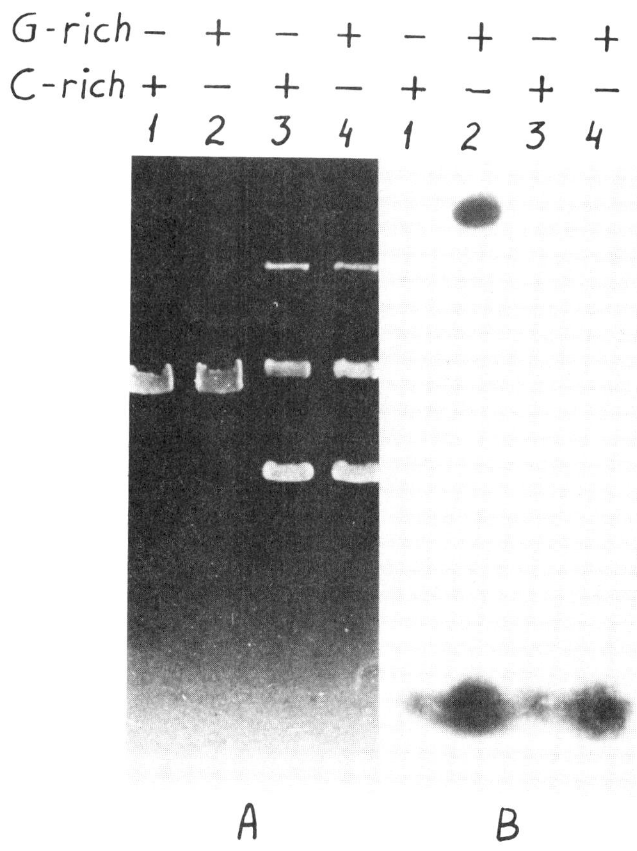

Figure 6: The same as in Figure 5, but the oligonucleotides were preincubated in the TES buffer (100 mM NaCl, 10 mM Tris-HCl, pH 8.0, 1 mM EDTA). Electrophoresis was performed in the buffer: 100 mM Na-acetate, 20 mM Tris-HCl, pH 8.0, 1 mM EDTA. The other conditions are the same as in Figure 5.

our present experiments we observe no oligonucleotide binding to the double helix, and this directly shows that the telomeric sequences are unable to form triplexes. The absence of masking binding made it possible to demonstrate a distinct binding of the $C_3A_2C_4A_2C$ oligonucleotide to the complementary unstructured G-rich strand of the insert in the (C,A)-hairpin state. As was discussed at length in (28), our method makes it possible to observe only very strong, effectively irreversible binding. Estimations based on the equations in (28) show that the lifetime of the duplex state for the oligonucleotides used in the present study and under our ambient conditions is large enough.

We did not observe any binding of the $(G_4T_2)_2$ molecules to the single-stranded G-rich part of the (C,A)-hairpin, though one could expect them to form parallel four-stranded complexes as described in (29). Again, a possible explanation could be the destabilizing effect of low pH on the G_4 tetrads. One should also bear in mind that in our experiments the oligonucleotide concentration was about 100 times lower than in (29). Thus, our conditions were extremely unfavourable for a multistranded complex.

Discussion

We have demonstrated that the sequence under study adopts, under superhelical stress and acid pH, an unusual conformation. Our data are most consistent with the model in Figure 3. However, other possibilities cannot be excluded at the moment. Specifically, we cannot completely exclude the possibility of formation of the triplex H form by our insert which carries, along with the canonical TAT and CGC^+ triads, non-canonical base-triads, such as CGA and ATC.

It follows from our model in Figure 3 that the sequence requirement for the (C,A)-hairpin is a poly(A,C) · poly(G,T) mirror repeat (we call it an (A,C)-palindrome). This remains to be tested in experiments similar to the ones in (9), which demonstrated the H palindrome to be the sequence requirement for the H form.

Is it accidental that telomers have (A,C)-palindromic sequences which can adopt the (C,A)-hairpin structure under superhelical stress? At the ends of chromosomes telomeric sequences exist predominantly in the single-stranded state. However, similar sequences were found inside chromosomes (30,31). The ability of sequences to adopt the (C,A)-hairpin structure may prove to be of some biological significance.

Acknowledgments

We thank A.S. Borovik, S.A. Grachev, V.I. Ivanov, Y.S. Lazurkin, V.G. Nikiforov, A. Rich, I.Y. Skuratovskii, E.D. Sverdlov and A.V. Vologodskii for discussions.

References and Footnotes

1. L.F. Liu and J.C. Wang, *Proc. Natl. Acad. Sci. USA 84*, 7024-7027 (1987).
2. H.-Y. Wu, S. Shyy, J.C. Wang and L.F. Liu, *Cell 53*, 433-440 (1988).
3. G.N. Giaever and J.C. Wang, *Cell 55*, 849-856 (1988).

4. M. Gellert *et al.*, *Cold Spring Harbor Symp. Quant. Biol. 43*, 35-40 (1979).
5. D.M.J. Lilley, *Proc. Natl. Acad. Sci. USA 77*, 6468-6472 (1980).
6. N. Panayotatos and R.D. Wells, *Nature 289*, 466-470 (1981).
7. A. Rich, A. Nordheim and A.H.-J. Wang, *Ann. Rev. Biochem. 53*, 791-846 (1984).
8. V.I. Lyamichev, S.M. Mirkin and M.D. Frank-Kamenetskii, *J. Biomol. Struct. Dyn. 3*, 667-669 (1986).
9. S.M. Mirkin *et al.*, *Nature 330*, 495-497 (1987).
10. O.N. Voloshin *et al.*, *Nature 333*, 475-476 (1988).
11. J.C. Hanvey, M. Shimizu and R.D. Wells, *Proc. Natl. Acad. Sci. USA 85*, 6292-6296) (1988).
12. E. Henderson *et al.*, *Cell 51*, 899-908 (1987).
13. M. Budarf and E. Blackburn, *Nucl. Acids Res. 15*, 6273-6292 (1987).
14. C.C. Hentschel, *Nature 295*, 714-716 (1982).
15. A. Larsen and H. Weintraub, *Cell 29*, 609-622 (1982).
16. V.I. Lyamichev, S.M. Mirkin and M.D. Frank-Kamenetskii, *J. Biomol. Struct. Dyn. 3*, 327-338 (1985).
17. V.I. Lyamichev, S.M. Mirkin and M.D. Frank-Kamenetskii, *J. Biomol. Struct. Dyn. 5*, 275-282 (1987).
18. J.C. Hanvey, J. Klysik and R.D. Wells, *J. Biol. Chem. 263*, 7386-7396 (1988).
19. Y. Kohwi and T. Kohwi-Shigematsu, *Proc. Natl. Acad. Sci. USA 85*, 3781-3785 (1988).
20. M. Vojtiskova *et al.*, *FEBS Lett. 234*, 295-299 (1988).
21. H. Htun and J.E. Dahlberg, *Science 241*, 1791-1796 (1988).
22. B. Johnston, *Science 241*, 1800-1804 (1988).
23. D.M. Gray, R.L. Ratliff, V.P. Antao and C.W. Gray, in *Structure & Expression, Vol. 2: DNA and Its Drug Complexes*, (Eds., R.H. Sarma and M.D. Sarma) Adenine Press, NY, 147-166 (1987).
24. C.R. Cantor and P.R. Schimmel, *Biophysical Chemistry,* Freeman, San Francisco, CA (1980).
25. B. Johnston and A. Rich, *Cell 42*, 713-724 (1985).
26. W. Herr, *Proc. Natl. Acad. Sci. USA 82*, 8009-8013 (1985).
27. B. Johnston, *J. Biomol. Struct. Dyn. 6*, 153-166 (1988).
28. V.I. Lyamichev, S.M. Mirkin, M.D. Frank-Kamenetskii and C.R. Cantor, *Nucl. Acids Res. 16*, 2165-2178 (1988).
29. D. Sen and W. Gilbert, *Nature 334*, 364-366 (1988).
30. M.-Ch. Yao, E.H. Blackburn and J. Gall, *J. Cell Biol. 90*, 515-520 (1981).
31. J.M. Cherry and E.H. Blackburn, *Cell 43*, 747-758 (1985).

Structure & Methods, ISBN 0-940030-32-2
Volume 3: DNA & RNA, ISBN 0-940030-31-4
Eds., Ramaswamy H. Sarma & Mukti H. Sarma, © Adenine Press 1990

The Structure and Formation of Triple-Stranded H-DNA

Han Htun and James E. Dahlberg
Department of Physiological Chemistry
University of Wisconsin-Madison
1300 University Avenue
Madison, WI 53706

Abstract

Under negative torsional stress or low pH, polypyrimidine-polypurine sequences, such as $(dT\text{-}dC)_n$:$(dA\text{-}dG)_n$, can assume an H-DNA conformation, which contains single-stranded and triple-stranded regions and makes a flexible kink, termed a hinge. Formation of H-DNA is affected by a number of factors, including copolymeric length, pH, salt, and level of negative supercoiling. Once formed, an H-DNA structure may be 'trapped' in a local energy minimum, so the initial nucleation event is important in determining the actual H-DNA conformer observed. A comprehensive model for H-DNA formation is presented, and a standard nomenclature is proposed for describing the various H-DNA conformers. Our model for the formation of H-DNA explains why increasing negative torsional stress promotes the use of the 3′ half of the donated strand when that strand lies within the major groove of a right-handed acceptor helix.

Introduction

Polypyrimidine-polypurine sequences can adopt a number of unorthodox DNA conformations. Synthetic copolymer studies have shown that these sequences can form self-paired polypyrimidine structures (2-7), self-paired polypurine structures (7-12), triple-stranded structures (4,7,13-32), and four-stranded structures (7,12,33-39; also see Saenger 40). In addition, theoretical and stereochemical considerations have led to the suggestion that in the double-stranded state, these sequences may exist not only in the standard right-handed DNA conformations (40,41) but also in a variety of underwound conformations (42-46).

When present within negatively supercoiled molecules, polypyrimidine-polypurine sequences exhibit unusual sensitivity to digestion by single-strand-specific nucleases, such as nuclease S1 (reviewed in 44,47 and 48). The structure responsible for this sensitivity has been controversial. In spite of its specificity for single-stranded over double-stranded nucleic acid (49), nuclease S1 is thought to recognize the phosphodiester backbone conformation rather than the unpaired base (50-52). As such, cleavage does not necessarily imply single-strandedness (42-44,52-56). In addition, base-specific chemical reagents, such as osmium tetroxide, hydroxylamine, diethyl pyrocarbonate, and chloracetylaldehyde, which have been used to probe the nuclease

S1-sensitive structure, have not resolved the controversy, since these 'single-strand-selective' reagents can also react with certain double-stranded DNA conformations (57-61; reviewed in ref. 62). Thus, numerous models have been proposed for the nuclease S1-sensitive structure at polypyrimidine-polypurine sequences (27,42-45,52-55,63-73).

One model that has gained widest acceptance as the basis for the nuclease S1-sensitivity of $(TC \cdot AG)_n$ sequences and other palindromic polypyrimidine-polypurine sequences is the triple-stranded and single-stranded structure, first proposed by Lee and Morgan in 1984 (27) and modified to a form called H-DNA (68) by Frank-Kamenetskii and co-workers in 1986 (69). In this structure, half of the Watson-Crick duplex is disrupted and the released polypyrimidine strand is folded back, enabling it to progress down the major groove of the other half of the repeat. This third strand, designated the donated strand, associates with purines in the helical half of the repeat (the acceptor region) by Hoogsteen base pairs, forming dT-dA · dT and dC-dG · dC^+ base triplets. The single strand at the 'fold-back' tip and the displaced polypurine strand would render $(TC \cdot AG)_n$ sequences and other palindromic polypyrimidine-polypurine sequences in the H-DNA conformation susceptible to digestion by single-strand-specific nucleases.

A large body of evidence has been advanced in support of the triple-stranded H-DNA model (48,67,69-72,74-86). While these observations establish the presence of a 'fold-back' structure (particularly, ref. 48,65,75,80 and 83), they do not distinguish between structures containing triple and single strands from those containing self-paired polypyrimidine and self-paired polypurine strands (67-77,79-86). These latter structures are formal possibilities and cannot be ruled out, since the chemical nature of these self-pairs have not been fully determined (2-12) and numerous unusual types of interactions continue to be reported (87-91). Another recently mentioned formal possibility is a fold-back, four-stranded structure (71,73; see ref. 92 for an illustration of one such model).

We found that polypyrimidine-polypurine sequences are the site of nuclease S1 sensitivity in the genes of three small nuclear RNA multigene families: those for human U1 RNA (65), human U2 RNA (93), and *Xenopus laevis* embryonic U1 RNA genes (94). Subsequently, we proceeded to solve the structure responsible for the nuclease S1 sensitivity of one of these sequences: the $(dT\text{-}dC)_n$:$(dA\text{-}dG)_n$ sequences (48,78), abbreviated as $(TC \cdot AG)_n$ associated with the human U1 and U2 RNA genes.

Using two dimensional gel electrophoresis of DNA topoisomers, we found, in mid-1985, that at any one linking number a $(TC \cdot AG)_{18}$ copolymer could rearrange at pH 5 to yield two distinct topoisomeric forms, which do not interconvert (95). We then observed that longer copolymers could rearrange to yield multiple topoisomeric forms. The multiplicity and non-interconvertibility of topologically distinct (and hence energetically non-equivalent) structures show that several metastable forms can be 'trapped' in a local energy minimum. A range of locations within a $(TC \cdot AG)_n$ sequence could serve as the 'fold-back' point, which would determine the number of (TC · AG) repeats in the 'fold-back' structure (by defining the registry of the intra-copolymeric interaction) as well as the number of negative supercoils relaxed. The metastability of individual structures resulted from the presence of a highly energetically favorable triple-stranded DNA structure (see section on energetics, below).

The structure responsible for the nuclease S1 sensitivity of $(TC \cdot AG)_n$ sequences is called H-DNA (96). To facilitate the description of the various H-DNA structures formed at these and other palindromic polypyrimidine-polypurine sequences, a standard nomenclature is proposed (48). Our model for the formation of H-DNA explains why at levels of negative supercoiling equivalent to 0.05 or greater (i.e., 'bacterial' levels), the donated 'third' strand is derived from the 3′ half of the polypyrimidine (e.g., in the case of $(TC \cdot AG)_n$) or polypurine (e.g., in the case of $(C \cdot G)_n$) strand (48).

Demonstration of Single-Stranded Regions

Initially, we showed that a $(TC \cdot AG)_{18}$ sequence located 1.8 kilo-base pairs downstream of a human U1 RNA gene is unusually sensitive to digestion by single-strand-specific nuclease S1 (65). Nuclease S1 cleaved the $(TC)_{18}$ sequence near its center, to give a unimodal distribution of cleavage products, and it cleaved the $(AG)_{18}$ sequence on either side of its center to give a bimodal distribution of cleavage products. To determine whether nuclease S1 sensitivity was a result of single-stranded regions within the $(TC \cdot AG)_{18}$ sequence, the nuclease S1-sensitive structure was examined for its ability to hybridize to complementary single-stranded nucleic acids and probed with chemical reagents that react with exposed bases (78).

Incubation of negatively supercoiled molecules containing the nuclease sensitive $(TC \cdot AG)_{18}$ structure with single-stranded $(TC)_{18}$ sequence, cloned into circular M13 phage DNA, resulted in the formation of 1:1 complexes between the double-stranded and single-stranded molecules (Figure 1A). Complexes were not observed when the M13 DNA contained the complementary $(AG)_{18}$ sequence in place of the $(TC)_{18}$ sequence, or when the negatively supercoiled DNA contained a shorter $(TC \cdot AG)_5$ sequence, which does not form a nuclease S1-sensitive structure (78,95; data not shown). The specificity of the interaction between the $(TC \cdot AG)_{18}$ sequence in the supercoiled molecule and the $(TC)_{18}$ sequence in the single-stranded M13 DNA can be seen by the predominance of single points of contact (indicated by arrow-heads) shared between the two DNAs.

To examine whether the observed complexes were due to the presence of a nuclease S1-sensitive structure rather than the presence of the $(TC \cdot AG)_{18}$ sequence *per se*, we took advantage of our earlier observation that a supercoiled DNA complexed with M13 DNA has retarded gel electrophoretic mobility (78). A series of DNA topoisomers with the $(TC \cdot AG)_{18}$ sequence was prepared by treatment with topoisomerase I and various ethidium bromide concentrations. The purified DNAs were pooled and incubated at pH 5 (100 mM Na^+) either in the presence or absence of single-stranded M13 DNA containing the $(TC)_{18}$ sequence, and then analyzed by two-dimensional gel electrophoresis (Figure 1B).

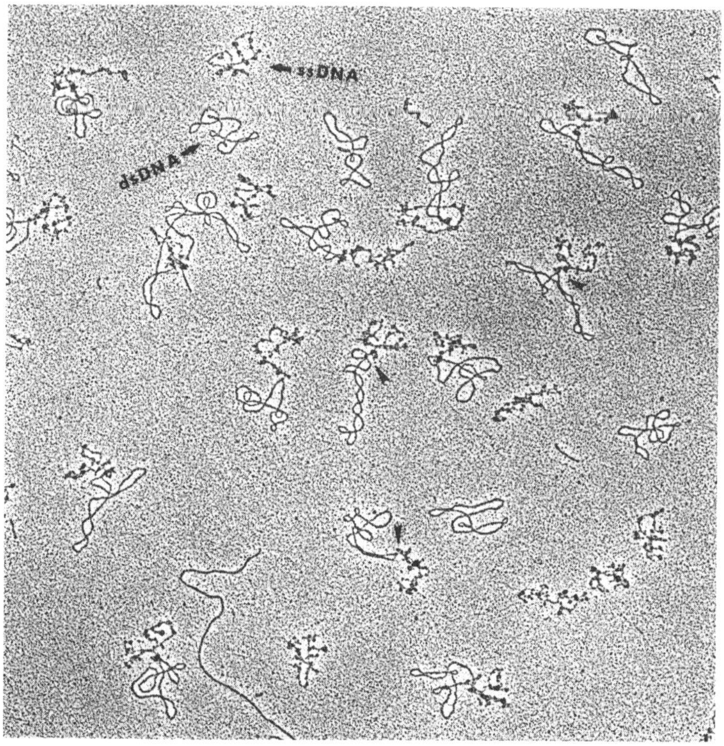
ssDNA
dsDNA

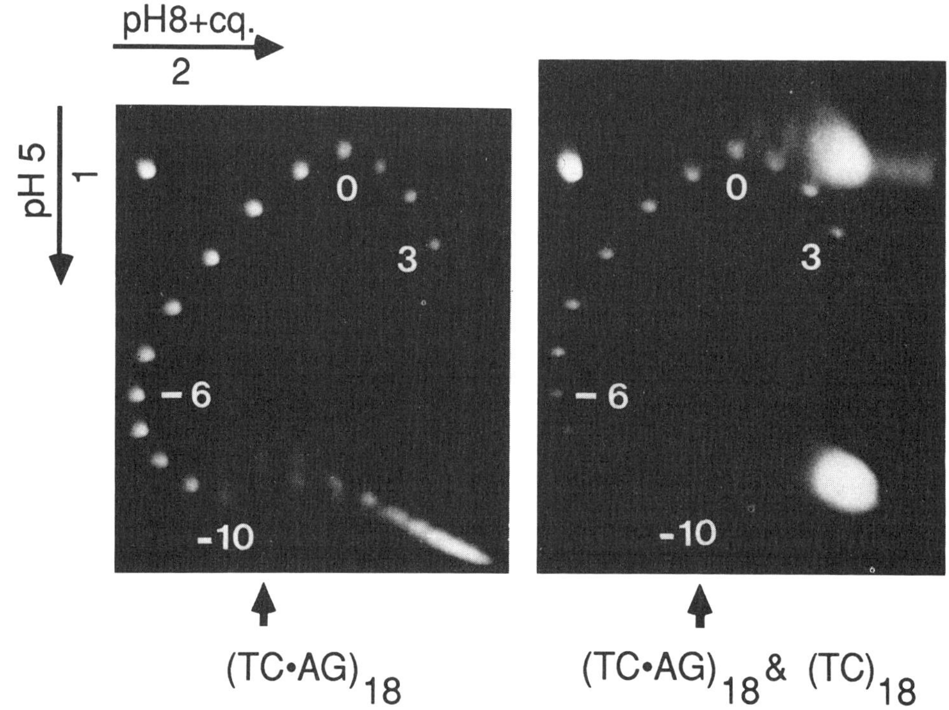
pH8+cq.
2
pH 5
1
0
3
-6
-10
(TC•AG)18
(TC•AG)18 & (TC)18

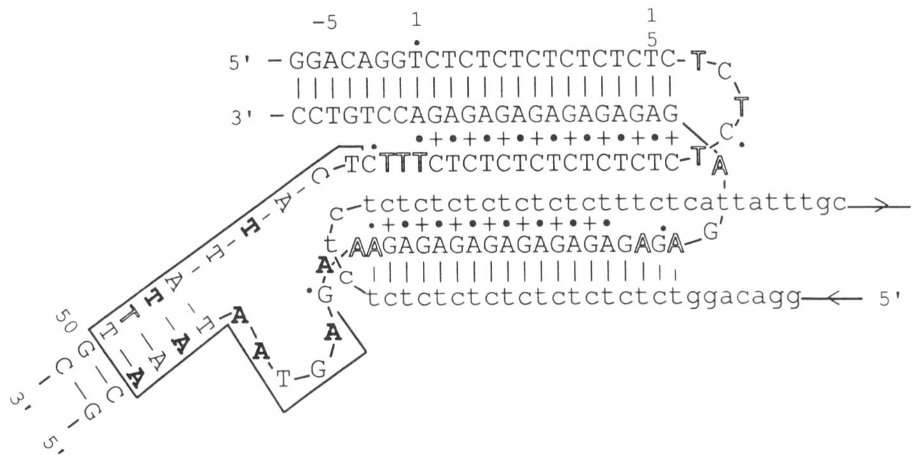

Figure 1: Complex formation and chemical probing to demonstrate the presence of single strands within the H-DNA conformation. (A) Visualization of complexes under the electron microscope. Negatively supercoiled DNAs (0.1 ug) with a (TC · AG)$_{18}$ insert derived from a region 1.8 kilo-base pairs downstream of a human U1 RNA gene, HU1-1 (65), was incubated in 20 ul of 0.2 M NaOAc (pH 5.0) with a four-fold molar excess of M13mp9 single-stranded DNA (0.2 ug) containing a (TC)$_{18}$ insert at 37°C overnight. Following incubation, complexes were spread (as in ref. 104) and examined under the electron microscope. An arrow-head indicates the site of contact between the two DNAs. ssDNA: collapsed single-stranded M13 DNA containing a (TC)$_{18}$ sequence; dsDNA: negatively supercoiled DNA with a (TC · AG)$_{18}$ sequence. [Taken with permission from Htun, ref. 95.] (B) Two-dimensional gel electrophoresis of (TC · AG)$_{18}$-containing topoisomers after incubation with the (TC)-$_{18}$containing single-stranded M13 DNA. A series of DNA topoisomers with the (TC · AG)$_{18}$ sequence was prepared by treatment with topoisomerase I at various concentrations of ethidium bromide. The mixture of purified topoisomers was separated by two-dimensional gel electrophoresis (left-hand panel) or it was first incubated with the (TC)$_{18}$-containing single-stranded M13 DNA, as described earlier except 33.3 mM Na_3 Citrate (pH 5.0) buffer was used instead of the NaOAc buffer before electrophoresis in a 1.5% agarose gel (right-hand panel). The first dimension (top to bottom) was in 33.3 mM Na_3 Citrate (pH 5.0) at 9°C. After equilibrating at room temperature in 40 mM tris-base, 25 mM sodium acetate, 0.9 mM sodium salt of EDTA, and chloroquine phosphate (cq.) at 3 ug per ml, the DNAs were separated in the second dimension (left to right) in this latter buffer but at 9°C. The second condition does not support H-DNA formation and leads to the dissociation of the complexes. The numbers refer to the linking (number) difference relative to the most relaxed (slowest migrating) topoisomer in the pH 5 dimension. The upward arrow points to the topoisomers which remain partly in the duplex and H-DNA conformations (transition midpoint) during the course of the first dimensional electrophoresis. See reference 105 for a more detailed discussion of the two-dimensional gel electrophoretic technique, and Figure 2C of reference 48 for a comparison of the effect of ionic strength and cation on the structural transition. (C) Summary of the chemical reactivity data for the (TC · AG)$_{18}$ structure in the M13 DNA complex. Negatively supercoiled plasmid DNA (represented by upper case letters) was probed for exposed nucleotides using a thymine-specific reagent, osmium tetroxide, and an adenine-specific reagent, diethyl pyrocarbonate. The reactive nucleotides in the uncomplexed plasmid DNAs are indicated by bold letters without serif, except in the case of adenines A23 to A35 (see the H-y3(16) conformer in Figure 4). In the plasmid DNA complexed to the M13 DNA (represented by lower case letters), these adenines are hybridized to the (TC)$_{18}$ sequence resulting in their loss of reactivity to diethyl pyrocarbonate. Bold letters with serif indicate the additional sites of reactivity in plasmid DNA due to complex formation. Note the disruption of basepairs in plasmid DNA from (C40, G40) to (T45, A45) which are otherwise paired in the uncomplexed DNA (see Figure 4). Also, see the legend of Figure 4 for additional clarification of the various symbols. [Taken with permission from Htun and Dahlberg, ref. 78. Copyright 1988 by the AAAS.]

At pH 5 and 100 mM NaCl, the (TC · AG)$_{18}$ sequences in plasmids with a linking number difference of at least −10 (relative to the most relaxed topoisomer) undergo a structural change to the nuclease S1-sensitive structure (left-hand panel, Figure 1B; also, see Figure 4-3 of ref. 95). That change is evident in the slower migration of the DNAs, due to the relaxation of negative supercoils (48). The topoisomers that had undergone this structural change were able to form complexes with the (TC)$_{18}$-containing M13 DNA (right-hand panel). Because the second dimension condition (left to right) does not support complex formation, the DNAs with retarded mobilities in the first dimension have normal mobilities in the second dimension. The two large bright spots near the right-hand edge of the second panel are M13 DNA that had (top) or had not (bottom) been complexed to the (TC · AG)$_{18}$ sequence.

The requirement for an altered (nuclease S1-sensitive) structure to support formation of complexes between the (TC · AG)$_{18}$ sequence and (TC)$_n$ sequences in single-stranded, closed-circular M13 DNA (78,95) contrasts with the conditions needed for formation of complexes between (TC · AG)$_n$ sequences in duplex DNA and single-stranded (TC)$_n$ oligonucleotides (26-30,76; unpublished data). In this latter case, formation of the intermolecular complex with a short oligonucleotide requires a (TC · AG)$_n$ sequence but not a nuclease-sensitive structure.

We also tested the existence of single-stranded regions within the nuclease S1-sensitive structure by probing the structure with osmium tetroxide and diethyl pyrocarbonate (78). These chemicals react preferentially at the C5-C6 positions of thymines and at the N7 position of adenines, respectively, when the bases are exposed as in single-stranded DNA or in altered double-stranded conformations. The modified sites were mapped by transcription with phage RNA polymerases and sizing of the prematurely terminated products against a standard RNA sequencing ladder. Figure 1C summarizes the results of probing the structure complexed to a (TC)$_{18}$ repeat in M13 DNA, while Figure 4 summarizes that of probing the uncomplexed structure.

Nucleotides from the (TC · AG)$_{18}$ repeat in plasmid DNA are in upper case letters, whereas those from the (TC)$_{18}$ repeat in M13 are in lower case letters. The pattern of reactivity is consistent with the triple-stranded H-DNA model in which the 3′ half of the (TC)$_{18}$ sequence folds back onto the acceptor half and winds back down to the 'base.' Single-stranded regions exist at the 'fold-back' region and in the 5′ half of the (AG)$_{18}$ sequence.

When not complexed with the (TC)$_{18}$ sequence of the M13 DNA, nucleotides in the middle (T17, T19, and T21) and at the 3′ end (T37, T38, T39 and T48) of the polypyrimidine sequence are hyper-reactive to osmium tetroxide and hence exposed, while bases in the 5′ half (A17 to A38) of the polypurine sequence are hyper-reactive to diethyl pyrocarbonate. Furthermore, nucleotides from C40 to T45, and G40 to A45 are base paired in the uncomplexed DNA (see H-y3(16) conformer in Figure 4).

When complexed with M13 DNA, the plasmid DNA showed similar osmium tetroxide reactivity in the polypyrimidine strand; however, the diethyl pyrocarbonate reactivity of the polypurine strand was greatly reduced (from A23 to A36) - demonstrating the single-strandedness of the 5′ half of the $(AG)_{18}$ sequence (Figure 1C). Base pairing of these formerly reactive purines with the complementary single-stranded $(TC)_{18}$ sequence in M13 DNA would account for their lack of reactivity. Because the interaction is between two closed DNA circles, the M13 DNA and the D-loop of the single-stranded $(AG)_{18}$ sequence, there can be no net winding of the two DNAs. Thus, the M13 DNA probably exits from the polypurine D-loop by winding the $(TC)_{18}$ repeat back on itself; at the pH 5, that would favor the formation of another triple-stranded structure. This second triplex structure might account for the stability of the complex, which survives gel electrophoresis, both at pH 5 (Figure 1B) and pH 7.8 (in the absence of chloroquine; Figure 4A of ref. 78).

Although the junctional reactivity at one end of the copolymeric sequence extends outwards to include a few additional residues (T44, T47, A41, A44, A45, A47, and A49) presumably due to steric requirements imposed by the intermolecular complex, the lack of new regions of reactivity within the copolymer indicates that the M13 DNA did not induce the formation of a new structure in the plasmid DNA or significantly alter the existing structure. While other hypothetical structures involving self-paired polypyrimidines/self-paired polypurines (2-12,65,68,88-91) or four-stranded structures (37-39,71,73,92) could be consistent with the chemical reactivity profile of the uncomplexed DNA, those structures are not consistent with that of the plasmid DNA in the intermolecular complex (78). Thus, the chemical probing of uncomplexed and complexed plasmid DNA establishes the single-strandedness of the reactive 5′ half of the $(AG)_{18}$ sequence and places the complementary, unreactive 3′ half of the $(TC)_{18}$ sequence within a triple-stranded structure (Figure 1C). Our previously observed nuclease S1 cleavage near the middle of the $(TC)_{18}$ sequence (65) is explained by the single-stranded polypyrimidine loop at the 'tip' of the triple-stranded structure.

Despite its single-strandedness, the displaced half of the polypurine sequence can have a defined structure. The modulated pattern of nuclease S1 cleavage at every other nucleotide suggests that these purines are stacked as pairs (43,52,54,65). When the single-stranded, 5′ half of the $(AG)_{18}$ sequence (indicated by the large box) was exposed to diethyl pyrocarbonate, the unpaired purines were uniformly reactive toward the chemical at 22°C in a pH 5 buffer with 100 mM Na^+ concentration (Figure 2, lane 1) but they had varying reactivities at 12.5°C in a different pH 5 buffer containing 1 mM Mg^{2+} concentration (lane 2). This change in the pattern of chemical reactivity between the two conditions suggests that the single-stranded polypurines chain can adopt at least two different structures, depending on conditions.

Demonstration of the Kink in H-DNA

The folding back of the polypyrimidine strand on itself as it proceeds down the acceptor helix should result in the introduction of a severe kink in the molecule (78,83). Such a kink would retard the electrophoretic mobility of a DNA fragment, and this retardation would increase as the kink is placed closer to the center of the fragment. Although negative supercoiling promotes formation of H-DNA, it is not

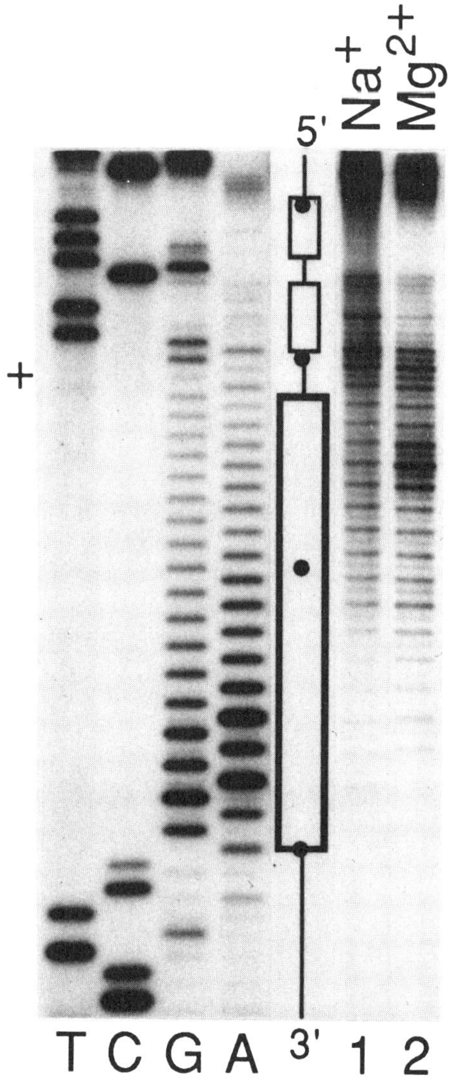

Figure 2: The $(AG)_n$ single strand can have a defined structure. The $(TC \cdot AG)_{18}$ sequence in the H-DNA conformation was probed with diethyl pyrocarbonate and assayed by transcription with T7 RNA polymerase, as described previously (78). The H-DNAs were formed in negatively supercoiled DNAs at room temperature in a pH 5 buffer: 100 mM NaOAc (lane 1) or 20 mM HOAc/1 mM $Mg(OAc)_2$ adjusted with tris-base (lane 2). DNAs (19 ug/ml) were reacted with 10 ul of DEPC in 400 ul buffer. Reaction for lane 1 was for 40 min. at room temperature (with vortexing every 5 min.), whereas that for lane 2 was for 4 hours at 12.5°C (with vortexing every 30 min.). In the latter case, longer reaction times were necessary due to reduced solubility of the reagent at the lower temperature. The large box indicates the $(AG)_{18}$ region, while the two smaller boxes the (A+T)-rich direct repeats. The nucleotide in the template that directed the incorporation of the chain-terminating 3′ deoxynucleoside triphosphate is indicated on the right by A, G, C, and T. The plus (+) sign indicates the position of a misincorporated nucleotide in the sequencing ladder; the corresponding nucleotide in the template is an A. The 5′ and 3′ symbols show the polarity of the $(AG)_{18}$-containing strand. The solid dots denote every 20th nucleotide starting at the 3′ end of the $(AG)_{18}$ sequence.

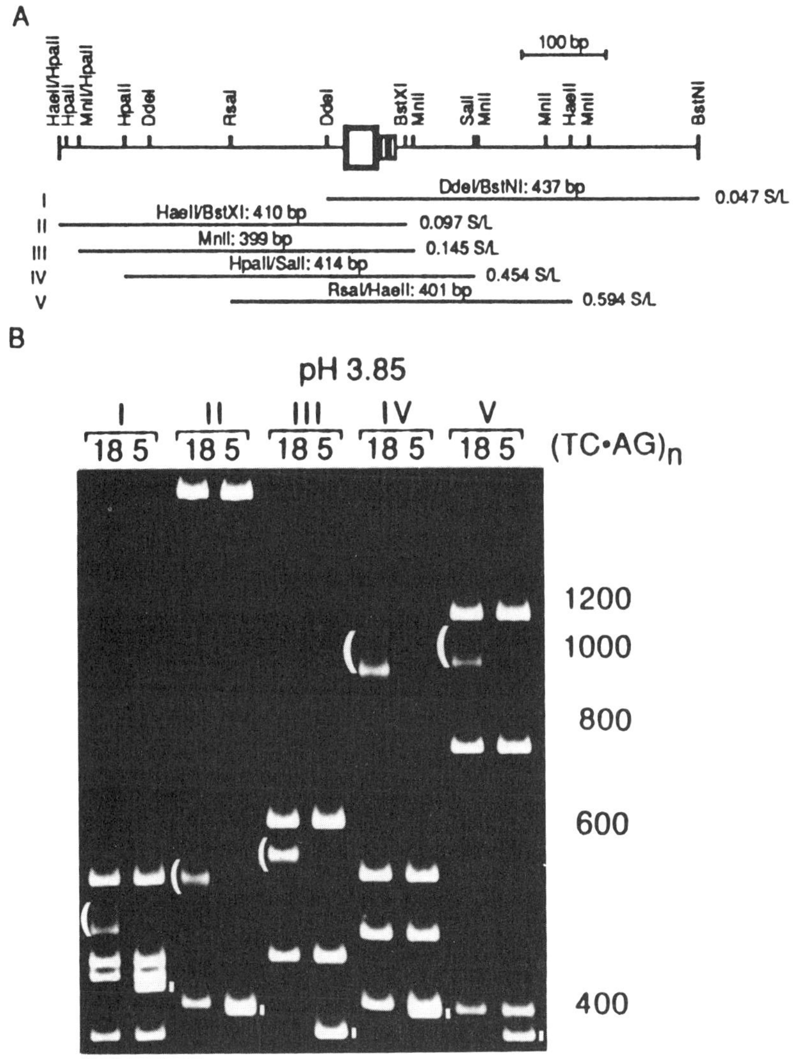

Figure 3: Kinking in H-DNA as demonstrated by retardation of electrophoretic mobilities. (A) Map of restriction fragments containing the $(TC \cdot AG)_n$ sequence at various locations. The fragments were between 399 and 437 bp long, including the 36-bp $(TC \cdot AG)_{18}$ sequence. Fragments with the $(TC \cdot AG)_5$ sequence were 26 bp shorter and had a T → C transition 57 nucleotides to the right of the sequence; S/L indicates the ratio of the number of base pairs in the shorter and longer flanking regions in each fragment. [Taken with permission from Htun and Dahlberg, ref. 78. Copyright 1988 by the AAAS.] (B) Electrophoresis of restriction fragments containing $(TC \cdot AG)_n$ sequences that formed H-DNA. Numerals I to V refer to the fragments mapped in (A) and 18 or 5 refers to the number of (TC · AG) repeats in the fragment. The pH 3.85 condition allows the formation of H-DNA in relaxed DNA fragments containing $(TC \cdot AG)_{18}$ but not $(TC \cdot AG)_5$ sequence (78,95). The parentheses on the left indicate the mobilities at pH 3.85 of the fragments containing the $(TC \cdot AG)_{18}$ sequence. As the S/L ratio increases, the fragments migrate more slowly relative to those with the $(TC \cdot AG)_5$, indicated by short white bars on the right. The retarded bands have varying intensities (see text for discussion). The numbers on the right of the gel indicate the approximate length in base pairs of linear fragments containing B-DNA. Electrophoresis was performed in 5% (60:1) polyacrylamide gel containing 33.3 mM Na_3 Citrate (pH 3.85) prepared as previously described (78).

essential at sufficiently low pH (54,65,78,93,95), so we were able to make H-DNA in linearized DNA restriction fragments (78,95). Plasmid DNAs containing the $(TC \cdot AG)_{18}$ sequence were digested with restriction enzymes to produce fragments about 400 nucleotides long with the repeated sequence at various distances from the center (Figure 3A); these fragments were electrophoretically separated in a polyacrylamide gel at pH 3.85 (Figure 3B). As a control, we used identical fragments with a shorter insert, a $(TC \cdot AG)_5$ sequence, which does not form H-DNA even in negatively supercoiled molecules (48,54,65,95).

The mobilities of the H-DNA bearing fragments decreased as the repeat was located closer to the center of the fragment, indicating that the repeat introduced a kink in the DNA (78). The heterogeneity of the retarded fragments (note the varying intensity and width of the bands to the right of the white open parentheses in Figure 3B) indicates that not all molecules adopt one time-averaged structure. The observed heterogeneity could result from differences in the H-DNA conformations. In addition, the introduction of a kink with limited flexibility, which we termed a hinge (resulting from unpaired nucleotides at the bottom of the triple helix; 78), might contribute to the presence of these electrophoretically distinct species.

Nomenclature for H-DNA Structures

We propose a standard nomenclature for describing H-DNA structures (48). The H-DNA conformation refers to the presence of triple-stranded and displaced single-stranded regions, independent of the nature of the pairing responsible for stabilization of the triplex. Expected presence of a hinge-like flexibility of the kink in all H-DNAs is an additional justification for the name H-DNA, since it is hinged-DNA (78).

In forming H-DNA structures at $(TC \cdot AG)_n$ sequences, the donated 'third' strand, which forms Hoogsteen pairs with the Watson-Crick duplex is a polypyrimidine strand (abbreviated as 'y' for pyrimidines). The source of this third strand can either be from the 5′ or 3′ half of the polypyrimidine sequence. To distinguish between these two possibilities, H-DNA structures in which the donated polypyrimidine strand comes from the 5′ half should be indicated as **H-y5** and those from the 3′ half as **H-y3** conformers. The number of base triplets within H-DNA should be indicated by a number within parentheses, immediately following the designated conformation. The **H-y3(16)** and **H-y5(15)** conformers are illustrated in Figure 4.

In addition to the **H-y** DNA conformations, poly(C) · poly(G) sequences have been proposed to adopt a triple-stranded and single-stranded (and hence H-DNA) conformation, where the 5′ or 3′ half of the polypurine strand serves as the donated 'third' strand (70,86). These would be the **H-r** DNA conformations, where the 'r' indicates the donated purines. Similarly, the **H-r** DNAs can be described as either **H-r5** or **H-r3** depending on the source of the donated purines.

A Model for H-DNA Formation

Some H-DNA conformers are stable even when they are not at their lowest free

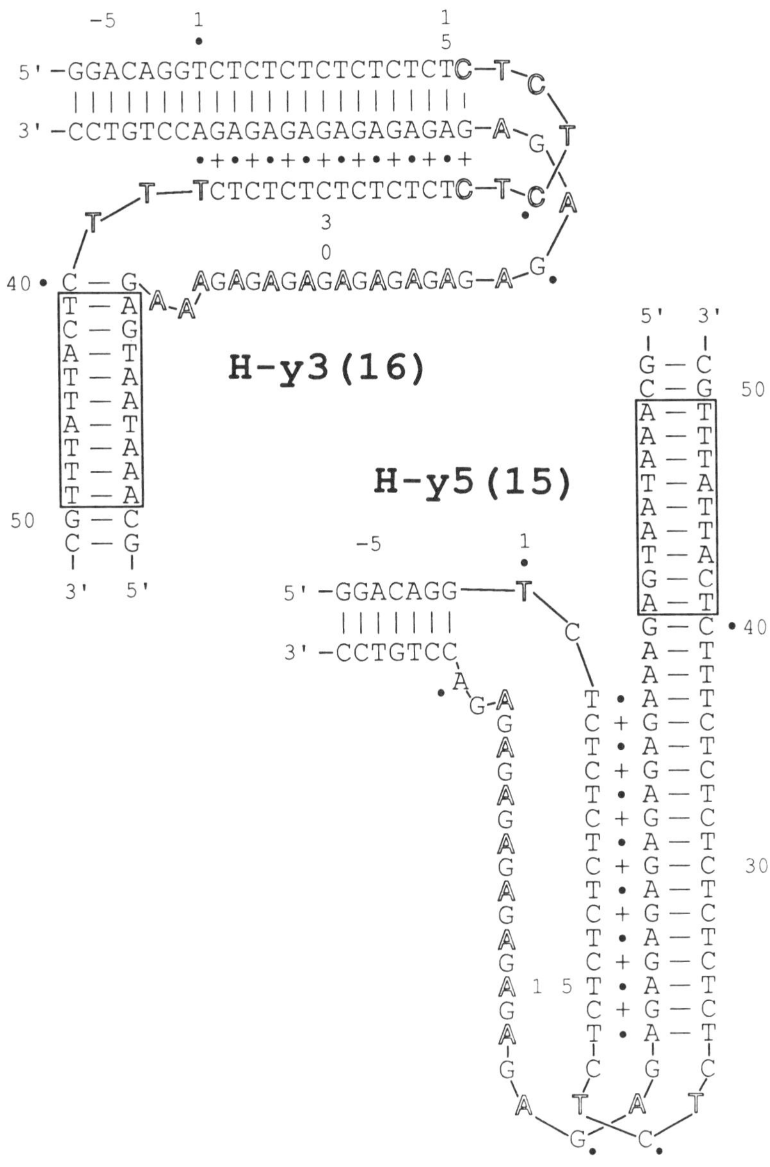

Figure 4: Nomenclature for describing the H-y DNA conformers. Alternative use of the 3′ or 5′ half of the $(TC)_n$ repeat as the donated strand leads to H-y3 or H-y5 conformers, respectively. Watson-Crick base pairs (in the flanking and acceptor helices) are shown as lines and Hoogsteen base pairs between the acceptor purines and uncharged [T] or protonated [C^+] pyrimidines are shown by • and +, respectively. Residue numbers and the box denoting a flanking region sequence are shown. Outlined letters indicate nucleotides that are reactive to diethyl pyrocarbonate (**A**), osmium tetroxide (**T**) or methoxylamine (**C**) when the DNAs are in the H-y DNA conformations. The two illustrated structures are H-y3(16) and H-y5(15) DNAs. The number of base triplets is indicated in the parentheses. See text for a description of the H-r conformers. [Taken with permission from Htun and Dahlberg, ref. 48. Copyright 1989 by the AAAS.]

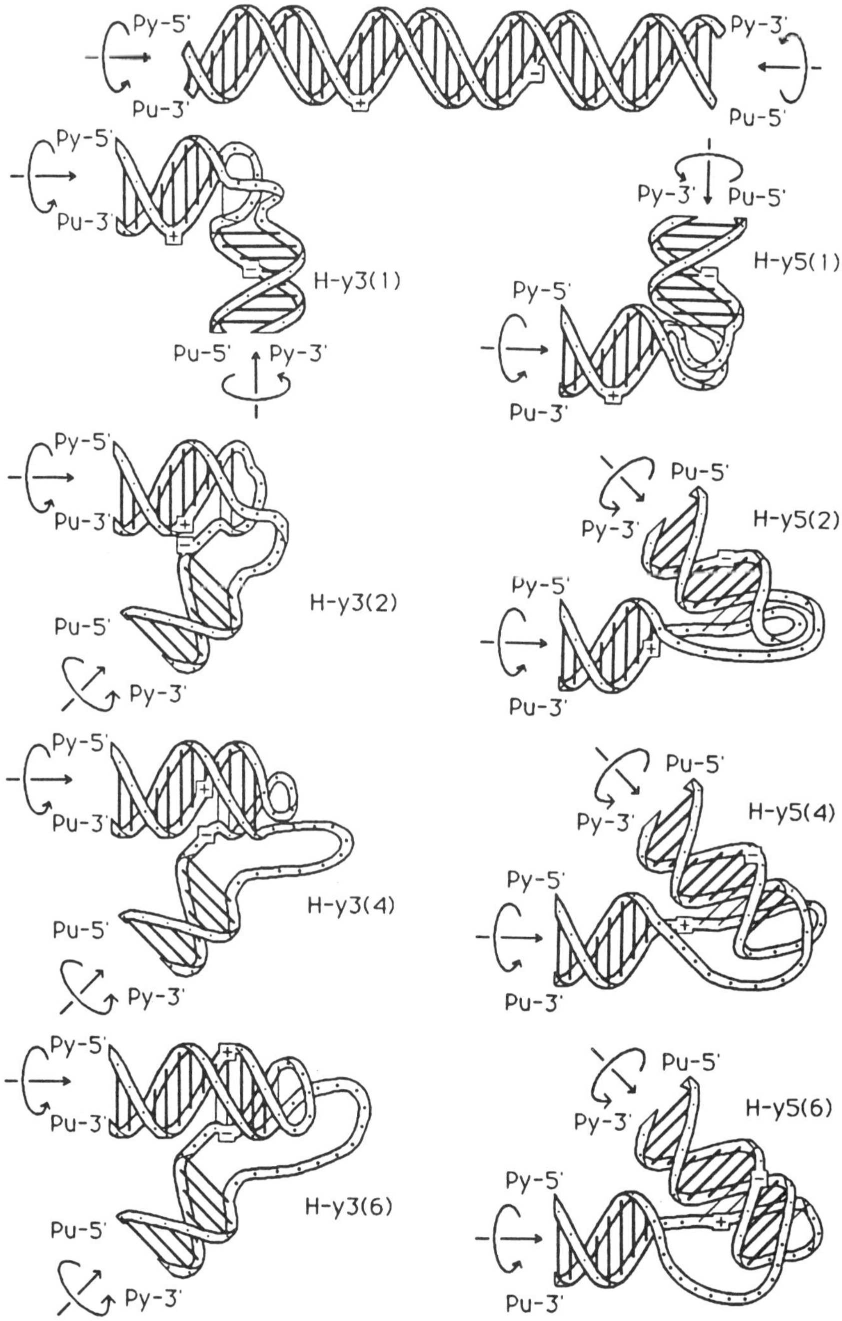
Py-5'
Pu-3'
Py-3'
Pu-5'
H-y3(1)
H-y5(1)
H-y3(2)
H-y5(2)
H-y3(4)
H-y5(4)
H-y3(6)
H-y5(6)

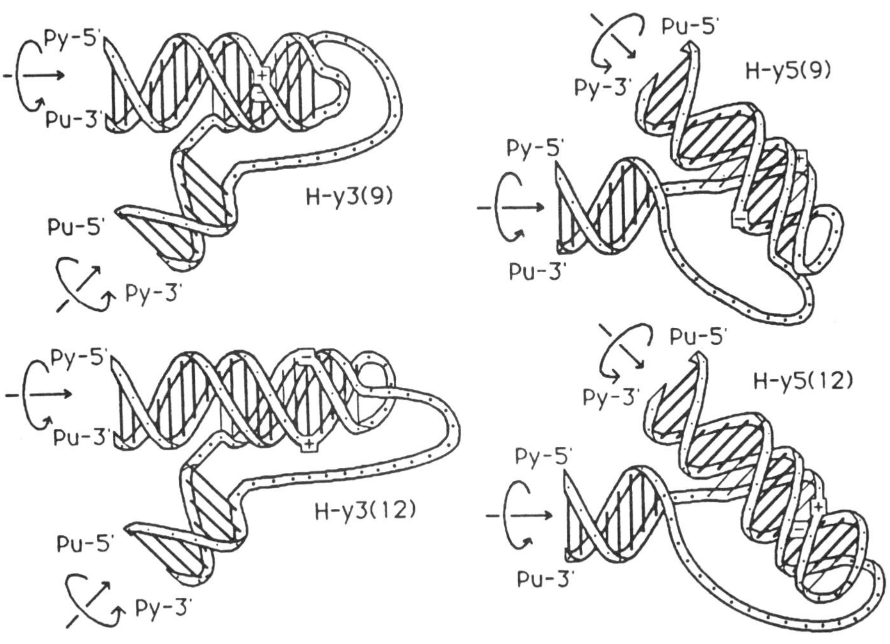

Figure 5: A model for the formation of H-DNA. Left and right sides, the formation of H-y3 and H-y5 conformer, respectively; parentheses, the lengths of the triplex; curved arrows, direction of rotation that relaxes negative supercoiling; straight arrows, the direction that nucleotides move as they are recruited into the H-DNA structure during its elongation; thick lines, Watson-Crick base pairs; thin lines, Hoogsteen pairs; plus (+) and minus (−) signs located 13 nucleotides apart on the phosphodiester backbone of the polypyrimidine strand illustrate the progression of nucleotides from the flanking region duplex into the body of the triplex. The nucleotides in the single-stranded polypurine loop are stacked in pairs along one side of the triplex (43,52,54,65). All helices have arbitrarily been drawn with 11-bp or triplexes per turn. H-DNA formation is initiated by breathing within the middle of the (TC · AG) repeat, allowing the duplex to kink back on itself. Nucleation occurs by alignment of a pyrimidine at the end of one duplex (the donor) in the major groove of the other (the acceptor), allowing formation of the Hoogsteen pair at the tip of the triplex (as described in Figure 6). Elongation occurs when the two helices rotate coordinately, allowing the acceptor helix (shown above) to spool up pyrimidines as they are released by denaturation of the donor helix (below); both rotations are propelled by the force associated with negative supercoiling. The structure is thereby elongated until either the donor or the acceptor helix no longer has nucleotides that can be incorporated into the triplex. The single-stranded nucleotides at the end of the donor helix (78) provide for a small amount of supercoiling relaxation in the absence of further denaturation (48). [Taken with permission from Htun and Dahlberg, ref. 48. Copyright 1989 by the AAAS.]

energy levels (44,48,95,97). That is evident from the two-dimensional gel in the left-hand panel of Figure 1B. Once a requisite level of supercoiling is introduced to stabilize the B → H transition, topoisomers with the same linking number can assume multiple conformations that relax different amounts of negative supercoiling (seen as additional spots in the first (vertical) dimension; see also Figure 2 of ref. 48 and Figures 4-2 and 4-3 of ref. 95). The faster migrating species of the pair has an alternate structure that relieves three negative supercoils and the slower migrating species has a structure relieving four negative supercoils. The inability of all molecules to achieve the same, lowest energy level shows that the H-DNA conformers are trapped in metastable states.

We propose that H-DNA formation involves a transition state that determines which conformer is to be made, regardless of whether the final structure is at the lowest possible free energy (48,95,97). Moreover, for DNA in one H-DNA conformation to be converted to another, the molecule must pass back through the same transition state. Thus, interconversion to achieve the lowest possible free energy becomes progressively more difficult as more (stabilizing) repeats are incorporated into any H-DNA structure.

We define a nucleation structure as the first intermediate that is committed to form a particular conformer of H-DNA (48,95). While this is most conveniently envisaged as the structure in which only one base triplet has formed, at the 'tip' of what is to be the triple helix, the commitment to form a particular nucleation structure must be made in an earlier transition state involving a pre-nucleation rotation of flanking helices (see below).

Once nucleation has occurred, H-DNA is elongated by mutual rotation of the two flanking region duplexes (Figure 5). Rotation of the donor duplex denatures it, releasing the single-stranded purine chain plus a pyrimidine that is spooled onto the acceptor duplex, as the latter rotates. Both of these duplex rotations relax negative supercoiling in the rest of the molecule (48), explaining why supercoiling promotes H-DNA formation (47,63-65,93).

The multiplicity of H-DNA conformers noted by us here and elsewhere (48,95,97) can result from several factors. The most obvious one is the actual site of nucleation: if it is displaced from the center of the repeat, the resulting H-DNA triplex has less than the maximal length. The other primary cause of heterogeneity results from the way in which the 'tip' of the triplex is made (Figure 6). As the polypyrimidine strand folds back, to go from being part of a Watson-Crick duplex to being the third, Hoogsteen-paired part of a triplex, it must traverse the axis of the acceptor helix. In order to form the nucleation structure, the donated pyrimidine must be placed in the major groove of the acceptor helix, about 180 degrees away from where it emerged at the end of the Watson-Crick helix. That can be achieved by rotation of the flanking helices by a half turn in two different ways. When they rotate by a half turn in the positive sense, to orient the third strand over the major groove of the acceptor, no net rotation actually occurs. That is because this half-turn positive rotation cancels the half-turn negative rotation that denatures the six nucleotides in forming the 'tip.' In

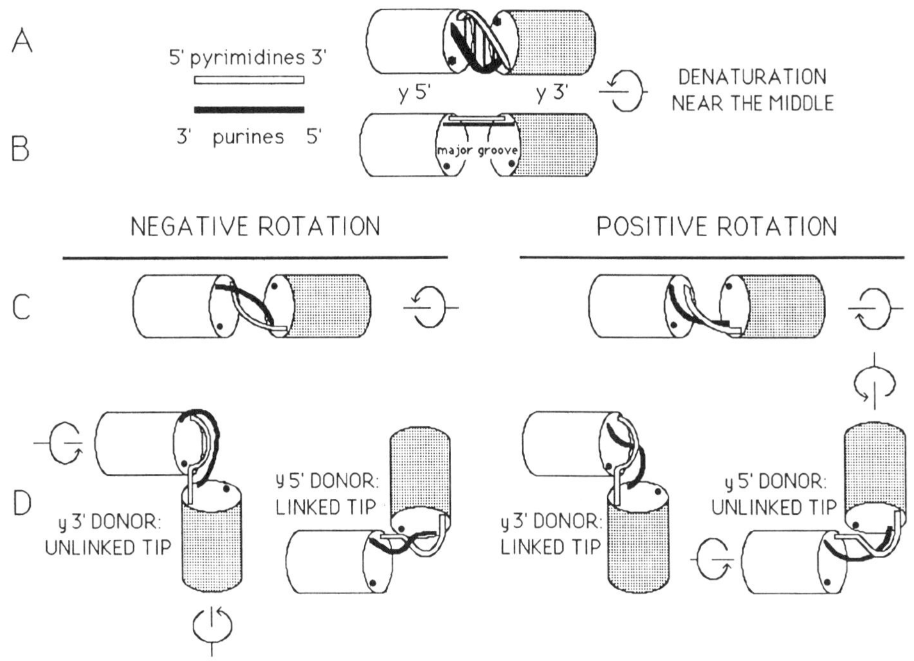

Figure 6: The role of pre-nucleation rotation in the determination of donor and acceptor polarities in H-DNA. The two flanking duplexes are represented by cylinders and the major groove by a spot. Prior to nucleation, the two helices (A) may be thought to undergo two half-turn rotations: denaturation of nucleotides to make the loop and first donated pyrimidine (B) and orientation of a donor pyrimidine opposite an acceptor major groove (C). The two flanking duplexes containing the 5′ and 3′ halves of the polypyrimidine repeat are represented by white and gray cylinders, respectively. For clarity, only one of the two flanking duplexes is rotated. While the rotation associated with denaturation, as illustrated, occurs only in the negative sense (relaxing negative supercoils in the DNA) (B), rotation to reorient the pyrimidines at the end of one duplex opposite the major groove of the other duplexes can be in either the negative or positive sense (C). The sense (direction in space) of this latter rotation determines whether formation of the nucleation structure will be topologically significant ($-1/2$ plus $-1/2 \approx -1$ turn) or neutral ($-1/2$ plus $+1/2 \approx 0$ turn). Furthermore, it dictates which half of the polypyrimidine is to be donated as the third strand. To avoid local linking of strands at the tip (where the polypurine would be forced to pass through the polypyrimidine loop), only two of the four possible structures drawn in (D) can be used to nucleate H-DNA formation: negative pre-nucleation rotation from the structure in (B) results in use of the 3′ region of the polypyrimidine as donor, whereas positive pre-nucleation rotation results in use of the 5′ region. Extensive negative supercoiling would be expected to foster negative rotation (leading to left-hand structure in C) and give rise to H-y3 DNA nucleation structure (left-hand corner of D), whereas low pH or little negative supercoiling would allow the DNA duplex (A) to kink directly back on itself (with the separation of strands at the site of kinking) and give rise to H-y5 DNA (right-hand corner of D). [Taken with permission from Htun and Dahlberg, ref. 48. Copyright 1989 by the AAAS.]

contrast, orientation of the two helices by pre-nucleation in the negative sense results in a net rotation of minus one (Figure 6).

To avoid local linking of the strands at the tip (which we postulate would be very unfavorable energetically), the choice of the donated strand is determined by the sense of the pre-nucleation rotation (48,95). Hence, the 5′ half of the polypyrimidine chain must be the donated strand in formation of a nucleation structure with no net rotation, giving rise to H-y5 DNA. This structure can be envisaged to proceed through a simple 'break' in the linear molecule, with no net rotation, allowing the DNA to be kinked. In contrast, if the DNA undergoes a complete negative rotation prior to nucleation, only the 3′ half of the polypyrimidine chain can be used as a donor, giving rise to H-y3 DNA.

Because of differences in rotations prior to nucleation, the topological (and hence, energetic) consequences of forming H-y3 DNA differ from those of making H-y5. Formation of H-y3 DNA from $(TC \cdot AG)_{18}$ results in the relaxation of about one more negative supercoil than does formation of H-y5, due to the additional rotation prior to nucleation. Since the donor duplex needs only to fold back on the acceptor to make H-y5 DNA, this conformer would be expected to predominate at low levels of negative supercoiling. In contrast, formation of the H-y3 nucleation structure requires one complete turn of the two chains about each other - an event that would be promoted by high levels of negative supercoiling. In experiments designed to test these predictions, we found that high levels of supercoiling do indeed support H-y3 formation, whereas low levels support H-y5 formation, as expected (48).

Because most investigators use highly negatively supercoiled DNAs (negative supercoiling density of 0.05 or greater), they usually make the H-y3 conformers. Thus, until now, most reports on the structures of H-DNA noted an unexplained bias toward utilization of the 3′ half of the polypyrimidine chain as the donor (47,56,70-72,77-82,84-86). The enigma of why that should be is now explained by our model of H-DNA formation (48). [We note that the model as developed for the H-y conformers can also be applied to the H-r conformers (70,72,86).]

Energetics of H-DNA Structures

When the pH is lowered from 8 to 5, synthetic double-stranded $(TC \cdot AG)_n$ copolymers spontaneously rearrange to a triple-stranded structure, containing two $(TC)_n$ and one $(AG)_n$ strands (25-27). The released $(AG)_n$ strands associate to form either a two- or four-stranded self-paired structure (7, 12). The spontaneity of the rearrangement suggests an energetically favorable process in which formation of a highly stable triple-stranded structure is sufficient to drive the displacement of the fourth strand. We note that the displaced strands are free to interact with each other, thereby contributing to the overall reduction in free energy.

Formation of H-DNA from long regions of DNA differs in two important respects from the situation with oligonucleotides. First, the displaced polypurines are not as free to interact with each other, so the free energy change per base pair is likely to be less with long DNAs than with oligonucleotides. Secondly, the ends of H-DNA triplex, at both its tip and its base, contain single-stranded regions that make a constant positive (unfavorable) contribution to the free energy of formation. Favorable free energy contributions are derived from the relaxation of negative supercoils in the plasmid DNA and, as inferred from Table I, from the conversion of two regions of duplex to a triplex plus single strand.

We estimated the relative energetic cost of H-DNA formation by measuring, under defined conditions, the degree of negative supercoiling required to support formation of H-y3 DNA for $(TC \cdot AG)_n$ repeats of different lengths (95,97). Table I shows that at pH 5, the energetic cost of converting duplex to H-DNA decreases as the length of the copolymer increases. Since the energetic costs of forming the single-stranded ends are roughly equivalent in all H-y3 nucleation structures, the decreased requirement for negative supercoiling energy shows that the bonding energies per nucleotide in H-DNA are more favorable than in duplex DNA.

A change in condition that increases the energetic cost of forming H-DNA conformation, by preferentially stabilizing the duplex state or destabilizing the triplex state, would impose a greater need for negative supercoiling or a longer $(TC \cdot AG)$ repeat that could be incorporated into triplex. In a paper to be published elsewhere (97), we show that at higher pH, where formation of $(G \cdot C^+)$ Hoogsteen pairs is not as favored, fewer alternate forms of H-DNA are stable, reflecting the requirement to maximize triplex length. Furthermore, at higher pH, more supercoiling energy is required to support the transition from duplex to H-DNA: that is evident both in the higher number of negative supercoils that must be introduced into the plasmids (greater linking deficiency) and in the fact that the resulting structures are primarily in the H-y3 conformation.

Similar effects have been observed with different concentrations and types of cations, which affect the formation of H-DNA, presumably by their influence on the relative stability of the H-DNA and double-stranded DNA structures (97). (For example, compare Figure 1B above with Figure 2C of ref. 48; note differences in the ratio of H-y3 to H-y5 conformers immediately following the structural transition.) In general, increasing the concentration of monovalent cation ions has a greater stabilizing effect on $(TC \cdot AG)_n$ sequences in the double-stranded than triple-stranded structure, accounting also for the fact that H-DNA formation in linear DNA at pH 4.53 occurs only under low salt concentrations (65).

Functions of H-DNA

In spite of what we now believe to be reasonably comprehensive models of H-DNA structure and formation, the functions that this conformation may have *in vivo*, if any, remain to be determined. H-DNA can exist at physiological pH (78) and antibodies against triplex DNAs stain eukaryotic nuclei (98,99). The findings by others (100-102) and ourselves (48), that $(TC \cdot AG)_n$ repeats are present about once every 130-150 kilo-base pairs in human DNA and that polypyrimidine-polypurine sequences are over-represented in eukaryotic DNA, imply a possible widespread use, such as in chromatin structure, gene expression, or DNA replication.

Table I
Energetics of H-y3 DNA Formation at (TC · AG)$_n$ Sequences
[Taken with permission from Htun, ref. 95.]

Name[a]	(TC · AG)$_n$[b]	Size (bp)	Polypyrimidine	Sequence[c]
			−1	
pTC5tt2A[h]	5	3015	GG (TC)$_5$	TTTCTC
pTC9tt2A	9	3023	GG (TC)$_9$	TTTCTC
pTC11tt2A	11	3027	GG (TC)$_{11}$	TTTCTC
pTC13A$^{\Delta 9}$	13	3016	GG (TC)$_{13}$	------
pTC15B	15	3029	GG (TC)$_{15}$	------
pTC18tt2A	18	3041	GG (TC)$_{18}$	TTTCTC
pTC19tt4B	24	3047	GG (TC)$_{19}$TT(TC)$_4$	------
pTC25tt4B[j]	30	3059	GG (TC)$_{25}$TT(TC)$_4$	------

[a]All DNAs were obtained by replacing the 8-bp *Sac-Bam*HI polylinker of pGEM-2 DNA (2869-bp; Promega Corp., Madison, Wis.) with the corresponding fragment from a region 1.8-kbp downstream of human U1 RNA genes. The human DNA sequences in pTC18tt2A, pTC5tt2A, pTC25tt4B, pTC19tt4B, and pTC15B DNAs were from pHU1-1H, pHSD-1, pHSD-5, pHSD-4, and pHSD-6, respectively (65). Other DNAs are derived from pTC18tt2A DNA after treating with nuclease S1 and repairing the nuclease S1-generated ends; these DNAs are identical to pTC18tt2A DNA, except where indicated in the table.
[b]Trivial name used to refer to the DNA with a (TC · AG)$_n$ copolymer.
[c]Only the polypyrimidine sequence at and about the polypyrimidine-polypurine region is shown (see Figure 2-5 of ref. 95 for the sequence of the entire *Sac*I-*Bam*HI insert).
[d]Alternate structure formation at a (TC · AG)$_n$ sequence in a pH 5 buffer [20 mM acetic acid and 1 mM magnesium acetate (adjusted to pH 5 with Tris-base); see also Figure 2 of ref. 48].
[e]Linking (number) difference relative to that of the most relaxed state when half of the topoisomers adopt an alternate conformation.
[f]Values within parentheses are expected values: [{[number of base pairs with (TC · AG)$_n$ repeats]/11} + 0.67] (see ref. 48).
[g]Assumes the validity of the expression: [1.1*RT*](midpoint)^2 - (midpoint - supercoils relaxed)^2]/size, where *R* is 1.98 calories per mole-deg. and *T* is temperature in degrees Kelvin (or 287° K, in present case); otherwise, the values are in arbitrary units (see ref. 105-107).
[h](TC · AG)$_5$ is not sensitive to nuclease S1 (54,65,95).
[i]Formation of a cruciform structure at a 39-bp inverted repeat of pGEM-2 DNA (see Figure 2A of ref. 48).
[j]See Figure 2D of ref. 48 for the extent of negative supercoil relaxation.

It is prudent not to assume that all H-DNA structures have the same function (47,95). We previously noted that the transient introduction of a hinge into an otherwise rigid, linear DNA would bring previously distant DNA sequences into close proximity for a brief, defined period, perhaps facilitating both DNA compaction and interaction between DNA-bound proteins (48,78). Also, the over representation of polypyrimidine-polypurine repeat sequences at sites of illegitimate recombination (103) may indicate a role for these sequences in homogenization of multigene families (65,93).

The structures studied here illustrate what certain DNA sequences *can* do, rather than what they do spontaneously; perhaps specific proteins facilitate or modulate

Table I
continued

	Mid-point[e]	Structural transition[d] Number of negative supercoils relaxed[f]	Free energy requirement[f,g] (kcal/mole)
+1 +10			
ATTATTTGCA	12.3[i]	3.8[i] (3.5)	16.4[i] (15.5)
ATTATTTGCA	11.7	3.2 (2.4)	13.4 (10.4)
ATTATTTGCA	9.9	3.0 (2.8)	10.4 (9.7)
---------A	8.7	3.3 (3.0)	9.6 (9.0)
ATTCTTTGCA	8.2	3.4 (3.4)	9.1 (9.1)
ATTATTTGCA	6.3	4.0 (4.0)	8.7 (8.7)
ATTCTTTGCA	5.3	- -	- -
ATTCTTTGCA	4.2	- -	- -

formation of H-DNA *in vivo*. Now that such a structure is known to exist and the topological and structural implications are evident, it would be of interest to learn if other sequences present in eukaryotic DNAs can form similar hinge-like structures.

Acknowledgments

We thank Dr. Frank P. Johnston for stimulating discussion throughout the course of this work; Dr. Maria Schnos and Selma Sachs for teaching one of us (H.H.) electron microscopy techniques; Professor Ross Inman for the use of his electron microscope; Drs. Vladmir D. Axelrod and Harry Osterman for a generous supply of 3′ deoxyribonucleoside triphosphates; and colleagues at the National Cancer Insitute (Frederick, Md.) for use of the facility during the preparation of this manuscript. This work was done while H.H. was a graduate student in the Genetics Training Program at the University of Wisconsin-Madison and was supported by grants to J.E.D. from the National Institutes of Health (GM-30220) and the National Science Foundation (PCM 8309618).

References and Footnotes

1. Present address: Division of Chemistry and Chemical Engineering, 147-75, California Institute of Technology, Pasadena, CA, 91125.
2. R.A. Langridge and A. Rich, *Nature 198*, 725 (1963).
3. R.B. Inman, *J. Mol. Biol. 9*, 624 (1964).
4. D. Thiele, C. Marck, C. Schneider and W. Guschlbauer, *Nucleic Acids Res. 5*, 1997 (1978).
5. D.M. Gray, M. Vaughan, R.L. Ratliff and F.N. Hayes, *Nucleic Acids Res. 8*, 3695 (1980).
6. D.M. Gray, T. Cui and R.L. Ratliff, *Nucleic Acids Res. 12*, 7565 (1984).
7. V.P. Antao, D.M. Gray and R.L. Ratliff, *Nucleic Acids Res. 16*, 719 (1988).
8. J.R. Fresco, *J. Mol. Biol. 1*, 106 (1959).
9. A. Rich, D.R. Davies, F.H.C. Crick and J.D. Watson, *J. Mol. Biol. 3*, 71 (1961).
10. S.B. Zimmerman, *Biopolymers 14*, 889 (1975).
11. A. Dugaiczyk, D.L. Robberson and A. Ullrich, *Biochemistry 19*, 5869 (1980).

12. J.S. Lee, D.H. Evans and A.R. Morgan, *Nucleic Acids Res. 8*, 4305 (1980).
13. G. Felsenfeld, D.R. Davies and A. Rich, *J. Am. Chem. Soc. 79*, 2023 (1957).
14. M. Riley, B. Maling and M.J. Chamberlin, *J. Mol. Biol. 20*, 359 (1966).
15. F.B. Howard, J. Frazier and H.T. Miles, *J. Biol. Chem. 246*, 7073 (1971).
16. S. Arnott and E. Selsing, J. Mol. Biol. 88, 509 (1974).
17. S.L. Broitman, D.D. Im and J.R. Fresco, *Proc. Natl. Acad. Sci. 84*, 5120 (1987).
18. M.N. Lipsett, *J. Biol. Chem. 239*, 1256 (1964).
19. F.B. Howard, J. Frazier, M.N. Lipsett and H.T. Miles, *Biochem. Biophys. Res. Comm. 17*, 93 (1964).
20. C. Marck and D. Thiele, *Nucleic Acids Res. 5*, 1017 (1978).
21. C. Marck, D. Thiele, C. Schneider and W. Guschlbauer, *Nucleic Acids Res. 5*, 1979 (1978).
22. J.L. Campos and J.A. Subirana, *J. Biomolec. Struct. & Dyn. 5*, 15 (1987).
23. M. Cooney, G. Czernuszewicz, E.H. Postel, S.J. Flint and M.E. Hogan, *Science 241*, 456 (1988).
24. J.H. Miller and H.M. Sobell, *Proc. Natl. Acad. Sci. 55*, 1201 (1966).
25. A.R. Morgan and R.D. Wells, *J. Mol. Biol. 37*, 63 (1968).
26. J.S. Lee, D.A. Johnson and A.R. Morgan, *Nucleic Acids Res. 6*, 3073 (1979).
27. J.S. Lee, M.L. Woodsworth, L.P. Latimer and A.R. Morgan, *Nucleic Acids Res. 12*, 6603 (1984).
28. H.E. Moser and P.B. Dervan, *Science 238*, 645 (1987).
29. T. LeDoan, L. Perrouault, D. Praseuth, N. Habhoub, J.-L. Decout, N.T. Thuong, J. Lhomme and C. Helene, *Nucleic Acids Res. 15*, 7749 (1987).
30. A.G. Letai, M.A. Palladino, E. Fromm, V. Rizzo and J.R. Fresco, *Biochemistry 27*, 9108 (1988).
31. P. Rajagopal and J. Feigon, *Nature 339*, 637 (1989); *ibid. 340*, 322 (1989).
32. C. de los Santos, M. Rosen and D. Patel, *Biochemistry 28*, 7282 (1989).
33. R.K. Ralph, W.J. Connors and H.G. Khorana, *J. Am. Chem. Soc. 84*, 2265 (1962).
34. M. Gellert, M.N. Lipsett and D.R. Davies, *Proc. Natl. Acad. Sci. 48*, 2013 (1962).
35. D.M. Gray and F.J. Bollum, *Biopolymers 13*, 2087 (1974).
36. S.B. Zimmerman, G.H. Cohen and D.R. Davies, *J. Mol. Biol. 92*, 181 (1975).
37. S. McGavin, *J. Mol. Biol. 55*, 293 (1971).
38. D. Johnson and A.R. Morgan, *Proc. Natl. Acad. Sci. 75*, 1637 (1978).
39. S. McGavin, *J. Theor. Biol. 77*, 83 (1979).
40. W. Saenger, *Principles of Nucleic Acid Structure*, Springer-Verlag, New York (1984).
41. A.G.W. Leslie, S. Arnott, R. Chandrasekaran and R.L. Ratliff, *J. Mol. Biol. 143*, 49 (1980).
42. C.R. Cantor and A. Efstratiadis, *Nucleic Acids Res. 12*, 8059 (1984).
43. D.E. Pulleyblank, D.B. Haniford and A.R. Morgan, *Cell 42*, 271 (1985).
44. D.E. Pulleyblank, in *Nucleic Acids and Molecular Biology*, Vol. 2, (F. Eckstein & D.M.J. Lilley, Eds.) Springer-Verlag, pp. 31-48 (1988).
45. G. Yagil and J.L. Sussman, *EMBO J. 5*, 1719 (1986).
46. M. Bansal and N. Pattabiraman, *Biopolymers 28*, 531 (1989).
47. R.D. Wells, D.A. Collier, J.C. Hanvey, M. Shimizu and F. Wohlrab, *FASEB J. 2*, 2939 (1988).
48. H. Htun and J.E. Dahlberg, *Science 243*, 1571 (1989).
49. V.M. Vogt, *Methods Enzymol. 65*, 248 (1980).
50. K. Shishido and T. Ando, in *Nucleases* (S.M. Linn & R.J. Roberts, Eds.) Cold Spring Harbor Laboratory, pp. 155-185 (1982).
51. H.R. Drew, *J. Mol. Biol. 176*, 535 (1984).
52. D.E. Pulleyblank, M. Glover, C. Farah and D.B. Haniford, in *Unusual DNA Structures* (R.D. Wells & S.C. Harvey, Eds.) Springer-Verlag, New York, pp. 23-42 (1988).
53. E. Schon, T. Evans, J. Welsch and A. Efstratiadis, *Cell 35*, 837 (1983).
54. T. Evans and A. Efstratiadis, *J. Biol. Chem. 261*, 14771 (1986).
55. F. Wohlrab, M.J. McLean and R.D. Wells, *J. Biol. Chem. 262*, 6407 (1987).
56. J.C. Hanvey, J. Klysik and R.D. Wells, *J. Biol. Chem. 263*, 7386 (1988).
57. B.H. Johnston and A. Rich, *Cell 42*, 713 (1985).
58. W. Herr, *Proc. Natl. Acad. Sci. 82*, 8009 (1985).
59. K. Nejedly, M. Kwinkowski, G. Galazka, J. Klysik and E. Palecek, *J. Biomol. Struct. & Dyn. 3*, 467 (1985).
60. M.J. McLean, J.E. Larson, F. Wohlrab and R.D. Wells, *Nucleic Acids Res. 15*, 6917 (1987).
61. N. Vogt, L. Marrot, N. Rousseau, B. Malfoy and M. Leng, *J. Mol. Biol. 201*, 773 (1988).
62. R.D. Wells, S. Amirhaeri, J.A. Blaho, D.A. Collier, J.C. Hanvey, W.-T. Hsieh, A. Jaworski, J. Klysik, J.E. Larson, M.J. McLean, F. Wohlrab and W. Zacharias, in *Unusual DNA Structures* (R.D. Wells & S.C. Harvey, Eds.) Springer-Verlag, New York, pp. 1-21 (1988).

63. C.C. Hentschel, *Nature 295*, 714 (1982).
64. H.A.F. Mace, H.R.B. Pelham and A.A. Travers, *Nature 304*, 555 (1983).
65. H. Htun, E. Lund and J.E. Dahlberg, *Proc. Natl. Acad. Sci. 81*, 7288 (1984).
66. T. Kohwi-Shigematsu and Y. Kohwi, *Cell 43*, 199 (1985).
67. D. Christophe, B. Cabrer, A. Bacolla, H. Targovnik, V. Pohland and G. Vassart, *Nucleic Acids Res. 13*, 5127 (1985).
68. V.I. Lyamichev, S.M. Mirkin and M.D. Frank-Kamenetskii, *J. Biomol. Struct. & Dyn. 3*, 327 (1985).
69. V.I. Lyamichev, S.M. Mirkin and M.D. Frank-Kamenetskii, *J. Biomol. Struct. & Dyn. 3*, 667 (1986).
70. Y. Kohwi and T. Kohwi-Shigematsu, *Proc. Natl. Acad. Sci. 85*, 3781 (1988).
71. P. Parniewski, G. Galazka, A. Wilk and J. Klysik, *Nucleic Acids Res. 17*, 617 (1989).
72. J. Bernues, R. Beltran, J.M. Casasnovas and F. Azorin, *EMBO J. 8*, 2087 (1989).
73. F. Wohlrab and R.D. Wells, *J. Biol. Chem. 264*, 8207 (1989).
74. V.I. Lyamichev, S.M. Mirkin and M.D. Frank-Kamenetskii, *J. Biomol. Struct. & Dyn. 5*, 275 (1987).
75. S.M. Mirkin, V.I. Lyamichev, K.N. Drushlyak, V.N. Dobrynin, S. A. Filippov and M.D. Frank-Kamenetskii, *Nature 330*, 495 (1987).
76. V.I. Lyamichev, S.M. Mirkin, M.D. Frank-Kamenetskii and C.R. Cantor, *Nucleic Acids Res. 16*, 2165 (1988).
77. O.N. Voloshin, S.M. Mirkin, V.I. Lyamichev, B.P. Belotserkovskii and M.D. Frank-Kamenetskii, *Nature 333*, 475 (1988).
78. H. Htun and J.E. Dahlberg, *Science 241*, 1791 (1988).
79. B.H. Johnston, *Science 241*, 1800 (1988).
80. J.C. Hanvey, M. Shimizu and R.D. Wells, *Proc. Natl. Acad. Sci. 85*, 6292 (1988).
81. D.A. Collier, J.A. Griffins and R.D. Wells, *J. Biol. Chem. 263*, 7397 (1988).
82. M. Vojtiskova, S. Mirkin, V. Lyamichev, O. Voloshin, M. Frank-Kamenetskii and E. Palecek, *FEBS Lett. 234*, 295 (1988).
83. J. Stokrova, M. Vojtiskova and E. Palecek, *J. Biomol. Struct. & Dyn. 6*, 891 (1989).
84. M. Shimizu, J.C. Hanvey and R.D. Wells, *J. Biol. Chem. 264*, 5944 (1989).
85. J.C. Hanvey, M. Shimizu and R.D. Wells, *J. Biol. Chem. 264*, 5950 (1989).
86. Y. Kohwi, *Nucleic Acids Res. 17*, 4493 (1989).
87. E. Henderson, C.C. Hardin, S.K. Walk, I. Tinoco, Jr. and E.H. Blackburn, *Cell 51*, 899 (1987).
88. J.H. van de Sande, N.B. Ramsing, M.W. Germann, W. Elhorst, B.W. Kalisch, E.V. Kitzing, R.T. Pon, R.C. Clegg and T.M. Jovin, *Science 241*, 551 (1988).
89. R. Chattopadhyaya, S. Ikuta, K. Grzeskowiak and R.E. Dickerson, *Nature 334*, 175 (1988).
90. V.I. Lyamichev, S.M. Mirkin, O.N. Danilevskaya, O.N. Voloshin, S.V. Balatskaya, V.N. Dobrynin, S.A. Filippov and M.D. Frank-Kamenetskii, *Nature 339*, 634 (1989).
91. M.J.J. Bloomers, J.A.L.I. Walters, C.A.G. Haasnoot, J.M.A. Aelen, G.A. van der Marel, J.H. van Boom and C.W. Hilbers, *Biochemistry 28*, 7491 (1989).
92. V.I. Lim and A.L. Mazanov, *FEBS Lett. 88*, 118 (1978).
93. H. Htun, E. Lund, G. Westin, U. Pettersson and J.E. Dahlberg, *EMBO J. 4*, 1839 (1985).
94. A. Krol, E. Lund and J.E. Dahlberg, *EMBO J. 4*, 1529 (1985).
95. H. Htun, *H-DNA: Its Structure and Formation*, Ph. D. thesis, University of Wisconsin-Madison (Madison, 1989).
96. On the basis of our two-dimensional gel electrophoretic results, we have for a number of years presented our conclusion in support of the triple-stranded and single-stranded structure as shown in Figure 4: *Biological Effects of DNA Topology*, Cold Spring Harbor, N.Y. (September 1986); *Unusual DNA Structures*, First Gulf Shores Symposium, Gulf Shores, Ala. (April 1987); and *Biomolecular Stereodynamics*, Fifth Conversation, Albany, N. Y. (June 1987).
97. H. Htun and J. E. Dahlberg, manuscript in preparation.
98. J.S. Lee, G.D. Burkholder, L.J.P. Latimer, B.L. Haug and R.P. Braun, *Nucleic Acids Res. 15*, 1047 (1987).
99. G.D. Burkholder, L.J.P. Latimer and J.S. Lee, *Chromosoma (Berlin) 97*, 185 (1988).
100. H.C. Birnboim, *J. Mol. Biol. 121*, 541 (1978).
101. H. Manor, B. Sridhara Rao and R.G. Martin, *J. Mol. Evol. 27*, 96 (1988).
102. A.M. Beasty and M.J. Behe, *Nucleic Acids Res. 16*, 1517 (1988).
103. A.K. Konopka, *Nucleic Acids Res. 16*, 1739 (1988).
104. R.B. Inman and M. Schnos, *J. Mol. Biol. 49*, 93 (1970).
105. J.C. Wang, L.J. Peck and K. Becherer, *Cold Spring Harbor Symp. Quant. Biol. 47*, 85 (1982).
106. R.E. Depew and J.C. Wang, *Proc. Natl. Acad. Sci. 72*, 4275 (1975).
107. D.E. Pulleyblank, M. Shure, D. Tang, J. Vinograd and H.P. Vosberg, *Proc. Natl. Acad. Sci. 72*, 4280 (1985).

Structure & Methods, ISBN 0-940030-32-2
Volume 3: DNA & RNA, ISBN 0-940030-31-4
Eds., Ramaswamy H. Sarma & Mukti H. Sarma, © Adenine Press 1990

Triplexes, Duplexes, and Homopurine Complexes Formed from Homopurine and Homopyrimidine DNA Oligonucleotides

Juli Feigon[1]*, Dara Gilbert[1], Ponni Rajagopal[1], Edmond Wang[1], Gijs A. van der Marel[2] and Jacques H. van Boom[2]

[1]Department of Chemistry and Biochemistry
and the Molecular Biology Institute
University of California
Los Angeles, CA 90024

[2]Gorlaeus Laboratory
P.O. Box 9502
2300 RA Leiden, The Netherlands

Abstract

Homopurine:homopyrimidine sequences are widely occurring in the eucaryotic genome and appear to have unusual structures which may be involved in genetic regulation and in chromosome replication. In order to help elucidate these structures, we have investigated the complexes formed by the homopurine $d(GA)_4$ and homopyrimidine $d(TC)_4$ DNA oligonucleotides using 1 and 2 dimensional ^{1}H NMR spectroscopy. We have identified at least four different structures formed by these DNAs; a B-DNA duplex, a triplex composed of one homopurine and two homopyrimidine strands, another heterocomplex containing both strands, and a homocomplex of the $d(GA)_4$ strand. We review data on the duplex and triplex and present new information on a $d(AG)_4$ self-complex.

Introduction

Repeating DNA sequences of $d(GA)_n \cdot d(TC)_n$, as well as other naturally occurring homopurine:homopyrimidine stretches of DNA, show a pH and supercoil density dependent conformational change that indicates that these sequences can adopt non B-DNA structures (reviewed in 1). Several models have been proposed for these alternative conformations (2-4). Recent evidence strongly supports a model in which such sequences can, under appropriate conditions, form an intramolecular triplex composed of TAT and CGC^+ triplets with the excess $d(GA)_n$ looped out as a single strand (5-9). The proposed structure of the triplex part of the model is based in

*Author to whom correspondence should be addressed.

part on earlier studies which indicated that homopolymers of $d(GA)_n$ and $d(TC)_n$ form a triplex composed of one homopurine and two homopyrimidine strands at low pH (10), and on fiber diffraction data on $T_n \cdot A_n \cdot T_n$ triplexes (11).

Homopurine:homopyrimidine sequences are overrepresented in the eucaryotic genome (12). Diverse functions have been suggested for these sequences, depending on their locations, including roles in chromosome folding, selective pairing of chromosomes during meiosis, recombination, and genetic regulation (1). The latter role has been suggested because such sequences frequently flank transcribed genes and show a hypersensitivity to DNAse I and single strand specific nucleases which is usually pH and supercoil density dependent (13-16). Although the intramolecular pyr · pur · pyr triplex model explains most of the data obtained on these triplexes, there is also some evidence that under some conditions other structures may be forming (17,18,8).

The formation of intermolecular DNA triplexes is also currently an area of great interest because of their potential role in chromosome mapping (19) and in antisense gene therapy (20). For the former application, Dervan and co-workers have attached Fe(II)-EDTA cleaving reagents to homopyrimidine DNA oligonucleotides and then assayed for binding of these oligonucleotides to plasmid DNA containing the complimentary DNA sequence by the cleavage pattern observed (21). Their results substantiated models for triplex formation in which the second homopyrimidine strand binds parallel to the purine strand via Hoogsteen base pairing in the major groove. The high sequence specificity of these complexes may make them useful reagents for cleavage of large fragments in chromosomal DNA (19). Triplex formation is also promising in the area of antisense DNA where formation of DNA triplexes or RNA-DNA triplexes may be useful to repress protein synthesis at the level of transcription (22). In a preliminary experiment of this type, Hogan and co-workers showed that a mostly homopurine 27 base DNA oligonucleotide bound to the complementary region 115 base pairs upstream from the transcription origin of the human *c-myc* gene and repressed *c-myc* transcription *in vitro* (23). This particular system is also of interest because the triplex formed is predominantly a pyr · pur · *pur* triplex. Although evidence has been presented by other workers for triplexes of this type (24,25), relatively little has been established about their structure, including the base pairing scheme. The proposed existence of pyr · pur · pur triplexes also raises the question of whether *intra*molecular triplexes of this type may also form.

We have initiated NMR studies on homopurine-rich and homopyrimidine-rich DNA oligonucleotides in order to obtain detailed information on the structure, sequence specificity, and stabilities of triplexes and other alternative conformations formed from these oligonucleotides. In this paper, we review the NMR results we have obtained on the duplex, triplex, and other complexes formed from $d(GA)_4$ + $d(TC)_4$, with emphasis on the information obtained on the $d(TC)_4 \cdot d(GA)_4 \cdot d(TC)_4$ triplex (26,27). We also present new information on formation of self-complexes of $d(GA)_4$ and the closely related $d(AG)_4$.

Duplex Formation from $d(TC)_4$ and $d(GA)_4$. Spectra of the aromatic, H1′, H2′,H2″, and

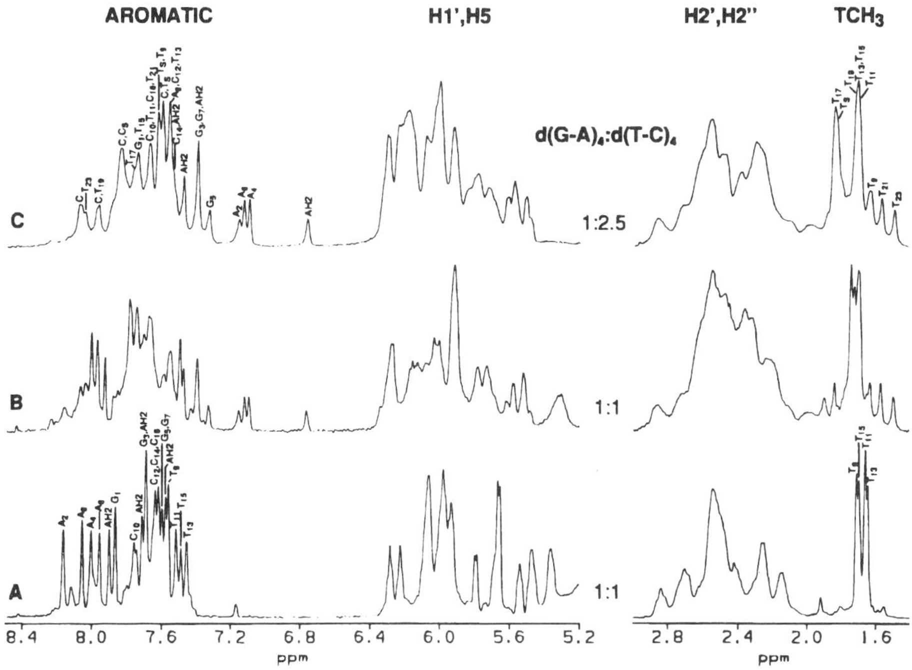

Figure 1: 500 MHz ^{1}H NMR spectra of the aromatic, H1′ and H2′,H2″, and methyl regions of $d(GA)_2$ + $d(TC)_4$ under different conditions in D_2O. (A) 1:1 $d(GA)_4 \cdot d(TC)_4$ at 15°C in 20 mM phosphate, pH 7.3, 50 mM NaCl, 5 mM $MgCl_2$. Under these conditions, the predominant form is the duplex DNA. Assignments of the duplex aromatic and methyl resonances are indicated. (B) 1:1 $d(GA)_4 \cdot d(TC)_4$ at 35°C in 20 mM phosphate, pH 5.5, 50 mM NaCl, 5 mM $MgCl_2$. The sample contains predominantly a mixture of duplex and triplex. (C) 1:2.5 $d(GA)_4 \cdot d(TC)_4$ at 35°C in 10 mM phosphate, pH 5.5, 100 mM NaCl, 5 mM $MgCl_2$. The major form of the DNA present is the triplex form, as well as some single-stranded $d(TC)_4$. Assignments of the triplex aromatic and methyl resonances are indicated. Peaks labelled C are from the second homopyrimidine strand bound to the major groove in the triplex. The single-stranded thymine methyl resonances are identified as T_s. Some resonances which were mislabeled in (26) have been correctly indicated here. Spectra were acquired with a sweep width of 5000 Hz, 2 second recycle delay, 64-128 transients, and 8K complex points. The spectra were resolution enhanced by double exponential multiplication.

TCH_3 resonances of $d(GA)_4$ and $d(TC)_4$ under different conditions are shown in Figure 1. At pH 7 and above, the oligonucleotides $d(TC)_4$ and $d(GA)_4$ combine to form a B-DNA duplex (Figure 1a), as determined by our analysis of NOESY spectra obtained on such complexes (27). Assignments of all but the H5′,H5″ resonances were obtained for this duplex using standard sequential assignment procedures for B-DNA type duplexes (28-30) and some of these assignments are indicated on the figure. Excess $d(TC)_4$ strand in some of the samples appeared as single-strand. In the absence of magnesium, this duplex is very unstable and is already partially melted at 20°C. In contrast, the DNA octamer $[d(ACGTACGT)]_2$, which contains the same number of AT and GC base pairs, melts at least 20°C higher in the same salt conditions (Gilbert and Feigon, unpublished results). The unusually low melting temperature for this homopurine:homopyrimidine duplex indicates that there may be something unusual about this B-DNA structure and may help explain why such sequences can adopt alternative conformations so readily.

Duplex-Triplex Equilibrium. As the pH of a sample containing equimolar amounts of $d(GA)_4$ and $d(TC)_4$ is lowered to pH 6.1 and below, resonances from an alternative conformation become readily observable (Figure 1b). These new resonances arise from a triplex containing one $d(GA)_4$ strand and two $d(TC)_4$ strands (Scheme I). Addition of excess $d(TC)_4$ pushes the equilibrium towards the triplex form; the sample in Figure 1c contains primarily triplex with some excess single $d(TC)_4$ strand.

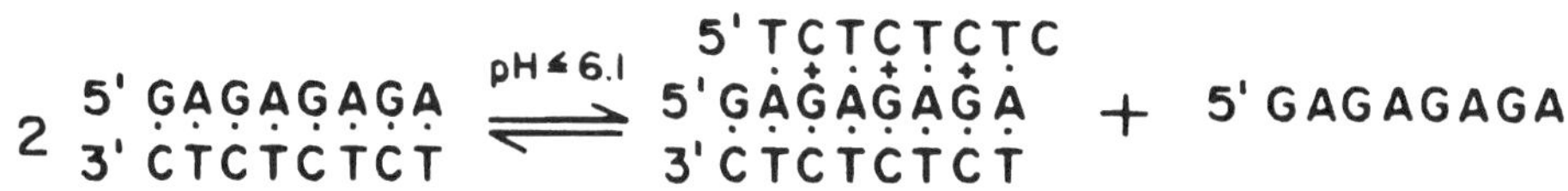

Scheme I

Exchange Between Duplex and Triplex. A NOESY spectrum of the sample under the conditions shown in Figure 1c is shown in Figure 2. This spectrum is considerably more complicated than that obtained for the duplex. Assignments of the resonances in this structure presented a much greater challenge than those for the B-DNA duplex. Standard sequential assignment techniques could not be used since the structure at this point was not known, and in any case sequential connectivities were not observed. Fortunately, we were able to obtain assignments of the base and H1′ resonances in the triplex, without making any assumptions about the structure, by exchange spectroscopy (31) (NOESY and ROESY (32)). A portion of a ROESY spectrum of the sample under conditions where duplex, triplex, and single strands are present, is shown in Figure 3a. Exchange crosspeaks are observed between the triplex and the duplex and between the triplex and single-stranded $d(TC)_4$, but not between duplex and single-strand, as illustrated in Figure 3b. This exchange indicates that triplex formation proceeds by binding of the second $d(TC)_4$ strand to a $d(GA)_4 \cdot d(TC)_4$ duplex.

Evidence for an Additional Heterocomplex. One-dimensional spectra of samples of $d(GA)_4$ and $d(TC)_4$ taken under conditions where the predominant conformation is a B-DNA duplex contain some additional resonances which do not correspond to resonances identified for the triplex (e.g., peaks at 7.17 and 8.13 ppm in Figure 1a). These resonances occur in samples from pH 6.1 to 8.3 in the absence and presence of Mg^{+2} at all strand concentrations studied. In NOESY spectra of such samples, these resonances show exchange crosspeaks to the duplex. The aromatic region of a NOESY spectrum of the sample under conditions where the predominant conformation is a B-DNA duplex is shown in Figure 4, with some of these exchange crosspeaks indicated by arrows. Since exchange crosspeaks are observed to both the $d(GA)_4$ and the $d(TC)_4$ strand, it appears that an additional heterocomplex is present in these samples. Although triplexes containing one homopyrimidine and two homopurine strands have also been reported by Fresco and colleagues (24,25), we do not believe that this heterocomplex corresponds to a pyr · pur · pur triplex since the resonances from this complex did not increase in intensity in the presence of excess $d(GA)_4$ strand. We have been unable to find conditions where there is more than a small amount of this heterocomplex, so we have not been able to characterize it further. Interestingly, in samples containing a mixture of triplex and duplex at pH 6.1,

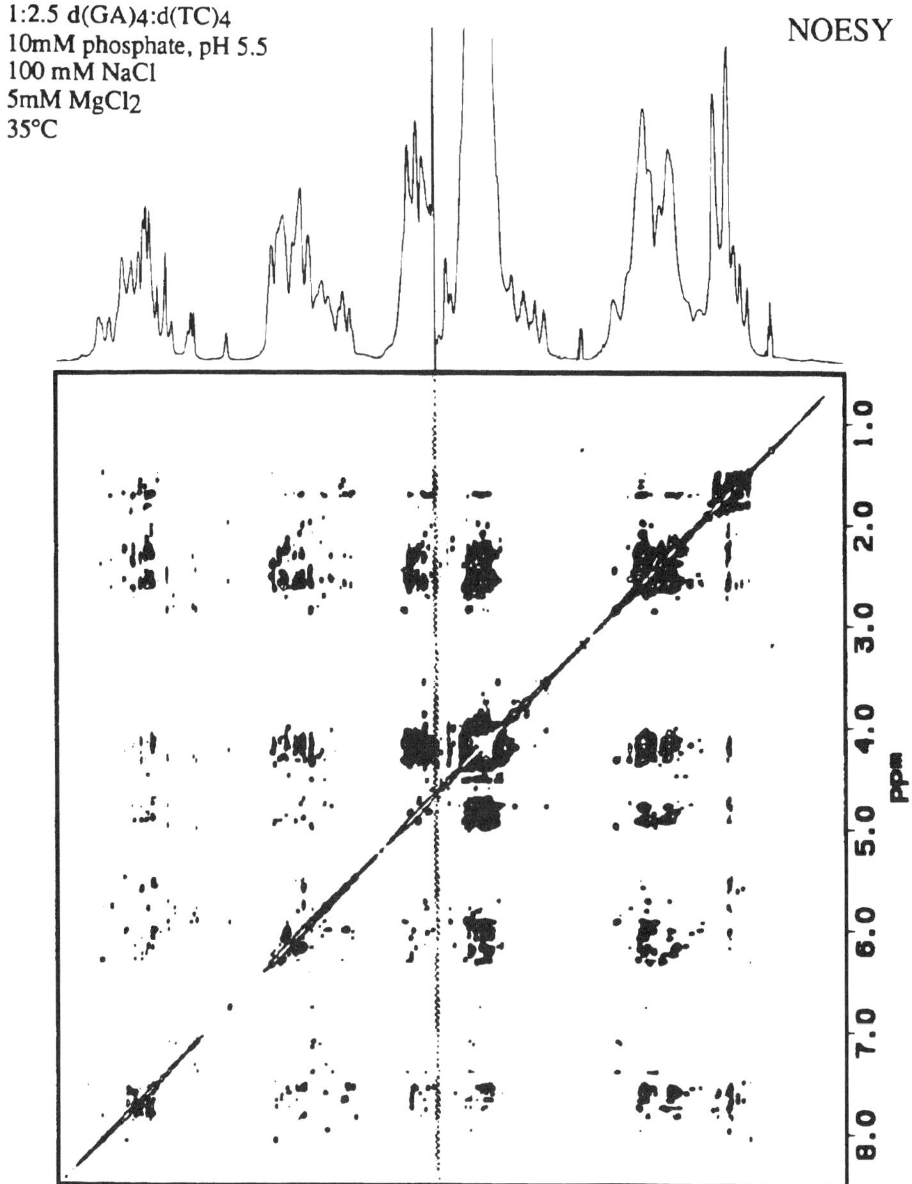

Figure 2: NOESY spectrum of 1:2.5 $d(GA)_4 \cdot d(TC)_4$ in 10 mM phosphate, pH 5.5, 100 mM NaCl, 5 mM $MgCl_2$, 35°C. Sample contains 2 mM $d(GA)_4$ and 5 mM $d(TC)_4$ and is primarily triplex under these conditions with the excess $d(TC)_4$ present as single strand. The spectrum was acquired with a sweep width of 5000 Hz in both dimensions, 1K complex points in t_2, 64 scans per t_1 value, and 322 t_1 values were collected. Residual HDO was irradiated during the recycle delay of 2 s and τ_m = 350 msec. The t_1 domain was zero-filled to 1K complex points prior to Fourier transformation, and the data was apodized by a squared sine-bell function phase shifted by 40° in t_2 and 60° in t_1. The one-dimensional spectrum at the top was acquired with 8K complex points, 64 acquisitions, and irradiation of the residual HDO during the 2 second recycle delay (adapted from 27).

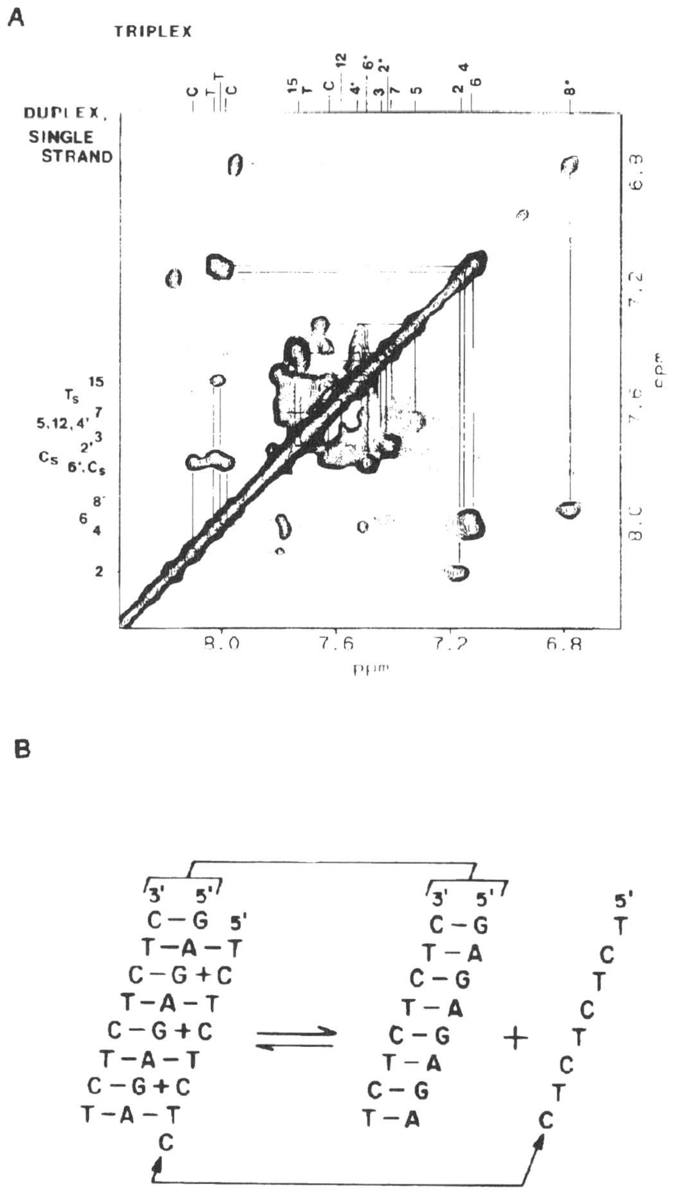

Figure 3: (A) Aromatic region of a ROESY spectrum of 1:1.25 $d(GA)_4 \cdot d(TC)_4$ in 20 mM phosphate, pH 5.5, 50 mM NaCl, 5 mM $MgCl_2$, 42°C. Sample is 2 mM in $d(GA)_4$ and 2.5 mM in $d(TC)_4$. Exchange crosspeaks are seen between duplex and triplex and between triplex and single $d(TC)_4$ strand. Assignments of triplex and duplex resonances are indicated on the tops and sides of the spectra, respectively. T_s indicates resonances from $d(TC)_4$ single-strand, numbers with * are AH2 resonances, and C, T are the Hoogsteen base paired pyrimidine strand H6 resonances. The spectrum was acquired with a 4 KHz spin-lock field applied during the mixing time of 116 msec. the sweep width was 5000 Hz in both dimensions and 1k complex points were collected in t_2. 259 t_1 values of 64 scans each were collected. Spectra were zero-filled to 1K in the t_1 dimension and apodized with a squared sine-bell function phase shifted by 65°. (B) Schematic illustrating exchange between triplex and duplex and single $d(TC)_4$ strand.

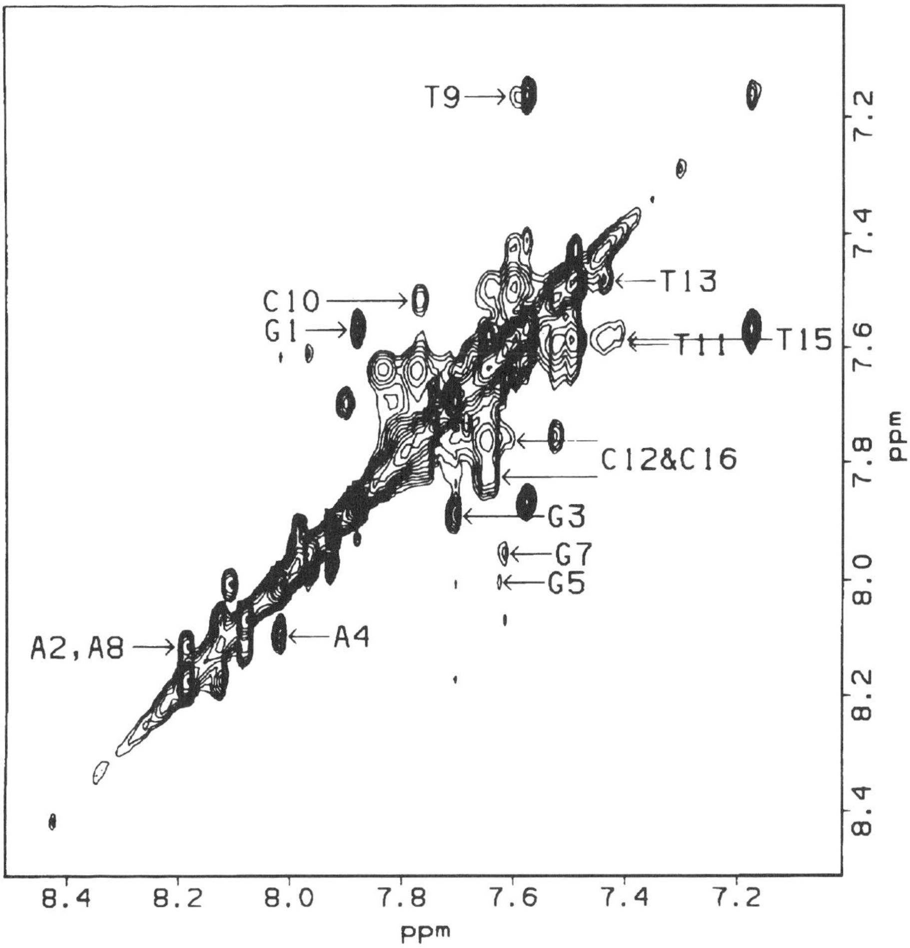

Figure 4: Aromatic region of a NOESY spectrum of the same under conditions where the predominant conformation is a B-DNA duplex. Exchange crosspeaks between the duplex and an unidentified heterocomplex are observed. Assignments are indicated for some of these exchange crosspeaks, with the arrows pointing toward the heterocomplex resonances. Sample is 1:1.3 $d(GA)_4 \cdot d(TC)_4$ in 20 mM phosphate, pH 8.3, 50 mM NaCl, 15°C and is primarily duplex under these conditions with the excess $d(TC)_4$ present as single strand. The spectrum was acquired as in Figure 2 except 282 t_1 values were collected and the data in both dimensions were apodized by a squared sine-bell function phase shifted by 65°.

exchange crosspeaks between the duplex and the unknown heterocomplex but not between the duplex and the triplex were observed. We therefore studied the triplex at pH 5.5.

Triplex Formation from $d(GA)_4$ and 2 $d(TC)_4$. The spectral changes observed in samples containing $d(GA)_4$ and $d(TC)_4$ on lowering the pH and in the presence of excess $d(TC)_4$ strand are consistent with pyr · pur · pyr triplex formation. NOESY (Figure 2) and DQF-COSY spectra were obtained on the sample shown in Figure 1c. Figure 5 shows the portion of the DQF-COSY spectrum containing the crosspeaks between CH6-CH5. Eight CH6-CH5 were observed as expected for a structure containing

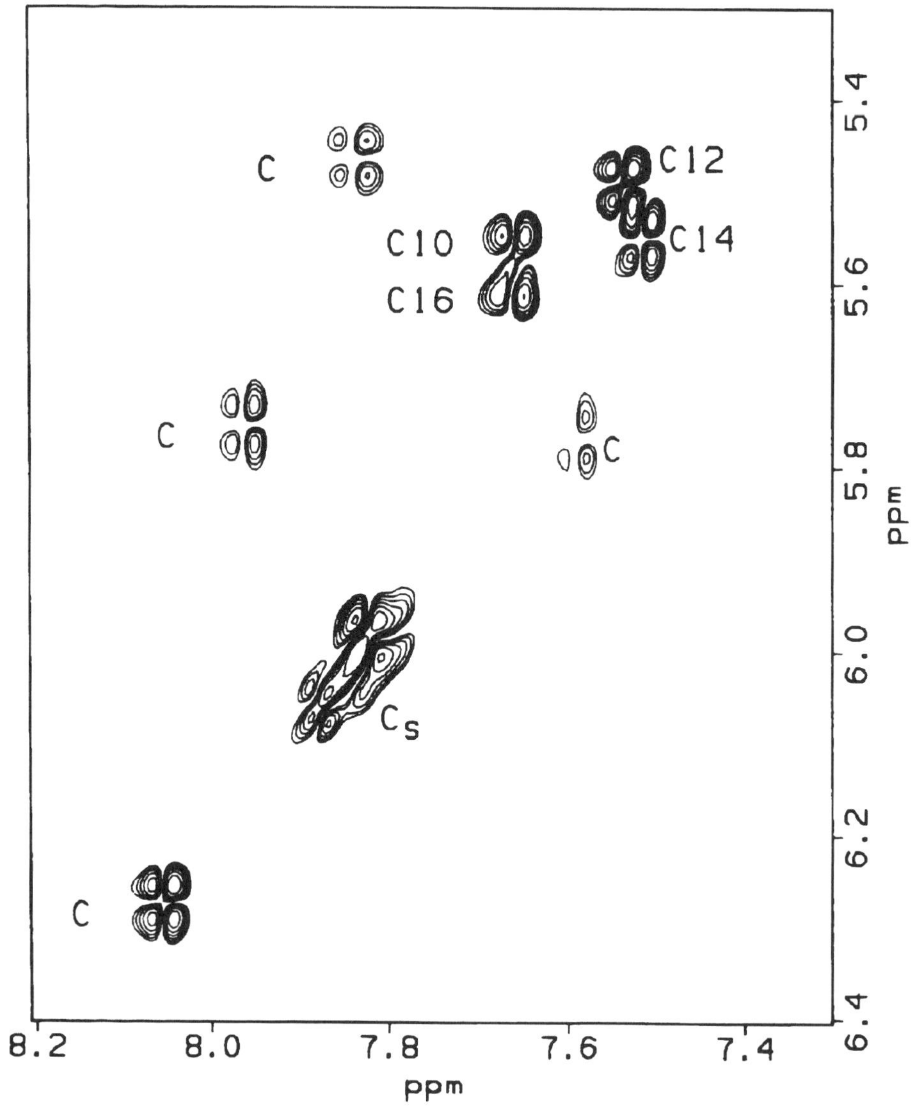

Figure 5: DQF-COSY spectrum of the triplex at 35°C. Region of crosspeaks between the CH5 and CH6 resonances is shown. Sample is the same as Figure 2. Crosspeaks from the second pyrimidine strand are identified as C; crosspeaks arising from some excess single-stranded $(TC)_4$ are identified as C_s.

two $d(TC)_4$ strands. Additional crosspeaks in this region arise from some excess single-stranded $d(TC)_4$. Similarly, eight TH6-TMe crosspeaks from the triplex plus some single-strand crosspeaks were observed (not shown).

Spectra of the imino region of the triplex also reveal additional imino resonances arising from hydrogen bonding of the second $d(TC)_4$ strand in the triplex (Figure 6a). At low temperatures, eight imino resonances were observed in the duplex, corresponding to 4 Watson-Crick AT and 4 Watson-Crick GC^+ base pairs (27). Seven

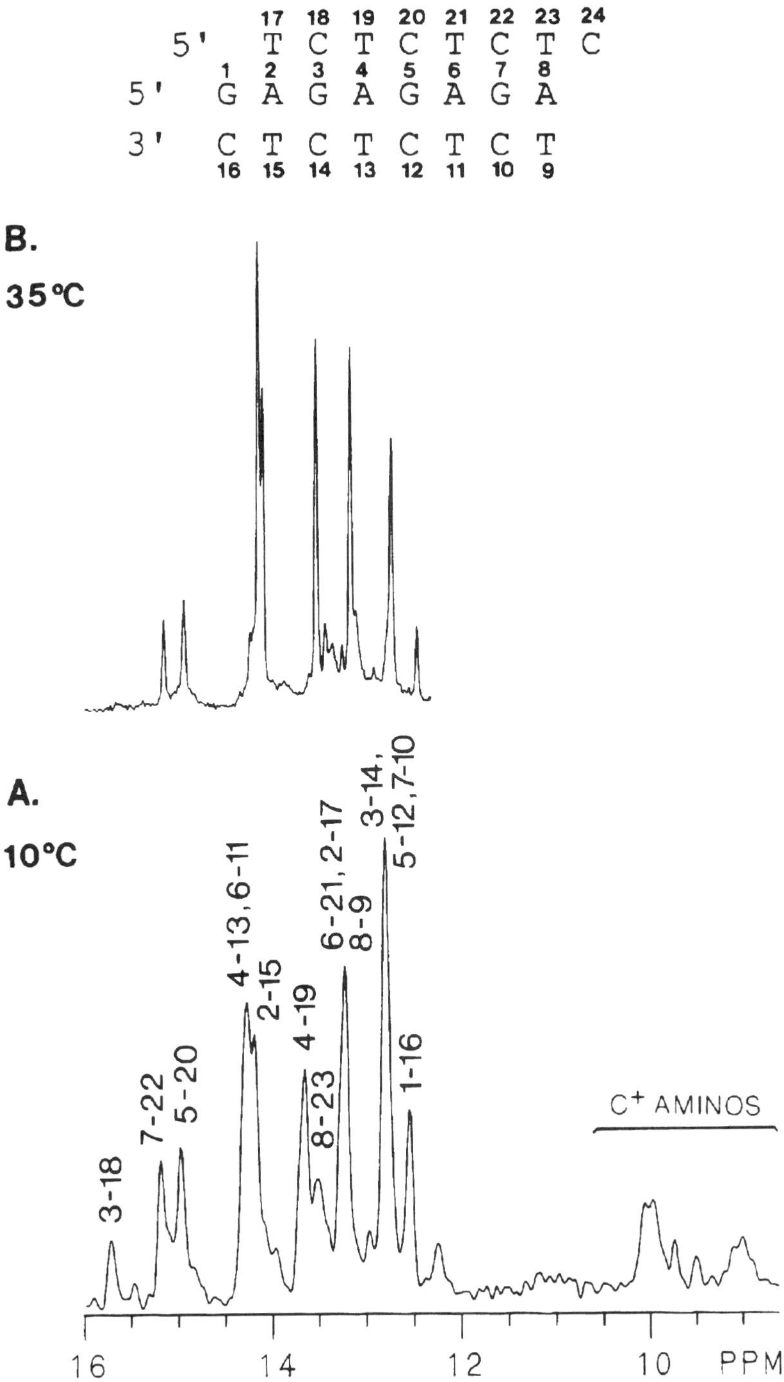

Figure 6: Imino proton spectra of the triplex at (A) 10°C and (B) 35°C. Sample is the same as Figure 1c but in 90% H_2O/10% D_2O. Spectra were acquired with a $1\bar{1}$ spin echo pulse sequence (90°_x-τ-90°_{-x}-Δ-90°_ϕ-2τ-$90^\circ_{-\phi}$-Δ) (45). Assignments are indicated for the imino resonances.

additional imino resonances were observed at low temperatures in the triplex, which we identified as arising from 4 AT and 3 GC Hoogsteen base pairs (see below). These resonances were sequentially assigned via imino-imino NOEs observed in spectra of the triplex in H_2O (Figure 7). Proposed models for pyr · pur · pyr triplexes have one purine and one pyrimidine strand Watson-Crick base paired in an A′-DNA

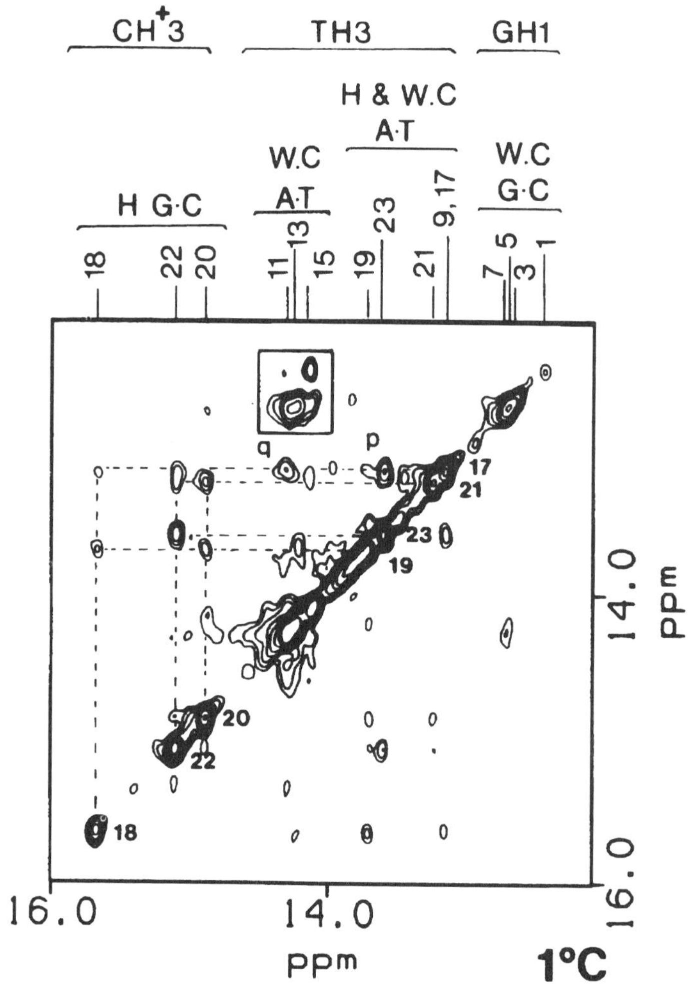

Figure 7: Portion of a phase sensitive NOESY spectrum of the triplex in H_20 (90% H_2O 10% D_2O) at 1 °C showing the region containing the imino proton resonances and their crosspeaks. Sequential assignments for the Hoogsteen base paired iminos are indicated by the dotted lines. Crosspeaks between Watson-Crick base paired iminos are boxed. Some exchange crosspeaks between the two triplex forms (see text) are labeled **p**, **q**. The sample contains 1:2.5 $d(GA)_4 \cdot d(TC)_4$, 10 mM phosphate, pH 5.5, 25 mM NaCl. Spectra were acquired by replacing the third 90 pulse with a $1\bar{1}$ spin echo pulse sequence and phase cycling appropriately in order to suppress the large water resonance (45). The carrier was centered at the water resonance and the delay τ was adjusted so that both the imino and the aromatic resonances were at regions of maximum excitation (τ = 300 μsec). The sweep width was 14048 Hz in both dimensions, the mixing time was 150 msec, and 215 t_1 values of 128 acquisitions each were collected. The t_1 dimension was zero-filled to 2K complex points prior to Fourier transformation. The spectrum was apodized by a squared sine-bell function (skew = 1.6) and phase shifted by 85° in both dimensions (adapted from 26).

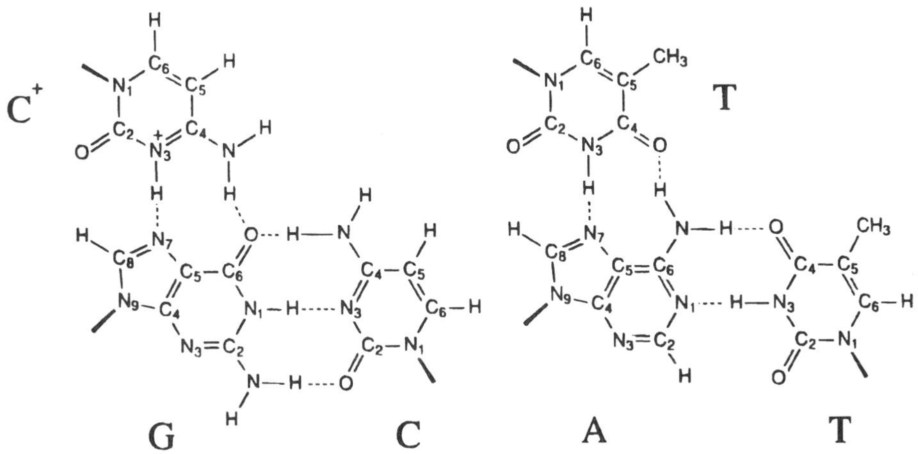

Scheme II

type helix, with the second homopyrimidine strand Hoogsteen base paired in the major groove to the purine strand. This results in base triplets as illustrated above (Scheme II). Hoogsteen base pairing of GC base pairs requires protonation of the C at N3. The lowfield shifted imino resonances which we assigned to Hoogsteen GC^+ base pairs resonate at around 15-16 ppm. This is the same region which Kallenbach, *et al.* assigned to a protonated C imino in RNA CGC^+ triplets formed from oligo G plus CMP (33). We observed crosspeaks from the imino resonances in the third strand to the AH8 resonances in spectra of the triplex taken at 30°C, thus confirming that AT Hoogsteen base pairs are present (Figure 8). At this temperature, the imino resonances from the GC^+ base pairs are exchanging too rapidly with water to give rise to crosspeaks. However, at lower temperatures we also observe crosspeaks between the GC^+ iminos and the GH8 resonances. These assignments were confirmed by obtaining spectra on samples which had been prepared with $d(GA)_4$ deuterated at the H8 position (27), since there is a lot of resonance overlap in these spectra and the assignments to H8 had to be made unambiguously.

Binding of the second $d(TC)_4$ strand parallel to the $d(GA)_4$ strand could result in a triplex with a 5′ dangling end or a 3′ dangling end (Scheme III). Observation of 4 TA and 3 GC^+ Hoogsteen base pairs indicated that the predominant triplex formed has a 3′ dangling end. However, we did see some additional crosspeaks in the NOESY spectra in H_2O and D_2O which indicate that a small proportion of the triplex with the 5′ dangling end is also formed. Close examination of the one dimensional spectra of the triplex reveals that these additional crosspeaks arise from some small resonances in the spectrum which mostly appear as shoulders on the main resonances. The predominance of the triplex with 4 TA and 3 GC^+ rather than 3 TA and 4 GC^+ Hoogsteen base pairs may indicate that Hoogsteen AT base pairs are more stable than Hoogsteen GC^+ base pairs at the pH studied. Spectra of the imino proton resonances in water at higher temperatures (Figure 6b) show that the C^+ iminos exchange much more rapidly than the Hoogsteen AT iminos, although it is not clear from this whether this is due to an intrinsically faster exchange rate for these protons or to a shorter lifetime for the base pairs.

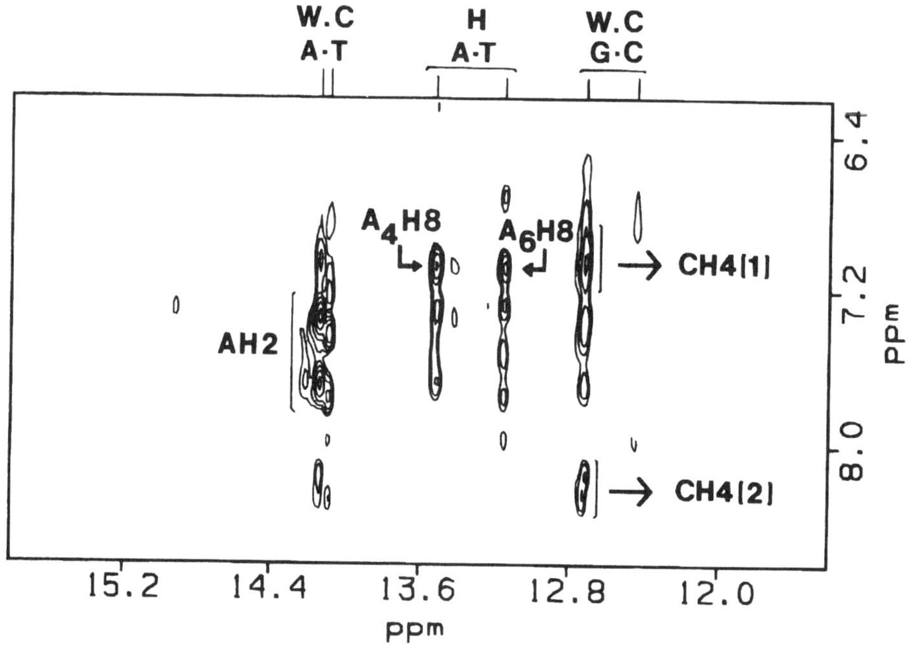

Figure 8: Portion of a phase sensitive NOESY spectrum of the triplex in H_2O (90% H_2O:10% D_2O) at 30°C showing the region containing the crosspeaks between the imino and the aromatic and amino resonances. Assignments for crosspeaks between the Watson-Crick AT imino and AH2, the Hoogsteen AT imino and AH8, and the Watson-Crick GC imino and C amino resonances are indicated. Crosspeaks from Hoogsteen GC^+ resonances are absent at this temperature. The sample is the same as Figure 6. The spectrum was acquired and processed as in Figure 7 except it was apodized in t_1 and t_2 by 60 and 45 degree phase shifted sinebell squared functions, respectively (adapted from 27).

```
        17 18 19 20 21 22 23 24
  5'     T  C  T  C  T  C  T  C          5'   T C T C T C T C
      1  2  3  4  5  6  7  8
5'    G  A  G  A  G  A  G  A                5'  G A G A G A G A
3'    C  T  C  T  C  T  C  T                3'  C T C T C T C T
     16 15 14 13 12 11 10  9
```

Scheme III

Models for triplex structures based on fiber diffraction of poly(A)-poly(U)-poly(U) and poly(dA)-poly(dT)-poly(dT) (11) show an A′-DNA structure with a C3′-endo sugar pucker for all three strands. In order to obtain further information on the glycosidic torsion angles and sugar pucker, we also obtained a MINSY (34) spectrum on the triplex. In this experiment, the H2′H2″ region of the spectrum was irradiated during the mixing time of a NOESY experiment. This allowed us to obtain direct NOEs from the aromatic to the H3′ resonances without the usual spin diffusion through the H2′,H2″ protons. The results of these experiments are shown in Figure 9. For B-DNA, with S-type sugar pucker (average C2′-endo) the inter and intrabase H8,H6 to H3′ distances are 4-5 Å, while for A-DNA with N-type sugar pucker (average C3′-endo) the distances are 2.5-3.1 Å (35). We therefore expect strong

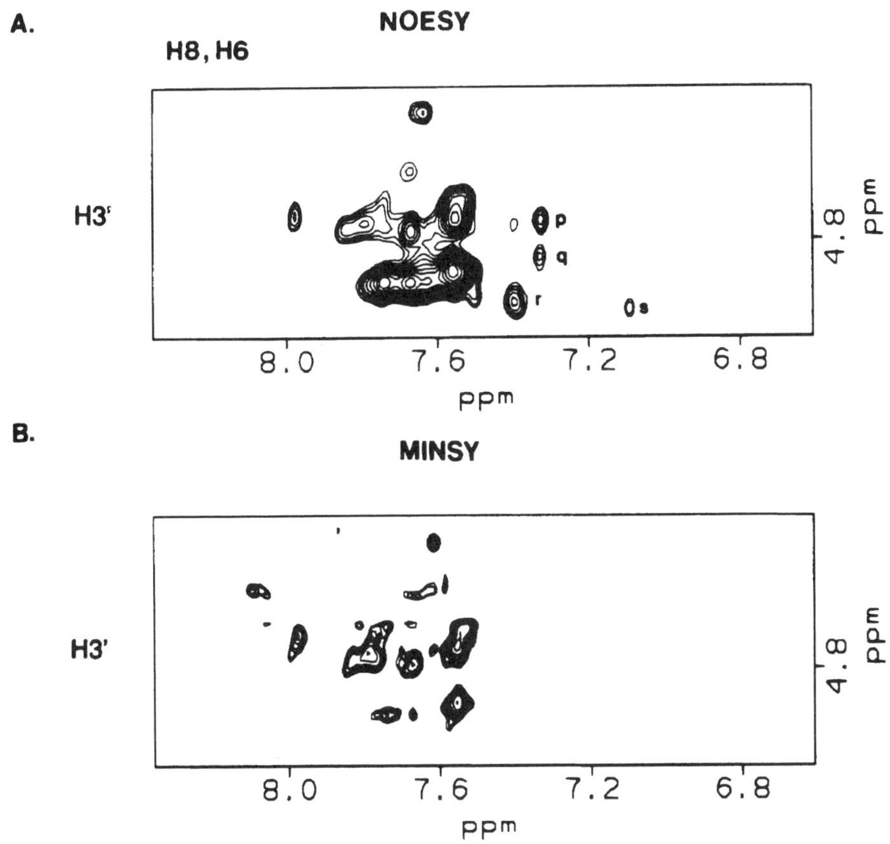

Figure 9: Portions of NOESY (A) and MINSY (B) spectra of the triplex at 35°C. Region of crosspeaks between the aromatic and H3′ protons are shown. In (A) GH8-H3′ crosspeaks are labeled p, q, and r and AH8-H3′ crosspeak is labeled s; these crosspeaks are absent in (B). The sample contained 1:2 $d(GA)_4 \cdot d(TC)_4$, 20 mM phosphate, pH 5.5, 50 mM NaCl, and 5 mM $MgCl_2$. The control NOESY spectrum was acquired with a τ_m = 200 msec. The MINSY spectrum was acquired under the same conditions as the NOESY except that the region of the spectrum containing the H2′,H2″ resonances was completely saturated during the mixing time, and residual HDO was not irradiated during the recycle delay. 2K complex points were collected with 64 scans per t_1 value and 261 t_1 values were collected. The spectra were zero-filled in t_1 and apodized with a squared sine-bell phase shifted by 90° in both dimensions (adapted from 27).

H8,H6-H3′ NOEs for an A-DNA type sugar pucker and weak or no NOEs for a B-DNA type sugar pucker. A comparison of the crosspeaks appearing in the NOESY and MINSY experiment indicated that the crosspeaks in this region arising from the purine residues disappear in the MINSY experiment while those from the pyrimidines remain. Thus it appears that for this triplex the pyrimidine sugars are closer to an A-DNA type sugar pucker while the purine sugars are closer to a B-DNA type sugar pucker. We were unable to obtain more quantitative information on sugar pucker from the DQF-COSY spectrum due to extreme spectral overlap in this region.

Self Complexes from $d(GA)_4$ and from $d(AG)_4$. Spectra of the single strands of $d(TC)_4$ and $d(GA)_4$ revealed some interesting features. At 15°C, samples containing $d(TC)_4$

only showed partially resolved spectra with narrow linewidths indicative of a single-stranded structure. In contrast, d(GA)$_4$ at 15°C showed broad resonances indicative of some kind of self-complex (27). As the temperature was raised, the aromatic resonances shifted to lower field and sharpened. We have investigated the self-complexes formed by both d(GA)$_4$ and by d(AG)$_4$. Spectra of the aromatic and H1′ regions of d(AG)$_4$ as a function of temperature are shown in Figure 10. At 1°C, the aromatic region of the spectrum of d(AG)$_4$ shows partially resolved, relatively sharp resonance lines. By 10°C the resonances have begun to broaden and shift to lower field. The sharp resonances which appear between 7.2 and 7.6 ppm at 1°C have almost completely disappeared by 20°C, and the spectrum appears broad and unresolved. As the temperature is raised further, the resonance lines once again

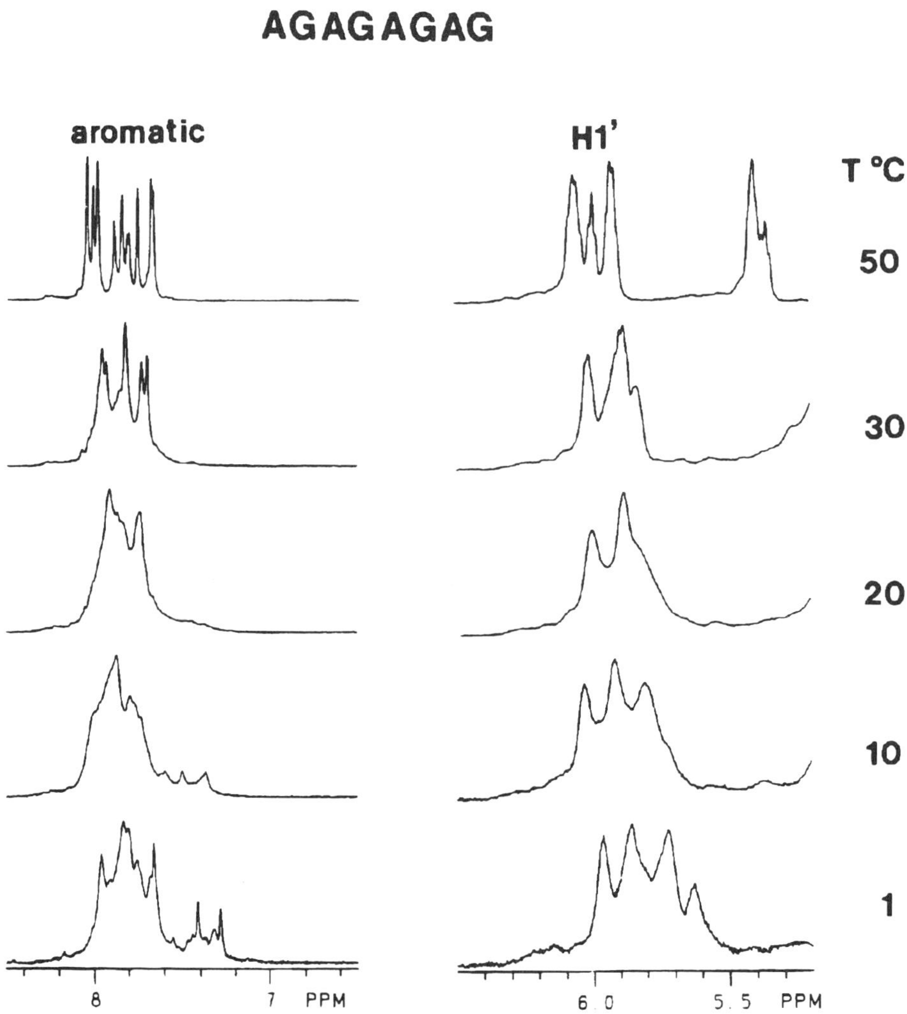

Figure 10: One dimensional spectra of the aromatic and H1′ resonances of d(AG)$_4$ in D_2O as a function of temperature. Sample contains d(AG)$_4$ in 20 mM phosphate, pH 7, 50 mM NaCl, and 5 mM $MgCl_2$.

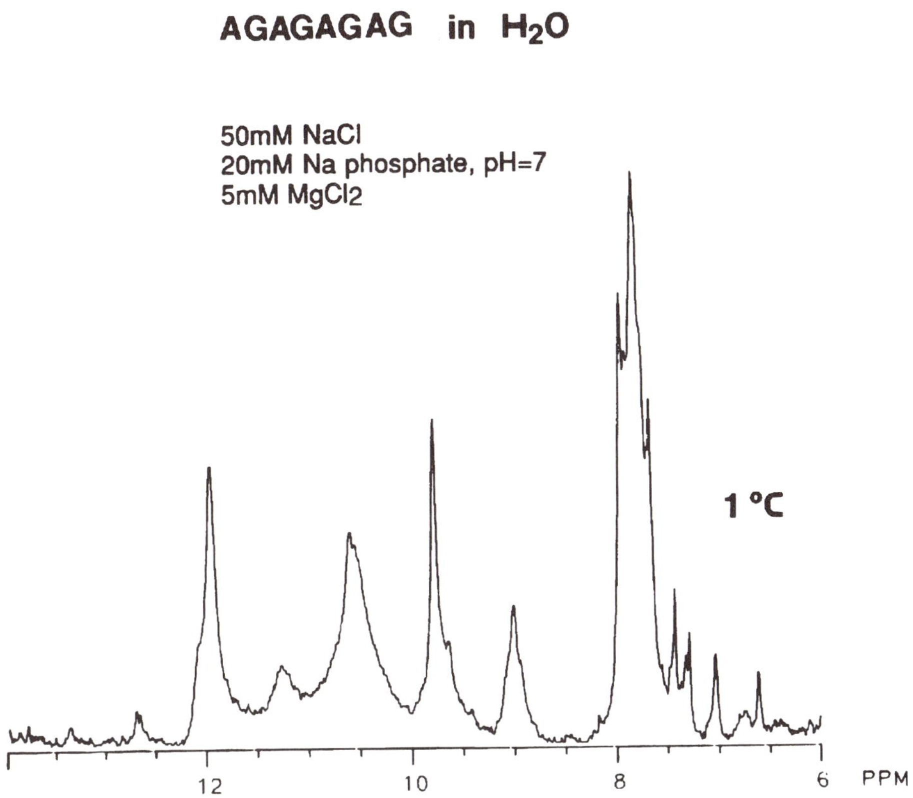

Figure 11: One dimensional spectrum of the imino, amino, and aromatic resonances of $d(AG)_4$ in 90% H_2O/10% D_2O at 1°C. Sample buffer is the same as Figure 10. The spectrum was acquired with a $1\bar{1}$ spin echo pulse sequence with the excitation maximum at 12.3 ppm.

begin to sharpen and by 50°C, the aromatic region of $d(GA)_4$ shows sharp, well resolved lines. The H1′ region of the spectrum behaves in a similar fashion. These spectra indicate that at low temperatures $d(AG)_4$ is forming at least one specific self-complex and that as the temperature is raised this self-complex(es) is in intermediate exchange with single-strand.

Further evidence for formation of at least one specific self-complex at low temperatures is obtained from spectra of $d(GA)_4$ and $d(AG)_4$ in H_2O. A spectrum of the imino, amino, and aromatic regions of $d(AG)_4$ at 1°C is shown in Figure 11. Hydrogen bonding of at least some of the G imino protons is indicated by the resonance intensity at around 12 ppm. Additional resonances between 8.5 and 11.5 ppm must arise from G imino (most likely non-hydrogen bonded) and hydrogen bonded G amino and/or A amino protons. Preliminary NOESY spectra in water showed a crosspeak between the hydrogen bonded and non-hydrogen bonded amino resonances at 9 and 7 ppm, respectively (not shown). No crosspeaks from any of the other exchangeable resonances were observed.

Self-complexes of G-rich oligonucleotides have been previously observed (36,37), and duplex (36) or tetraplex (37) structures containing G-G base pairs have been proposed as models for telomere structures. The model for the tetraplex structures has the Gs in all four strands hydrogen bonded via Hoogsteen base pairs. If such structures were forming with $d(AG)_4$ and $d(GA)_4$, the adenines would then most likely not be forming base pairs at neutral pH. A protonated self-complex of poly d(AG) had been reported by Antao *et al.* (38) at pH 4.0, but they do not observe a self-complex at higher pHs. An alternative structure, in which a duplex of mis-matched GA base pairs were formed, would allow all of the bases to form base pairs. GA base pairs have been observed in both crystal and NMR structures. In the crystal G(anti)-A(anti) (39), G(anti)-A(syn) (40), and G(syn)-A(anti) (41) base pairing schemes have all been reported, apparently depending on the sequence studied. NMR results on some GA mismatches have further shown that at least in some cases the base pairing structure obtained in a given oligomer is dependent on pH, with G(anti)-A(anti) base pairs observed at neutral pH and above and G(syn)-A^+(anti) Hoogsteen base pairs postulated at low pH (42). The crystal structure on d(CCAAGATTGG) showed that the GA mis-match did not significantly distort the helix (43), and therefore it might be predicted that GA base pairs could form a stable duplex. Work is in progress to determine which, if any, of these structures is being formed in the homopurine oligonucleotides $d(GA)_4$ and $d(AG)_4$.

Summary

The homopurine $d(GA)_4$ and homopyrimidine $d(TC)_4$ octamers form several different complexes depending on conditions. Some of the structures which these DNA oligonucleotides might form are summarized in Table I. Both a B-DNA duplex and a pyrimidine:purine:pyrimidine triplex were readily observed, with triplex formation favored by low pH and excess pyrimidine strand. However, we found no evidence for formation of a pyrimidine:purine:*purine* triplex under any of the wide range of conditions studied. Spectra of the pyrimidine strand alone at neutral pH and above indicated no higher order structure, although other workers have proposed a duplex structure for $d(TC)_n$ at much lower pH (38,44). The purine

Table I

Possible Structures Formed from 5′ d(GAGAGAGA)+ 5′ d(TCTCTCTC)

homopurine:homopyrimidine duplex	$d(GA)_4 \cdot d(TC)_4$
homopyrimidine:homopurine:homopyrimidine triplex	$d(TC)_4 \cdot d(GA)_4 \cdot d(TC)_4$
homopyrimidine:homopurine:homopurine triplex	$d(TC)_4 \cdot d(GA)_4 \cdot d(GA)_4$
homopurine duplex	$d(GA)_4 \cdot d(GA)_4$
homopurine tetraplex	$d(GA)_4 \cdot d(GA)_4 \cdot d(CA)_4 \cdot d(GA)_4$
homopyrimidine duplex	$d(TC)_4 \cdot d(TC)_4$
other heterocomplexes	?

$d(GA)_4$ and $d(AG)_4$ strands both form some sort of at least partially base paired self-complex at low temperatures, but the stoichiometry and structure of these self-complexes has not yet been determined. An additional heterocomplex of unknown structure is also formed in small amounts under a range of conditions and exchanges readily with the B-DNA duplex.

Although the presence of several different conformations in the same sample precluded obtaining a detailed three dimensional structure on the triplex, significant information on the structure and stability of this pyrimidine:purine:pyrimidine triplex was obtained. We unambiguously confirmed that the second pyrimidine strand binds by Hoogsteen base pairing in the major groove of a Watson-Crick base paired duplex. The conformation of the pyrimidine sugars is A-DNA like, but the purines have a B-DNA type sugar pucker. Of the two possible triplexes which could form in which the pyrimidine strand is parallel to the purine strand, the one with four TAT and three C^+GC triplets predominates. This fact, along with the exchange behavior of the iminos, indicates that the TA Hoogsteen base pairs are more stable than GC^+ Hoogsteen base pairs in the pH range studied.

Acknowledgments

This research was supported by National Institutes of Health Grant R01 GM 37254 and Office of Naval Research Contract N00014-88-K-0180.

References and Footnotes

1. R.D. Wells, D.A. Collier, J.C. Hanvey, M. Shimizu and F. Wohlrab, *FASEB J. 2*, 2939-2949 (1988).
2. D.E. Pulleyblank, D.B. Haniford and A.R. Morgan, *Cell 42*, 271-280 (1985).
3. T. Evans and A. Efstratiadis, *J. Biol. Chem. 261*, 14771-14780 (1986).
4. V.I. Lyamichev, S.M. Mirkin and M.D. Frank-Kamenetskii, *J. Biomol. Str. & Dyn. 3*, 667-669 (1986).
5. S.M. Mirkin, V.I. Lyamichev, K.N. Drushlyak, V.N. Dobrynin, S.A. Filippov and M.D. Frank-Kamenetskii, *Nature 330*, 495-497 (1987)
6. O.N. Voloshin, S.M. Mirkin, V.I. Lyamichev, B.P. Belotserkovskii and M.D. Frank-Kamenetskii, *Nature 333*, 475-476 (1988).
7. H. Htun and J.E. Dahlberg, *Science 243*, 1571-1576 (1989).
8. H. Htun and J.E. Dahlberg, *Science 241*, 1791-1796 (1988).
9. B.H. Johnston, *Science 241*, 1800-1804 (1988).
10. J.S. Lee, D.A. Johnson and A.R. Morgan, *Nucl. Acids Res. 6*, 3073-3091 (1979).
11. S. Arnott and E. Selsing, *J. Mol. Biol. 88*, 509-521 (1974).
12. M.J. Behe, *Biochem. 26*, 7870-7875 (1987).
13. J.G. McCarthy and S.M. Heywood, *Nucl. Acids Res. 15*, 8069-8085 (1987)
14. T. Evans, E. Schon, G. Gora-Maslak, J. Patterson and A. Efstratiadis, *Nucl. Acids Res. 12*, 8043-8058 (1984).
15. A. Larsen and H. Weintraub, *Cell 29*, 609-622 (1982).
16. J.M. Nickol and G. Felsenfeld, *Cell 35*, 467-477 (1983).
17. J. Bernués, R. Beltrán, J.M. Casasnovas and F. Azorin, *EMBO J. 8*, 2087-2094 (1989).
18. Y. Kohwi and T. Kohwi-Shigematsu, *Proc. Natl. Acad. Sci. USA 85*, 3781-3785 (1988).
19. S.A. Strobel, H.E. Moser and P.B. Dervan, *J. Am. Chem. Soc. 110*, 7927-7929 (1988).
20. C. Hélène and N.T. Thuong, *Current Communications in Molecular Biology*, Cold Spring Harbor Laboratory (D.A. Melton, ed.), pp. 47-51 (1988).
21. H.E. Moser and P.B. Dervan, *Science 238*, 645-650 (1987).
22. D. Praseuth, L. Perrouault, T. Le Doan, M. Chassignol, N. Thuong and C. Hélène, *Proc. Natl. Acad. Sci. USA 85*, 1349-1353 (1988).

23. M. Cooney, G. Czernuszewicz, E.H. Postel, S.J. Flint and M.E. Hogan, *Science 241*, 456-459 (1988).
24. S.L. Broitman, D.D. Im and J.R. Fresco, *Proc. Natl. Acad. Sci. USA 84*, 5120-5124 (1987).
25. A.G. Letai, M.A. Palladino, E. Fromm, V. Rizzo and J.R. Fresco, *Biochem. 27*, 9108-9112 (1988).
26. P. Rajagopal and J. Feigon, *Nature 339*, 637-640 (1989).
27. P. Rajagopal and J. Feigon, *Biochemistry 28*, 7859-7870 (1989).
28. J. Feigon, W. Leupin, W.A. Denny and D.R. Kearns, *Biochem. 22*, 5943-5951 (1983).
29. R.M.. Scheek, N. Russo, R. Boelens and R. Kaptein, *J. Am. Chem. Soc. 105*, 2914-2916 (1983).
30. D.R. Hare, D.E. Wemmer, S.H. Chou, G. Drobny and B.R. Reid, *J. Mol. Biol. 171*, 319-336 (1983).
31. A. Bax and D.G. Davis, *J. Magn. Res. 63*, 207 213 (1985).
32. J. Feigon, A.H.-J. Wang, G.A. van der Marel, J.H. van Boom and A. Rich, *Nucl. Acids Res. 12*, 1243-1263 (1984).
33. N.R. Kallenbach, W.E. Daniel, Jr. and M.A. Kaminker, *Biochem. 15*, 1218-1223 (1976).
34. W. Massefski, Jr. and A.G. Redfield, *J. Magn. Res. 78*, 150-155 (1988).
35. K. Wüthrich, *NMR of Proteins and Nucleic Acids*, John Wiley & Sons, New York (1986).
36. E. Henderson, C.C. Hardin, S.K. Walk, I. Tinoco, Jr. and E.H. Blackburn, *Cell 51*, 899-908 (1987).
37. D. Sen and W. Gilbert, *Nature 334*, 364-366 (1988).
38. V.P. Antao, D.M. Gray and R.L. Ratliff, *Nucl. Acids Res. 16*, 719-738 (1988).
39. G.G. Privé, U. Heinemann, S. Chandrasegaran, L.-S. Kan, M.L. Kopka and R.E. Dickerson, *Science 238*, 498-504 (1987).
40. W.N. Hunter, T. Brown, and O. Kennard, *J. Biomol. Str. Dyn. 4*, 173-191 (1986)
41. T. Brown, G.A. Leonard, E.D. Booth and J. Chambers, *J. Mol. Biol. 207*, 455-457 (1989).
42. X. Gao and D.J. Patel, *J. Am. Chem. Soc. 110*, 5178-5182 (1988).
43. G.G. Privé, U. Heinemann, S. Chandrasegaran, L.-S. Kan, M.L. Kopka and R.E. Dickerson, *Structure & Expression, Vol. 2: DNA and Its Drug Complexes* (W.K. Olson, M.H. Sarma, R.H. Sarma and M. Sundaralingam, eds.), Adenine Press, Guilderland, NY, pp. 27-48 (1988).
44. M.H. Sarma, G. Gupta and R.H. Sarma, *FEBS Lett. 205*, 223-229 (1986).
45. V. Sklenar, B.R. Brooks, G. Zon and A. Bax, *FEBS Lett. 216*, 249-252 (1987).

Structure & Methods, ISBN 0-940030-32-2
Volume 3: DNA & RNA, ISBN 0-940030-31-4
Eds., Ramaswamy H. Sarma & Mukti H. Sarma, © Adenine Press 1990

The Intramolecular Poly(dG)-Poly(dG)-Poly(dC) Triple Helix Structure Forms at a Neutral pH in the Presence of Mg^{++} Ions

Terumi Kohwi-Shigematsu and Yoshinori Kohwi
La Jolla Cancer Research Foundation
10901 North Torrey Pines Road
La Jolla, California 92037

Abstract

Poly(dG)-poly(dC) sequences, when studied in supercoiled plasmid DNA, revealed a capability of inducing altered DNA conformation upon neighboring DNA region in a sequence independent and unidirectional manner. With newly devised chemical cleavage method to map DNA bases modified with chloroacetaldehyde, a chemical that reacts with unpaired DNA bases, we found that poly(dG)-poly(dC) sequences in the presence of Mg^{++} ions, adopt a tetra-stranded structure containing a dG · dG · dC triple helix structure. The dG · dG · dC triplex is a Mg^{++} induced structure and forms at a neutral pH as well as acidic pH. In the absence of Mg^{++}, a protonation-induced dC^+ · dG · dC triplex is formed under acidic conditions by the same poly(dG)-poly(dC) sequences. A 16 contiguous dG residues in the 5′ flanking sequence of the chicken adult β^A globin gene also adopts a dG · dG · dC triplex structure at neutral pH in the presence of Mg^{++} ions. Other cationic metals, such as Ca^{++} and Mn^{++} ions also induce a dG · dG · dC triplex structure at the 16 contiguous residues whereas Zn^{++}, Co^{++}, and Cu^{++} ions do not promote the triplex structure formation.

Introduction

Certain types of DNA sequences preferentially adopt DNA structures that deviate from normal B-DNA structure when placed in supercoiled plasmid DNA. These DNA sequences with intrinsic potential of adopting non-B DNA structures may be of biological significance because the DNA sequences within and near these sequences that are known to be involved in the regulation of gene expression often exhibit this structural property (1-4). These observations suggest that in addition to providing sequence information to be recognized by proteins, DNA may actively participate in the regulation of gene expression using its potential to alter its conformation.

Non-B DNA structures have been detected with the use of S1 nuclease, other endonucleases, as well as chemical probes. We have previously introduced bromoacetaldehyde (BAA) (1) and chloroacetaldehyde (CAA) (5) as probes to study DNA structures. Among various chemical probes, both BAA and CAA play unique roles as they both react specifically with unpaired adenine and cytosine as well as, to a limited extent, guanine residues (6 and references within). Because of this specificity, these chemicals have been successfully used to probe DNA structures containing unpaired bases not only in supercoiled plasmid DNA but also in chromatin as well (1,2 and 4). The BAA or CAA reactive structure was detected at specific sites within regulatory regions of genes *in vivo*, and the occurrence of the structure correlated with the activity of the genes. For example, in the case of human cytomegalovirus major immediate early gene, a CAA reactive site occurs *in vivo* at -836 ± 10 bp from the mRNA cap site in the part of regulatory region that can both positively or negatively affect promoter activity (4). Also for chicken adult β^A globin gene, a BAA reactive region occurs at -10 bp from the cap site *in vivo* (1). In both cases, the CAA or BAA reactive sites occur when the corresponding genes are actively transcribed.

In supercoiled plasmid DNA, in addition to the CAA or BAA reactive sites observed *in vivo* within the regulatory regions of the genes, multiple other sites nearby were also CAA reactive. For the chicken adult β^A globin gene, the major CAA reactive site in supercoiled DNA was a 16 contiguous dG sequence located in the promoter region (1). Recently an erythrocyte specific protein factor that specifically bind this contiguous dG sequence was reported (7). We have focused on poly(dG)-poly(dC) sequences asking what exact conformation these types of sequences adopt and if such structural property is important for regulation of gene expression. Here we describe in detail the analysis for the unusual structural property of poly(dG)-poly(dC) sequences employing synthetic sequences as well as the naturally occurring sequences in the chicken adult β^A globin gene.

Materials and Methods

Chemicals. BAA was prepared by refluxing 25 g of bromoacetaldehyde diethylacetal (Eastman Organic Chemicals) for 45 minutes in 125 ml of 50% sulfuric acid (wt/vol). The mixture was then distilled, and the pH was adjusted to pH 4.5, and then redistilled. CAA was purchased from Fluka as a 50% (vol/vol) solution in water. CAA was distilled twice before use. Hydrazine, formic acid and piperidine were purchased from Sigma.

Plasmid DNA. Supercoiled $pC_\delta104$ plasmid (8) contains a mouse immunoglobulin $C_\delta$sequence inserted at the Pst I site by the G-tailing method.

The pCATCG30 plasmid (6) has a 30 bp poly(dG)-poly(dC) sequence inserted in the Sma1/Sac1 site of the pUC13 plasmid, which also contains the bacterial chloramphenicol acetyltransferase gene inserted into the Hind III site. Supercoiled plasmid, pBSTN1 (9), contains the region from -303 to $+167$ of the chicken adult β^A globin gene.

Chemical Modification of DNA. Twenty to fifty micrograms of supercoiled plasmid DNA was incubated with various amounts of CAA per 100 µl reaction mixture at 37°C for 1 hour. The reaction mixture contained either 50 mM NaOAc (pH5) or 50 mM Tris.HC1 (pH7.2) in the presence or absence of 2 mM Mg^{++}.

Mapping of BAA or CAA Modified Sites. Four micrograms of the BAA or CAA modified

DNA was cleaved with a restriction enzyme and then radiolabeled either at the 5′ end with T4 kinase or at the 3′ end with the Klenow fragment of DNA polymerase I. The subsequent method to cleave DNA at the chemically modified sites using either S1 nuclease (8) or chemical cleavage method (6) is reviewed in the Results and Discussion section.

Results and Discussion

Poly(dG)-Poly(dC) Sequence Induces Altered Conformation Upon Neighboring Region: (S1 Nuclease Cleavage at the BAA Modified Sites)

When supercoiled plasmid DNAs harboring poly(dG)-poly(dC) sequences, at bacterial superhelical density, were reacted with BAA at pH 5 in the presence of Mg^{++}, BAA reactive sites were detected not only at the center of the poly(dG)-poly(dC) sequence, but also at the neighboring sequences located 3′ to the deoxyguanine residues (8). These reactions at two different regions occurred within the same plasmid DNA molecule. When the poly(dG)-poly(dC) sequence was adjacent to a variety of neighboring sequences, it was always the neighboring sequences 3′ of the dG tract that was unpaired indicating that the poly(dG)-poly(dC) sequence has a potential of inducing its neighboring region to adopt an unpaired conformation in a sequence-independent and undirectional manner (Figure 1).

We have further examined the effect of the length of poly(dG)-poly(dC) tracts, and its potential in inducing altered DNA conformation upon neighboring sequences. The BAA modified sites were mapped by employing S1 nuclease to cleave the DNA at this site of modification, since BAA modified remains single-stranded even after the DNA is digested with restriction enzymes (8). The longer the poly(dG)-poly(dC) tract, the more extensive the conformational effect was as indicated by a longer

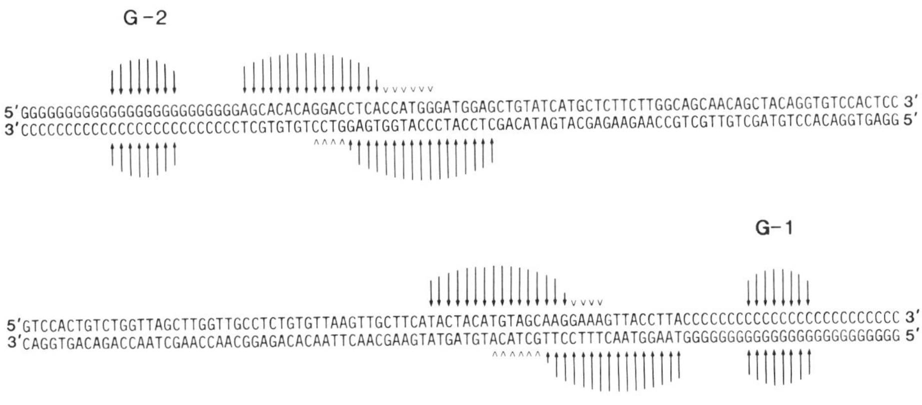

Figure 1: The mapping of BAA-modified sites for plasmid pC_8104 containing two sets of poly(dG)-poly(dC) sequences. The distribution of the cleavage sites generated by S1 nuclease treatment of BAA modified pC_8104 plasmid are shown by arrows. (Ref. Kohwi-Shigematsu and Kohwi, *Cell 43*, 199-206 (1985)).

stretch of the neighboring sequence being reactive with BAA (data not shown). The length of 40 base pair tract induces approximately 40 base pairs of the neighboring sequences to adopt base-unpaired conformation. The length of 22 base pair tract influence 20 base pairs of the neighboring region. The length of 16 base pairs of the tract induce approximately 3 or 4 base pairs of its neighboring region to be unpaired.

In every case, the conformational alternation was observed in the neighboring region 3′ of the poly(dG) tract at pH 5 and in the presence of Mg^{++} ions. The structural basis for this unusual behavior of poly(dG)-poly(dC) sequence was explored as described below.

The Chemical Cleavage Method to Identify the DNA Sites Modified with BAA or CAA

We considered that the reason for the neighboring sequence being base-unpaired is that the sequence flanking the poly(dG)-poly(dC) tract is part of the non-B DNA structure adopted by the poly(dG)-poly(dC) sequences. This hypothesis was tested by devising an alternative chemical cleavage method to identify the exact positions of the BAA modified sites without the use of S1 nuclease. Such method allowed a better understanding of the non-B DNA structure adopted by the poly(dG)-poly(dC) sequence. Since S1 nuclease may have its own specificity for the substrate conformation, we devised a direct method to chemically cleave the DNA at the sites of BAA modification (6).

The principle of the method relies on the fact that when a particular DNA base is CAA or BAA modified, the electronic structure of the modified DNA base becomes altered in comparison to the corresponding unmodified base, and thus the CAA or BAA modified base becomes reactive to the second set of chemicals which normally do not react with that particular base before CAA or BAA modification. For example, hydrazine specifically reacts with cytosine residues in the presence of salt. However, we found that hydrazine also reacts with CAA modified adenine residues. Formic acid reacts specifically with guanine and adenine residues. In addition to these two residues, it also reacts with CAA or BAA-modified cytosine residues. These differences in reactivity then leads to differential susceptibility to the subsequent piperidine reaction. Thus, when analyzed on a sequencing gel, additional bands appear that correspond to the CAA or BAA modified adenine bases within the cytosine ladder, and CAA or BAA modified cytosine bases within the guanine and adenine ladder. (The reaction scheme is shown in Figure 2.) The arrow represents enhancement of the intensity of bands due to chemical modification.

The advantage of this method is that it does not require enzymes to cleave DNA, and it allows detection of a single base modified with BAA or CAA within a plasmid DNA molecule.

The BAA Modified Sites as Mapped with S1 Nuclease vs. Chemical Cleavage Method

Two different methods for mapping the BAA modified bases were employed for a

	control	CAA reacted
HZ / piperidine	C	C↑ A G
DMS / piperidine	G	G A C
FA / piperidine	G,A	G↑ A↑ C

Figure 2: The chemical cleavage scheme. The DNA bases at which the DNA cleavages occur are shown: C, cytosine; G, guanine; and A, adenine. The arrows show enhanced cleavage rate. HZ, hydrazine; DMS, dimethylsulfate; FA, formic acid.

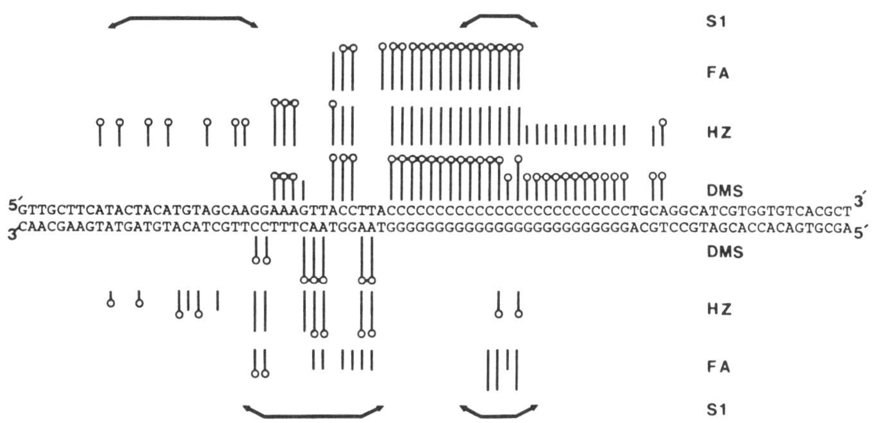

Figure 3: Summary of the chemical cleavage pattern for CAA-modified supercoiled pC_8104 plasmid DNA. DNA bases that show enhanced cleavage are indicated by vertical lines, relative degree of enhancement is indicated by different lengths. Open circles represent cleavage (bands in addition to those normally expected on a sequencing ladder) due to CAA modification at that site. Double-headed arrows indicate the regions that are cleaved by S1 nuclease for the CAA-modified DNA sites in pC_8104 plasmid. (Kohwi and Kohwi-Shigematsu, *Proc. Natl. Acad. Sci. USA 85*, 3781-3785 (1988)).

supercoiled pC_8104 plasmid DNA, harboring two regions of 25 bp poly(dG)-poly(dC) tracts, modified with BAA at pH 5 in the presence of 2 mM Mg^{++} ions. The methods were: 1) with the use of S1 nuclease, and, 2) with the direct chemical cleavage method. (The result is summarized in Figure 3.)

The chemical cleavage method revealed that the 5′ half of the contiguous cytosine stretch was reactive to CAA, while the 3′ half of the stretch was virtually unreactive to CAA. In contrast, S1 nuclease cleaved at the center of the contiguous cytosine stretch. This indicates that there exists a region that is CAA reactive yet uncleaved by S1 nuclease, suggesting that S1 nuclease does not necessarily cut DNA at unpaired DNA bases. This result suggests that the CAA reactive region, the 5′ half of the contiguous cytosine stretch, is not single-stranded (see below). In the bottom strand containing contiguous guanine residues, the CAA reactivity was limited to specific guanine residues located at the center of the stretch as detected by either chemical cleavage or S1 cleavage method. Both cleavage methods revealed CAA reactivity for the neighboring sequences 3′ of the poly(dG) sequence.

This non-B DNA structure was found to form in a pH independent manner in the presence of Mg^{++}, as the typical CAA reaction pattern was unchanged from pH5 to 8 (Figure 4).

The Structural Basis for the Conformational Effect Exerted by Poly(dG)-Poly(dC) Sequence upon Neighboring DNA Region

The non-B DNA structure which is consistent with the observed CAA reaction patterns was proposed as shown in Figure 5, the left structure. It is basically a tetra-stranded structure that is formed via a sharp folding of poly(dG)-poly(dC) sequences in halves at the center. This tetra-stranded structure contains a dG · dG · dC triple helix consisting of both halves of the poly(dG) strand and the 5′ half of the poly(dC) strand. The 3′ half of the poly(dC) strand remains base unpaired but closely associated with the triple helix. This is concluded because the 3′ half of the poly(dC) strand is not accessible to the subsequent S1 nuclease digestion yet it was continuously CAA reactive.

The 3′ half of the poly(dC) strand and its complementary strand which is part of a dG · dG · dC triplex structure need to be re-oriented in space before they can be base-paired once again. This requires a certain amount of unwinding of the DNA helix. Thus, this non-B DNA structure once formed by the poly(dG)-poly(dC) sequence accompanies the neighboring region to be unpaired. There is one other important aspect to further explain the unidirectionality of the conformational effect. One can envision an alternative isomeric form for the dG.dG.dC triplex which involves the 3′ half of the poly(dC) tract instead of the 5′ half of the poly(dC) strand. Although the reason is yet unknown, according to our data, only the isomer containing the 3′ half of the poly(dC) strand is detected. Because of this preference one isomer over the other, only base pairing neighboring effect on region 3′ of the poly(dG) tract is observed.

It is worth emphasizing the fact that this intramolecular triple helix can be readily formed at bacterial superhelical density at a neutral pH and in the presence of Mg^{++} as low as 0.2 mM, and therefore, this is clearly different from those structures that are induced by protonation as described below.

Dynamic Property of Poly(dG)-Poly(dC) Sequences

The inherent potential of poly(dG)-poly(dC) sequence in forming non-B DNA structure was further examined in the absence of Mg^{++} ions using CAA as the probe. In the absence of Mg^{++}, it was the 5′ half of the poly(dG) tract being CAA reactive as well as the center cytosine residues within the poly(dC) tract. Also, the neighboring region 5′ instead of 3′ of the poly (dG) tract revealed CAA reactivity

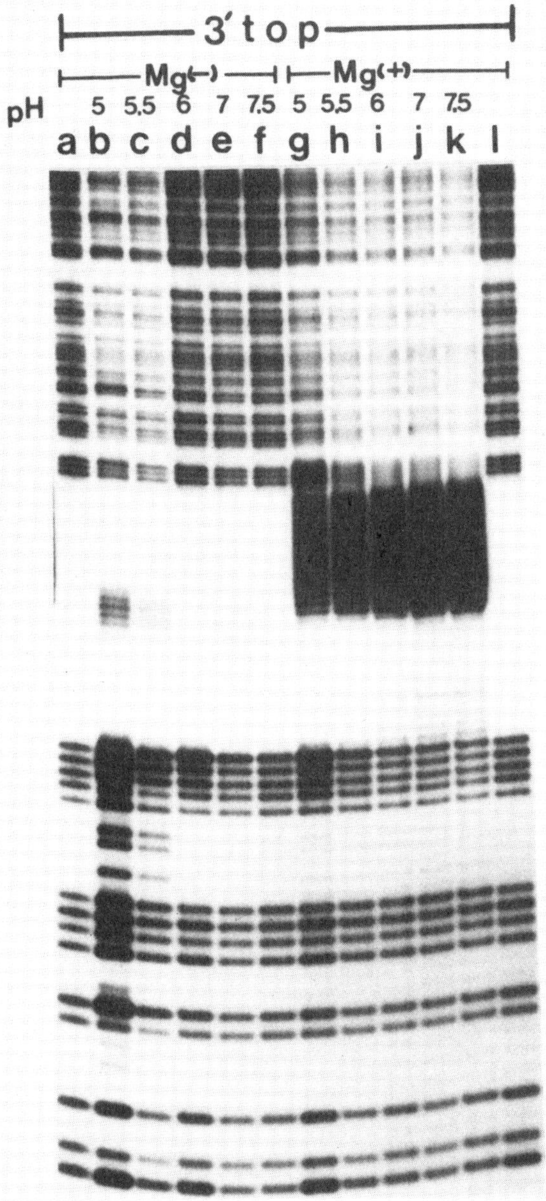

Figure 4: pH dependency on triple-helical structure. Supercoiled plasmid pCATCG30 was treated with 2 μl of CAA in 50 mM Tris-Maleic acid buffer at pH 5, 5.5, 6, 7, and 7.5 in the presence or absence of 2 mM $MgCl_2$. The BanI/HindIII DNA fragment labeled at the 3′ end of the HindIII site (top strand) was then isolated and subjected to Maxam-Gilbert chemical reaction with formic acid. Lanes a and i, CAA-untreated control DNA. pH had no effect on control DNA. (Kohwi and Kohwi-Sigematsu, *Proc. Natl. Acad.Sci. USA 85*, 3781-3785 (1988)).

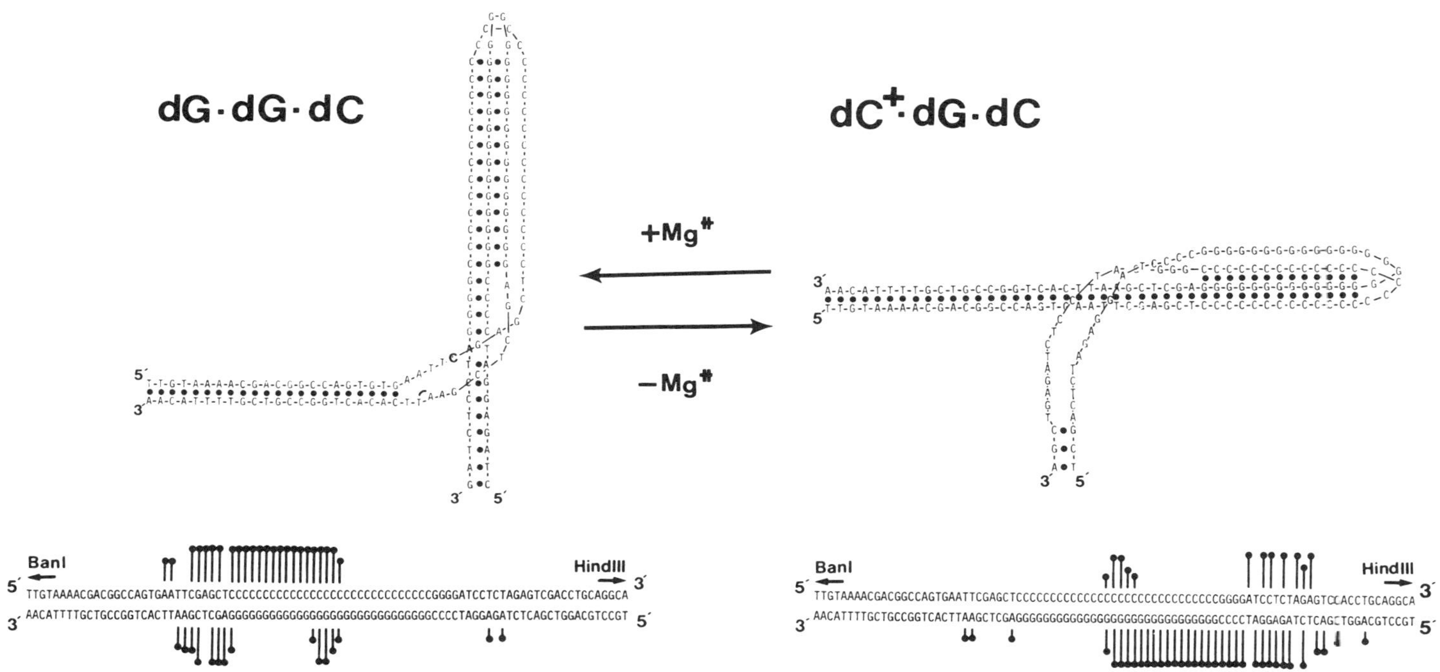

Figure 5: The dynamic structural property of poly(dG)-poly(dC) sequence in supercoiled plasmid DNA. Left panel represents the structure proposed based on the CAA reaction pattern obtained in the presence of Mg^{++}, and the right panel represents the structure in the absence of Mg^{++}. The CAA reaction pattern for each condition is shown by the vertical bars with black circles.

(Figure 5, right structure). Furthermore, this typical CAA reactive pattern was observed in a pH dependent manner. The reactivity was diminished above pH 5.5 when supercoiled plasmid with bacterial density was employed (6).

Based on the CAA reaction pattern observed and its pH dependency, the structure adopted by poly(dG)-poly(dC) tract in the absence of Mg^{++} was concluded as a tetra-stranded structure containing a $dC^{+} \cdot dG \cdot dC$ triplex. This protonated triplex was first reported as H-form (10) and studied by a number of groups (11-16). The $dC^{+} \cdot dG \cdot dC$ base triplet is formed when one of the cytosines is protonated.

Poly(dG)-poly(dC) sequences adopt a tetra-stranded DNA structure containing either a $dG \cdot dG \cdot dC$ triplex or a $dC^{+} \cdot dG \cdot dC$ triplex depending on the presence or the absence of Mg^{++} (Figure 5) (6). This demonstrates a dynamic property for these DNA sequences in forming non-B structures. Because of this dynamic property and the preference of one particular isomer over the other for both $dG \cdot dG \cdot dC$ and $dC^{+} \cdot dG \cdot dC$ triplex formations, the unidirectional conformational effect exerted by the poly(dG)-poly(dC) sequence in the presence of Mg^{++} is reversed in directionality by simply deleting Mg^{++}.

Naturally Occurring Poly(dG)-Poly(dC) Sequence within the Chicken Adult β^{A} Promoter Region

There exists a poly(dG)-poly(dC) tract of 16 base pair within the 5′ flanking region of the chicken adult β^{A} globin gene. This relatively short stretch of poly(dG)-poly(dC) tract also adopts a $dG \cdot dG \cdot dC$ triplex structure in the presence of Mg^{++} at a neutral pH (17). When various cationic metals in addition to Mg^{++} ions were examined, Ca^{++} and Mn^{++} ions were also found to induce the 16 bp poly(dG)-poly(dC) sequence to adopt a $dG \cdot dG \cdot dC$ triplex structure (Figure 6). However, in the absence of these divalent cations, the other $dC^{+} \cdot dG \cdot dC$ structure (the H-form), does not form. Our study shows that at bacterial superhelical density, 16 base pair tract is too short to be able to adopt a $dC^{+} \cdot dG \cdot dC$ triplex structure.

In the presence of Zn^{++}, Cu^{++} or Co^{++} ions, on the other hand, the $dG \cdot dG \cdot dC$ triplex does not form by this sequence, and the 16 bp tract of the poly(dG)-poly(dC) adopt normal double-stranded conformation (Figure 6). In the presence of these metal ions, a direct repeat sequence adjacent to the poly(dG)-poly(dC) sequence adopt another type of non-B DNA structure. This result demonstrates that certain metal ions have specific effects in stabilizing particular DNA structures (17).

Specific metal ion-effect on the structure may have an important biological significance. The contiguous dG stretch in the 5′ flanking region of the chicken adult β^{A} globin gene adopts two different chromatin structures *in vivo*: in cells that do not express the β-globin gene, this dG stretch is not associated with nucleosomes and is hypersensitive to nuclease digestion (18), whereas, in mature erythrocytes in which the gene is transcriptionally active, the dG stretch is protected from the nuclease attack (19). The nuclease hypersensitive structure might correspond to a $dG \cdot dG \cdot dC$ triplex structure adopted by the contiguous dG stretch. A DNA binding protein

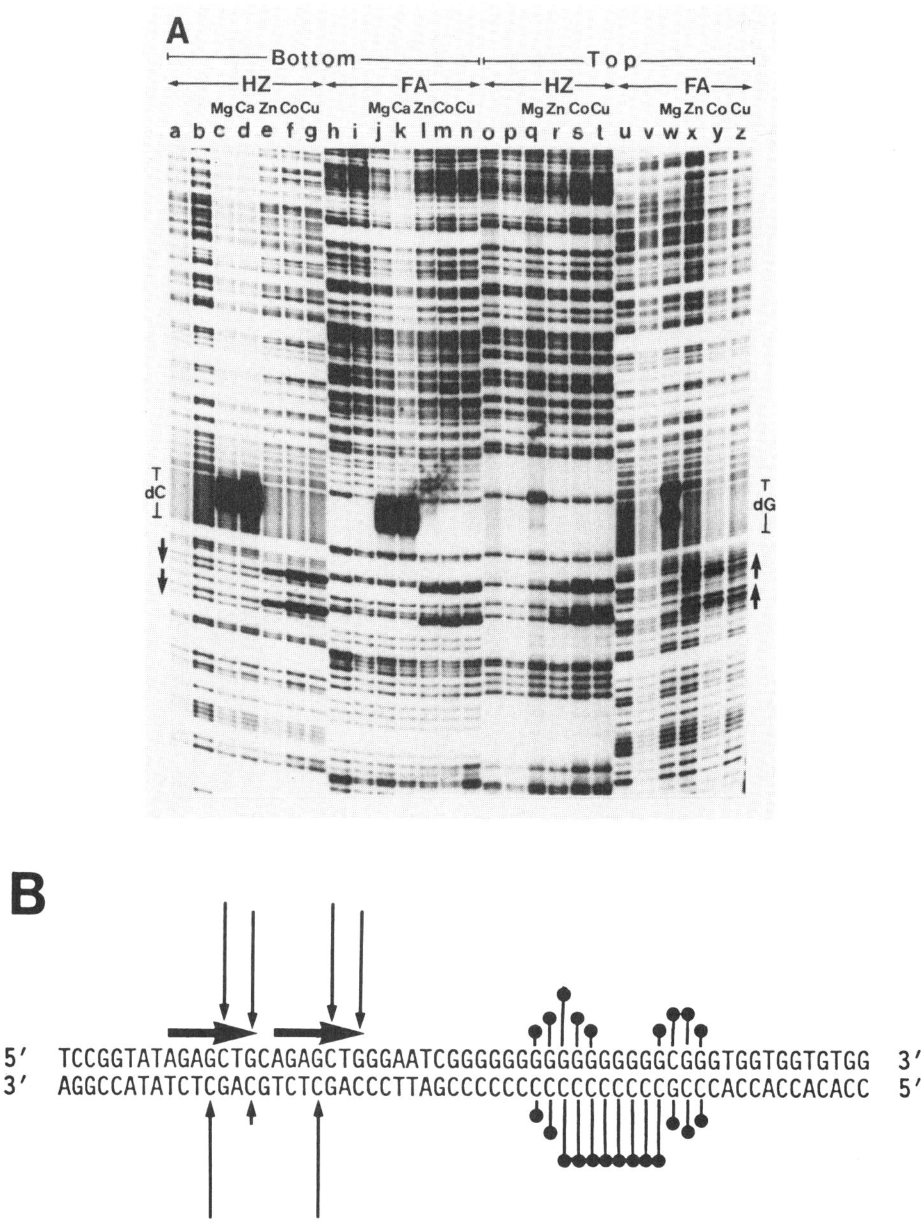

Figure 6: Effects of various metal ions on the non-B DNA structures adopted by the 5′ sequence of the chicken adult β^A globin gene. (A) Supercoiled plasmid, pBSTN1, was treated with 0 µl (control, lane b, i, p and v) or with 4 µl of CAA either in the absence of (lanes a, h, o and u) or in the presence of 2 mM of metal ions (Mg^{++}, lanes c, j, q and w; Ca^{++}, lanes d and k; Zn^{++}, lanes e, l, r and x; Co^{++}, lanes f, m, s and y; Cu^{++}, lanes g, n, t and z) in 25 mM Tris-Maleic acid (pH 7.0). The HindIII-EcoRI fragments were isolated from a native polyacrylamide gel and were subjected to reaction with either hydrazine (HZ) or formic acid (FA). The DNA's were then cleaved by piperidine reaction. (B) Summary to the chemical cleavage patterns for CAA modified DNA. (⚲) indicates the CAA modified sites in the presence of Mg^{++} and Ca^{++} ions. (↑) indicates the CAA modified sites in the presence of Zn^{++}, Co^{++} and Cu^{++} ions. (Y. Kohwi, *Nucleic Acids Res. 17*, 4493-4502 (1989)).

(BGP1) which specifically binds to the dG stretch is restricted to erythrocyte lineage and most abundant in mature erythrocytes (7). Interestingly, this protein requires Zn^{++} for the DNA-binding activity. Our data shows that when both Mg^{++} and Zn^{++} are present, the dG · dG · dC triplex formation is inhibited provided that the Zn^{++} concentration is sufficient (17). It is intriguing to speculate that the potential of DNA to adopt a particular conformation in response to metal ions is utilized for specific DNA-protein interactions at the time of transcriptional complex formations.

Poly(dG)-poly(dC) sequence is an example of a homopurine-homopyrimidine sequence. Homopurine-homopyrimidines with different sequences are found in various regulatory regions such as adenovirus major late promoter (20), and human epidermal growth factor receptor gene promoter (21,22). In our assay, all homopurine-homopyrimidine sequences if they are long enough (usually more than 14 bp) adopt CAA reactive structures. However, they are not always the same conformations as described here. It is important to note that sequence plays a dominant role in determining the specific structure formed. And the sequences' response to metal ions in forming non-B DNA structures is also dramatically different depending on the sequences. These points will be elaborated elsewhere in the future.

Acknowledgments

This work was supported by a grant from the National Institute of Health (R01-CA39681) to T. Kohwi-Shigematsu.

References and Footnotes

1. Kohwi-Shigematsu, T., Gelinas, R. and Weintraub, H., *Proc. Natl. Acad. Sci. USA 80*, 4389-4393 (1983).
2. Bode, J., Pucher, H-J. and Maass, K., *Eur. J. Biochem. 158*, 393-401 (1986).
3. Siegfried, E., Thomas, G.H., Bond, U.M. and Elgin, S.C.R., *Nucleic Acids Res. 14*, 9425-9444 (1986).
4. Kohwi-Shigematsu, T. and Nelson, J.A., *Molecular Carcinogenesis 1*, 20-125 (1988).
5. Kohwi-Shigematsu, T., Manes, T. and Kohwi, Y., *Proc. Natl. Acad. Sci. USA 84*, 2223-2227 (1987).
6. Kohwi, Y. and Kohwi-Shigematsu, T., *Proc. Natl. Acad. Sci. USA 85*, 3781-3785 (1988).
7. Lewis, C.D., Clark, S.P., Felsenfeld, G. and Gould, H., *Genes and Development 2*, 863-873 (1988).
8. Kohwi-Shigematsu, T. and Kohwi, Y., *Cell 43*, 199-206 (1985).
9. Emerson, B.M., Lewis, C.D. and Felsenfeld, G., *Cell 41*, 21-30 (1985).
10. Lyamichev, V.I., Mirkin, S.M. and Frank-Kamenetskii, M.D., *J. Bio. Mol. Struct. Dyn. 3*, 327-338 (1985).
11. Mirkin, S.M. Lyamichev, V.I., Drushlyak, K.N., Dobrynin, V.N., Filippov, S.A. and Frank-Kamenetskii, M.D., *Nature (London) 330*, 495-497 (1987).
12. Voloshin, O.N., Mirkin, S.M., Lyamichev, V.I., Belotserkovskii. B.P. and Frank-Kamenetskii, M.D., *Nature 333*, 475-476 (1988).
13. Vojtiskova, M. and Palecek, E., *J. Biomol. Struct. Dyn. 5*, 283-296 (1987).
14. Hanvey, J.C., Klysik, J. and Wells, R.D., *J. Biol. Chem. 263*, 7386-7396 (1988).
15. Htun, H. and Dahlberg, J.E., *Science 241*, 1791-1796 (1988).
16. Johnston, B.H., *Science 241*, 1800-1804 (1988).
17. Kohwi, Y., *Nucleic Acid Research 17*, 4493-4502 (1989).
18. Jackson, P.D., Ph.D Thesis, John Hopkins University, Baltimore, Maryland (1986).
19. Jackson, P.D. and Felsenfeld, G., *Proc. Natl. Acad. Sci. USA 82*, 2296-2300 (1985).
20. Goding, C.R. and Russell, W.C., *Nucleic Acids Res. 11*, 21-36 (1983).
21. Johnson, A.C., Jinno, Y. and Merlino, G.T., *Mol. Cell. Biol. 8*, 4174-4184 (1988).
22. Ishii, S., Y.-H. Xu, R.M., Stratton, B.A., Roe, G., Merlino, G.T. and Pastan, I., *Proc. Natl. Acad. Sci. USA 82*, 4920-4924 (1985).

Structure & Methods, ISBN 0-940030-32-2
Volume 3: DNA & RNA, ISBN 0-940030-31-4
Eds., Ramaswamy H. Sarma & Mukti H. Sarma, © Adenine Press 1990

Chemical Probing of the DNA Polymorphic Structure *In Vitro* and *In Situ*

E. Paleček, P. Boublíková, F. Jelen, A. Krejčová, E. Makaturová, K. Nejedlý, P. Pečinka and M. Vojtíšková
Institute of Biophysics
Czechoslovak Academy of Sciences
612 65 Brno, Czechoslovakia

Abstract

Chemical probes reacting preferentially with single-stranded and some non-B DNA regions (especially osmium tetroxide, pyridine (Os,py) and diethyl pyrocarbonate (DEPC)) yielded important information about local DNA structures such as cruciforms, left-handed Z DNA, B-Z junctions, protonated triplexes (H-DNA) in homopurine · homopyrimidine tracts, etc. By means of DEPC and nuclease *Bal*31 recently we demonstrated supercoil-stabilized left-handed DNA in the plasmid $(dA\text{-}dT)_{16}$ insert in the presence of Ni^{2+} ions. Using electron microscopy we showed that H-form induces curvature in DNA.

To extend the possibilities of the detection of osmium-modified bases in DNA polyclonal antibodies against DNA modified with Os,py were elicited in rabbits. These antibodies do not cross-react with unmodified DNA and osmium-modified proteins and may become useful in studies of local open DNA structures *in vivo*. We tested a number of ligands to replace pyridine in the Os,py reagent and to improve the versatility of the osmium probes. 2,2′-bipyridine (bipy), 1,10-phenanthroline, bathophenanthroline disulfonic acid and tetramethylethylenediamine can be used as ligands in the osmium probes at concentrations substantially lower than that of pyridine. Os,bipy reacts with T, C and G residues in single-stranded DNA; the reaction with T is, however, much faster. We proposed a technique based on Os,bipy to probe the DNA structure in cells and demonstrated the existence of left-handed DNA and its structural junctions with B DNA in *E.coli* cells. Our results also suggest that the protonated H-DNA can exist in the cell and may be influenced by intracellular pH and DNA linking number.

Introduction

In the beginning of the 80's we were searching for chemicals binding covalently to nucleic acids which could serve as probes of the DNA polymorphic structure (1) and be at the same time an electroactive label of the polynucleotide chain (2). The ultimate aim of this search was to find chemicals suitable for probing DNA structure *in situ* (3). From the substances tested osmium tetroxide, pyridine (Os,py) (Figure 1) best fulfilled our requirements (2-6). It binds covalently to DNA showing selectivity for single-stranded and distorted double-stranded (ds) regions and the Os,py-

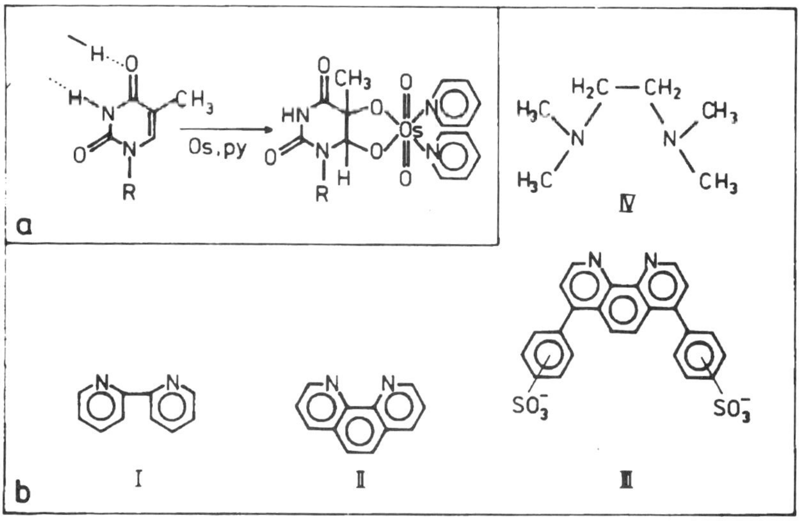

Figure 1: a) Formation of the adduct between thymine and osmium tetroxide, pyridine; ...., hydrogen bonding in the Watson-Crick base pair. b) Some ligands which can replace pyridine in the osmium complex: I, 2,2′-bipyridine (bipy); II, 1,10-phenanthroline (phe); III, bathophenanthroline (4,7-diphenyl-1,10-phenantroline) disulfonic acid (BPDS); IV, tetramethylethylenediamine (TMEN).

modified DNA produces catalytical polarographic (voltammetric) currents even at very low DNA concentrations (4). We showed that osmium binding sites in DNA are recognized and cleaved by nuclease S1 (6,7) and can be visualized in the electron microscope (6,8) provided the osmium-modified region is sufficiently large. At present, further methods of osmium binding sites detection are available (Figure 2), including those working at single-nucleotide resolution (based either on hot piperidine cleavage (9-12) of the DNA chain labilized at the site of the osmium modification or on the ability of the osmium adducts to terminate transcription (13) *in vitro*.

In recent years Os,py has been applied in numerous studies of local unusual structures stabilized by supercoiling (6-43). It has been shown that Os,py reacts with nucleotides in the cruciform loop (7,14), similarly to other chemical probes such as, e.g., diethyl pyrocarbonate (DEPC) (15,16). Os,py has been applied in studies of structure and properties of various cruciforms (7,14,17-21). This reagent seems to be so far the only chemical which is able to detect "open" four-way junction of the cruciform (14) and that of the synthetic Holliday junction (22). It thus appears that with Os,py detection of unstacking of bases (without rupture of hydrogen bonding) is possible.

Bases at the boundary between the right-handed and left-handed Z DNA in $(dC\text{-}dG)_n$ and $(dA\text{-}dC)_n$ segments (9,11,23-29) are hypersensitive to Os,py suggesting presence of structural distortions at the B-Z junctions. Hypersensitivity to Os,py was also observed in a curvature-inducing insert sequence dATATATTTTTTAGAGATTTTT (repeat about four times) of a supercoiled plasmid pK5/6T217 (30). Os,py has been applied to studies of the structure of homopurine · homopyrimidine tracts (31-36) as a probe specific for the homopyrimidine strand. Thymine mismatched with cytosine,

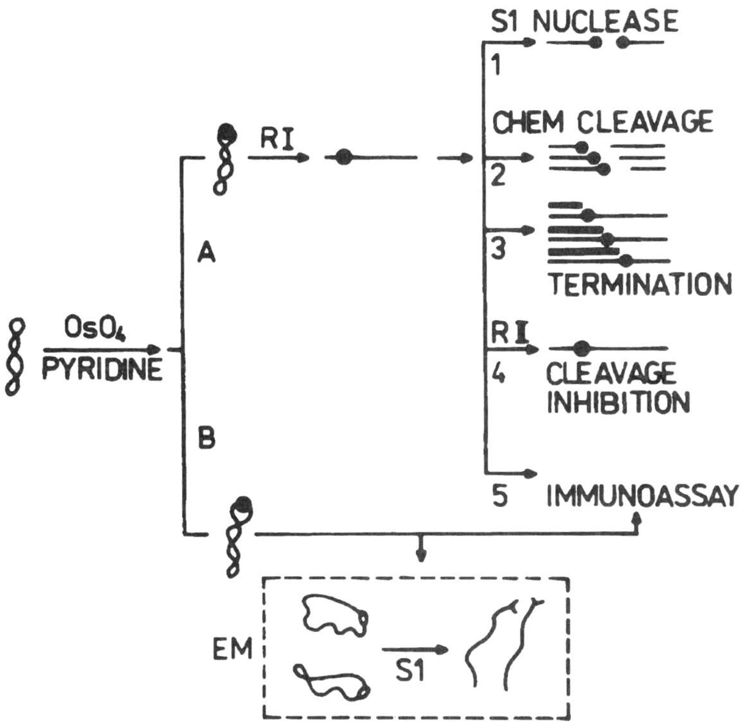

Figure 2: Scheme of treatment of supercoiled DNA with osmium tetroxide, pyridine and mapping of the osmium binding sites. To map the osmium binding sites DNA is cleaved by restrictase (RI) followed 1, by nuclease S1 digestion and gel electrophoresis of the resulting DNA fragments (5-7) or 2, by cleavage with hot piperidine and sequencing (9-11) using the principles of the Maxam-Gilbert method; 3, by DNA transcription (13) *in vitro* (which is terminated at modified bases in the template) and nucleotide sequencing; 4, if a structural distortion (e.g., in the region of the B-Z junction) is expected to occur within the recognition site of a particular restrictase (RII) (23,26), the site-specific modification of the distortion can be manifested by inhibition of the restriction cleavage; 5, osmium binding in restriction fragments can be determined by immunoassay (63) (e.g., DNA gel retardation or ELISA). Modification of large DNA regions may result in partial or full relaxation of the molecule (accompanied by changes in the electrophoretic mobility) and formation of a denaturation "bubble" visible in the electron microscope (EM) (6,8); nuclease S1 cleaves DNA in the "bubble"; the amount of bound osmium can be determined electrochemically (2-6).

guanine and thymine in heteroduplex DNA's were detected by Os,py (38) after piperidine cleavage and nucleotide sequencing. Extra thymines in self-complementary oligonucleotides were also hypersensitive to Os,bipy (V. Kolar, E. Palecek and U. Heinemann, unpublished); osmium binding was detected by spectrophotometric and electrochemical techniques.

Recently, Os,py was used in studies of structural changes induced in DNA by antitumor drug binding. In the presence of echinomycin specific thymine residues exhibited enhanced reactivity towards Os,py (39). Treatment of oligonucleotides and DNA restriction fragments with cis-diamminedichloroplatinum(II) resulted in hypersensitivity of a large number of thymine residues to Os,py (40) in the vicinity of the platinum adducts as well as away from them along the DNA molecules. Distortions in ds oligonucleotides by covalently bound acetylaminofluorene (AAF) residues and by apurinic sites were studied by Os,py, chloracetaldehyde (CAA) and DEPC (41). It has been found that AAF residues induce local DNA denaturation while bases in the vicinity of the apurinic site are not unpaired; hypersensitivity of two T residues adjacent to the apurinic site indicates, however, some distortion of the double helix.

Single-stranded (ss) regions in complexes between RNA polymerase and promoters were identified in DNA by means of Os,py (42). Using Os,py local conformational variations in supercoiled DNA's were detected (43) at sites defined as protein interaction sites and consensus sequence motifs of RNA polymerase II promoters.

Osminum Tetroxide: Different Reactivity of DNA Bases

In spite of extensive application of osmium tetroxide as a probe of the DNA structure the question of osmium tetroxide reactivity toward DNA bases has not been clarified up to now. It is known that in the absence of ligands osmium tetroxide reacts with T residues while the reaction with other bases is negligible (44,45). In 1977 Chang *et al.* (46) showed that in the presence of ligands such as pyridine and 2,2′-bipyridine (bipy) osmium tetroxide reacts with T and C. In 1978 Friedmann and Brown (47) proposed Os,py as an agent specific for T in ds DNA in Maxam-Gilbert nucleotide sequencing (48). Comparing these results one may ask (a) how can Os,py react with ds DNA if it is a probe of the structure not reacting with B DNA? and (b) is Os,py a T-specific agent or does it react with both T and C residues?

Earlier we showed (3,5) that at higher Os,py concentrations DNA may be denatured and modified at sites primarily not accessible to the reagent. Question (a) might thus be answered by assuming that under conditions used by Friedmann and Brown (47) DNA was denatured due to the high Os,py concentration. In contrast to Friedmann and Brown (47) who modified DNA at 0°C (with about 0.12 M OsO_4, 6.3% pyridine) in our experiments (3,5) modification was performed at room temperature. We studied (P. Pecinka and E. Palecek, unpublished) the influence of Os,py concentrations and ionic strength on DNA modification at 0°C and we found that at low ionic strengths and high Os,py concentrations even at 0°C modification of plasmid DNA can occur at sites primarily not available for the reaction.

To answer the question (b) we modified ss poly(dT), poly(dC), poly(dG) and poly(dA) with Os,py and Os,bipy under various conditions and measured the content of modified bases in each polynucleotide by means of absorption spectra and differential pulse stripping voltammetry (4) (Figure 3). Under conditions close to those used by Chang *et al.* (46) (e.g., 20 h treatment with 4 mM Os,bipy) both poly(dT) (not shown) and poly(dC) (Figure 3b) were strongly modified (Os/P ratio was 0,07 while no osmium modification was detected in poly(dA) (Figure 3e). Up to now it has been believed that Os,py and Os,bipy react only with pyrimidine bases (46,50). The guanine reaction is not yet well understood; it might be an addition on the N7-C8 double bond.

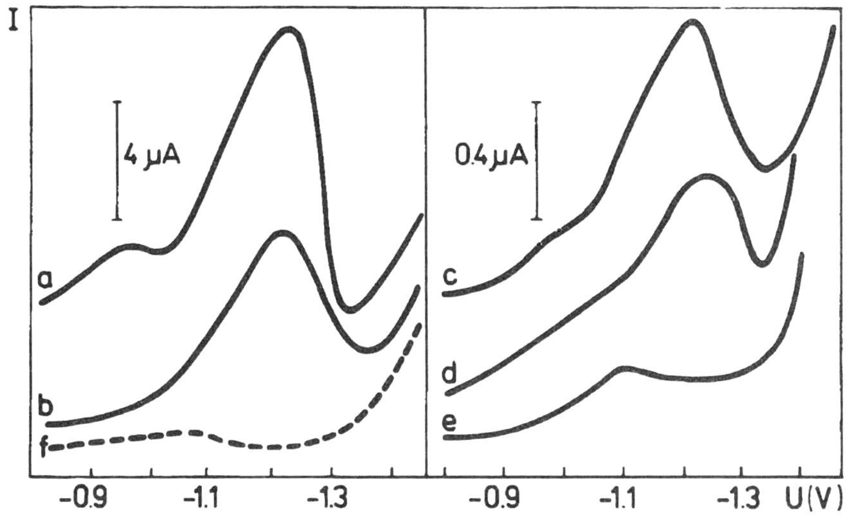

Figure 3: Stripping voltammograms of four Os,bipy treated polydeoxynucleotides. a) poly(dT); b) poly(dC); c) poly(dG); e) poly(dA) at 1 mM concentration (related to monomer content) in 35 mM sodium phosphate (pH 7.0) were treated with 4 mM osmium tetroxide, 4 mM 2,2′-bipyridine, 20 hours at 26°C. d) 0.25 mM poly(dC) in 50 mM sodium phosphate (pH 7.0) was treated with 1 mM osmium tetroxide, 1 mM 2,2′-bipyridine 15 minutes at 26°C; f) background electrolyte. Differential pulse stripping voltammetry (DPSV) (4) was performed at a polynucleotide concentration of 0.6 (µg/ml under the following conditions: pulse amplitude 50 mV, scan rate 10 mV, initial potential −0.8 V, accumulation time 120 s; background electrolyte: 0.3 M ammonium formate with 0.05 M sodium phosphate (pH 6.8). The bars represent the current scale showing that curves c,d,e were measured at a tenfold higher sensitivity of the instrument as compared to curves a,b,f. Prior to DPSV measurements the modified polynucleotides were twice extracted with chloroform and dialysed.

Under mild M conditions close to those used in probing of supercoiled DNA structure (i.e., 15 minute treatment with 1 mM Os,bipy at 26°C) poly(dT) was almost fully (Figure 3a) modified, while modification of poly(dC) (Figure 3d) corresponded to about 8%. Thus the amount of modifided T,C and G residues in DNA depends very much on reaction conditions. If Os,bipy is used to probe the structure of supercoiled DNA the fraction of bases available for the reaction is usually below 1%. Thus while the concentration of the total DNA and Os,bipy are roughly the same as under M conditions of our experiment with synthetic polynucleotides the concentration ratio of Os,bipy/reactive bases is more than 100× higher. Such a large excess of the osmium probe might result in modification of not only T but also C and G residues if available for the reaction; in fact modified C and G residues were observed by several authors (e.g., 32) using an osmium probe. On the other hand Os,py and Os,bipy can serve as an agent specific for Ts in Maxam-Gilbert sequencing of ss DNA if mild reaction conditions are used (e.g., 0.5 mM Os,py or Os,bipy, 15 minutes at 26°C).

Combination of Chemical Probes

The use of enzymatic probes such as nuclease S1 contributed significantly to the discoveries of supercoil-stabilized unusual structures (reviewed in 49). Application

Table I
Chemical Probes of the DNA Structure Reacting Preferentially with Single-Stranded and Non-B DNA Regions

Base specificity	Probe	Reference
T>>C,G	Os,py; Os,bipy	3,5,50
	$KMnO_4$	82
T>>C	OsO_4 (alone)	83, E. Palecek, unpublished
A>G	DEPC[a]	9,84
A,C	BAA[b], CAA[b]	24,25,85
G	glyoxal[b]	24,25,86
	N-hydroxylaminofluorene	87
C	$NaHSO_3$	86,87
	hydroxylamine	9
	methoxylamine	13

[a]Reacts also with Z DNA (purines in *syn* conformation).
[b]Disturbance of Watson-Crick pairing required.

of chemical probes has provided a deeper insight into these structures. Compared to enzymatic probes, chemicals have many advantages (23) which include the possibility of their application under a wide range of conditions, small probe size and known sites and mechanisms of attack. After the demonstration of the site-specific reactions of Os,py (reviewed in 50) and bromoacetaldehyde (BAA) with the cruciform loop and other supercoil-stabilized local unusual structures a number of other chemical probes has been introduced (Table I). These probes differ in their specificity toward bases and functional groups, etc.; such differences may influence sensitivity of bases contained in the unusual structure to the particular probe. So, with a proper combination of the chemical probe one can "feel for" the local structure and obtain detailed information about its spatial organization at single-nucleotide resolution.

Combination of probes was especially useful in the studies of the B-Z transition and structural distortions at the B-Z junctions (9,10,24,29) and in the elucidation of the structure of homopurine · homopyrimidine tracts (13,31-36). Using glyoxal and CAA, i.e., probes which require base unpairing for the reaction, we demonstrated the presence of unpaired bases in the B-Z junctions (24-26). Similar conclusions were drawn also by other authors (51,52) based on probing B-Z junctions with BAA and CAA.

Osmium Tetroxide: Effect of Ligands

Properties of the osmium probe can be significantly influenced by the osmium tetroxide ligands. In Os,py reagent 1 mM osmium tetroxide is usually combined with at least 1% (v/v) pyridine. One may expect that such a high concentration of pyridine would not be convenient, e.g., if Os,py is applied to probe DNA structure in the cell. In fact treatment of *E.coli* cells with Os,py induced early cell lysis (53). If pyridine is

Table II
Osmium Tetroxide Complexes with Different Ligands Tested for Their Ability to Site-Specifically Modify the ColE1 Cruciform in Supercoiled pColIR215 DNA

OsO_4 complex with:	site-specific modification
pyridine	+[a]
2,2′-bipyridine	+
4,4′-bipyridine	−
2,2′-dithiobrpyridine	−
1,10-phenanthroline	+[b]
bathophenanthroline disulfonic acid	+
2,9-dimethyl-1,10-phenanthroline	−
5-nitro-1,10-phenanthroline	−
tetramethylethylenediamine	+
8-hydroxy-5-quinoline	−
8-hydroxy-5-quinoline sulfonic acid	−
8-hydroxy-7-iodo-5-quinoline sulfonic acid	−

+, Site-specific modification detected by nuclease S1 (after DNA linearization with *Pst*I) in the presence of 2 mM OsO_4 and 2 mM ligand (10 min. at 37°C).
−, no site-specific modification detected under the given conditions.
[a]A presence of at least 0.5% pyridine necessary.
[b]In addition to the cruciform modification, reactions at multiple sites in the DNA molecule.

replaced in Os,py by 2,2′-bipyridine, more stable adducts with DNA are formed (3,5,24,26), osmium tetroxide and bipy can be applied at equimolar concentrations and even submillimolar concentrations of Os,bipy are sufficient for the detection of B-Z junctions in supercoiled plasmids (24). Using Os,bipy we developed a simple method for probing DNA structure in the cell (54,55). To improve the versatility of the osmium probes we tested (in addition to py and bipy) the ability of ten different ligands (Table II) to site-specifically modify the B-Z junction and the cruciform loop. We found (53, P. Boublikova and E. Palecek, unpublished) that in addition to Os,bipy, bathophenanthroline disulfonic acid (BPDS) and tetramethylethylenediamine (TMEN) in complexes with osmium tetroxide site-specifically modify the above mentioned structures at millimolar and submillimolar concentrations. Osmium tetroxide complex with 1,10-phenanthroline behaved under the same conditions less specifically, also showing reactions at other sites of the supercoiled and linear DNA molecules. Lower specificity of the phenanthroline complex in reactions with DNA may be useful in DNA footprinting *in vitro* and *in situ* (E. Palecek, unpublished).

Negative results obtained with many compounds presented in Table II do not mean that the given substance does not react at all with DNA; in fact with some of them we obtained positive results at higher probe concentrations. Os,bipy, Os,BPDS and Os,TMEN (Figure 1) greatly differ in their sizes and other properties. One may expect that these differences may come into play in the selectivity of the probes for specific DNA structures as well as in the probe penetration into the cell when applied to studies of DNA structure *in situ*.

Antibodies Against DNA-Os,py and DNA-Os,bipy

Immunological methods have proved to be of great value in the studies of non B DNA structures (56-59). These methods have also been used to study chemically modified DNA's (60-62) but eliciting antibodies against DNA chemically modified with a structural probe has not been reported. We attempted to generate antibodies against DNA-Os,py (anti-DNA-Os,py) and DNA-Os,bipy (anti-DNA-Os,bipy) which could (if sufficiently specific) significantly extend the applicability of Os,py and Os,bipy to probe structures of DNA's in their natural environment including DNA's in prokaryotic and eukaryotic cells. Polyclonal anti-DNA-Os,py were elicited in rabbits (63). Testing of specificity of the antisera and purified IgG by ELISA and/or retardation of the DNA electrophoretic mobility in agarose gels has revealed strong reaction with ss and ds DNA-Os,py, weak reaction with DNA-Os,bipy and no cross-reaction with unmodified DNA, RNA and proteins. RNA-Os,py showed a weak cross-reaction but no reaction with osmium-modified proteins was observed.

Our preliminary results suggest that application of anti-DNA-Os,py and anti-DNA-Os,bipy will make it possible to study not only specific structures in small plasmids but also local structures in chromosomal DNA's both *in vitro* and *in situ*. In addition to this anti-DNA-Os,py and anti-DNA-Os,bipy extend the possibilities of the detection of osmium-modified bases in DNA's (Figure 2). E.g., Os,py modification of 2-3 nucleotides in the cruciform loop (14,20) in supercoiled pAT32 DNA resulted in a marked retardation of the supercoiled molecules (Figure 4). After *Bgl*I cleavage

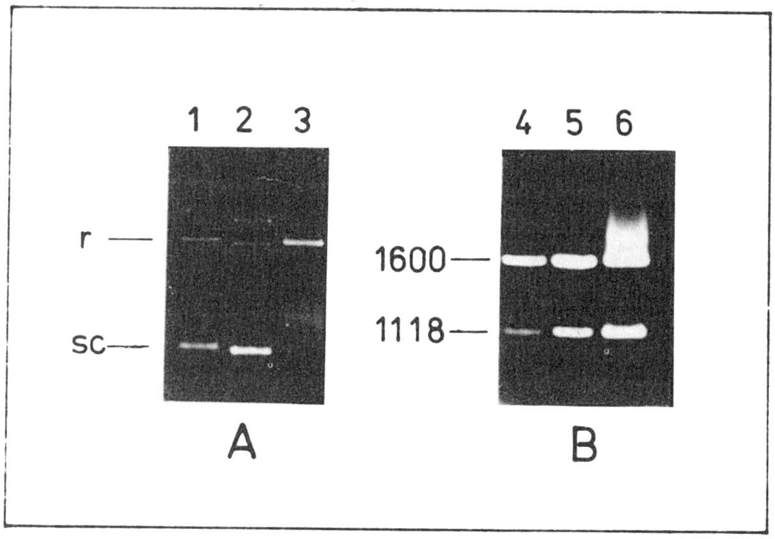

Figure 4: Gel retardation of pAT32 DNA-Os,py by anti-DNA-Os,py; DNA was modified with 1 mM OsO_4, 3% pyridine, 20 minutes at 20°C in 50 mM NaCl, 5 mM Tris-EDTA, pH 7.6 (14,20). Osmium-modified DNA samples were incubated with 20 μg of the anti-DNA-Os,py in a volume of 20 μl. A, supercoiled DNA; B, DNA cleaved with BglI. Unmodified DNA with antibody (lanes 1 and 4), Os,py-modified DNA without antibody (lanes 2 and 5), Os,py-modified DNA with antibody (lanes 3 and 6). 1% agarose gel.

of this Os,py-modified DNA only the longer fragment (containing the Os,py-modified bases in the middle of the $(dA\text{-}dT)_{16}$ insert) was retarded, while the shorter one was unretarded.

Polymorphy of $(dA\text{-}dT)_n$ Sequence: Supercoil-Stabilized Left-Handed DNA

In contrast to other alternating purine-pyrimidine sequences which form in natural DNA's supercoil-stabilized Z DNA (64,65) until recently no left-handed DNA had been reported in $(dA\text{-}dT)_n$ sequences. Recently Taillandier *et al.* (66,67) have shown that poly(dA-dT) · poly(dA-dT) at high NaCl concentration in the presence of Ni^{2+} (5 M NaCl, 95 mM $NiCl_2$) displays the CD, UV absorption and Raman spectra characteristic of Z DNA. Application of Os,py or Os,bipy in the presence of Ni^{2+} ions is difficult. So, we used DEPC and *Bal*31 nuclease to probe the $(dA\text{-}dT)_{16}$ insert in a supercoiled and linearized plasmid pAT32 in Ni^{2+} containing solutions (68). The DEPC modification patterns (Figure 5a) suggested that in a supercoiled plasmid left-handed DNA can be formed under conditions (2.0 M NaCl, 0.2 M $NiCl_2$) not sufficient to induce left-handed DNA in the linear plasmid and poly(dA-dT) · poly(dA-dT). Our preliminary experiments (K. Nejedly, unpublished) showed under the same conditions binding of a monoclonal anti-Z antibody to the pAT32 plasmid. Quite

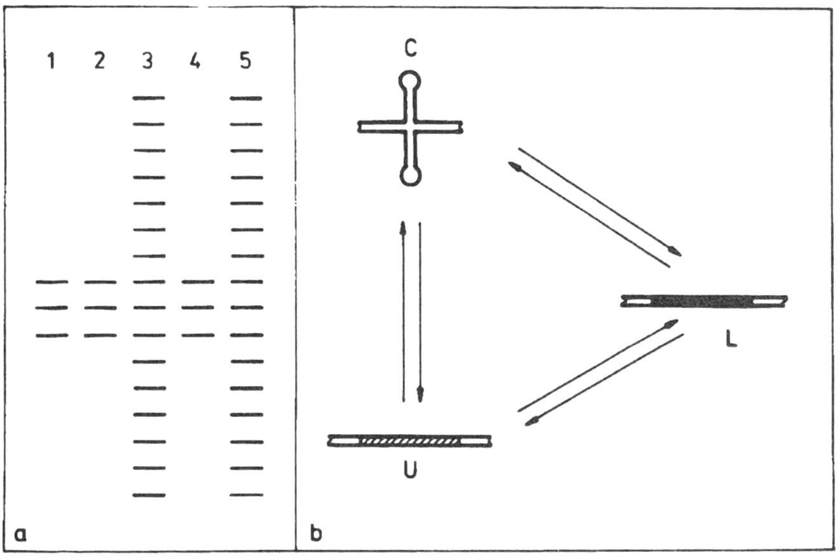

Figure 5: a) Schematic representation of the DEPC modification pattern (at single-nucleotide resolution) of the $(dA\text{-}dT)_{16}$ insert in a supercoiled pAT32 DNA; dependence on ionic composition of the reaction mixture (68). DNA was modified with DEPC (30 minutes at room temperature) in 25 mM Tris-HCl, pH 7.6 (lane 1) plus either 0.5 or 1.0 M $NiCl_2$, respectively (lanes 2 and 3) or in the same buffer with 0.2 M $NiCl_2$ plus 1.5 or 2.0 M NaCl, respectively (lanes 4 and 5). b) Schematic representation of a model of equilibria in $(dA\text{-}dT)_{16}$ segment in supercoiled DNA. At low ionic strengths conformation U is formed (14,20) (probably alternating structure with disturbed A-upon-T stacking, characterized by uniform modification with Os,py). Increase in ionic strength or decrease in temperature result in an equilibruim shift to the cruciform C. At higher ionic strengths in the presence of $NiCl_2$ left-handed DNA may be formed (68).

recently it has been shown that in $(dA\text{-}dT)_5$ segment left-handed helix may be formed at much lower Ni^{2+} concentration if this segment is flanked with other sequences forming Z DNA (69).

In linearized plasmids $(dA\text{-}dT)_n$ sequences (with n = 16 and higher but not with n = 8) display strong reactivity of thymines towards Os,py (12); it was suggested that these sequences adopt an altered conformation, probably close to the model of alternating dinucleotide structure (37). In supercoiled plasmids $(dA\text{-}dT)_n$ inserts adopt two different structures (14), one of them being a cruciform while the other is probably close to that found in the linear plasmids. A transition between these two forms depends on the ionic strength, temperature etc. The $(dA\text{-}dT)_n$ insert in a supercoiled DNA may thus undergo transitions (Figure 4b) between at least three structural forms; no such structural versatility has been found in any other DNA nucleotide sequence.

Structure of the Homopurine · Homopyrimidine Tracts

Frequent occurence and specific localization of the homopurine · homopyrimidine sequences in eukaryotic genomes suggest that these sequences may play a significant biological role. Unusual structures adopted by the homopurine · homopyrimidine tracts were originally detected by their hypersensitivity to single-strand selective nucleases. Several structural models were proposed to explain properties of homopurine · homopyrimidine tracts (reviewed in 70).

In 1987 we brought the first evidence based on the application of chemical probes (31) in favour of the intramolecular protonated triplex H-DNA (71-73) in the homopurine · homopyrimidine tract of a supercoiled and linearized plasmid pEJ4. We used (31) Os,py to probe the homopyrimidine strand and glyoxal as a probe for the homopurine strand in combination with nuclease S1 cleavage to detect the chemically modified bases. We showed the dependence of the site specific chemical modification of the homopurine · homopyrimidine sequence on pH, supercoiling and ionic strength and demonstrated at pH 5.6 the major modification in the middle of the homopyridine strand and a minor site 10-20 bp away from the major site. On the ground of our results we concluded that under the given conditions protonated triplex H-DNA is present in the supercoiled pEJ4 DNA. Our results also suggested that at pH 4.0 and 4.5 H-form can exist even in linearized pEJ4 DNA.

Using basically the same approach several laboratories including ours (13,32-36) published in 1988 modification patterns (Figure 6b) of the homopurine · homopyrimidine tracts at single-nucleotide resolution (using chemical cleavage of DNA instead of nuclease S1) which represent direct and compelling evidence of the intramolecular protonated triplex H-form DNA.

We used electron microscopy to visualize the triplex H-form in pEJ4 DNA (74). At pH 4.0 and 5.6 specific local changes were observed in supercoiled DNA by means of the formamide variant of the Kleinschmidt technique and the protein-free technique. These changes were absent in pUC19 DNA (from which the pEJ4 plasmid

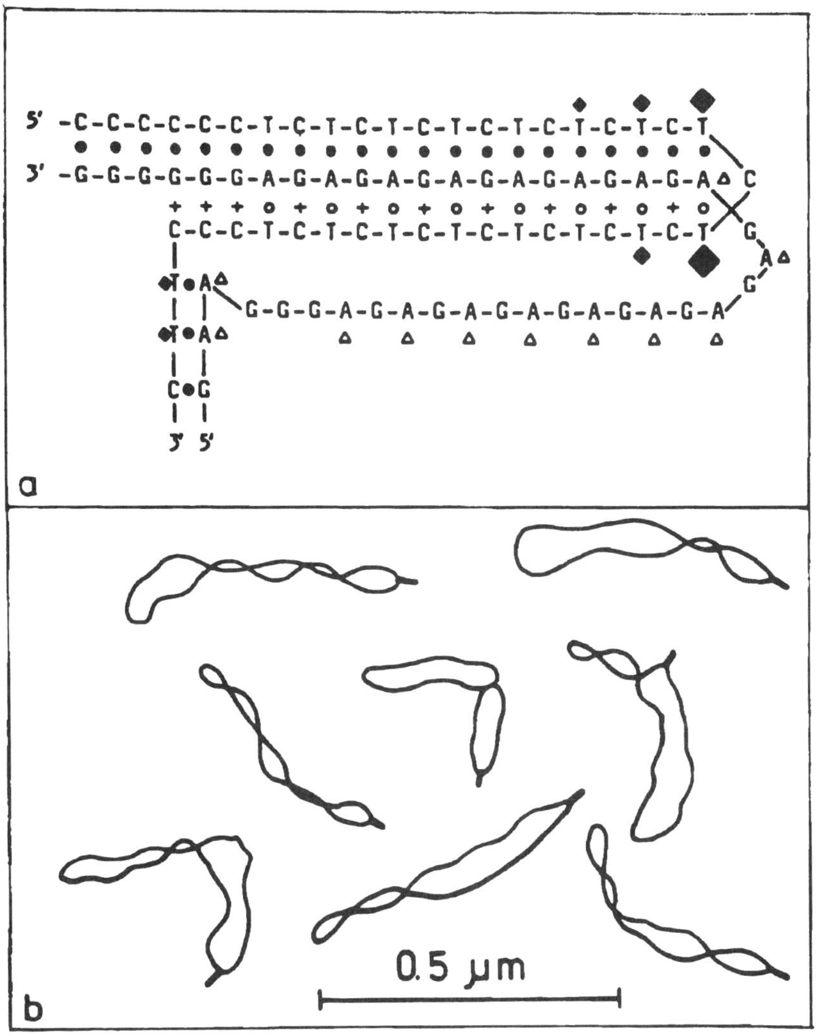

Figure 6: a) Protonated triplex H form in supercoiled pEJ4 DNA (34) which includes the Watson-Crick (•) duplex associated with the homopyrimidine strand by Hoogsteen base pairing (o,+) where the cytosines are protonated. The diamonds denote Os,py modified thymines while triangles show adenine residues modified by DEPC at pH 5.5 *in vitro*. b) Electron microscopy of supercoiled pEJ4 DNA (formamide spreading) at pH 5.6 (74). Graphical interpretation of molecules containing "stems".

was derived) as well as in pEJ4 specimens prepared at pH 7.6. Short "stems" observed in pEJ4 DNA at pH 5.6 appeared almost always at the apex of the plasmid, (Figure 6b) suggesting the presence of a curvature or a kink in the vicinity of the H structure. At pH 4.0 (i.e., under conditions where H-DNA can be formed even in the absence of DNA supercoiling) retardation of the electrophoretic mobility of DNA fragments containing homopurine · homopyrimidine insert was found by Htun and Dahlberg (13), suggesting the presence of a kink or hinge in the DNA molecule.

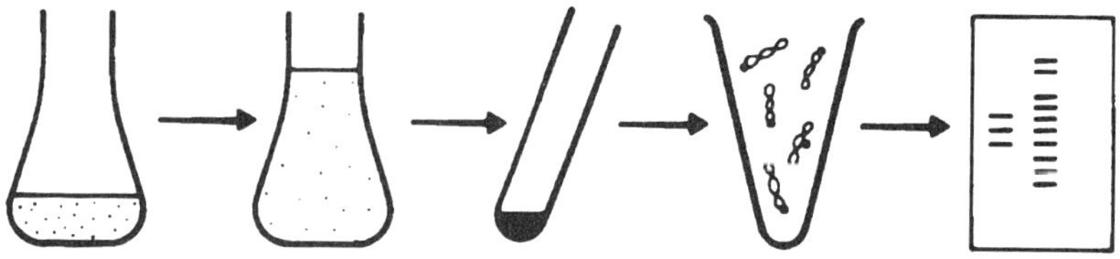

Figure 7: Schematic representation of the method of probing of plasmid DNA structure in bacterial cells by Os,bipy (54,55). a) Suspension of *E.coli* cells (2 mg of dry weight per ml) is treated with 2 mM OsO_4, 2 mM 2,2′-bipyridine for 20 to 60 minutes at room temperature (or at 37°C). b) The reaction is stopped by chilling to 0°C and tenfold diluting by an icecold buffer solution. c) Cells are spun down and thoroughly rinsed. d) plasmid DNA is isolated by the boiling method usually followed by isopycnic CsCl, ethidium bromide gradient centrifugation or some other purification step. e) Osmium binding sites are detected in the same way as with DNA modified with Os,bipy or Os,py *in vitro* (see Figure 2).

Polymorphy of the DNA Structure in the Cell

Our knowledge of the polymorphy of the DNA double helix *in vitro* has greatly improved in this decade. On the other hand little is known about the DNA structure in the cell mainly due to lack of suitable techniques. In 1987 we proposed a technique for the analysis of open local DNA structures in the cell (54,55). This technique is based on a chemical probe - Os,bipy - which penetrates easily into the bacterial cells without disturbing their integrity and site-specifically modifies bases in DNA accessible to the probe. The principles of this technique are shown in Figure 7. Using this technique we brought direct evidence of the existence of the left-handed DNA (54) and open unusual structure of $(dA\text{-}dT)_{16}$ sequence (55) in *E.coli* cells. At the same time Jaworski *et al.* (75) introduced a molecular genetic technique to study left-handed Z DNA in *E.coli* and showed that Z DNA exists and elicit a biological response *in vivo*. While the technique designed by Jaworski *et al.* (75) can be used to study Z DNA only, our chemical method (54,55) can be applied to studies of any DNA structure containing bases open to the chemical probe.

Does protonated triplex H-DNA exist in the cell? Recent studies of homopurine · homopyrimidine sequences (reviewed in 70) suggest that their triplex structure may play a significant biological role. From the results of immunofluorescence studies (81) it seems likely that triplexes are an inherent feature of eukaryotic DNA's, but strong evidence of the existence of the DNA triplex structure in the cell is missing.

We attempted to apply the Os,bipy technique (Figure 7) to study H-DNA of the pEJ4 plasmid in *E.coli* cells. The experiments were performed basically in the same way as with $(dC\text{-}dG)_n$ containing plasmids (54,55), but the cells were preincubated and modified in buffers of different pH values. Osmium binding sites were detected (after plasmid isolation and purification) by nuclease S1 cleavage (Figure 2) or with hot piperidine cleavage and nucleotide sequencing.

Os,bipy modification pattern at single-nucleotide resolution. Samples of pEJ4 DNA modified *in situ* at pH 4.5 and 7.6 were used for the analysis on sequencing gel at single-nucleotide resolution using basically the same procedure as described (34). Treatment of bacterial cells with Os,bipy at pH 4.5 resulted in a strong modification at the centre of the homopyridine tract (Figure 8a) with the strongest modification at T15. In addition to the modification of the central nucleotides appreciable modification was observed at thymines at the 3′ end outside the $(dT\text{-}dC)_{16}$ segment as well as at T31 at the 5′ end of this segment. In contrast to this result treatment of bacteria with Os,bipy at pH 7.6 resulted in a weak modification (not shown) differing only slightly from the background. These results basically agree with those obtained *in vitro* after Os,bipy modification of supercoiled pEJ4 DNA with Os,bipy (not shown) and with Os,py (Figure 6a) (34). It has been shown by several authors (13,31-36,76) that the Os,py pattern of the homopyridine strand in the H-form shows a strong modification of T residues in the centre of the $(C\text{-}T)_n$ sequence and a weaker modification at its boundary, differing from patterns observed in any of the local open structures (e.g., cruciform and B-Z junctions) so far studied (50). It is thus sufficiently characteristic to be used for the identification of the H-form in pEJ4 plasmid in *E.coli* cells. The specificity of the Os,bipy modification is important as no chemical probe reacting preferentially with single-stranded regions in the homopurine strand *in situ* has so far been introduced.

Intracellular pH values ($pH_{(in)}$) of E.coli cells harbouring the pEJ4 plasmid measured by the fluorescein method (77) were higher than pH of the external 0.1 M buffers ($pH_{(out)}$) (J. Slavik and E. Palecek, unpublished). At $pH_{(out)}$ 4.0, 4.5 and 5.0 $pH_{(in)}$ the values of $pH_{(in)}$ were, however, within the pH range in which the isolated pEJ4 DNA at native mean superhelical density ($\bar{\sigma}$) contains H-DNA in the homopurine · homopyrimidine tract (31,71).

Influence of superhelical density and pH. It has been demonstrated *in vitro* (71) that at higher $\bar{\sigma}$ the B → H transition takes place at higher pH values. To increase the linking number of the intracellular pEJ4 DNA we grew the cells in the media supplemented with 0.35 M NaCl (78). Figure 8c shows chloroquine-agarose gel of pEJ4 DNA isolated from bacterial cells after growth in low and high osmolarity media; an increase of the growth medium osmolarity resulted in a substantial oversupercoiling of pEJ4 DNA which was manifested in the gel containing chloroquine (1.25 µg/ml) by an increase in mobility.

Bacteria which were grown in high and normal osmolarity media were preincubated in buffers at various pH values and treated with Os,bipy. DNA was then isolated (Figure 7), linearized with EcoRI and cleaved at Os,bipy-modified sites with nuclease S1 (Figure 2). In a parallel experiment DNA samples isolated from the same bacteria were modified with Os,bipy *in vitro*.

In agreement with our previous work (31) Os,bipy modification *in vitro* resulted in the appearance of a strong band H (characteristic for the site-specific modification of the homopurine · homopyrimidine tract corresponding to about 2750 bp from the EcoRI site) (Figure 8b, lanes 12-14 and 19-21) at pH 4.0, 4.5 and 5.0; in DNA samples with higher σ (Figure 8b) H bands were slightly stronger (Figure 8b, lanes 18-20). Band H was absent in DNA samples modified at pH 7.6 (Figure 8b, lanes 15 and 22).

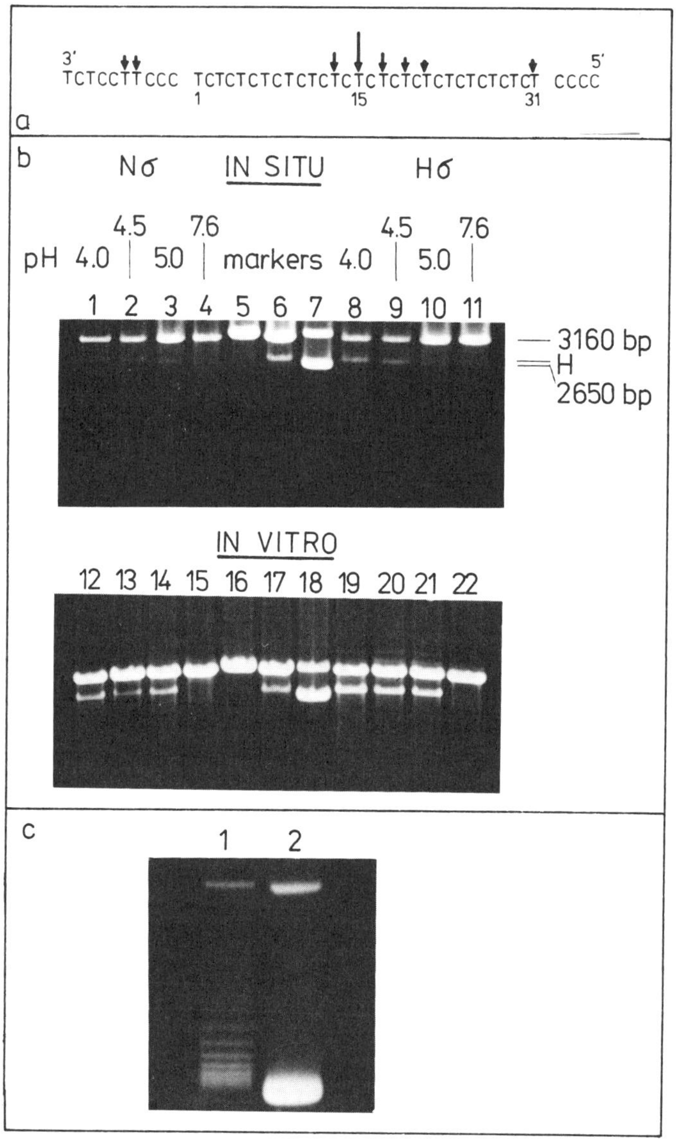

Figure 8: a) Nucleotide sequence of the homopyrimidine strand of pEJ4 DNA (a derivative of pUC19 DNA containing the 509-bp long fragment of sea urchin *P. miliaris* histone gene spacer region cloned in the polylinker). The arrows denote the Os,bipy hypersensitive sites (at pH 4.5) in plasmid pEJ4 contained in *E.coli* cells. b) Site-specific Os,bipy-modification of plasmid pEJ4 in *E.coli* cells (lanes 1-11) and *in vitro* (lanes 12-22). *E.coli* grown at normal osmolarity (native superhelical density, N σ) (lanes 1-4,12-15) and at high osmolarity (higher (H) σ) (lanes 8-11,19-22). Preincubation and modification at pH 4.0 (lanes 1,8,12,19), pH 4.5 (lanes 2,9,13,20), pH 5.0 (lanes 3,10,14,21) and pH 7.6 (lanes 4,11,15,22). DNA samples isolated by the boiling method (54) without further purification. c) Effect of *E.coli* growth at different osmolarities on pEJ4 DNA supercoiling. pEJ4 DNA isolated from bacteria grown in normal osmolarity media (M9 medium) (lane 1) and in high osmolarity media (M9 supplemented with 0.35 M NaCl) (lane 2). The gel contained 1.25 μg/ml of chloroquine. Under these conditions the more supercoiled topoisomers migrate more rapidly. (J. Novakova and E. Palecek, unpublished).

If the Os,bipy modification was performed *in situ* a strong band H was observed at pH 4.0 and 4.5 (Figure 8b, lanes 8 and 9) only DNA samples with higher σ (i.e., isolated from bacteria grown in a high osmolarity medium (Figure 8c)) and at pH 5.0 only a weak band H (Figure 8b, lane 10) appeared. In DNA samples with normal σ only weak bands H appeared at pH 4.0, 4.5 and 5.0 (Figure 8b, lanes 1-3). No band H was observed at pH 7.6 (Figure 8b, lanes 4 and 11) in DNA samples with both normal and higher σ.

On the basis of our results we conclude that H-form DNA can exist in *E.coli* cells and its formation in the cell may be influenced by the intracellular pH and DNA linking number. In eukaryotic cells where the homopurine · homopyrimidine sequences frequently occur (70) the superhelical densities of various DNA domains may be significantly different (79); $pH_{(in)}$ depends on the life cycle of the cells (e.g., low intracellular pH is common to resting cells) and its values in different cell compartments can substantially vary (80). On the other hand it has been shown that triplex structure can be formed *in vitro* at neutral pH at high superhelical density (13) and in the presence of magnesium (33a); longer homopurine · homopyrimidine sequences (32) can assume alternative structure at neutral pH at native σ and in the absence of Mg^{2+}.

Quite recently it has been shown (80a) that around the middle of the $(dT\text{-}dC)_n$ tracts the DNA replication is specifically arrested; the arrests is less prominent at pH 8.0 than at pH 6.5. It has been concluded that triplex structures may serve as pause or arrest signals for DNA replication and amplification. Further work will be necessary to explain the relations between the intracellular pH, and DNA linking number on one hand and the biological role of the DNA on the other hand. Of course the crucial experiments will have to be done with eukaryotic cells where the location and high occurrence of the homopurine homopyrimidine sequences suggest their biological importance.

Conclusions

In recent years chemical probes of the DNA structure, namely Os,py and DEPC, have been increasingly applied and contributed significantly to our knowledge of local DNA structures *in vitro*. A common feature of these structures is accessibility of bases in some regions to the chemical probe; the same region in the given local structure (in absence of the chemical modification) is usually cleavable by single-strand selective nucleases. These structures can thus be categorized as "open" structures. Does this opening of the DNA structure play a biological role? Do all the local DNA structures we can study *in vitro* exist in the cell? How do the specific DNA structures interact with other macromolecules in the cell? To answer these and other related questions further work concerning the DNA structural-functional relations will be necessary. The first results of probing DNA structure with osmium probes *in situ* suggest that these probes and antibodies against the probe-modified DNA's may represent important research tools in our efforts to understand better the role of the DNA structure in the cell.

References and Footnotes

1. E. Palecek, in *Progress in Nucleic Acids Res. Mol. Biol.*, (Ed., W.E. Cohn), Vol. 18, Academic Press, New York, p. 151 (1976).

2. E. Palecek, E. Lukasova, F. Jelen and M. Vojtiskova, *Bioelectrochem. Bioenerg. 8*, 497 (1981).
3. E. Lukasova, F. Jelen and E. Palecek, *Gen. Physiol. Biophys. 1*, 53 (1982).
4. E. Palecek and M.A. Hung, *Anal. Biochem. 132*, 236 (1983).
5. E. Lukasova, M. Vojtiskova, F. Jelen, T. Sticzay and E. Palecek, *Gen. Physiol. Biophys. 3*, 175 (1984).
6. G.C. Glikin, M. Vojtiskova, L. Rena-Descalzi and E. Palecek, *Nucl. Acids Res. 12*, 1725 (1984).
7. D.M.J. Lilley and E. Palecek, *EMBO J. 3*, 1187 (1984).
8. M. Vojtiskova, J. Stokrova and E. Palecek, *J. Biomol. Struct. Dyn. 2*, 1013 (1985).
9. B.H. Johnston and A. Rich, *Cell 42*, 713 (1985).
10. E. Palecek, *Studia Biophys. 114*, 39 (1986).
11. G. Galazka, E. Palecek, R.D. Wells and J. Klysik, *J. Biol. Chem. 261*, 7092 (1986).
12. J.A. McClellan, E. Palecek and D.M.J. Lilley, *Nucl. Acids Res. 14*, 9291 (1986).
13. H. Htun and J.E. Dahlberg, *Science 241*, 1791 (1988).
14. J.A. McClellan and D.M.J. Lilley, *J. Mol. Biol. 197*, 707 (1987).
15. P.M. Scholten and A. Nordheim, *Nucl. Acids Res. 14*, 3981 (1986).
16. J.C. Furlong and D.M.J. Lilley, *Nucl. Acids Res. 14*, 3995 (1986).
17. D.M.J. Lilley and L.R. Hallam, *J. Mol. Biol. 180*, 179 (1984).
18. K.M. Sullivan and D.M.J. Lilley, *Cell 47*, 817 (1986).
19. L.H. Naylor, D.M.J. Lilley and J.H. van de Sande, *EMBO J. 5*, 2407 (1986).
20. D.M.J. Lilley and J.A. McClellan, in *Structure and Expression*, (Eds., R.H. Sarma and M.H. Sarma), Vol. 2, Adenine Press, p. 073 (1987).
21. D.M.J. Lilley, K.M. Sullivan and A.I.H. Murchie, in *Nucleic Acids and Molecular Biology*, (Eds., F. Eckstein and D.M.J. Lilley), Vol. 1, Springer-Verlag, Berlin, p. 126 (1987).
22. D.R. Duckett, A.I.H. Murchie, S. Diekmann, E. von Kitzing, B. Kemper and D.M.J. Lilley, *Cell 55*, 79 (1988).
23. K. Nejedly, M. Kwinkowski, G. Galazka, J. Klysik and E. Palecek, *J. Biomol. Struct. Dyn. 3*, 467 (1985).
24. E. Palecek, P. Boublikova, G. Galazka and J. Klysik, *Gen. Physiol. Biophys. 6*, 327 (1987).
25. E. Palecek, P. Boublikova, K. Nejedly, G. Galazka and J. Klysik, *J. Biomol. Struct. Dyn. 5*, 297 (1987).
26. K. Nejedly, R. Matyasek and E. Palecek, *J. Biomol. Struct. Dyn. 5*, 261 (1988).
27. B.H. Johnston, *J. Biomol. Struct. Dyn. 6*, 153 (1988).
28. N. Vogt, L. Marrot, N. Rousseau, B. Malfoy and M. Leng, *J. Mol. Biol. 201*, 773 (1988).
29. N. Vogt, N. Rousseau, M. Leng and B. Malfoy, *J. Biol. Chem. 263*, 11826 (1988).
30. E. Palecek, E. Makaturova-Rasovska and S. Diekmann, *Gen. Physiol. Biophys. 7*, 379 (1988).
31. M Vojtiskova and E. Palecek, *J. Biomol. Struct. Dyn. 5*, 283 (1987).
32. D.A. Collier, J.A. Griffin and R.D. Wells, *J. Biol. Chem. 263*, 7397 (1988).
33. J.C. Hanvey, J. Klysik and R.D. Wells, *J. Biol. Chem. 263*, 7386 (1988).
33a. Y. Kohwi and T. Kohwi-Shigematsu, *Proc. Natl. Acad. Sci. USA 85*, 3781 (1988).
34. M. Vojtiskova, S. Mirkin, V. Lyamichev, O. Voloshin, M. Frank-Kamenetskii and E. Palecek, *FEBS Lett. 234*, 295 (1988).
35. J.C. Hanvey, M. Szimizu and R.D. Wells, *Proc. Natl. Acad. Sci. USA 85*, 6292 (1988).
36. B.H. Johnston, *Science 241*, 1800 (1988).
37. A. Klug, A. Jack, M.A. Viswamitra, O. Kennard, S. Shakked and T.A. Steitz, *J. Mol. Biol. 131*, 669 (1979).
38. R.G.H. Cotton, N.R. Rodrigues and R.D. Campbell, *Proc. Natl. Acad. Sci. USA 85*, 4397 (1988).
39. M.J. McLean and M. Warring, *Molecular Recognition 1*, 138 (1988).
40. L. Marrot and M. Leng, *Biochemistry 28*, 1454 (1989).
41. A. Schwartz, L. Marrot and M. Leng, *J. Mol. Biol. 207*, 445 (1989).
42. M. Buckle, A. Spassky, M. Herbert, D.M.J. Lilley and H. Buc, *Symposium on Local Changes in DNA Structure and Their Biological Implications*, Brno, Book of Abstracts, p. 11 (1988).
43. E. Di Mauro, G. Camilloni, S. Venditi, R. Negri and M. Caserta, *Sumposium on Local Changes in DNA Structure and Their Biological Implications*, Brno, Book of Abstracts, p. 17 (1988).
44. M. Beer, S. Stern, D. Carmalt and K.H. Mohlhenrich, *Biochemistry 5*, 2283 (1966).
45. K. Burton and W.T. Riley, *Biochem. J. 98*, 70 (1966).
46. Ch.-H. Chang, M. Beer and L.G. Marzilli, *Biochemistry 16*, 33 (1977).
47. T. Friedmann and D.M. Brown, *Nucl. Acids Res. 5*, 615 (1978).

48. A.M. Maxam and W. Gilbert, *Methods in Enzymology 65*, 499 (1980).
49. R.D. Wells, *J. Biol. Chem. 263*, 1095 (1988).
50. E. Palecek, in *Highlights of Modern Biochemistry*, (Eds.; A. Kotyk, J. Skoda, V. Paces and V. Kostka), VSP International Science Publishers, Zeist, p. 53 (1989).
51. T. Kohwi-Shigematsu, T. Manes and Y. Kohwi, *Proc. Natl. Acad. Sci. USA 84*, 2223 (1987).
52. M.J. McLean, J.E. Larson, F. Wohlrab and H. Weintraub, *Nucl. Acids Res. 15*, 6971 (1987).
53. P. Boublikova and E. Palecek, *Gen. Physiol. Biophys.*, in press.
54. E. Palecek, P. Boublikova and P. Karlovsky, *Gen. Physiol. Biophys. 4*, 593 (1987).
55. E. Palecek, E. Rasovska and P. Boublikova, *Biochem. Biophys. Res. Commun. 150*, 731 (1986).
56. D. Stollar, *CRC Crit. Rev. Biochem. 20*, 1 (1986).
57. D. Eilat, *Clin. Exp. Immunol. 65*, 215 (1986).
58. M. Leng, in *DNA - Ligand Interactions. From Drugs to Proteins*, (Eds.; W. Guschlbauer and W. Sanger), Plenum Press, New York, p. 257 (1987).
59. D. Stollar, in *Unusual DNA Structures*, (Eds.; R.D. Wells and S.C. Harvey), Birmingham, USA, p. 253 (1988).
60. T.W. Munns and M.K. Liszewski, in *Progress in Nucleic Acid Res. Mol. Biol.*, (Ed.; W. Cohn), Vol. 24, Academic Press, New York, p. 109 (1980).
61. P.T. Strickland and J.M. Boyle, in *Progress in Nucleic Acids Res. Mol. Biol.*, (Ed.; W. Cohn), Vol. 31, Academic Press, New York, p. 1 (1984).
62. M. Leng, *Biochimia 67*, 309 (1985).
63. E. Palecek, A. Krejcova, M. Vojtiskova, V. Podgorodnichenko, T. Ilyina and A. Poverenyi, *Gen. Physiol. Biophys. 8*, 491 (1989).
64. A. Rich, A. Nordheim and A.H.-J. Wang, *Annu. Rev. Biochem. 53*, 791 (1984).
65. T.M. Jovin, D.M. Soumpasis and L.P. McIntosh, *Annu. Rev. Phys. Chem. 38*, 521 (1987).
66. S. Adam, J. Liquier, J.A. Taboury and E. Taillander, *Biochemistry 25*, 3220 (1986).
67. J.P. Ridoux, J. Liquier and E. Taillandier, *Biochemistry 27*, 3874 (1988).
68. K. Nejedly, J. Klysik and E. Palecek, *FEBS Lett. 243*, 313 (1989).
69. J. Klysik, W. Zacharias, G. Galazka, M. Kwinkowski, B. Uznanski and A. Okruszek, *Nucl. Acids Res. 16*, 6915 (1988).
70. R.D. Wells, D.A. Collier, J.C. Hanvey, M. Shimizu and F. Wohlrab, *FASEB J. 2*, 2939 (1988).
71. V.I. Lyamichev, S.M. Mirkin and M.D. Frank-Kamenetskii, *J. Biol. Struct. Dyn. 3*, 327 (1985).
72. D. Christophe, B. Cabrer, A. Bacolla, H. Targovnik, V. Pohl and G. Vassart, *Nucl. Acids Res. 13*, 5127 (1985).
73. V.I. Lyamichev, S.M. Mirkin and M.D. Frank-Kamenetskii, *J. Biol. Struct. Dyn. 3*, 667 (1986).
74. J. Stokrova, M. Vojtiskova and E. Palecek, *J. Biomol. Struct. Dyn. 7*, 891 (1989).
75. A. Jaworski, W.-T. Hsieh, J.A. Blaho, J.E. Larson and R.D. Wells, *Science 238*, 773 (1987).
76. P. Parniewski, G. Galazka, A. Wilk and J. Klysik, *Nucl. Acids Res. 17*, 617 (1989).
77. J. Slavik, *FEBS Lett. 140*, 22 (1982).
78. C.F. Higgins, C.J. Dorman, D.A. Stirling, L. Waddell, I.R. Booth, G. May and E. Bremer, *Cell 52*, 569 (1988).
79. G.N. Giaever and J.C. Wang, *Cell 55*, 849 (1988).
80. I.H. Madshus, *Biochem. J. 250*, 1 (1988).
80a. A. Lapidot, N. Baran and H. Manor, *Nucl. Acids Res. 17*, 883 (1989.
81. J.S. Lee, G.D. Burkholder, L.J.P. Latimer, B.L. Haug and R.P. Braun, *Nucl. Acids Res. 15*, 1047 (1987).
82. J.A. Borowiec, Li Zhang. S. Sasse-Dwight and J.A. Gralla, *J. Mol. Biol. 196*, 101 (1987).
83. E.D. Sverdlov, G.S. Monastyrskaya and E.I. Budowsky, *Mol. Biol. USSR 11*, 116 (1977).
84. W. Herr, *Proc. Natl. Acad. Sci. USA 82*, 8009 (1985).
85. T. Kohwi-Shigematsu, R. Gelinas and M. Weintraub, *Proc. Natl. Acad. Sci. USA 80*, 4389 (1983).
86. D.M.J. Lilley, in *The Role of Cyclic Nucleic Acid Adducts in Carcinogenesis and Mutagenesis*, (Eds.; B. Singer and H. Bartsch), International Agency for Research on Cancer, Lyon, p. 83 (1985).
87. P. Rio and M. Leng, *J. Mol. Biol. 191*, 569 (1986).
88. E. Lukasova and E. Palecek, *Studia. Biophys. 60*, 61 (1976).

Structure & Methods, ISBN 0-940030-32-2
Volume 3: DNA & RNA, ISBN 0-940030-31-4
Eds., Ramaswamy H. Sarma & Mukti H. Sarma, *© Adenine Press 1990*

Free Energies Associated with Superhelical Deformations of DNA

Craig J. Benham
Department of Biomathematical Sciences, Box 1023
Mount Sinai School of Medicine
1 Gustave Levy Place
New York, NY 10029

Abstract

The linking difference ΔLk of a superhelically constrained topological domain may be partitioned between writhing and twisting deformations in a continuum of ways. Fixing ΔLk does not specify a pure state, but rather it determines an ensemble of states. The free energy $G(\Delta Lk)$ associated to superhelicity therefore is an ensemble average quantity. To calculate its value one must first determine the free energy of each state in the ensemble. That portion of this free energy arising from secondary structural transitions is relatively easily accounted for, at least in principle. The residual linking difference (i.e., that part of ΔLk not expressed as changes of twist consequent on secondary structural transitions) must be accommodated by torsional and flexural deformations whose free energies are determined by the mechanical properties of the molecule. Bending and torsional stiffnesses have been measured for DNA, with values depending on base sequence, secondary structure and environmental parameters. These experimental results implicitly ascribe to the molecule the mechanical properties of a symmetric, linearly elastic rod. This is the experimental basis on which any analysis of the energetics of superhelical conformations must be founded. This paper explores the implications of these elastic mechanical properties. Writhing and twisting are shown *not* to be statistically independently fluctuating quantities in nicked molecules, so derivations of the torsional stiffness of DNA that assume such independence are not valid. We also show that a quadratic free energy cannot be ascribed directly to writhing. Methods that determine $G(\Delta Lk)$ from separate free energies of ΔTw and ΔWr, constrained by the constancy of their sum, are shown to yield conclusions which disagree with those derived from the known mechanical properties of DNA.

Introduction

The superhelical constraint imposed on a topological domain of DNA is the constancy of its linking difference ΔLk. This topological constraint must be accommodated through the partitioning of ΔLk between torsional and flexural deformations according to White's formula (1):

$$\Delta Lk = \Delta Tw + \Delta Wr \qquad [1]$$

Here ΔTw expresses the change in total twist of the domain away from its relaxed value (2). This torsional deformation may involve either local transitions at susceptible sites to alternative secondary structures having different helicity than the B-form, and/or smooth elastic torsional deformations of the secondary structures away from their unstressed helicities (3). The flexural deformation is expressed by the change in the writhing number ΔWr, a parameter that measures the amount by which the domain's large-scale tertiary structure differs from its relaxed conformation under the prevailing environmental conditions (4,5).

In practice there are myriad ways that an imposed linking difference can be partitioned among the various torsional, flexural and transconformational deformations to which the domain is susceptible. Genomic DNA base sequences generally contain many local sites whose sequence renders them susceptible to transitions to alternative secondary structures. These may include cruciform extrusions at inverted repeats, transitions to Z-form at alternating purine-pyrimidine sites, and to H-form at long homo-pyrimidine runs. In addition, because any base pair can denature, a domain containing N base pairs has 2^N states of strand separation. Both theoretical and experimental results indicate that transitions to each of these alternative conformations can be driven by imposed negative linking differences (6-13).

The number of states of secondary structure available to a superhelical domain of specified sequence, although finite, will generally be extremely large. Each individual state expresses part of the imposed linking difference as the changes of twist consequent on the transitions to its particular collection of altered secondary structures:

$$\Delta Lk = \Delta Tw_{trans} + \Delta Lk_{res}. \qquad [2]$$

The residual linking difference, ΔLk_{res}, is the part of the superhelical deformation that is not accommodated in this way. It must be expressed as smooth elastic torsional and flexural deformations of secondary structure:

$$\Delta Lk_{res} = \Delta Tw_{res} + \Delta Wr. \qquad [3]$$

There are a continuum of ways in which this partitioning can be effected. For each particular partitioning, there are infinitely many ways in which the particular values of ΔTw_{res} and ΔWr can be accommodated by smooth elastic deformations.

The fixing of a particular value of the linking difference ΔLk determines not a single pure state of the domain, but rather an ensemble of states, here indexed by i. Each individual state in the ensemble has a particular free energy whose value G_i is determined by the local transitions and elastic deformations that characterize it. According to standard statistical-mechanical theory, the fractional occupancy of state i at equilibrium is given by (14):

$$p_i = \frac{e^{-G_i/kT}}{\Sigma_i\, e^{-G_i/kT}}\,. \qquad [4]$$

The free energy associated to ΔLk is an ensemble averaged quantity, that is related to the energetics of the component states by:

$$G(\Delta Lk) = \sum_i p_i G_i. \quad [5]$$

This superhelical free energy can vary in complex ways with the imposed linking difference (15). In different regimes of superhelicity the imposed constraint ΔLk can induce different types of deformations and/or transitions, which may be specific to the base sequence of the DNA involved. In addition, other sequence-specific effects such as natural curvature and variability of the mechanical properties of DNA can lead to different free energy functions $G(\Delta Lk)$ for distinct molecules.

DNA Energetics - Experimental Results

Free Energy of Elastic Deformation

All DNA secondary structures that have been investigated to date have been shown experimentally to have the mechanical properties of symmetric, linearly elastic rods. Each structure has an unstressed conformation, possibly sequence dependent, deformations away from which are opposed by linear restoring forces, hence require a quadratic free energy density (16,17). The total free energy needed to deform a domain of length L, having specified secondary structure and base sequence, away from its unstressed conformation by curvature changes $\kappa(s)$ and deformations of helicity $\tau(s)$ (both quantities have units of radians/length) is

$$G(\kappa,\tau) = \int_0^L \frac{A(s)\kappa^2(s)}{2} + \frac{C(s)\tau^2(s)}{2}\, ds. \quad [6]$$

The experimentally measured mechanical properties of DNA are the torsional stiffness C and one bending stiffness A. The values of these stiffnesses are known to depend upon the secondary structure involved, environmental conditions such as ionic strength and temperature, and base sequence (18-22). For many purposes it is sufficient to use sequence-averaged values of these stiffnesses. The bending and torsional stiffnesses of random sequence B-form DNA in solution have been measured to be $A = 2.63 \times 10^{-19}$ erg-cm and $C = 2.75 \times 10^{-19}$ erg-cm, respectively (21,22). The fact that there is one bending stiffness implies that bending requires the same free energy in all directions. This mechanical symmetry may result from the participation in flexural motions of the approximately cylindrically symmetric hydration shell.

Energetics of Conformational Transitions

Local transitions to alternative DNA secondary structures are known to be cooperative in nature. They are either heteropolymeric or homopolymeric, depending upon whether or not their energetics vary with base sequence. For a homopolymeric transition (such as transition to Z-DNA within a run whose sequence is $(G \cdot C)_m$) the free energy required to transform r runs containing a total of n base pairs to the alternate conformation is

$$G_{trans} = ar + bn. \quad [7]$$

Here a is the free energy needed to initiate a run of transition and b is the free energy per base pair required to effect the transition. The values of these energy parameters depend upon the transition involved and environmental conditions.

In a heteropolymeric transition the value of b depends on base sequence. For example, strand separation of r runs containing a total of n base pairs, of which n_{AT} are A · T's, requires free energy

$$G_{trans} = ar + n_{AT}b_{AT} + (n - n_{AT})\, b_{GC}\,. \qquad [8]$$

Here the initiation free energy $a = 7$ kcals arises from the extra stacking interaction that must be disrupted in denaturing the first base pair (23). The values of b_{GC} and b_{AT} have been measured using oligomers in solution (24,25). The problem of determining free energies for other transitions is considered in a later section.

Free Energy of Superhelicity

When a population of identical circular DNA molecules is either nicked then treated with ligase or exposed to nicking-closing enzyme, an equilibrium results in which a distribution of linking numbers is observed. Densitometer analysis shows this distribution to be Boltzmann to high accuracy (26,27). From the measurement of the variance of this distribution a phenomenological free energy of superhelicity can be calculated which has the functional form

$$G(\Delta Lk) = \frac{K(\Delta Lk)^2}{2}\,. \qquad [9]$$

The value measured by Pulleyblank *et al.* (27) for the free energy parameter is $K = 2220RT/N$, where N is the length of the molecule involved. These energetics were shown to be accurate for the three DNA's that were experimentally investigated. However, these measurements were performed only for linking differences in the range $|\Delta Lk| \leqslant 5$, a small interval around the relaxed state where the behavior of the molecule is relatively simple. Conformational transitions are energetically highly disfavored in this range, so $\Delta Lk = \Delta Lk_{res}$ here. The assumption that these identical energetics of residual linking remain accurate at substantial linking differences involves extrapolation of the experimental results far beyond the range where they were measured. This caution applies particularly to analyses of superhelically driven transitions.

The Energetics of States

Consider a circular topological domain of DNA of known base sequence that is supercoiled a fixed amount ΔLk. Each individual state within the ensemble of possible responses to this imposed linking difference is characterized by a particular secondary structure, in which the conformation of each base pair is specified. Distinct local regions of altered, non-B form structure will occur in different states. The specification of this secondary structure fixes both the mechanical properties (i.e., stiffnesses to bending and twisting) at each point along the molecule and the partitioning of the imposed linking difference between ΔTw_{trans} *and* ΔLk_{res} described in Equation [2] above.

In order to analyze the equilibrium distribution of a population among its available states, the free energy G_i associated to each state must be determined. This free energy decomposes into two parts

$$G_i = G_{res} + G_{trans}, \quad [10]$$

arising from the residual linking difference and from transitions, respectively.

The Energetics of Residual Superhelicity

The residual linking difference ΔLk_{res} is expressed as torsional and flexural deformations of the secondary structures of the molecule. The energetics of these deformations are derived directly from the known mechanical properties of the DNA as shown in Equation [6] above. It is not presently feasible to perform a complete and rigorous analysis of the relationship between the deformation energetics and ΔLk_{res}. In practice the level of detail that is appropriate to a given case will depend upon the goals of the analysis being performed.

Consider a case where the distribution of the residual linking difference between smooth torsional deformations and bending is to be examined explicitly:

$$\Delta Lk_{res} = \Delta Tw_{res} + \Delta Wr. \quad [11]$$

In principle, the stable mechanical equilibria of this system can be determined by standard methods of elasticity theory (28). Once the equilibrium structures are known, their free energies of deformation can be found from Equation [6]. Unfortunately, this approach has three important problems that limit its practical utility to simple cases.

First, the analysis required for a completely rigorous treatment of the problem is intrinsically extremely complex. Correct account must be taken of the sequence-dependent mechanical properties and unstressed shapes, including naturally curved regions. Moreover, the collection of all possible tertiary structures is very difficult to characterize. This is because the curvatures at all points are coupled together by the global requirement that the curve remain closed. Although these curvatures may vary, they cannot do so independently. (To specify the shape of a one-dimensional curve in three-dimensional space the values of two curvature parameters must be specified at each point. In differential geometry these are chosen to be the curvature and the torsion. In mechanical analyses they are the curvatures in the two principle directions of the cross-section at each point (29).) It is an unsolved problem in differential geometry to determine computationally tractable necessary and sufficient conditions on the curvatures of a curve to guarantee smooth closure. Thus it is not possible to specify the family of curvature functions whose associated curves are closed. Yet the complete analysis of this problem requires that the curvatures be known at each point because the bending energy derives from curvature. Thus, at present one cannot determine the collection of feasible tertiary structures in a way that allows a bending free energy to be associated to each.

Second, in general there will be many closed tertiary structures which satisfy the conditions of mechanical equilibrium for a particular value of the residual linking difference. The calculation of these equilibria is tractable in cases where the mechanical properties of the molecule are regarded as uniform. However, it is difficult in practice to distinguish the mechanically stable equilibria from the unstable ones. Multiple mechanically stable equilibria can exist for a particular value of ΔLk_{res}, a fact that is consistent with experimental observation (30-32).

Third, the actual equilibrium attained will be statistical, not mechanical, in nature. Due to thermal buffeting, torsional and flexural fluctuations will occur which cause the molecule to occupy an ensemble of states around the stable equilibria. Thus the free energy $G(\Delta Lk_{res})$ will itself be an ensemble-averaged quantity. Unfortunately, its value is difficult to calculate because the energetics of the possible conformations require their expression in terms of curvatures. Although these curvatures may vary, they can do so only subject to the constraint that the domain remains closed. As described above, the family of possible curvatures that satisfy this constraint has not been characterized in a tractable manner.

Fortunately, less detailed analyses are appropriate in most cases of practical interest. The sequence-dependent mechanical parameters often may be replaced by their averaged values, either globally or within blocks of the domain. In problems where the large scale structure of the domain is to be explicitly determined, one may assume that the tertiary structure instantly equilibrates to the mechanical equilibrium conformation. If there is more than one such, then each determines its own state. The free energy of superhelicity is the elastic deformation strain free energy of the mechanical equilibrium conformation. In practice this approach replaces the distribution around each equilibrium by the equilibrium itself.

A less detailed approach is adequate for treating many problems. To analyze superhelically driven secondary structural transitions, one need not know precisely how the residual linking difference is accommodated. Instead, one only requires the free energy $G(\Delta Lk_{res})$. In practice it is usually appropriate to use the best-fitting linear analysis in each region of ΔLk_{res} of interest, because experimentally it is difficult to measure higher-order effects with accuracy. This means a linear generalized force is associated with the residual linking difference, which gives rise to quadratic energetics:

$$G_{res} = \frac{K(\Delta Lk_{res})^2}{2} . \qquad [12]$$

In cases where non-linearities occur, they manifest themselves as differences in the value of K that are appropriate in different ranges of ΔLk_{res}. This approach accords with the energetics that were found experimentally to hold around the relaxed state (27).

Great care must be exercised in choosing the value of K for a given problem. The experimentally measured value $K = 2220RT/N$ applies only near the relaxed state (27). As shown below, the equilibrium state changes in complex ways as the linking difference varies, so the energy parameter K is expected to exhibit similar alterations. In the next section we show how the value of K at substantial negative linking differences may be estimated from experimental data on superhelically driven conformational transitions.

Energetic Information from Transition Data

The stress-induced DNA conformational transitions of practical importance are observed to occur at negative superhelicities (i.e., $\Delta Lk < 0$). They involve alternative secondary structures that have smaller unstressed helicity than the B-form, so that $\Delta Tw_{trans} < 0$. Examples include cruciform extrusion at inverted repeats, strand separations at AT-rich regions, and transitions to left-handed helices such as Z-DNA, or to triple helices such as the H-form. These transitions have been shown experimentally to occur at substantial negative linking differences (6-13). Clearly the application in this range of the free energy expression G_{res} that was measured at $-5 \leqslant \Delta Lk \leqslant 5$ involves a huge extrapolation from the data.

Under these circumstances the only feasible course of action in the analysis of superhelical conformational transition data is to assume that the coefficient K of the free energy of residual superhelicity is an unknown parameter. One determines the values of all the unknown parameters by fitting to the data. This has been done for two types of transition in the pBR322 molecule or engineered variants thereof.

The data of Peck and Wang on B-Z transitions in pBR322 plasmids engineered to contain different length Z-susceptible sites (10) were fit by least squares with three unknown parameters. These were the initiation free energy a for the B-Z transition, the free energy per base pair b needed for transition of the $(G \cdot C)_n$ susceptible site, (this transition is homopolymeric because all dinucleotide repeat units are identical), and the free energy parameter K for residual superhelicity. The values of the best-fitting parameters were found to be $a = 19.6RT$, $b = 0.828RT$, and $K = 0.691RT$, which corresponds to $K = 3015RT/N$ (15). The latter value is about 35% larger than that found near the relaxed state by Pulleyblank *et al.* (27). The B-Z transition energy parameters a and b also are 30-40% larger than those that result if the Pulleyblank value of K is assumed correct in this range of linking difference (10).

More recently, data on the strand separation transition in pBR322 DNA has been published by Kowalski *et al.* (33). The fitting of this data is simplified because the transition energy parameters a and b are known from other experiments. The initiation free energy a is the energetic cost of disrupting the extra stacking interaction that occurs when the first base pair is denatured, which is known to be approximately $a = 7$

kcals (23). The free energies of transition for each type of base pair are known from data on the denaturation of oligomers (24,25). The only unknown parameter remaining to be fit to the data is K, the free energy coefficient associated to residual superhelicity.

Kowalski found that the strand separation transition occurs at one or both of two possible sites, as detected by mung bean endonuclease cleavage. The relative frequencies of cleavage of the two sites varied with linking difference. The transition became detectable around $\Delta Lk = -19$, where some cleavage of the first site was observed. Around $\Delta Lk = -24$ cleavage at the second site was first noted. At $\Delta Lk = -28$ the molecule was cleaved at this second site 7% of the time, increasing to 25% at $\Delta Lk = -31$, the limit of the experiment. Because a first cleavage event relaxes the domain, this experiment did not determine whether strand separation occurred simultaneously at the two sites.

This author has developed a method of analysis of heteropolymeric superhelical transitions in long molecules of specified sequence, which will be presented in detail elsewhere. When this analysis is applied to the strand separation transition in superhelical pBR322 DNA, it predicts that denaturation will occur virtually exclusively at the two sites where Kowalski has detected it. At linking differences where cleavage was observed at both sites, the theory predicts that simultaneously existing strand separations occur. When various values of the parameter K were used in this analysis, the best fit to the experimental data was found for $K = 3000RT/N$, in agreement with the previous conclusions from the analysis of B-Z transition data. When the value $K = 2220RT/N$ was used, this analysis predicted no transition at any value of the linking difference examined by Kowalski *et al.* (33).

Implications of the Experimental Data

It has been experimentally established that DNA has the mechanical properties of a symmetric, linearly elastic rod. Any models that are created or assumptions that are made involving the energetics of superhelical deformations must be consistent with these mechanical properties and their consequences.

Onset of Writhing

A symmetric, linearly elastic rod will experience exchanges of stability, whereby qualitatively distinct classes of conformations become stable as thresholds of deformation are surpassed. Torsional deformations alone, once they exceed a threshold, have been shown to drive writhing as a form of elastic buckling. This occurs in both linear and circularly constrained rods, although the thresholds are significantly different in the two cases (34-36). Because the torsion angles between neighbor base pairs experience thermal fluctuations, the total twist deformation varies as the sum of independently varying random variables. If the length of the domain is sufficient, then the total torsional deformation can exceed the threshold for onset of writhing. The critical length at which the total torsional deformation has root-mean-square value equal to this threshold is

$$L_{crit} = \frac{12\pi^2 A^2}{CkT}. \quad [13]$$

This exchange of stability mechanically couples fluctuations of twist to writhing in nicked molecules.

Energetics of Writhing

The association of a free energy directly to writhing is complicated by the interactive, non-extensive nature of this geometric parameter (5). There is no local, intensive density whose integral yields *Wr*. Instead, the value of *Wr* measures the relative dispositions of all pairs of points on a curve. Although this parameter correctly measures the tertiary structure of superhelical DNA, it is deformations of curvature, not *Wr*, which actually require free energy. The relationship between curvature, total squared curvature and writhing is complex and not fully understood at present. Some workers have attempted to circumvent this problem by assuming that a free energy having a simple quadratic form is associated with writhing deformations (37):

$$G_w = \frac{K_w(\Delta Wr)^2}{2}, \quad [14]$$

This assumption is conjoined to the known quadratic free energy of twisting (assuming a constant value of the torsional stiffness *C*):

$$G_t = \frac{K_t(\Delta Tw)^2}{2}, \quad [15]$$

Here the free energy coefficient is related to the torsional stiffness by $K_t = 4\pi^2 C/L$. The free energy of superhelicity $G(\Delta Lk)$ can be computed as follows. The total free energy

$$G_w + G_t = \frac{K_w(\Delta Wr)^2}{2} + \frac{K_t(\Delta Tw)^2}{2} \quad [16]$$

is minimized subject to the constraint that the linking difference, which is the sum $\Delta Tw + \Delta Wr$, remains fixed. One finds at the minimum that $K_t\Delta Tw = K_w\Delta Wr$. This result states that the linking difference (or residual linking difference in cases where transitions occur) is partitioned in constant proportions between smooth twisting and writhing, regardless of the magnitude of ΔLk. Moreover, the free energy associated to superhelicity is quadratic, with coefficient K related to the parameters K_t and K_w as

$$K = \frac{K_t K_w}{K_t + K_w}, \quad [17]$$

so $K < K_t$ and $K < K_w$. This expression could be used to determine K_w, provided values of the other two quantities were known.

These conclusions contradict the result of the elastic analysis of the onset of writhing in superhelical molecules (35). That work found a threshold amount of linking difference to be required before the stable mechanical equilibrium conformation became writhed. The partitioning of the linking difference between twist and writhe at mechanical equilibrium was shown *not* to occur in constant proportions in rods having the mechanical properties of DNA. Thus, the conclusion of the above analysis, based on the association of a quadratic free energy directly to writhing, does not agree with the results of a direct analysis founded on the known mechanical properties of the molecule.

An ensemble-averaged free energy could, in principle, be determined for *Wr* in a case where bending is considered without reference to twisting. However, for superhelical problems the imposed constraint involves both twisting and writhing. The free energy of a state is determined by the torsional and flexural deformations that it experiences. The relationship between the flexural deformation free energy (an extensive parameter) and *Wr* (an interactive, not extensive, parameter) is sufficiently complex to preclude the expression of the former as a simple function of the latter (28).

Statistical Independence of ΔTw and Wr in Nicked DNA

In a nicked domain the twist and writhe are not topologically coupled together. Instead, both quantities may fluctuate, which causes their sum to vary. The variance of the sum of two random variables is related to their individual variances by (38)

$$Var(\Delta Lk_{res}) = Var(\Delta Tw_{res}) + Var(\Delta Wr) + 2Cov(\Delta Tw_{res}, \Delta Wr). \qquad [18]$$

The assumption of statistical independence implies that the covariance term equals zero. However, fluctuations in ΔTw_{res} and in ΔWr do *not* occur in a statistically independent manner in nicked circular molecules. A mechanical coupling, whereby twist fluctuations may drive writhe as a form of torsional buckling, has been described above. Because the sign of the driving torsional fluctuations is the same as that of the resulting writhing, this coupling contributes a positive term to the statistical covariance in long molecules (35).

There is another, purely geometric coupling between these parameters that contributes to this covariance for molecules of any length. Fluctuations of curvature that alter the total differential-geometric torsion of the molecule also change its twist. This fact may be demonstrated by expressing the shape of the domain using Euler angles (28). The local orientation of the DNA at each position s along its length is expressed by three angles, $\theta(s)$, $\phi(s)$, and $\psi(s)$, by which fixed space axes must be rotated to bring them into coincidence with local axes embedded in the structure. The unit tangent vector at each position is given by

$$\mathbf{T}(s) = (\sin\theta(s) \sin\phi(s), -\sin\theta(s) \cos\phi(s), \cos\theta(s)). \qquad [19]$$

The torsional deformation density δ_T, which is the rate (in radians/length) at which the helicity deviates from its unstressed value, is

$$\delta_T = \dot{\phi}(s)\cos\theta(s) + \dot{\psi}(s). \quad [20]$$

From this expression one sees that the total twisting deformation is given by

$$\Delta Tw_{res} = \frac{1}{2\pi}\left(\int_0^L \dot{\phi}(s)\cos\theta(s)ds + \int_0^L \dot{\psi}(s)ds\right). \quad [21]$$

The differential-geometric torsion $\tau(s)$ at each point s (29) is determined from the unit tangent vector to be:

$$\tau(s) = \dot{\phi}(s)\cos\theta(s) + \frac{\dot{\theta}^2\dot{\phi}\cos\theta + \dot{\theta}\ddot{\phi}\sin\theta - \dot{\phi}\ddot{\theta}\sin\theta}{\dot{\theta}^2 + \dot{\phi}^2\sin^2\theta}. \quad [22]$$

It follows that the total torsion of the curve is

$$\int_0^L \tau(s)\,ds = \int_0^L \dot{\phi}(s)\cos\theta(s)\,ds + \int_0^L \frac{dU}{1+U^2}, \quad [23]$$

where

$$U = \frac{\dot{\phi}\sin\theta}{\dot{\theta}}. \quad [24]$$

The second integral may be evaluated using the inverse tangent function, with appropriate care taken to choose the correct branch at points where $\dot{\theta} = 0$. For a smooth closed curve, such as occurs in nicked circular DNA, the values of the Euler angles must satisfy $\theta(0) = \theta(L)$, and $\phi(0) = \phi(L)$. (In a closed circular molecule the third Euler angle $\psi(s)$ must also close, but in a nicked molecule it need not do so.) It follows that the second integral will be an integer multiple of π. Yet the total torsion varies continuously as a curve is deformed by smooth bending. Because the second integral assumes only discrete values, it must be the first integral in the above equation that varies continuously with deformations. Because this first integral,

$$\int_0^L \dot{\phi}(s)\cos\theta(s)\,ds, \quad [25]$$

also occurs in the expression for the total twist ΔTw_{res}, it follows that the molecular twist varies continuously as random flexural deformations occur. Any flexural deformation that changes the total differential geometric torsion of a domain thereby also acts to twist it. In consequence, flexural deformations of a nicked circular domain induce, hence are geometrically coupled to, torsional deformations in molecules of all lengths.

Both mechanical and geometric couplings between twisting and flexure have been demonstrated in nicked circular molecules. It follows that fluctuations in ΔTw_{res} and in ΔWr do not occur in a statistically independent manner in these molecules. Any theoretical analysis that assumes such independence is based on a false premise (19,39).

Acknowledgments

This research was supported by grants DMB 86-13371 and DMB 88-96284 from the National Science Foundation.

References and Footnotes

1. J.H. White, *Am. J. Math 91*, 693 (1969).
2. J.H. White and W.R. Bauer, *J. Mol. Biol. 189*, 329 (1986).
3. C.J. Benham, *Ann. Rev. Biophys. Biophys. Chem. 14*, 23 (1985).
4. F.B. Fuller, *Proc. Natl. Acad. Sci. USA 68*, 815 (1971).
5. F.B. Fuller, *Proc. Natl. Acad. Sci. USA 75*, 3557 (1978).
6. D.M.J. Lilley, *Proc. Natl. Acad. Sci. USA 77*, 6468 (1980).
7. N. Panayotatos and R.D. Wells, *Nature 289*, 466 (1981).
8. C.J. Benham, *Biopolymers 21*, 679 (1982).
9. C.J. Benham, *Nature 286*, 637 (1980).
10. L.J. Peck and J.C. Wang, *Proc. Natl. Acad. Sci. USA 80*, 6206 (1983).
11. H. Htun and J.E. Dahlberg, *Science 243*, 1571 (1989).
12. W. Dean and J. Lebowitz, *Nature New Biol. 231*, 5 (1971).
13. C.J. Benham, *Proc. Natl. Acad. Sci. USA 76*, 3870 (1979).
14. D. Eisenberg and D. Crothers, *Physical Chemistry*, Benjamin-Cummings Pub. Co, Menlo Park, CA, p. 678-679 (1979).
15. C.J. Benham, *Cell Biophys. 10*, 193 (1987).
16. C.J. Benham, *Proc. Natl. Acad. Sci. USA 74*, 2397 (1977).
17. C.J. Benham, *Biopolymers 18*, 609 (1979).
18. M. Hogan, J. LeGrange and R. Austin, *Nature 304*, 752 (1983).
19. P.J. Hagerman, *Ann. Rev. Biophys. Biophys. Chem. 17*, 265 (1988).
20. T.J. Thomas and V. Bloomfield, *Nuc. Acids Res. 11*, 1919 (1983).
21. D. Shore and R.L. Baldwin, *J. Mol. Biol. 170*, 983 (1983).
22. M.T. Record, S. Mazur, P. Melancon, J. Roe, S. Shaner and L. Unger, *Ann. Rev. Biochem. 50*, 997 (1981).
23. D.M. Crothers and B.H. Zimm, *J. Mol. Biol. 9*, 1 (1964).
24. J. Marmur and P. Doty, *J. Mol. Biol. 5*, 109 (1962).
25. C. Schildkraut and S. Lifson, *Biopolymers 3*, 195 (1968).
26. R.E. Depew and J.C. Wang, *Proc. Natl. Acad. Sci. USA 72*, 4275 (1975).
27. D.E. Pulleyblank, M. Shure, D. Tang, J. Vinograd and H. Vosberg, *Proc. Natl. Acad. Sci. USA 72*, 4280 (1975).
28. C.J. Benham, *Biopolymers 22*, 2477 (1983).
29. J.J. Stoker, *Differential Geometry*, J. Wiley & Sons, New York, p. 53-70 (1969).
30. J. Shibata, J. Wilcoxson, J.M. Schurr and V Knauf, *Biochem. 23*, 1188 (1984).
31. G. Brady, D. Fein, H. Lambertson, V. Grassian, D. Foos and C.J. Benham, *Proc. Natl. Acad. Sci. USA 80*, 741 (1983).
32. G. Brady, D. Foos and C.J. Benham, *Biopolymers 23*, 2963 (1984).
33. D. Kowalski, D. Natale and M. Eddy, *Proc. Natl. Acad. Sci. USA 85*, 9464 (1988).
34. M. LeBret, *Biopolymers 18*, 1709 (1979).
35. C.J. Benham, *Phys. Rev. A 39*, 2582 (1989).
36. G. Manning, *Phys. Rev. A 34*, 668 (1986).
37. P. Wu, L. Song, J. Clendenning, B. Fujimoto, A. Benight and J.M. Schurr, *Biochem. 27*, 8128 (1988).
38. M. DeGroot, *Probability and Statistics*, Addison-Wesley, Reading, MA, p. 175 (1975).
39. A. Vologodskii, V. Anshelevich, L. Lukashin and M.D. Frank-Kamenetskii, *Nature 280*, 294 (1979) *et seq*.

Structure & Methods, ISBN 0-940030-32-2
Volume 3: DNA & RNA, ISBN 0-940030-31-4
Eds., Ramaswamy H. Sarma & Mukti H. Sarma, © Adenine Press 1990

Structure Destabilization and Condensation of Nucleic Acids by Intercalators

Jan Kapuscinski and Zbigniew Darzynkiewicz
Laboratory of Experimental Cell Research
Sloan - Kettering Institute for Cancer Research
1275 York Avenue
New York, N.Y. 10021

Abstract

Neutralization of negative charges of nucleic acids leads to condensation of these polymers. This effect can be induced either by multivalent ($m \geqslant 3$) nonaromatic (organic- or inorganic-) cations or by aromatic mono- or multivalent cations. The process is of interest because several intercalators (mutagens, antibiotics, antitumor agents) condense nucleic acids in the range of their pharmacological concentrations.

The kinetics, reversibility, specificity and equilibrium of intercalator induced condensation of polymers have been studied by light scattering monitored titrations, and analyzed using McGhee - von Hippel's model for cooperative ligand - polymer interactions. Thermodynamic calculations of acridine orange (AO) - induced condensation of poly(U) and double stranded (ds) DNA indicate that the cooperative transition of both polymers is enthalpy driven, while the nucleation process of poly(U) is entropy driven.

The molecular mechanism of the phenomenon is proposed, and its possible implications in the understanding of antitumor activity of some intercalating drugs, as well as in histochemical application of certain nucleic acids' fluorescent probes, is discussed.

Introduction

Polymers such as nucleic acids (NA) in polar solutions assume a random coil or worm-like conformation. Such conformation results from segment-segment electrostatic repulsive forces and strong segment-solvent interactions (solvation). The neutralization of polymer charges results in the spontaneous process of polymer condensation (1,2), due to elimination of repulsive forces (which leads to increased segment-segment interactions) and decreasing solvation (Figure 1). The neutralization of polymer charge does not necessarily have to be complete. For instance, neutralization of approximately 90% of phosphate charges of double stranded (ds) DNA is sufficient to cause its condensation (1). To achieve this degree of charge neutralization, "simple" cations (i.e., inorganic or organic cations which interact with DNA exclusively by ionic interaction) must have a valence of +3 or higher (1). This type of condensation

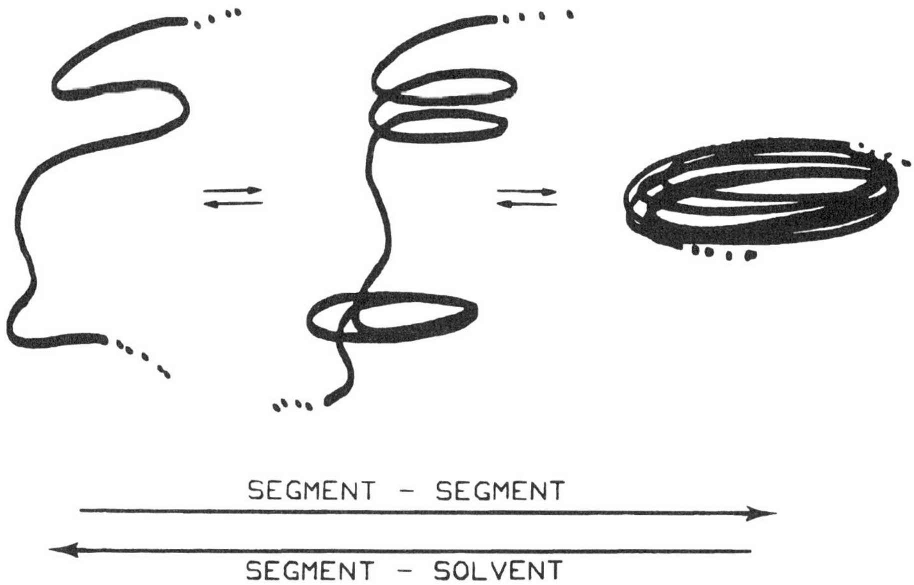

Figure 1: Schematic representation of the process of condensation of nucleic acids. Relevant forces for this process are polymer *segment-segment* and polymer *segment-solvent* interactions. An increase of the former or decrease of the latter can lead to spontaneous condensation (collapse) of the polymer. Condensation is a multi-phase process of compacting a worm-like or random coil molecule (left) into a compact particle (right) involving, most likely, the transitional forms, resembling e.g. beads on a string structure (in the middle). The compact particles have a tendency to aggregate; this process results finally in precipitation of the complex (not shown).

is of interest because NA *in situ* are usually in the form of condensed complexes with basic proteins. Thus, an asymmetrical DNA charge neutralization by the histone octamer has been proposed recently to explain polymer bending into the nucleosome structure (3).

In contrast to "simple" cations, several aromatic mono-cations are able to condense NA, some of them at 100 times lower concentration than the former (4). Because most intercalators, among them some antibiotics, mutagens, antitumor drugs and cytochemical probes of NA structure belong to this group, this phenomenon is of interest to researchers of various disciplines. Historically, the precipitation of NA by basic dyes, later known as intercalators, was occasionally noticed but treated as a nuisance. Usually the titrations were terminated when precipitation was observed. Most likely, the lack of interest in the phenomenon was the result of the then generally accepted mechanism, originally proposed by Bradley and Wolf (5). Their "stacking" model assumed pure ionic dye - NA interaction; the cooperativity of the transition and spectral changes of the ligand bound to single stranded (ss) NA were explained by dye stack formation on a lattice provided by NA backbone. This type of interaction, therefore, was not expected to be specific with respect to primary or secondary structure of NA. It should be mentioned, however, that at the time when this model was proposed, the ability of aromatic cations to interact with NA bases *via* dispersive forces (dye - bases stacking) was not yet known; Lermans' model of intercalation was published two years later (6).

Based on our studies of interactions of fluorescent dyes with NA, we proposed a new mechanism of complex formation (7-10). The main difference between our model and that proposed by Bradley and Wolf (5) is the assumption that the dye molecules form stacking complexes with NA bases (dye-base interactions) rather than dye-dye stacks attached electrostatically to phosphates, as proposed before. This new model allowed us to explain the metachromatic properties of two widely used fluorescent probes of NA, acridine orange (AO) (7,10) and pyronin Y(G) (11,12), to propose a new explanation for chromosome banding reactions (13) and explain differences in the pharmacological activity of certain antitumor agents (14,15).

In this paper we review the earlier findings, present new data and describe in greater detail the model of NA condensation by intercalating ligands.

Materials and Methods

Most materials and methods used in this paper have been described before (4,10). The light scattering measurements were made with an SLM 4800 spectrofluorometer (90° geometry) in which both monochromators were set at the same wavelength (350 nm) in ratio mode with Rhodamine G in ethyl glycol as a quantum counter. Titrations were performed in square (10 mm) quartz cuvettes equipped with a magnetic stirrer and enclosed with a septum through which small volumes of the dye stock solution (0.3-3 mM in H_20) were added without opening the instrument. Repetitive light scattering measurement at constant time intervals (5-10 sec.), data storage and processing was performed by HP 9826 computer interfaced with the instrument. Data corrections and calculations are described in the legend to figures. Concentrations of NA and dyes were measured colorimetrically as described (8). All solutions used in light scatter measurements were either passed through a 0.45 μ filter (directly into the cuvette used in the experiment) or centrifuged just before the experiment, to avoid dust particles which otherwise can cause unacceptable background light scattering.

Results and Discussion

Kinetics and Reversibility

Most intercalators at a dye/phosphate ratio (D/P) > 0.5 precipitate NA. Precipitation is a slow process, and the solid phase usually becomes visible only after several hours. The solubility of the precipitate is very low, and there are reasons to believe that, at this stage, the process does not obey the mass action law (7,9). The process is multi-staged, starting with a nucleation phase followed by condensation, and then aggregation of the condensed particles of the complex, leading to its precipitation (7,9,10). Light scattering measurement offers a most convenient method for the study of these processes. The intensity of light scattered at a given angle by the polymer solution is proportional (among other factors) to the number of macromolecules (scatterers) and their molecular form factor (S). The S factor increases

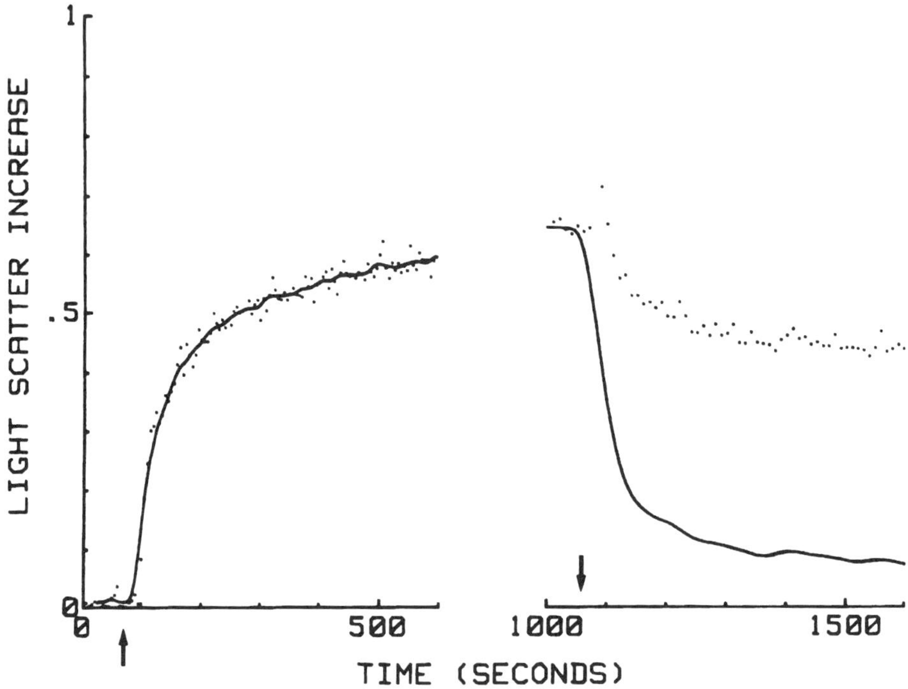

Figure 2A

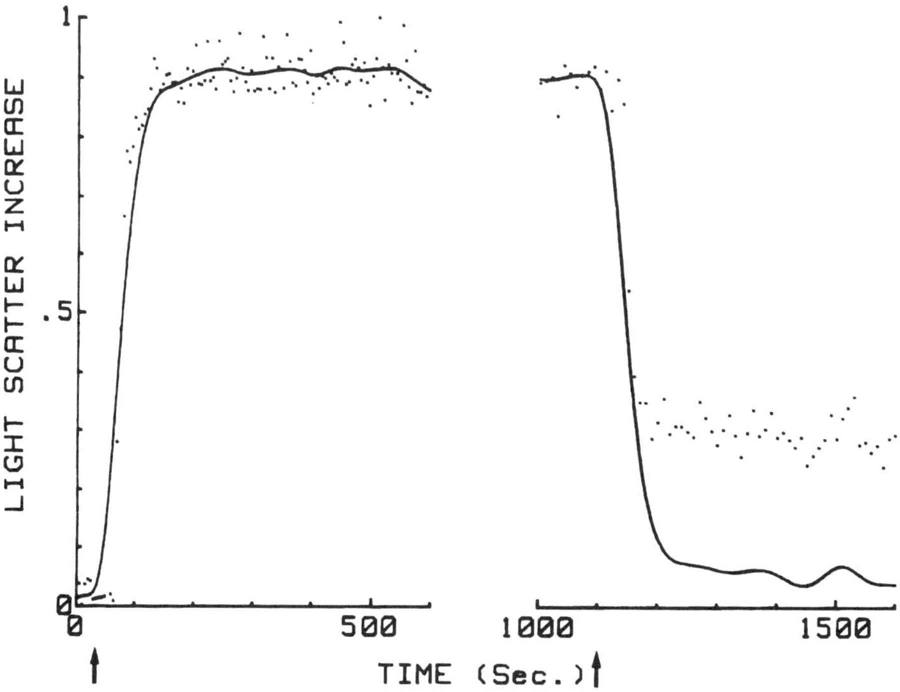

Figure 2B

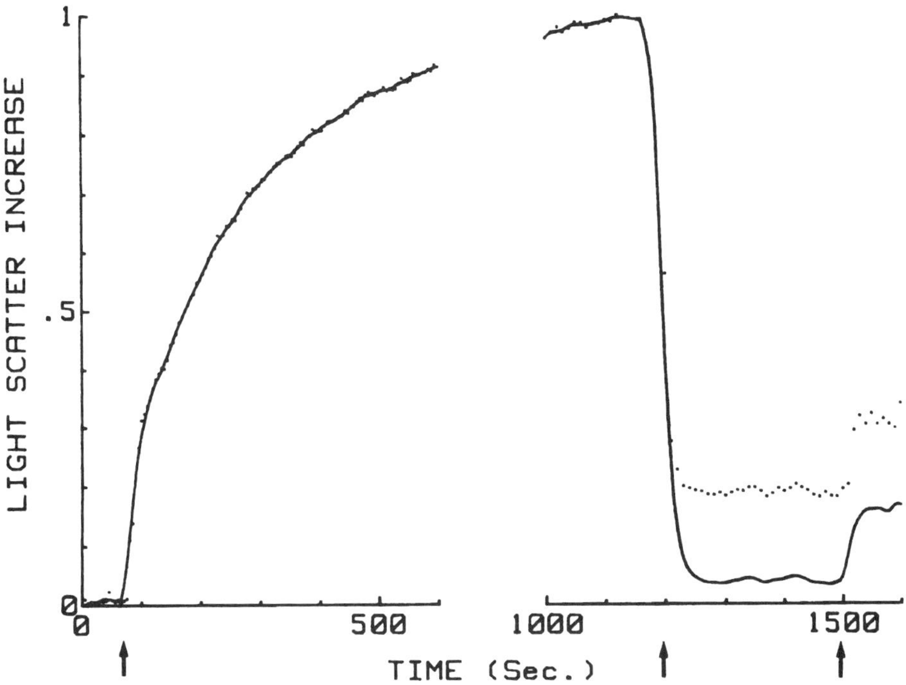

Figure 2C

Figure 2: Condensation - decondensation of NA by acridine orange (AO) monitored by light scattering measurement at 350 nm in 5 sec. (condensation) or 10 sec. (decondensation) increments, in 10 mM NaCl, 5 mM Hepes pH 6.9 at 25°C. The initial concentration of nucleic acids was: poly(A), 2 μM (A and B), sonicated calf thymus DNA 5 μM (C). The experimental data (points) were calculated by subtraction of the initial light scattering of the solution (before AO addition) and normalized (maximal value of transition = 1). Solid lines represent the smoothed transition; decondensation transitions were corrected for light scattering resulting from the addition of the decondensation agent. Additional control experiments on the stability of the condensed form of the complex were performed, to assure that the changes in light scattering during the decondensation phase were not the result of the aggregation of scatterers, and to establish corrections for the light scattering signal of decondensation agents (not shown). A) Condensation of poly(A) by AO. Left arrow indicates the moment of addition of AO (5 μM). Decondensation by addition of excess poly(A) (20 μM) - right arrow. Notice jump of the signal to 1 as a result of scattering by the added polymer. B) Condensation as in A), decondensation by addition of DNA (50 μM) - right arrow. C) Condensation of DNA by AO (15 μM) - added at the time indicated by the left arrow, decondensation by addition of an excess of DNA (5 μM) two times, at times indicated by central and right arrow. The solid line represents a correction only for light scattering resulting from addition of the first portion of the decondensation agent only to demonstrate the end of process (no substantial decrease of the signal after second addition).

dramatically after a long polymer molecule condenses into a compact sphere (16); this results in an increase of light scatter intensity. On the other hand, aggregation of particles decreases the number of scatterers and signal intensity.

In diluted NA solutions (concentrations at μM range) condensation is an intramolecular process (10), and aggregation of particles is delayed for several hours. In such a state the transition can be reversed by addition of excess of NA (Figure 2), by increase of temperature, addition of inorganic salts or polar solvent (7,9). Analysis

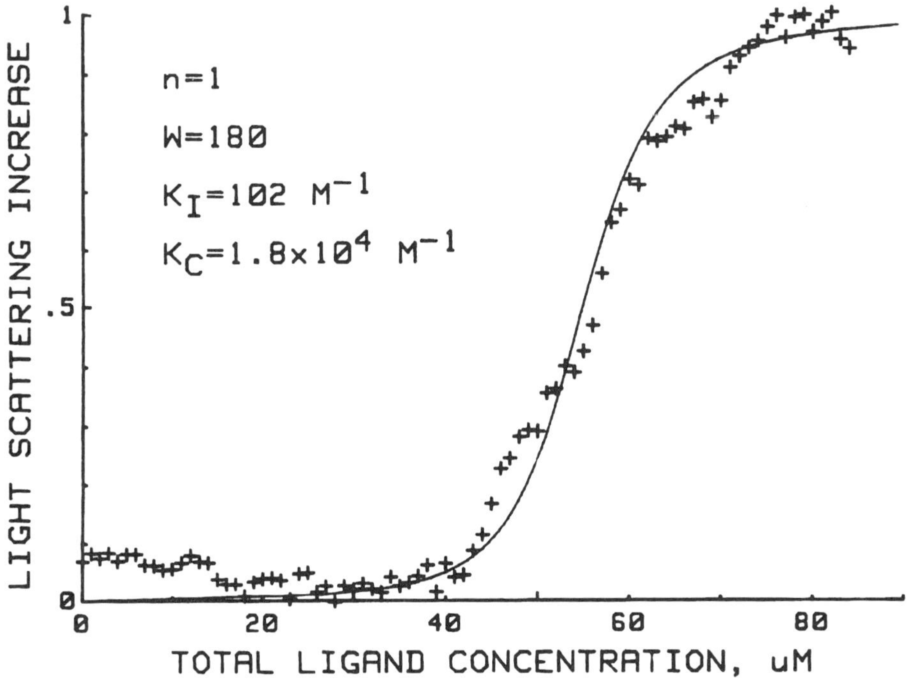

Figure 3: Light scattering (350 nm) monitored titration of poly-L-glutamic acid (MW = 2-15 K, Sigma, Catalog # P 4636) 2.5 ml of concentration 1 µM (monomer) with AO in 0.15 M NaCl, 5 mM Hepes pH 7 at 25°C. The ligand was added at a speed of 22 nmole/min. The experimental points (+) were normalized as described in legend to Figure 2; the solid line represents the best fit of McGhee-von Hippel isotherm Equation [1] drawn by computer, using parameters listed in the picture. The method of calculation is described in the text.

of transition curves presented in Figure 2 indicate that the kinetics of NA condensation, especially ds polymer, is several orders of magnitude slower than intercalative binding, which is in the msec. range (17). Also, for this reason, ds polymers are very effective condensation - reversing agents (Figure 2 B,C).

Equilibrium

Figure 3 demonstrates a typical transition of light scattering monitored titration of a polyanion with a condensation ligand. The sigmoidal shape of this curve indicates a cooperative process. To analyze this process a McGhee-von Hippel model for cooperative ligand-polymer interaction has been used (18):

$$\frac{r}{C_F} = K_I(1-nr)\left[\frac{(2W-1)(1-nr)+r-R}{2(W-1)(1-nr)}\right]^{n-1}\left[\frac{1-(n+1)r+R}{2(1-nr)}\right]^2 \qquad [1]$$

$$R = \{[1-(n+1)r]^2+4Wr(1-nr)\}^{1/2} \qquad [1a]$$

Where: K_I (intrinsic association constant) represents the binding of the ligand molecule to the isolated binding sites of the polymer; K_C (cooperative association constant) - the ligand binding in a singly contiguous fashion ($K_C = K_I W$, where W is the cooperativity parameter); r is binding density; C_F is concentration of free ligand; n is the binding site size expressed in monomer unit (18).

The last parameter (n) can be easily obtained from an independent experiment, e.g., using the precipitation method (7) to estimate the stoichiometry of the complex. Previously published data indicate that n value corresponds with the valence of the ligand (7,15). This conclusion is in agreement with the necessity for neutralization of polymer charges in order for condensation to occur; accordingly, for AO and other monocationic ligands $n \simeq 1$. K_I an W were calculated by computer using experimental data (standard deviation minimalization) and are listed in Figure 3; the curve representing the best fit of experimental points was then computer-drawn based on Equation [1].

The above calculations were made based on the assumption that the normalized light scattering signal is proportional to the binding density r. Actually, the transition monitored by light scattering is shifted somewhat into higher ligand concentrations as compared to the transition monitored by fluorescence (10). Also, examination of the transition indicated that it had at least three distinct phases. These phases represent most likely different transitional topological forms with different S values, rather than subpopulations of polymer with different MW. This conclusion is based on the evidence that three fractions of polymer with MW = 2-15 K, 15-50 K and 50-100 K had similar multiphase transitions (not shown). The last observation indicates also that the affinity of the ligand is independent of polymer MW, at least within 2-100 K range. The proposed method of affinity measurement is, therefore, an approximation. The approximate affinity parameters of AO induced condensation of poly(U) and ds DNA, measured as described above, are listed in Table I.

Another, and actually simpler method of assessing the affinity of ligands is based on measurement of the *critical free ligand concentration* (C_c), i.e., free ligand concentration in the midpoint of the transition (4,19). C_c can be calculated from the total ligand concentration at the midpoint of the transition (C_m) by subtraction of bound ligand concentration (C_b). The last value can be obtained from the known polymer concentration (C_p) based on stoichiometry of the condensation reaction:

$$C_b = 1/2\ C_p/n \qquad [2]$$

Table I
Affinity Parameters of AO-induced Condensation of Poly(A) and ds DNA Measured in 10 mM NaCl, 5 mM Hepes, pH 6.9 at 20°C

Polymer:	$K_C \times 10^{-4}$, M^{-1}	K_I, M^{-1}	W
poly(U)	9.2 ± 0.5	91 ± 20	1010 ± 200
calf thymus DNA	2.1 ± 0.1	51 ± 7	400 ± 60

K_C, K_I and W are cooperative and intrinsic association constant, and cooperativity parameter, respectively. The results are mean values of three measurements ± S.D.

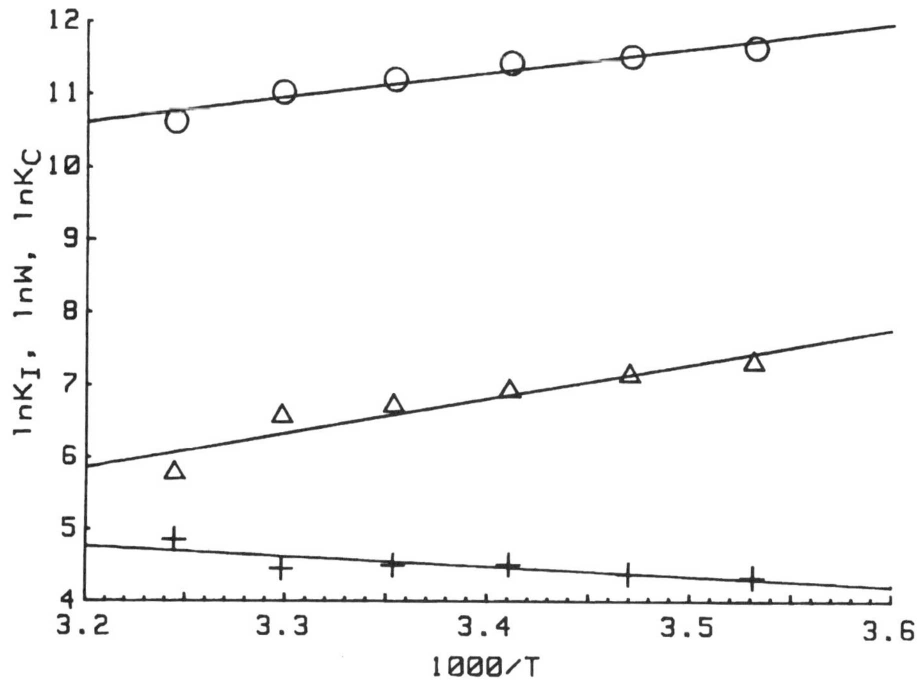

Figure 4A

$$C_c = C_m - C_b \quad [2a]$$

When these calculations are applied to ds NA, a correction for the portion of the ligand bound by the fraction of NA in ds conformation ($1/2\ C_p$) should be made (10). Relationship between C_c and the cooperative association constant can be expressed as:

$$K_C = 1/C_c \quad [3]$$

Equation [3] is correct for $n = 1$; for $n > 1$ it gives only approximate results (15). There is no simple way, however, to obtain K_I or W parameters from C_c.

Thermodynamics

The affinity of AO - induced condensation of poly(U) and ds DNA was measured in the temperature range 10-35°C, and data were analyzed using van't Hoff plot (Figure 4). There is good linearity of ln K_C *vs* 1/T for both tested polymers. Partition of cooperative association constants, however, into K_I and W parameters is less accurate, but it is sufficient to estimate their temperature dependent pattern. The thermodynamic data of these processes are listed in Table II. The free energy change ($\Delta G°$) for both intrinsic and cooperative association of AO to poly(U) and DNA are also included. One can see from these data that while most processes are enthalpy-driven, the intrinsic association constant for AO - poly(U) interaction is entropy-driven. Also, the interesting feature is the highly unfavorable entropy change of K_I

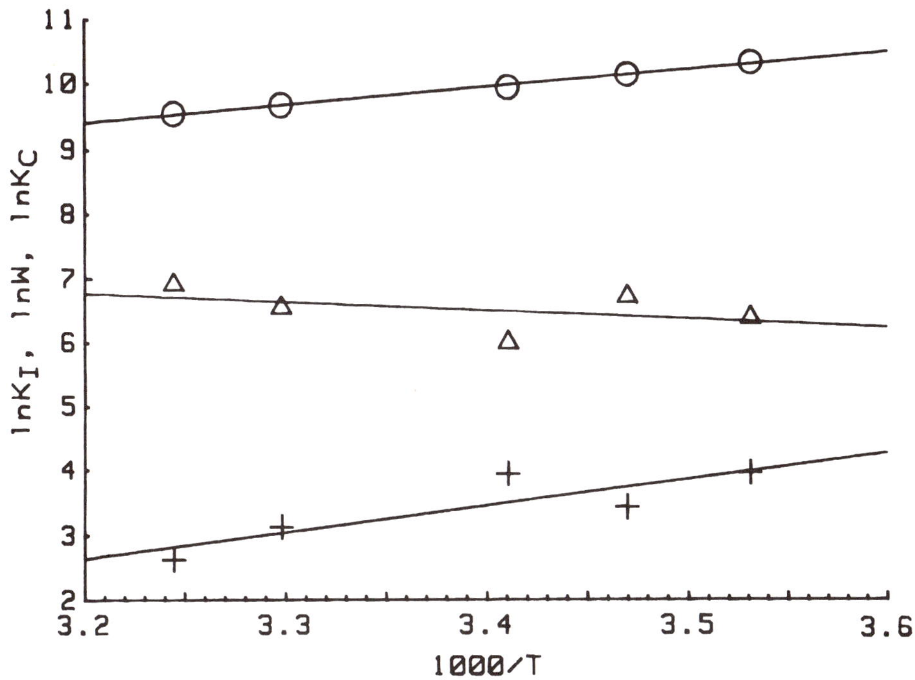

Figure 4B

Figure 4: Van't Hoff plots AO interactions with (A) - poly(U) and (B) -calf thymus DNA measurement in 0.15 M NaCl, 5 mM Hepes pH 6.9, at temperature range 10-35°C: (—+—) - $\ln K_I$, (—Δ—) - $\ln W$, (—O—) - $\ln K_C$. The regression data (intercept, slope, standard error of estimation) for poly(U): K_I(9.25, −1400, 0.12), W(−9.42, 4770, 0.21), K_C(−0.23, 3390, 0.11) and ds DNA: K_I(−10.32, 4050, 0.34), W(11.1, −1360, 0.36), K_C(0.768, 2700, 0.03). Thermodynamics of these reactions calculated from above data are listed in Table II.

for DNA which is then reversed in the cooperative interaction. Although, the above data indicate usefulness of the experimental techniques and calculations based on McGhee - von Hippel's model to approach the complex mechanism of intercalator - induced condensation of NA, further studies are needed for general thermodynamic characterization of the phenomenon.

Specificity of Condensation

Studies of condensation of numerous synthetic and natural NA by several aromatic cations (4,8,10,14,15,20) indicate that this process is highly specific with regard to the primary and secondary structure of NA. Results of these studies can be summarized by the following conclusions:

1. Single stranded polymers are more active then double stranded.

2. RNA is generally more reactive than DNA of similar strandeness and base composition.

Table II
Thermodynamics of AO Induced Condensation of Poly(U) and Calf Thymus DNA Measured by Light Scattering Monitored Titrations in 0.15 M NaCl, 5 mM Hepes, pH 6.9 at Temperature Range 10-35°C

	K_C			K_I		
	ΔG°20C Kcal/mole	ΔH° Kcal/mole	ΔS° e.u.	ΔG°20C Kcal/mole	ΔH° Kcal/mole	ΔS° e.u.
poly(U)	−6.66	−6.47	−0.46	−2.6	+2.8	+18.4
ds DNA	−5.79	−5.36	+1.53	−2.3	−8.1	−20.5

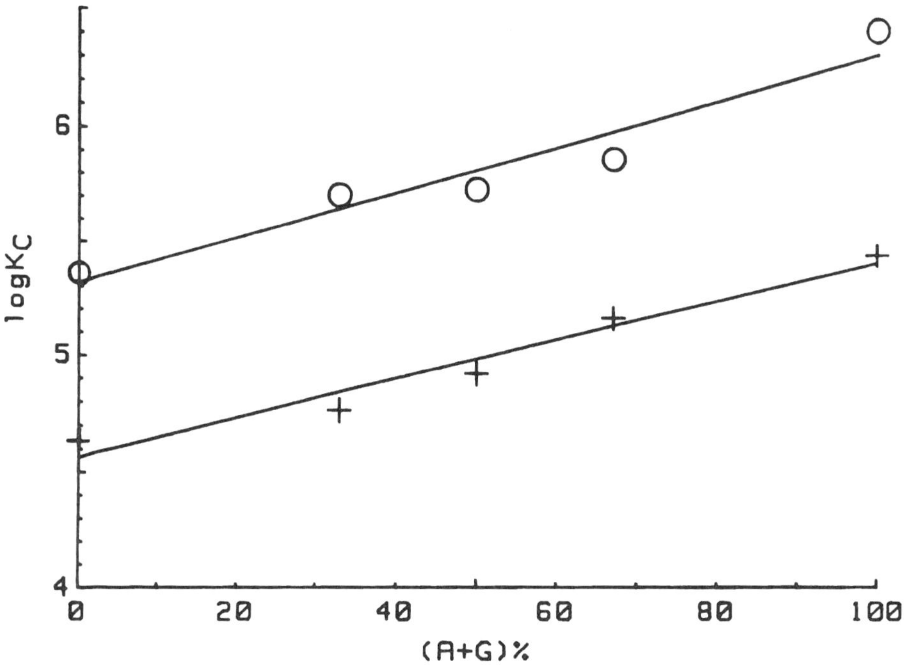

Figure 5: Relationship between cooperative association constant of Ametantrone (−+−) and Mitoxantrone (−O−) and purine content of random RNA copolymers: poly(C,U), poly(A,C,U), poly(U,G), poly(A,G,U) and poly(A,G) (P.L. Biochemicals) in 0.15 M NaCl, 5 mM Hepes pH 7.0 at 25°C. Calculated using Equation [3], data from (14).

3. Long purine sequences are more reactive than pyrimidine sequences. This is most evident from the data showing a linear dependence of logK_C of two antitumor agents Mitoxantrone and Ametantrone, from the purine content of random ribopolymers (Figure 5).

4. Synthetic homopolymer duplexes are more reactive than alternating isomeric polymers.

5. Among the polymers with the same sugar backbone, the ligand - base interactions play a dominant role over the secondary (helix *vs* coil) structure of ss NA.

Mechanism

The specificity of intercalator induced condensation can not be explained by the classic model of dye-dye stacks bound by electrostatic forces to NA (5). Based on studies of the spectral properties of condensed complexes of NA with fluorescent ligands, we proposed a new mechanism for the phenomenon ((7,10) and references cited therein). This mechanism can be summarized as follows:

1. The condensation of NA is the result of neutralization of its charge.

2. The driving force for condensation of NA by aromatic cations (intercalators included) is their high affinity to ss polymers. This affinity results from both electrostatic (ionic) and specific stacking (ligand - NA bases) interactions.

3. Double stranded NA can bind aromatic cations by intercalation, or minor groove mode ($r \leqslant 0.25$), and undergo condensation at higher binding density (r up to 1). Upon condensation the secondary structure of the polymers is destroyed as there is evidence of DNA denaturation at these high binding densities.

4. Condensation of NA by aromatic cations is a highly cooperative process.

At first sight, the denaturation of ds NA by intercalators proposed by this model appears to be an unlikely event, in lieu of the well known propensity of these ligands (as well as ligands binding to DNA grooves) to stabilize ds NA. For instance, the free energy change of AO intercalation is equal to −6.4 Kcal/mole (calculated based on data from ref. (19)) as compared to −5.7 Kcal/mole for AO induced condensation (Table II). Therefore, at low D/P ratio and binding density of intercalation (up to 0.25 per base pair), this type of binding is thermodynamically preferred over condensation. The products of intercalation and condensation, however, have different stoichiometry; the latter may contain up to four times as much as of the ligand as the former. Thus, at higher D/P ratio, the weaker but more numerous bindings become energetically preferable. Thermodynamics calculations (9) indicate that the free energy change generated by this cooperative process, overcomes the double helix stabilizing forces (base pairing, base pair stacking and intercalation or groove binding); in effect the ds structure undergoes destabilization (denaturation). The destabilization of ds NA was confirmed in experiments which provided evidence, that during formation of condensed complexes of ds DNA with several intercalators, there was increased accessibility of the polymer bases to ss - specific external probes (8,10). The schematic representation of both types of ligand - NA interactions is presented in Figure 6.

Numerous pharmacologically active compounds (antibiotics, antineoplastic agents, mutagens) as well as cytochemical fluorescent probes are intercalators or ligands that can condense NA. It is of interest, therefore, to know how the processes of intercalation and condensation take place *in situ*, in cells, i.e., in situations where ss and ds NA (RNA and DNA) are present and compete for the ligand. No mathematical model available in the literature, which can describe such a complex situation,

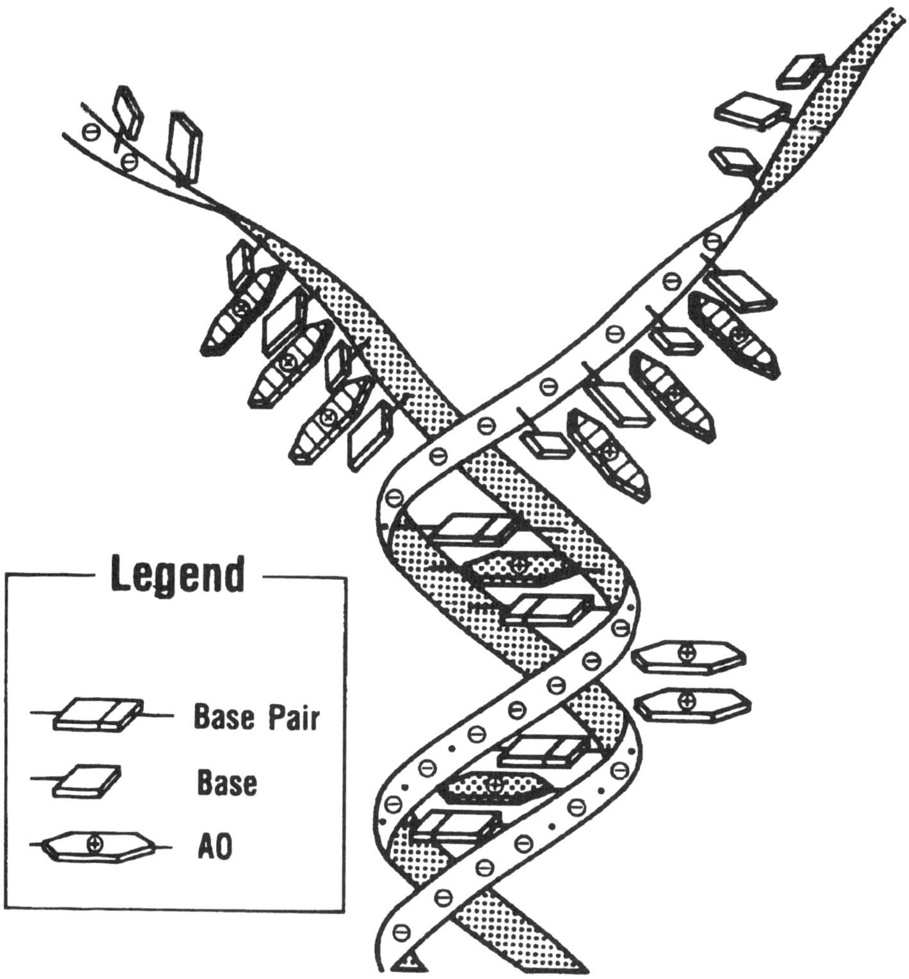

Figure 6: Schematic representation of different modes of AO binding to NA. At low dye concentration and D/P ratio, AO binds to ds NA by intercalation (lower part of the figure) and the dye fluoresces green (AO molecules filled with dots). At increased D/P ratio, binding of AO to ss NA becomes thermodynamically preferable and, thus, the double helix is destabilized (upper part of the structure, AO molecules dashed). Both electrostatic and dye - base stacking interactions are involved in the AO - ss NA complex formation, and the process is highly cooperative. The high binding density of AO binding to ss NA (one molecule per nucleotide) results in polymer charge neutralization, which in turn leads to condensation of the product (not shown) In the condensed form the product luminescences red. This luminescence is phosphorescence and can only be observed upon complex condensation. In solution this emission can not be observed because of collision quenching with solvent and/or oxygen molecules (7).

exists. A descriptive model which can be used for explanation of such processes, however, is proposed (Figure 7). The conclusions made based on this model are in agreement with histochemical and cytochemical observation, and explain the specificity and mechanism of action of some fluorescent probes of NA, such as AO or pyronin Y(G), which the old "dye-dye stacking" model failed to address (11,12).

The most characteristic feature of condensation of nucleic acids, and perhaps the

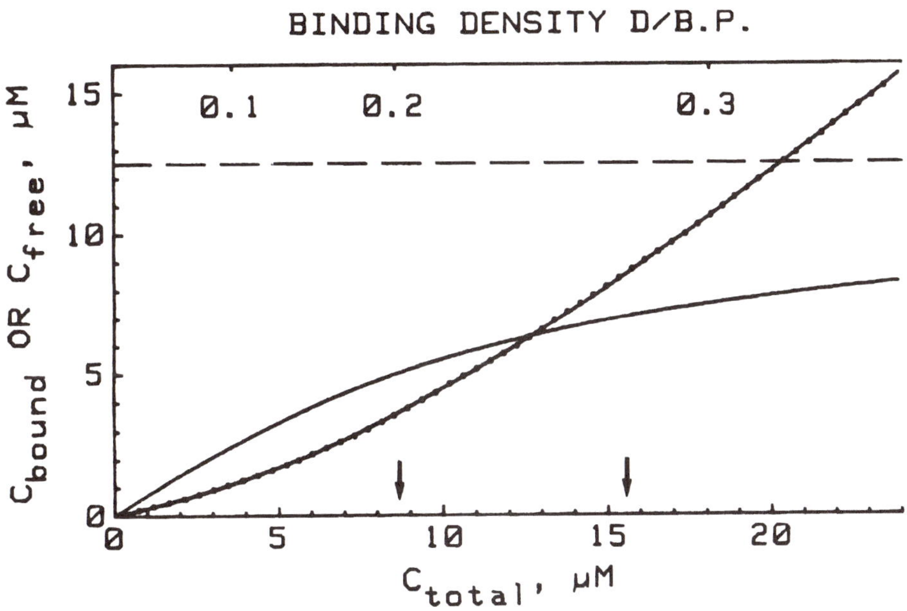

Figure 7: Computer simulation of ds DNA (0.1 mM P) titration with AO. Concentrations of bound (C_{bound}, solid line) and free ligand concentration (C_{free}, specked line) *vs* total ligand concentration (C_{total}) were calculated based on McGhee - von Hippel's model of non-cooperative polymer - ligand association (18). Association constant $K_i = 5.0 \times 10^4$, n = 2 b.p. (19). Broken line represents maximal concentration of bound dye calculated based on neighboring exclusion model. As is evident, C_{bound} increases sharply from onset of titration, and then its rate of increase slows down after binding density reaches approximately 0.25 (the increase is asymptotic to the maximal value depicted by the broken line). During titration the free dye concentration increases (solid line); when it approaches C_c value of most reactive RNA (e.g., long purine-rich sequences, C_c = 4.5 µM, left arrow on the C_{total} axis), this portion of RNA undergoes condensation. During this reaction RNA becomes a sink for the ligand so the C_{free} and binding density of DNA complex do not increase substantially until all RNA condenses. Then C_{free} increases again till it approaches C_c value of more resistant RNA (e.g., ribosomal RNA, C_c = 7.4 µM, right arrow) and so on. When C_{free} reaches value close to C_c of ds DNA (approx. 50 µM) this polymer will also be denatured and condensed. Taking into account the fact that intercalative AO complexes fluoresce green and AO condensed complexes phosphoresce red (see legend to Figure 6), the above scheme matches closely a well known histochemical observation during staining of cells with progressively increasing dye concentration. From the onset of the staining all NA emit green (only intercalative binding into ds RNA and DNA), then RNA in cytoplasm becomes red (RNA as the more sensitive become denaturated and condensed first). After further increase in AO concentration all NA in the cell are red, reflecting denaturation and condensation of ds DNA. This process can be reversed by removing part of the dye or increasing the temperature; decrease in temperature has the opposite effect because condensation is an exoergic process (Table II).

least understood, is cooperativity of the process. According to the classic model proposed by Bradley and Wolf (5), this phenomenon arises from cooperative dye - dye stack formation supported by the polymer. This explanation can be rejected based on the observation that cooperative condensation can be induced by "simple" cations (e.g., $Co[NH_3]_6^{+3}$ or spermine), cations with no ability for stack formation, and also based on the evidence that dye - dye stack building is an anticooperative process (21). The presence of aromatic systems (e.g., bases in NA) in the polymer is not a prerequisite for cooperativity, because aliphatic polymers such as polyglutamic acid, undergo cooperative condensation in interactions with aromatic (Figure 3) or "simple" cations (not shown). Therefore, there is no special structural or electronic requirement for both the polyanion or the cationic ligand (except its valence as described above) to restrict cooperative condensation. The only common denominator, essential for condensation to occur, is the neutralization of polymer charges. According to Manning (1,2), on electrostatic neutralization there is a spontaneous bending of DNA, and large negative free energy change resulting from non-electrostatic sources. This phenomenon most likely explains the cooperativity. Namely, when a segment of the polymer is neutralized by the ligand, there is release of energy from the polymer's spontaneous bending, which is added to the free energy change of ligand association, and manifested in the form of cooperativity.

The higher affinity of aromatic ligands (intercalators) to induce condensation of NA compared to "simple" cations can be explained by the fact that the former have, in addition to pure electrostatic interactions, specific non-electrostatic interactions (7,10,19) with NA bases (dye - bases stacking, dispersion forces).

Conclusions

Intercalator induced condensation has already found practical applications as a qualitative and quantitative analytical method for NA (4,22). This type of interaction explains differential specificity of two fluorescent probes of NA, AO and pyronin Y(G), towards DNA *vs.* RNA, and also explains the mechanism of metachromatic stainability of NA by these or other ligands.

The condensation of NA in situ can be observed at pharmacological concentrations of some intercalating antitumor agents (12,14,15,20,23); it is possible, therefore, that this type of interaction is involved in antineoplastic or toxic side effects of Mitoxantrone, Ametantrone or Ditercalinium (14,15) and perhaps other drugs.

The mechanism of cooperative dye - polymer interaction may be similar to cooperative protein - NA interaction and, therefore, could provide a general model describing binding of biologically important molecules to NA.

Acknowledgments

We are grateful to Dr. Myron R. Melamed for his constant support and encouragement and Mrs. Sally Carter for her assistance in the preparation of the manuscript. This work was supported by U.S. Public Health Service Grants CA 28704 and R37 CA 23296. This work was presented in part at the *Sixth Conversation in Biomolecular Stereodynamics*, June 6-10 , 1989, SUNY at Albany.

References and Footnotes

1. G.S. Manning, *Q. Rev. Biophys. 11*, 179 (1978).
2. G.S. Manning, *Biopolymers 19*, 37 (1980).
3. G.S. Manning, K.K. Ebralidse, A.D. Mirzabekov and A. Rich, *J. Biomol. Struct. Dyn. 6*, 877 (1989).
4. J. Kapuscinski and Z. Darzynkiewicz, *Proc. Natl. Acad. Sci. USA 81*, 7368 (1984).
5. D.F. Bradley and M.K. Wolf, *Proc. Natl. Acad. Sci. USA 45*, 944 (1959).

6. L.S. Lerman, *J. Mol. Biol. 3*, 18 (1961).
7. J. Kapuscinski, Z. Darzynkiewicz and M.R. Melamed, *Cytometry 2*, 201 (1982).
8. J. Kapuscinski and Z. Darzynkiewicz, *Nucleic Acids Res. 11*, 7555 (1983).
9. J. Kapuscinski, Z. Darzynkiewicz and M.R. Melamed, *Biochem. Pharmacol. 32*, 3679 (1983).
10. J. Kapuscinski and Z. Darzynkiewicz, *J. Biomol. Struct. Dyn. 1*, 1485 (1984).
11. J. Kapuscinski and Z. Darzynkiewicz, *Cytometry 8*, 129 (1987).
12. Z. Darzynkiewicz, J. Kapuscinski, F. Traganos and H.A. Crissman, *Cytometry 8*, 138 (1987).
13. Z. Darzynkiewicz and J. Kapuscinski, *Cytometry 9*, 7 (1988).
14. J. Kapuscinski and Z. Darzynkiewicz, *Proc. Natl. Acad. Sci. USA 83*, 6302 (1986).
15. J. Kapuscinski, F. Traganos and Z. Darzynkiewicz, *Cancer Lett. 42*, 185 (1988).
16. R.W. Wilson and V.A. Bloomfield, *Biochemistry 18*, 2192 (1979).
17. W.D. Wilson, Y.H. Wang, C.R. Krishnamoorthy and J.C. Smith, *Biochemistry 24*, 3991 (9185).
18. J.D. McGhee and P.H. von Hippel, *J. Mol. Biol. 86*, 469 (1974).
19. J. Kapuscinski and Z. Darzynkiewicz, *J. Biomol. Struct. Dyn. 5*, 127 (1987).
20. Z. Darzynkiewicz, J. Kapuscinski, S.P. Carter, F.A. Schmid and M.R. Melamed, *Cancer Res. 46*, 5760 (1986).
21. B.H. Robinson, A. Loffler and G. Schwarz, *J. Chem. Soc., Faraday Trans. 1; 69*, 56 (1973).
22. J. Kapuscinski and Z. Darzynkiewicz, *U.S. Patent No. 4, 801*, 550 (1989).
23. Z. Darzynkiewicz, D. Evenson, J. Kapuscinski and M.R. Melamed, *Exp. Cell Res. 148*, 31 (1983).

Structure & Methods, ISBN 0-940030-32-2
Volume 3: DNA & RNA, ISBN 0-940030-31-4
Eds., Ramaswamy H. Sarma & Mukti H. Sarma, © Adenine Press 1990

Modeling of Nucleic Acids in the Size Range 100-10,000 Nucleotides: DNA Plasmids and Ribosomal RNAs

Stephen C. Harvey, Robert K.-Z. Tan and Arun Malhotra
Department of Biochemistry
University of Alabama at Birmingham
Birmingham, Alabama 35294

Abstract

We have developed a molecular mechanics method for modeling nucleic acids that are one to two orders of magnitude larger than can be treated by conventional methods. In order to do this, the level of detail in the models must be substantially reduced. Instead of the traditional all-atom description for macromolecules, we introduce pseudoatoms chosen so that particular properties of interest can be modeled. For DNA supercoiling, we maintain detail down to the level of individual basepairs, which are treated as planes connected by springs with characteristics that mimic the known elastic properties of DNA. In this case, three pseudoatoms are needed to represent a basepair, since three points define a plane. For RNA folding, the molecule is treated as a collection of beads on a string, with one pseudoatom per nucleotide. Here we review the method and describe recent applications. These include DNA supercoiling and looping, and the structure of the 16S RNA in the 30S ribosomal subunit.

Introduction

Molecular mechanics methods, including energy minimization and molecular dynamics, are powerful tools for investigating questions of structure and dynamics in macromolecules (1). They are particularly useful for refining model structures based on data from x-ray crystallography and NMR.

The principal advantage of traditional all-atom molecular mechanics models is the level of detail that they contain. At the same time, however, this detail imposes serious limitations on the size of systems that can be modeled, because of computational demand. A nucleic acid the size of tRNA (76 nucleotides, molecular weight around 25,000) is about as large a molecule as can be treated at the all-atom level by these methods. For systems of this size, particularly if one includes a reasonable number of explicit solvent molecules, the simulation of intramolecular motions by molecular dynamics is limited to time periods well below one nanosecond. Because of these considerations, one of the most important tasks facing molecular modelers is the development of methods capable of treating larger molecular systems, and, for the case of molecular dynamics, capable of simulating longer time periods.

There are two possible approaches to this problem. One is to simply wait until computer technology provides several orders of magnitude more power than is currently available. The second option is to reduce the level of detail in the models. We have been developing new molecular mechanics algorithms for large nucleic acids following the latter approach. The heart of our method is the introduction of pseudoatoms to represent suitable structural subunits. In many traditional molecular mechanics simulations on macromolecules, it is common to include hydrogen atoms with the heavy atom to which they are bound, using, for example, a single united atom to represent a methyl group. In our method, by contrast, the pseudoatoms are chosen to simplify the modeling problem, but they do not always correspond to identifiable collections of atoms. This point will be clarified later on.

In this paper we review the methodology we have developed for modeling large nucleic acids. Since these models are not all-atom models, but are instead low resolution models containing relatively few pseudoatoms, we call them "succinct models" (2). We also review the results of two applications of this methodology. The first is to the investigation of supercoiling and looping in DNAs ranging from a few hundred to a few thousand base pairs in size (2-4). Second is a method for folding RNAs, with a test case involving tRNA and an application to the structure of the 16S RNA in the 30S ribosomal subunit (5-6).

Methods

In molecular mechanics molecular structures are represented by a collection of point masses (atoms in the traditional molecular mechanics approach; pseudoatoms in this work). The interactions between these particles are described by a potential energy function that contains information on optimal distances and geometry. Normal potential functions (1) contain terms for the deformation of the covalent structure of macromolecules, including the stretching of bonds, the bending of bond angles, and rotations about bonds. The so-called nonbonded interactions describe the van der Waals and electrostatic interactions between atoms.

The pseudoatoms used in our method are chosen in order to facilitate the simulation of particular types of molecular properties. These pseudoatoms may or may not represent identifiable collections of real atoms. For example, in early studies on protein folding, the protein chain was modeled with two pseudoatoms per amino acid. A set of pseudobonds was used to string these residues together, with a bond length equal to the average distance between successive α carbons (7). We have chosen a similar model for RNA folding, with one pseudoatom per nucleotide. In this case the question of which real atoms are incorporated into which pseudoatoms is straightforward. On the other hand, our model for DNA supercoiling represents each basepair as a plane by introducing three pseudoatoms per basepair, since three points define a plane. One of these pseudoatoms is located at the center of the double helix, so that pseudobonds between successive central pseudoatoms connect the basepairs to one another. The second and third pseudoatoms in each basepair serve only to define the geometry of the basepair plane with respect to neighboring basepair planes, and to identify the location of the major groove. For this model, then, there is no simple one-to-one correspondence between the real atoms and the pseudoatoms. The model has been constructed so that the elastic properties of DNA are mimicked, and so that the variations in helical parameters can be determined as we move along the double helix. More detailed information on the construction of these models and on the form of the potential energy functions used for them can be found in previous papers (2, 4-6).

DNA Supercoiling and Looping

Our method for treating large DNA molecules and examining questions related to supercoiling have been previously described, along with some results (2-4). In this report we briefly review the most important aspects of the methodology and describe our most recent results.

Our model, with three pseudoatoms per basepair, is intermediate in detail between the all-atom models of molecular mechanics (1) and the continuum elastic models for DNA supercoiling (8-10). Conceptually, we treat double stranded DNA as if the basepairs were planes connected by springs; the properties of the springs are chosen to mimic the known elastic properties of the molecule.

When a "relaxed" molecule (relaxed in the sense of being torsionally unstressed), is closed into a circle, the molecule is stressed by the bending necessary to achieve closure. It will move in such a way as to reduce the bending energy, by twisting and writhing, producing a lower energy structure in which the deformation energy is distributed between bending and twisting. Figure 1 shows how such a molecule behaves when optimized on the computer using a combination of energy minimization and molecular dynamics. The starting structure has a relatively high potential energy, all of it in the form of bending. As it twists and writhes, the molecule first adopts toroidal or roseate conformations, but it eventually arrives at the classically interwound conformation, which has a very low energy. As described in our earlier study (4), closed circular DNA molecules that are either overwound or underwound by a linking difference of ± 1 favor a closed circular form that is nearly planar and unwrithed, but at higher linking differences the molecule is highly writhed. This result was predicted by theoretical studies on continuum elastic models (10-11). In our hands, the lowest energy form for molecules whose absolute linking difference exceeds one or two is always the interwound form.

The combined effects of protein binding and DNA supercoiling on gene regulation can be explained in some instances by the phenomenon of DNA looping (13). The interactions of proteins with DNA at two distant sites causes the DNA to loop. The resulting structure is very similar to the loops that exist at the ends of interwound closed circular DNA molecules.

Our first investigation of the DNA looping phenomenon has focused on the superloop model of Higgins *et al.* (12). This model has been invoked to explain the combined effects of supercoiling and the binding of integration host factor protein on the expression of two converging and competing Mu promoters. To build a model for

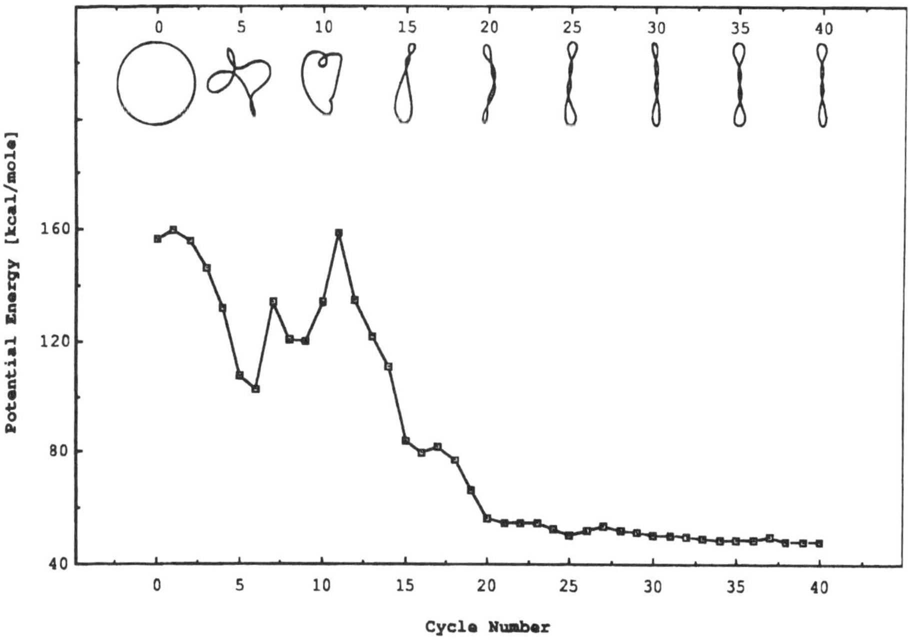

Figure 1: Refinement profile for the simulated annealing of a model underwound closed circular DNA molecule with 360 basepairs and a linking deficit of three turns. The upper part of the figure shows the structure at intervals of five cycles of annealing, while the lower part shows the energy after each cycle. Each cycle of annealing includes 2000 to 4000 steps of molecular dynamics with a timestep of 25 to 40 fs, followed by 500 to 1000 steps of conjugate gradient energy minimization. See text for discussion.

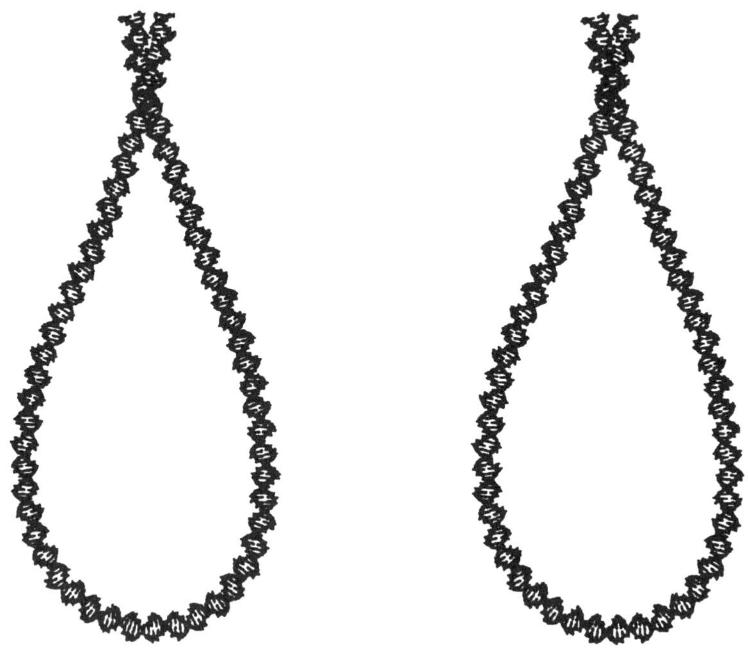

Figure 2: Our model for a DNA superloop (12).

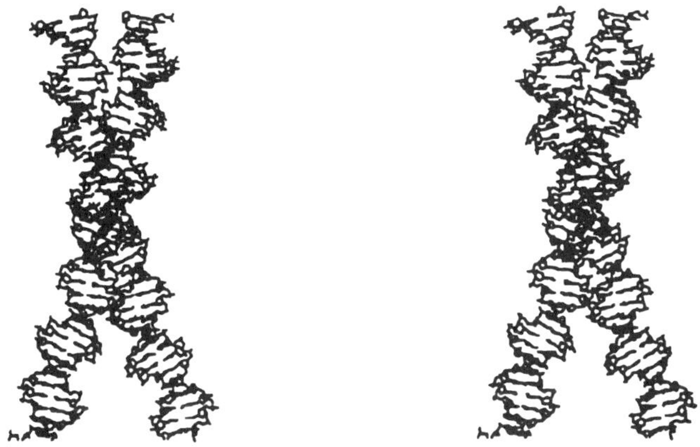

Figure 3: Detailed view of the crossover point for the DNA superloop.

the superloop, the loop structure from one of our supercoiled models was rescaled to provide a loop of appropriate size and dimensions, and then refined with energy minimization. The resulting structure is shown in Figure 2, while Figure 3 is an enlargement of the crossover point. Note that, although the structures were refined with our low resolution model having only three pseudoatoms per basepair, we are able to convert these to ordinary all-atom representations using AUGur, a program developed in our laboratory for studying sequence-structure relationships in DNA (14). In the superloop model, the crossover point blocks entry of RNA polymerase to one promoter or the other, with the preference being dictated by the level of supercoiling. Our method allows the development of detailed models for these structures, and offers opportunity for examination of the effects of changes in sequence or DNA supercoiling on them.

RNA Folding

A low resolution model for RNA, treating each nucleotide as a single particle, allows us to treat RNAs containing over 1000 residues and permits the investigation of the structure of large RNAs. Here we briefly review the methodology and describe our model for the 16S RNA in the 30S ribosomal subunit.

It is interesting to observe that, although a great deal of effort has been put into the prediction of the three dimensional structures of proteins, relatively little research has been carried out on how to predict the three dimensional structure of RNAs. There are two reasons, both related to the prediction of secondary structure, that give reason for optimism in developing methods for predicting the three dimensional structure of an RNA from its primary sequence. First, the algorithms for predicting secondary structure are much more reliable for nucleic acids than they are for proteins. Whereas the latter have reliabilities in the range of 60-70% for the prediction of α helical regions and β sheet regions, the secondary structure for RNAs of moderate size can be predicted with high reliability. In the case of large RNAs (the 16S RNA has 1,542 nucleotides), quite accurate consensus predictions can be made if sequences are available for the RNA obtained from a variety of organisms, because sequence comparisons often allow the determination of conserved regions of secondary structure. The second reason that information on secondary structures is more important in nucleic acids than in proteins is that it provides long distance structural information. Even if one could predict α helices and β sheet regions in proteins with high reliability, the former are local structures, and there are no methods for predicting which regions of β sheet will associate with one another and whether they will do so in parallel or antiparallel fashion. RNA secondary structures, on the other hand, generally contain information on close physical contact between regions which are distant from one another in the primary sequence.

The principal obstacle to predicting the three dimensional structure of an RNA from its primary sequence is that RNAs probably do not form the kind of compact structures that globular proteins do. In the case of RNA-protein complexes, such as the ribosome, however, the proteins serve as a scaffold holding the various regions of the RNA in a definite relationship with one another. From the standpoint of predicting the three dimensional RNA structure, the ribosomal proteins can be considered to be a scaffold through which the RNA must be strung. There is a growing body of experimental information on RNA-RNA and RNA-protein contacts in the 30S ribosomal subunit, and the addition of that information to the secondary structure information should allow the development of reasonable three dimensional models for the RNA. Such models have been built manually, using either physical models (15) or computer graphics methods (16,17).

We have developed an automated computer algorithm for folding large RNAs using the information described above. Manually built models have the advantage that stereochemical intuition can be applied at every stage of the development process. On the other hand, building and manipulating such models is laborious and difficult, and the final result of weeks or months of work is a single model. The 16S RNA in the ribosome is a very underdetermined system - the model has many more degrees of freedom than experimentally determined distances - so a wide range of models should be compatible with the data. It would be desirable to have a rapid, automated procedure for building these models, so that a large number of alternatives could be examined. Such examination should produce information on which regions of the structure are relatively well defined and which regions are poorly determined.

During the development phase of this project, we applied our algorithm to a test case where the crystal structure was already known, transfer RNA. In addition to providing an opportunity for comparing alternative algorithms, this allowed us to investigate how increasing the quantity of information that went into the model would gradually narrow the range of models compatible with the data. Figure 4 shows the sequential folding for one particular case. We begin with a random walk chain containing 76 pseudoatoms, one for each nucleotide. These are connected by pseudobonds with a bond length of 6.0 Å in single stranded regions, and 5.9 Å in regions where the cloverleaf model would predict helical structures. The latter distance is that between successive phosphate groups in A-RNA. At the first stage of refinement, pseudobonds are introduced between pairs of phosphate atoms in the

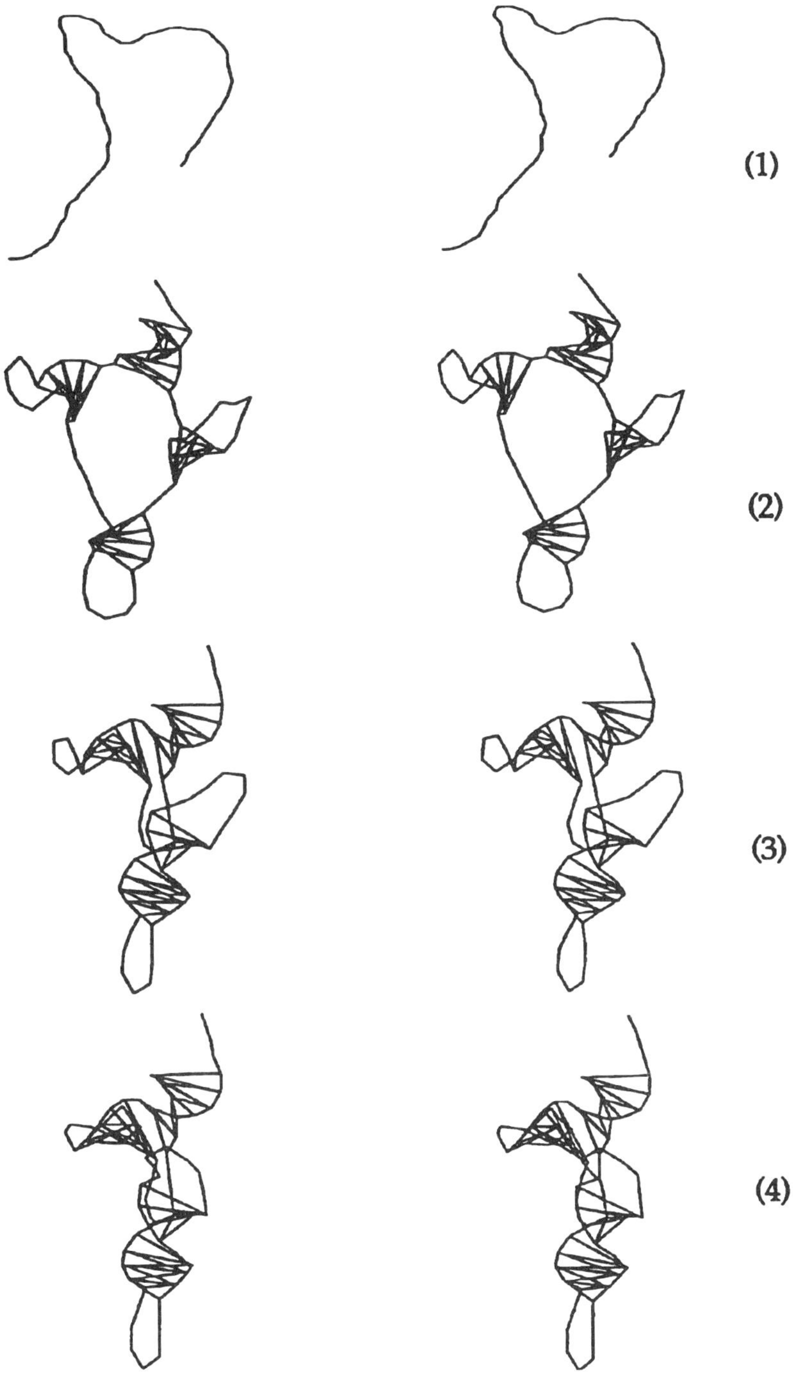

Figure 4: Generation of a three dimensional model for tRNA, starting with a random chain model. At successive stages of refinement, additional distance constraints are introduced. Proceeding downward from the top of the figure, these correspond to the secondary structure, stem stacking, and contacts between residues 18-19 of the D loop and residues 55-56 of the T loop. See text for discussion.

predicted stem regions. Since each pair of atoms has six degrees of freedom, six constraints per basepair are needed to guarantee the correct three dimensional structure. Five of these constraints are pseudobonds, while the sixth is an improper torsion. The latter is needed to guarantee chirality of helical regions; an example of such a pseudotorsion at the top of the anticodon stem would be defined by the succession of phosphates for residues 2, 1, 72, 71. When this set of constraints is applied and the system is optimized, the resulting structure is a three dimensional model for the familiar cloverleaf tRNA structure (Figure 4).

It is a logical assumption that, wherever possible, RNA stems will stack on one another to form essentially continuous double helices. Stem stacking can be guaranteed with six constraints per pair of stems. For ideal double helical geometry, these constraints are identical to those for stacking successive basepairs in the stem regions. In the case of a molecule with a cloverleaf secondary structure, three stacking patterns will be possible. If we suppose that experimental information was provided on the correct stacking pattern in tRNA (acceptor stem on the T stem; anticodon stem on the D stem), when we add appropriate constraints and refine the model until they are satisfied, we obtain a structure that begins to look like a recognizable tRNA (Figure 4).

If we suppose that one additional piece of experimental information were available on a contact between two residues that are remote from one another in a primary structure, we should be able to improve the model further. In the present case, we have used the distances defined by the hydrogen bonding patterns between residues 18 and 19 in the D loop and residues 55 and 56 in the T loop. A slight improvement in the structure is obtained when those constraints are added to the model (Figure 4). Since the pseudoatoms that we use are located at the phosphate groups, and the interphosphate distances for these last two constraints is so large, the structure of the elbow region where those groups are in contact in the crystal structure is not reproduced by this model. None the less, it is interesting that a model which so clearly resembles the crystal structure can be obtained with such a modest amount of input information.

This is, of course, only one of a range of models that is compatible with the simulated experimental data we have described. Figure 5 shows a collection of models that satisfy the distance constraints described above. All of them bear a general resemblance to tRNA, although none of them is really very close to the correct structure. It is important to note that the apparent relative motions of the two arms in the models of Figure 5 is not a prediction about intramolecular flexibility in tRNA. It is, rather, a statement about the uncertainty in the angle between the two arms. This uncertainty is not surprising, given the nature of the distance constraints that were included in the models. An important aspect of our methodology is that it allows quantitative error estimates to be associated with structural parameters. (In the case of the angle between the two arms of the model tRNAs, we have observed all orientations from side-by-side parallel to side-by-side antiparallel arrangement. The two arms are never observed to be colinear, nor are any nearly colinear arrangements generated.)

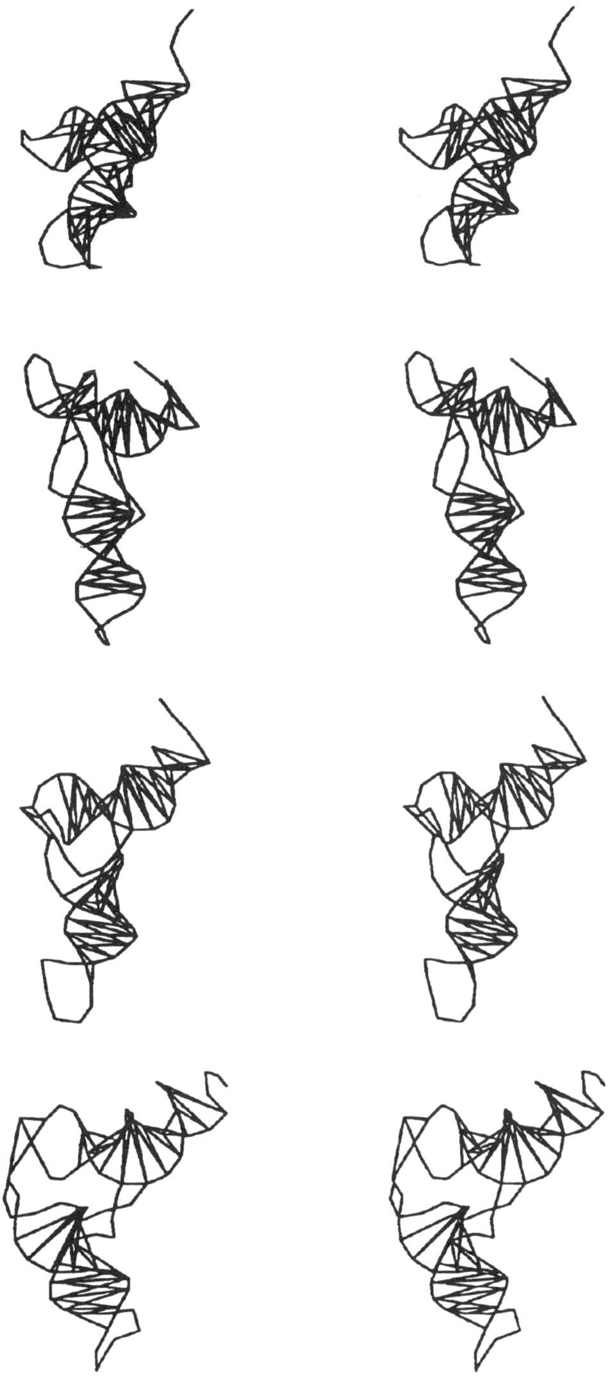

Figure 5: Several structures generated for tRNA, subject to the same sets of distance constraints. Each of these was generated following the procedure of Figure 4, but starting with a different random walk chain. All of these models are consistent with the distance constraints, so the differences between them illustrate the range of uncertainty in models built only with those constraints.

The 16S RNA in the 30S Ribosomal Subunit

We have used the procedure above to fold the 16S ribosomal RNA into a variety of structures that are compatible with the available experimental data. In addition to the consensus secondary structure, this data includes intramolecular crosslinking data between pairs of nucleotides within the RNA, intermolecular crosslinking between specified nucleotides and the ribosomal proteins, and chemical protection data (15,16). We interpret the chemical protection data in the following way. If a particular protein prevents a particular nucleotide from reacting with a chemical probe, we make the simplest assumption, which is that the nucleotide and the protein are in contact. For all the distance constraints between the proteins and nucleotides, we use a distance that is the sum of the radius of the protein and the radius of A-RNA.

Figure 6 shows a starting structure, with a random walk chain for the backbone of the 16S RNA, with the center of mass of this chain superposed on the center of mass of the 21 proteins of the 30S subunit. Notice that, prior to optimization, the RNA lies almost entirely outside of the ribosome. Figure 7 shows the final structure for the

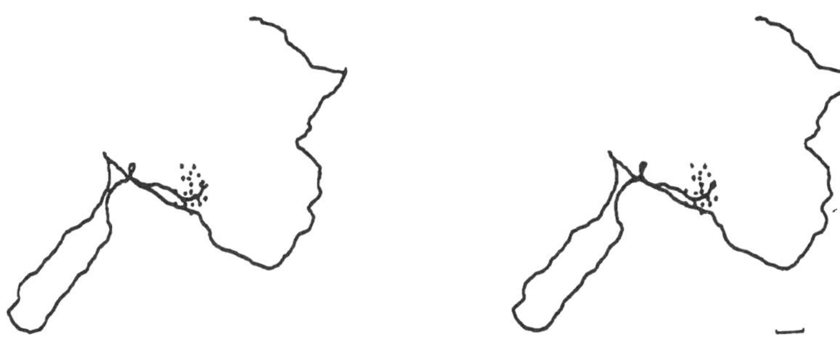

Figure 6: Initial unrefined model for the 16S RNA in the 30S ribosomal subunit. Note that the RNA (line) lies almost entirely outside of the framework of proteins (collection of dots). Scale bar = 100 Å.

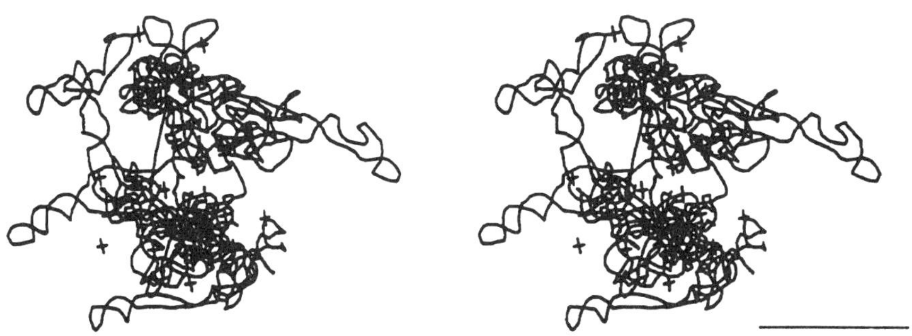

Figure 7: Backbone of the refined model obtained from the random walk chain of Figure 6 when all distance constraints are satisfied. Centers of the 21 ribosomal proteins are shown by crosses. The parts of the RNA that lie outside of the ribosome correspond to regions where there is no crosslinking data to provide information on position. The view is from the cytoplasmic side of the ribosome, with the same orientation as Figure 18 of reference 16. The general features of this model and that of reference 16 are similar. Scale bar = 100 Å.

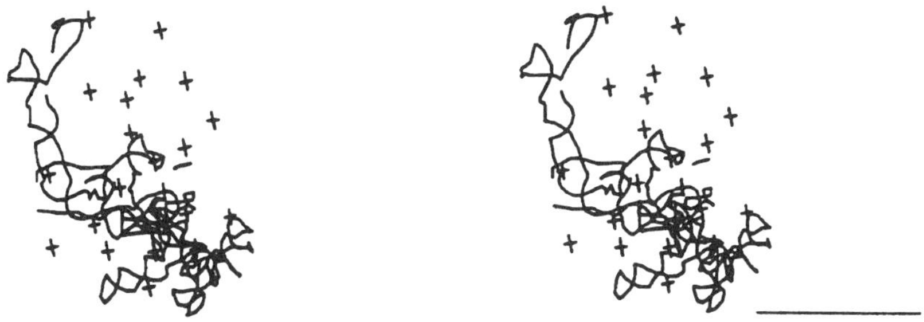

Figure 8: The well-defined regions of the 5′ domain of the model in Figure 7, including residues 38-65, 104-143, 179-436, and 498-546. Scale bar = 100 Å.

Figure 9: The well-defined regions of the central domain of the model in Figure 7, residues 558-915. Scale bar = 100 Å.

Figure 10: The well-defined regions of the 3′ domain of the model in Figure 7, including residues 920-990 and 1046-1397. Scale bar = 100 Å.

model, with one pseudoatom for each of the 1542 nucleotides of the RNA. Figures 8-10 show some details of the model. The locations of the principal regions of the RNA are similar to those proposed in manually built models (15-17).

As mentioned above, one of the advantages of our method is the ability to generate a number of models, all of which are compatible with the experimental data, allowing an investigation of the uncertainty in the models. We have refined four models, and Figure 11 shows the range of variation in them. The four models have been superpositioned (the ribosomal proteins provide a reference framework), and the root mean square deviation in the position of each nucleotide is calculated for the four models. This process is repeated for every nucleotide in the chain, producing the results shown in Figure 11. When we use all of the data described above, we find that some regions in the models are quite well defined, within a deviation of about ± 10 Å. In other regions, the uncertainty is very large, exceeding ± 60 Å. These regions

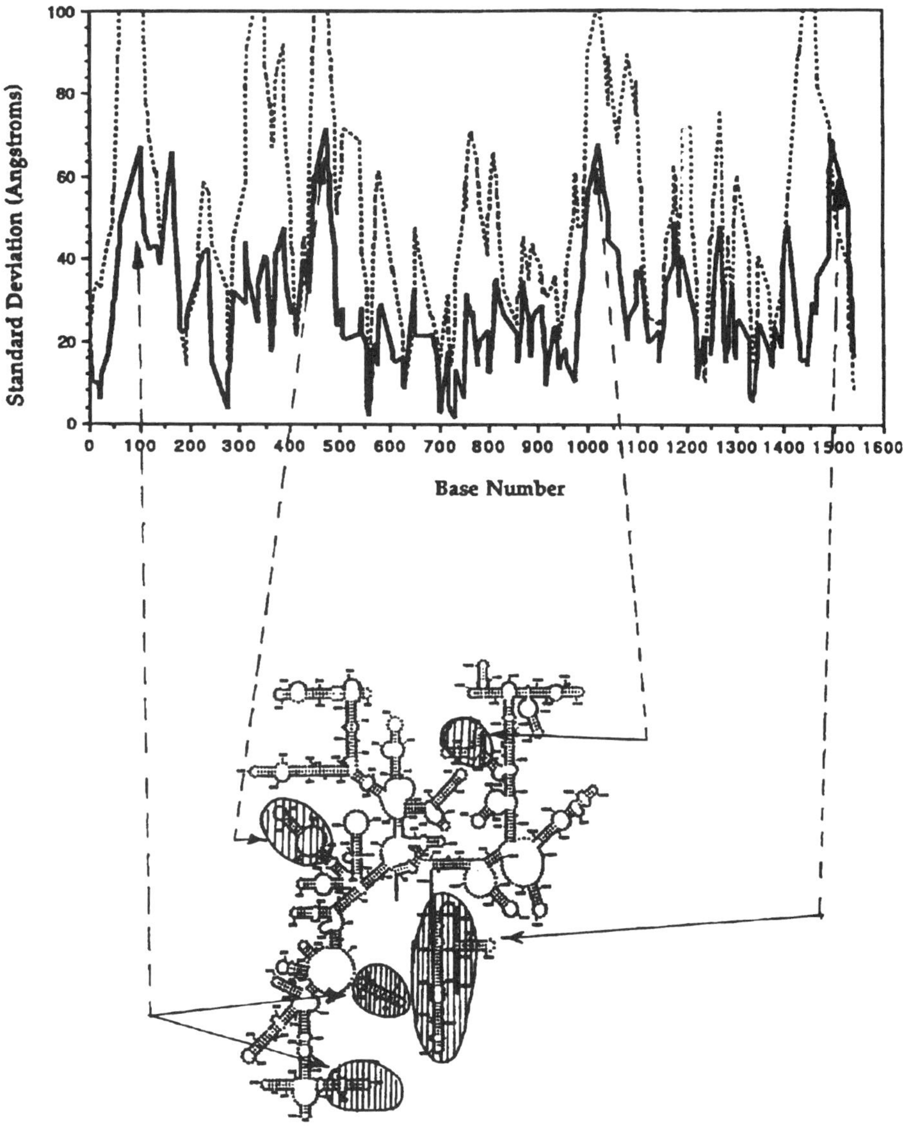

Figure 11: Variability between models for the 16S RNA in the 30S ribosomal unit. All models satisfy the same distance constraints, but each was built from a unique initial random walk chain. The upper part of the figure shows the root mean square fluctuation in the position of each nucleotide along the chain for four models refined using the information on secondary structure, chemical crosslinking, and chemical protection (solid line), and for four other models refined using only the information on secondary structure and chemical crosslinking patterns (broken line). The lower part of the figure shows the accepted secondary structure ofthe 16S RNA (from reference 16, with permission). High variability in our models represents the most poorly defined regions of the molecule; four of those are identified here.

correspond quite well with the regions that Stern *et al.* left out of their model, because of large uncertainty in where they should be placed (16).

The process described in the proceeding paragraph has been carried out a second time, using all of the crosslinking data, but omitting the base protection data. A comparison of the uncertainty curves in Figure 11 shows that the inclusion of the base protection data reduces the variability substantially. This illustrates how a relatively small number of measurements using a different experimental technique can provide significant improvements in the quality of structural models for the ribosome.

Acknowledgments

Supported by a grant from the National Science Foundation (GM-87-06551). We are grateful to the Alabama Supercomputer Network for a grant of computer time, and to the Artherosclerosis Research Unit for access to a computer graphics system. We are indebted to Dr. Hans De Loof and to Mr. Martin Jones for stimulating discussions and technical assistance.

References and Footnotes

1. McCammon, J.A. and Harvey, S.C., *Dynamics of Proteins and Nucleic Acids*, Cambridge University Press, London (1987).
2. Tan, R.K.Z. and Harvey, S.C., in *Theoretical Biochemistry and Molecular Biophysics*, Lavery, R. and Beveridge, D., Eds., Adenine, New York, in press.
3. Harvey, S.C. and Tan, R.K.Z., in *Unusual DNA Structures*, Wells, R.D., and Harvey, S.C., Eds., Springer, New York, (1987).
4. Tan, R.K.Z. and Harvey, S.C., *J. Mol. Biol. 205*, 573-591 (1989).
5. Malhotra, A., Tan, R.K.Z. and Harvey, S.C., *Proc. Natl. Acad. Sci. USA* (submitted).
6. Malhotra, A. and Harvey, S.C., in *Topics in Molecular and Structural Biology*, Goodfellow, J., Ed., Macmillan, London, in press.
7. Levitt, M. and Warshel, A., *Nature 253*, 694-698 (1975).
8. Selepova, P. and Kypr, J., *Biopolymers 24*, 867-882 (1985).
9. Shimada, J. and Yamakawa, H., *J. Mol. Biol. 184*, 319-329 (1985).
10. Tsuru, H. and Wadati, M., *Biopolymers 25*, 2083-2096 (1986).
11. LeBret, M., *Biopolymers 18*, 1709-1725 (1979).
12. Higgins, N.P., Collier, D.A., Kilpatrick, M.W. and Krause, H.M., *J. Biol. Chem. 264*, 3035-3042 (1989).
13. Ptashne, M., *Nature 322*, 697-701 (1986).
14. Tan, R.K.Z., Prabhakaran, M., Tung, C.S. and Harvey, S.C., *Comput. Applics. Bioscis. 4*, 147-151 (1988).
15. Brimacombe, R., *Biochemistry 28*, 4207-4214 (1988).
16. Stern, S., Weiser, B. and Noller, H.F., *J. Mol. Biol. 204*, 447-481 (1988).
17. Nagano, K., Harel, M. and Takezawa, M., *J. Theor. Biol. 134*, 199-256 (1988).

Structure & Methods, ISBN 0-940030-32-2
Volume 3: DNA & RNA, ISBN 0-940030-31-4
Eds., Ramaswamy H. Sarma & Mukti H. Sarma, © Adenine Press 1990

Structural Determination of Yeast $tRNA^{Phe}$ Transcripts by NMR

K.B. Hall[1] and J.R. Sampson[2]
[1]Department of Biochemistry
Brandeis University
Waltham, MA 02254

[2]Division of Biology
California Institute of Technology
Pasadena, CA 91125

Abstract

Structures of *in vitro* transcripts of yeast $tRNA^{Phe}$ have been studied by NMR and by nuclease mapping. The conformational change that the transcript undergoes upon the addition of Mg^{++} can be described as a change from a cloverleaf to the normal folded L-form. This structural flexibility has been tentatively correlated to the activity of the transcript in aminoacylation. Structures for several other sequence variants, including C19G56 and C19C56, have been proposed. The alteration of the tertiary base-pair G19C56 has little effect on the tRNA folding, wherease its disruption in C19C56 appears to destabilize several surrounding interactions.

Introduction

One goal of a structure:function study is to define the relative contributions of functional elements and structural elements to biological activity. The classic approach of such a study is to construct a mutant, then to test its function and analyze its structure. Engineering the mutant and measuring its function always proceed more rapidly than the corresponding structural determination, especially when the molecules involved are large.

The tRNA:synthetase complex provides several advantages for a biophysical approach. This is true in part because there are crystal structures of tRNA and synthetase available for reference (1,2), but also because the technology is in place to produce variant tRNA sequences and mutant proteins that can both be used to probe the interaction. These methods have yielded information on the specific sequences that constitute recognition points for the tRNA:synthetase interaction in several tRNAs (3,4,5,6) and for the more complex tRNA:ribosome interactions (7). Most of these studies have involved biochemical or *in vivo* assays of biological activity, and so the contribution of structural effects of mutations is addressed indirectly.

We have been interested in the interaction of yeast $tRNA^{Phe}$ with its cognate synthetase, to define the elements of the tRNA necessary for recognition by the protein.

Yeast $tRNA^{Phe}$ has been the subject of many structural investigations (1,8,9) but for our experiments, we have taken advantage of *in vitro* transcription by T7 RNA polymerase to produce the sequence of $tRNA^{Phe}$ or sequence variants (10). The major advantage of this method is that any variant sequence can be synthesized, including those that would not be produced *in vivo*. The other advantage is that the relatively large amounts necessary for biophysical studies, in this case, for NMR, can be produced easily. A potential disadvantage is that these *in vitro* transcribed molecules lack all modified bases.

Using the T7 transcripts of yeast $tRNA^{Phe}$ sequences, five nucleotides have been identified as possible specific recognition sites for the cognate synthetase (11). These are A73 at the 3′ end, G20 in the D-loop, and G34, A35, and A36 in the anticodon loop. These five nucleotides are spatially distal, indicating that the yeast phenylalanyl-tRNA synthetase must span the entire length of the tRNA and suggesting that the structural integrity of the tRNA will be important for proper recognition by the synthetase.

We have used NMR to study the structure of the $tRNA^{Phe}$ transcript (12). The NMR methods used here are similar to those previously used in studies of yeast $tRNA^{Phe}$ (8,9) in which the imino protons from base-paired nucleotides are used to determine stacked sequences and tertiary interactions. The power of the method now is in the use of selected sequence variants whose NMR spectra and spectral properties can be compared to those of the normal sequence to study the structural effects of the base or base-pair substitution. In this way, we can compare the biochemical function with the structural information obtained from NMR.

Materials and Methods

Construction of templates for *in vitro* synthesis reactions has been described (10). The conditions for large scale synthesis reactions for NMR are described in Hall *et al.* (12). The average yield from these syntheses was 1 mg/ml of transcription reaction. Typical NMR samples contained between 5 and 10 mg of purified tRNA transcript to give final concentrations between 1 and 2 mM.

Samples for NMR experiments were dialyzed against several changes of 0.1 M EDTA pH 8 at room temperature to remove any residual divalent cations left from the synthesis and purification, and then against the desired buffer. NMR spectra were recorded on the 500 MHz spectrometer in the laboratory of A.G. Redfield at Brandeis University. A 2-1-4 pulse was used to observe imino protons as described previously (13).

Results and Discussion

The $tRNA^{Phe}$ Transcript

In the presence of 5 mM free Mg^{++}, the transcript adopts the expected folded tertiary structure, as determined by NOE data from NMR experiments (12). The secondary

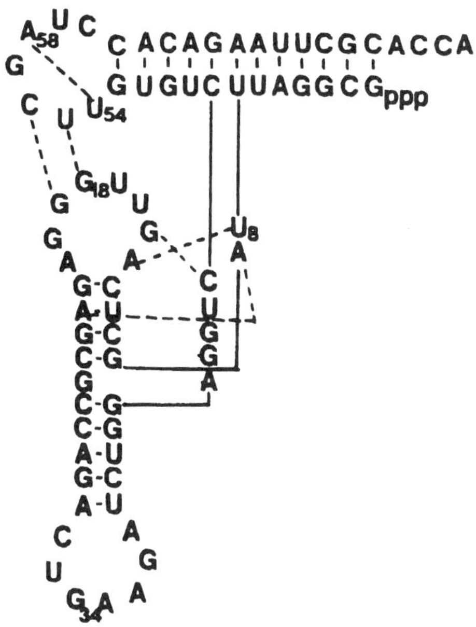

Figure 1: A model of the structure of the yeast tRNA^{Phe} transcript in the presence of Mg^{++}. The tertiary interactions indicated are those that have been identified by NMR experiments. Nuclease mapping experiments indicate that the nucleotides on the 3′ side of the anticodon loop are stacked.

and tertiary interactions that we have identified by NMR are shown in Figure 1. The imino proton spectrum of the transcript is not identical to that of the modified tRNA^{Phe}, however, for it exhibits less chemical shift dispersion, making assignments more difficult (see Figure 2 and Table I for the spectrum and assignments). Apparently, the modified bases contribute to the chemical shift dispersion of the spectra, probably through a combination of electronic and local structural effects that produce unique chemical and magnetic environments.

The structure of the transcript has been probed by several biochemical methods. It has been shown that there is a specific Pb-cleavage site between D17 and G18 in tRNA^{Phe} which is a useful probe of the integrity of the D- and T-loop interactions (14). Experiments showed that the rate of Pb-cleavage of the transcript is similar to that of yeast tRNA^{Phe} (15,16). In addition, nuclease mapping of the transcript in the presence of 5, 15, and 35 mM $MgCl_2$ showed that it is mostly resistant to nuclease cleavage in these conditions (data not shown) indicating that the structure is compact. Only the anticodon loop nucleotides U33, G34, and A35 of the transcript and of tRNA^{Phe} (17,18) are accessible to cleavage by single-strand-specific nucleases. Although the adjacent A31U39 base-pair at the end of the anticodon stem is not identified in the NMR spectrum of the transcript (12), the absence of cleavage at A31 in nuclease mapping experiments suggests that this nucleotide is stacked. Thus the anticodon stem/loop of the transcript in the absence of mC32, mG34, Y37 and ψ39, still retains considerable structure in the presence of at least 5 mM Mg^{++}.

An ordered anticodon stem-loop structure is important for aminoacylation at least because G34, A35, and A36 constitute part of the synthetase recognition set. It is possible that in the absence of m^5C40, ψ39, and the anticodon modifications, there are deviations from the normal anticodon structure of tRNA^{Phe}. Such changes in fact are suggested by reactivity of these nucleotides in the transcript to specific chemical probes. An altered structure in this loop could partially account for the 4-fold increase in K_m of the transcript for the synthetase relative to that of tRNA^{phe}. As an extreme example of an altered anticodon conformation, previous aminoacylation experiments using a modified tRNA^{Phe} molecule broken between the hypermodified Y37 and adenosine 38 in the anticodon loop showed that the broken tRNA was a poor substrate for aminoacylation at high ionic strength (19).

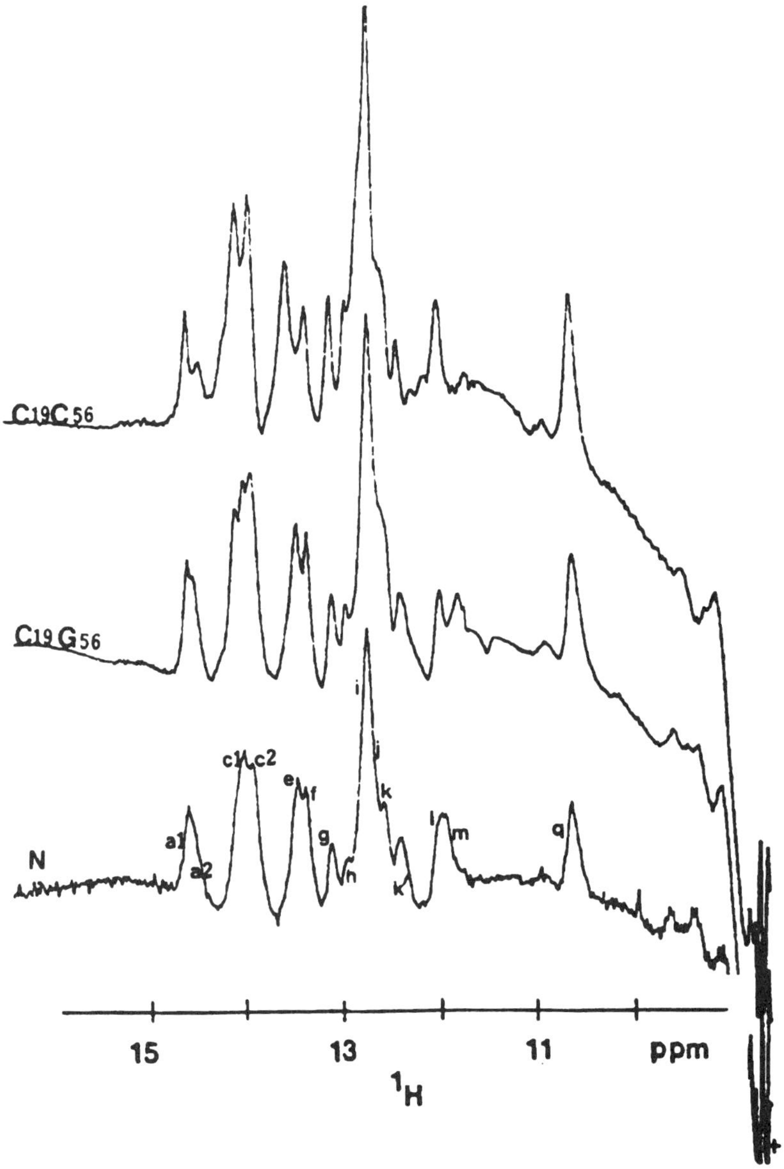

Figure 2: Imino proton NMR spectra of the normal $tRNA^{Phe}$ transcript (N) and of the two sequence variants C19G56 and C19C56. Each transcript is about 2 mM in 10 mM free Mg^{++}, 100 mM NaCl, 10 mM NaCacodylate at 25°C in 90% H_2O, 10% ^2H_2O. Spectral width was 8 kHz, with the carrier centered in the middle of the imino proton region. A 2-1-4 pulse was used to minimize water excitation. Spectra were apodized and line-narrowed.

While all these data indicate that the transcript is folding into a structure very similar to that of the native $tRNA^{Phe}$ in the presence of Mg^{++}, other data indicate that in the absence of Mg^{++}, the structure of the transcript is altered. Previous aminoacylation data (10) showed that the activity of the transcript is more sensitive

Table I
Imino Proton Assignments

Peak	Assignment
a1	U6A67
a2	U8A14
c1	A5U68
	U50A64
c2	U12A23
	U54A58
e	U7A66
	U52A62
f	A29U41
g	C13G22
h	C11G24*
i	C2G71
	C49G65
	G53C61
	G10C25*
	C28G42
j/k	G3C70
	G51C63
k′	G15C48
	G30C40
l	G4U69
m	G18U55
q	G4U69

*Considered tentative. Table adapted from (12).

to the $MgCl_2$ concentration than is native tRNA^{Phe}. In addition, the transcript exhibits a broader melting profile at lower Mg^{++} concentrations than does tRNA^{Phe}. NMR experiments showed that there were large changes in the imino proton spectrum of the transcript as a function of the Mg^{++} concentration (12). NOE experiments with the transcript in the absence of Mg^{++} or at low $[Mg^{++}]/[tRNA]$ ratios (<5) showed that only a portion of the acceptor stem was intact (12), and other NOE patterns did not extend far enough to allow the unambiguous identification of the D-, T-, or anticodon stem structures. Also, this structure was apparently lacking several of the AU pairs normally found in the tRNA cloverleaf.

One possible explanation for these biochemical and structural data was that the transcript adopts an alternative conformation in low $MgCl_2$ concentrations. There is no evidence for any alternative conformations of yeast tRNA^{Phe} from either NMR experiments (20) or nuclease mapping studies (17). However, *E. coli* tRNA$_2^{Gly}$ (17,21), *E.coli* tRNA^{Phe} (22), and *E. coli* tRNA$_3^{Gly}$ (23) do have conformational isomers that are dependent on the $MgCl_2$ concentration. Significantly, these tRNAs have fewer modified bases than does yeast tRNA^{Phe}, which suggests that in the absence of modified nucleotides, the transcript structure might be destabilized enough to adopt an alternative structure.

While the NMR data on the low-Mg^{++} form could not rule out the possibility that

Table II
Aminoacylation Kinetics

	15 mM $MgCl_2$			2 mM $MgCl_2$		
tRNA	K_m (nM)	V_{max}	V_{max}/K_m	K_m (nM)	V_{max}	V_{max}/K_m
G19C56	310	(100)	(1.0)	340	15	0.14
C19G56	310	200	2.0	280	25	0.27
C19C56	1350	80	0.18	1200	15	0.035
C8A14	560	60	0.33	1000	3	0.008

G19C56 is the wild-type sequence. Aminoacylation conditions as described in Sampson and Uhlenbeck (1988).

the transcript adopted an alternative structure, nuclease mapping of the transcript in the absence of $MgCl_2$ suggests that no rearrangement of the normal secondary structure has occurred. Only those nucleotides expected to be found in loops are cleaved by single-strand specific nucleases. These data suggest that the normal tRNA stems and loops are present. In the absence of $MgCl_2$, nuclease cleavage is observed at many of the nucleotides that are normally involved in tertiary interactions, including those between the D and T-loops and between the D-loop and other parts of the molecule (U8A14 and G15C48), suggesting that many of the normal tertiary interactions are disrupted.

It seems likely that this extended (cloverleaf) conformation corresponds to the structure of the transcript in conditions when it is a poor substrate for aminoacylation. As shown in Table II, the K_m of the reaction is independent of Mg^{++} concentration whereas the k_{cat} is reduced more than 6-fold at the lower Mg^{++} concentration. The constant K_m implies that the extended form of the tRNA does not impede protein binding at the initial binding step as it might through steric hindrance by the extended tRNA arms. These aminoacylation results and the structural correlations have precedent in previous work of Loftfield *et al.* (24). In those studies using the native yeast $tRNA^{Phe}$, aminoacylation activity was carefully measured as a function of Mg^{++} and spermine concentrations. On the basis of separate physical studies, the tRNA substrate activity was correlated to structural changes induced by the divalent ions. It is possible that when the tRNA tertiary structure is altered, the number of specific contacts are reduced such that the aminoacylation cannot proceed. In analogy with the hypothesis of Loftfield *et al.*, the reaction could be blocked at the level of an enzyme:substrate intermediate with insufficient energy to progress to the next step, and in fact the lowered k_{cat} for the transcript suggests that this low-Mg^{++} structure is less able to proceed through the reaction pathway.

Variant Conformations

Combining *in vitro* transcription with tRNA variants produces a system that allows measurement of both biological activity (aminoacylation activity) and structural integrity (via NMR and biochemical probes). By combining the two measurements, it should be possible to determine the contributions of functional changes and structural alterations to the larger question of protein:RNA interactions. For the tRNA:synthetase system, we have focused first on the structure of variants with altered nucleotides from the recognition set, and then variants with mutations in conserved tertiary interactions.

U20 tRNA

One example of a recognition set variant is the G20 to U20 mutant. G20, which crystal structures show as unpaired and single-stranded, was identified as an element of the recognition set by the 14-fold decrease in k_{cat}/k_m for aminoacylation activity of the U20 variant (10). The decrease in aminoacylation activity could alternatively be explained by a disruption of structure as a result of the substitution of U at position 20.

Structural analysis of the U20 variant first by Pb-cleavage indicated that the specific interactions between the D- and T-loop are intact (15). Second, the NMR spectrum and more importantly, the NOE patterns of the U20 variant are virtually identical to those of the wild-type tRNA. Within the limits of the NMR analysis, there is no conformational change that occurs as a result of this substitution (12). The U20 variant apparently contains all the normal base-pairs and tertiary interactions that were identified in the wild-type sequence (Figure 3). Thus these data further support the conclusion that U20 does not structurally perturb the tRNA structure and confirm the identification of G20 as a recognition nucleotide for the synthetase.

Assuming that the G20 and U20 tRNAs are structurally isomorphic, then a possible interpretation of the aminoacylation data is that the 6-fold increase in the K_m of the U20 sequence relative to the G20 sequence (10) is due to the loss of a specific contact with G20. The smaller 2.5-fold decrease in V_{max} is more difficult to interpret. It has been established for several tRNA-synthetase systems that aminoacyl bond formation occurs only upon formation of a cognate complex that itself depends on an induced conformational change of the tRNA (25). Similarly, it is possible that formation of a G20:protein interaction may be a critical step in a path involving conformational changes in either protein or tRNA or in the formation of a transition state that leads to aminoacylation.

G19C56 Variants

Tertiary interactions contribute to the global folding of all RNA molecules. Crystal structures of tRNAs provide the only detailed information on the conformations of these interactions, showing that they are often noncanonical pairs that participate in additional hydrogen-bonding to phosphates or counterions. Structural studies of specific tRNA variants with altered tertiary interactions should allow an evaluation of the contribution of each tertiary basepair to the local and global tRNA structure and stability. This structural information can then be used to interpret changes in the biological activity of the variant.

The tertiary interaction that we have been studying is the G19C56 base-pair. This is a conserved interaction in all tRNAs, so that the structural and biological effects of

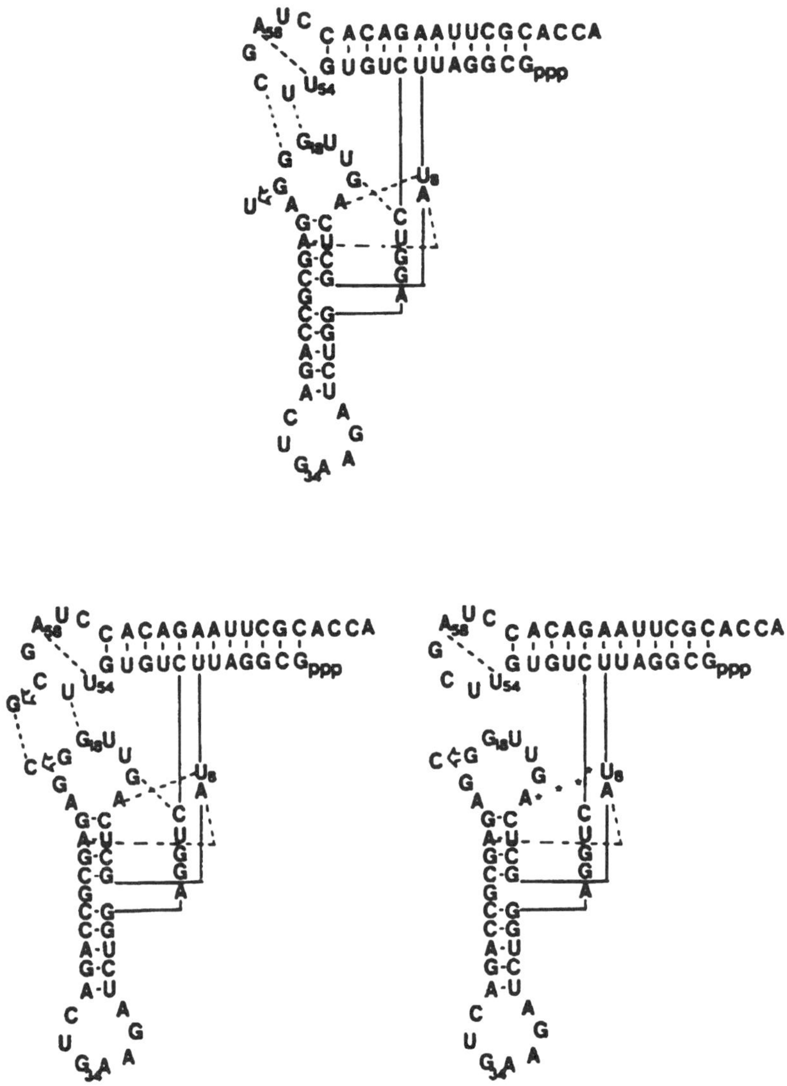

Figure 3: Models of the structures of the three variants. Again the tertiary base pairs identified by NMR are indicated; the A58U54 base pair is identified in the model of the C19C56 variant, although it has not been found in the NMR spectrum, since the nuclease data indicate that the T-loop is structured. NMR data show that the U8A14 base pair in the C19C56 variant is unstable, so that interaction has been indicated by asterisks.

its mutation or disruption in yeast $tRNA^{Phe}$ might be more generally applicable. The crystal structure shows that G19C56 is located more than 7A from the nearest base-pair. It was therefore not surprising that in the NMR spectra of the modified $tRNA^{Phe}$ the position of the resonance from the imino proton of G19C56 is deduced, for no NOE is observed from the adjacent G18U55 (8). In the NMR spectrum of the wild-type transcript, we have been unable to locate the G19C56 imino proton, for there is again no NOE from the imino proton of the G18U55 base-pair. These data suggest that the structure of this region may be similar in the transcript and native tRNA^{Phe}, even though the transcript lacks the modified bases at positions 54, 58, and 55.

Having made spectral assignments for the protons from the bases around this tertiary base pair, we then proceeded to use these assignments to assess what, if any, structural changes occurred in the tRNA when the G19C56 base-pair is altered. Two sequence variants, C19G56 and C19C56, were used for structure:function studies. In the C19G56 variant, the tertiary base-pair was anticipated to be retained although the sequence was inverted, while in the C19C56 variant, it was expected to be absent.

NMR spectra of these two variants are compared to that of the normal sequence in Figure 2. Analysis of the NMR data of the C19G56 variant indicates that there has been some structural change around this base-pair. The resonance assigned to the adjacent G18U55 (peak m, see Table I) has shifted upfield by more than 0.1 ppm, and it is now possible to find an NOE to a resonance assigned to the C19G56 imino proton, located in peak i. This new NOE suggests that the structure around this region has changed, such that the distance between C19G56 and G18U55 is less than 5A, to account for the observed NOE. The rate of lead cleavage for this mutant is normal, indicating that no large structural changes have occurred in this region. Peak m in the C19G56 variant is now more thermally labile than in G19C56, indicating that this structure is less stable. As Figure 3 shows, although the C19G56 variant has apparently suffered some structural changes, the stems are intact and most of the tertiary interactions can be identified.

In contrast, the spectrum of the C19C56 variant shows several obvious changes from that of the normal G19C56 sequence. Notably, the resonances assigned to the tertiary base-pairs between the D- and T-loops are either absent or greatly destabilized. In particular, the resonance assigned to the adjacent G18U55 is absent from the spectrum (peak m in the G19C56 spectrum), and there is a loss of intensity of the resonance assigned to the tertiary pair U8A14 (peak a2). Thus the C19C56 variant has apparently lost several base-pairs, but the structure (see Figure 3) is not disrupted. These data for the C19C56 variant may illustrate a general phenomenon, in which structural changes can propagate from local structural perturbations or single base-pair disruptions, although the extent and magnitude of such a propagation would depend on the position and context of the initial deformation.

These structural data for the tRNA^{Phe} variants provide some insight for interpretation of the aminoacylation data (see Table II). The K_m of the C19G56 variant and the normal G19C56 tRNA are identical, indicating that the structural changes observed around the C19G56 inversion neither interfere with nor facilitate initial binding of the tRNA to the synthetase. In contrast, the 5-fold increase in K_m of the C19C56 variant could be due to the inability of this variant to maintain a stable D- and T-loop interaction. If this instability simply gave rise to an extended structure, then in analogy to the binding of the low-Mg^{++} transcript, the K_m should be unchanged. Somehow, the structure of this variant actively interferes with initial binding.

It might be anticipated that the structural sensitivity to Mg^{++} shown by the normal sequence would also be shown by these variants. In fact, their imino proton spectra also show a Mg^{++}-dependence, where the spectrum of the U20 variant at low Mg^{++} concentrations is again indistinguishable from that of the normal sequence, while the spectra of the C19G56 and C19C56 variants are each different. Because the 15 mM $MgCl_2$ in aminoacylation experiments is expected to mask any structural alterations in these variants, experiments were also done at 2 mM $MgCl_2$. Those experiments (see Table II) showed that the relative substrate activity of the two tertiary variants with respect to the normal sequence is not Mg^{++}-dependent, suggesting that some features of the low-Mg^{++} form are present in all three tRNAs even though their NMR spectra are not identical. For comparison, the Mg^{++}-dependence of the C8-A14 variant is also shown in Table II. Both the K_m and k_{cat} of this variant relative to the normal sequence exhibit dependence on the counterion concentration, suggesting that a specific Mg^{++}-binding site has been disrupted. The Mg^{++}-binding site at C8A14, in the 8-12 turn, appears to be qualitatively different from the sites in the D-loop (26,27). The 8-12 turn is very sharp, with the Mg^{++} ion hydrogen-bonded to the phosphate oxygens of those bases. It may be that this bound magnesium-hydrate confers the particular structure to the 8-12 turn, whereas in the D-loop, other interactions such as base-stacking contribute to structural stability.

Keeping in mind that tRNA molecules are very large from the NMR perspective (26,000 MW) these results show that NMR can be used to address the question of structural effects due to sequence changes. These data can then be used to interpret biochemical data, which in this case describes the synthetase:tRNA interaction. These studies can now be extended to other sequence variants, both to provide a check on the assignments, and to continue the structure:function study of synthetase:tRNA interaction.

Acknowledgments

This work was supported by grants from the National Institutes of Health to O.C. Uhlenbeck (GM 37552) and A.G. Redfield and from the Lucille P. Markey Charitable Trust (K.B.H.). We give many thanks to Al Redfield for his continuing support and the use of his 500 MHz NMR at Brandeis University and to Olke Uhlenbeck for his enthusiasm and perspective.

References and Footnotes

1. Rich, A. and RajBhandary, U.L., *Ann Rev. Biochem. 45*, 819 (1976).
2. Westhof, E., Dumas, P. and Moras, D., *J. Mol. Biol. 184*, 119 (1985).
3. Schulman, L. and Pelka, H., *Science 242*, 765 (1988).
4. Hou, Y.-M. and Schimmel, P., *Nature 333*, 140 (1988).
5. McClain, W.H. and Foss, K., *Science 240*, 793 (1988).
6. McClain, W.H. and Foss, K., *Science 241*, 1804 (1988).
7. Smith, D. and Yarus, M., *J. Mol. Biol. 206*, 503 (1989).
8. Heerschap, A., Haasnoot, C.A.G. and Hilbers, C.W., *Nucleic Acids Res. 11*, 4483 (1983).
9. Roy, S. and Redfield, A.G., *Nucleic Acids Res. 9*, 7073 (1981).
10. Sampson, J.R. and Uhlenbeck, O.C., *Proc. Natl. Acad. Sci. 85*, 1033 (1988).
11. Sampson, J.R., DiRenzo, A.B., Behlen, L.S. and Uhlenbeck, O.C., *Science 243*, 1363 (1989).

12. Hall, K.B., Sampson, J.R., Uhlenbeck, O.C. and Redfield, A.G., *Biochem. 28*, 5794 (1989).
13. Redfield, A.G., *NATO ASI 107*, 1 (1986).
14. Brown, R., Dewan, J., and Klug, A., *Biochem 24*, 4785 (1985).
15. Sampson, J.R., Sullivan, F.X., Behlen, L.S., DiRenzo, A.B. and Uhlenbeck, O.C., *Cold Spring Harbor Symp. on Quant. Biol. 52*, 267, (1987).
16. Behlen, L., Sampson, J.R., DiRenzo, A.B. and Uhlenbeck, O.C., submitted (1989).
17. Wrede, P., Wurst, R., Vournakis, J. and Rich, A., *J. Biol. Chem. 254*, 960 (1979).
18. Peattie, D.A. and Gilbert, W.A., *Proc. Natl. Acad. Sci. 77*, 4679 (1980).
19. Bruce, A.G. and Uhlenbeck, O.C., *Biochem. 21*, 855 (1982).
20. Heerschap, A., Walters, J.A.L.I. and Hilbers, C.W., *Nucleic Acids Res. 14*, 983 (1986).
21. Eisinger, J. and Gross, N., *Biochem. 14*, 4031 (1975).
22. Hyde, E.I. and Reid, B.R., *Biochem. 24*, 4315 (1985).
23. Hyde, E.I., *Eur. J. Biochem. 155*, 57 (1986).
24. Loftfield, R.E., Eigner, E.A. and Pastuszyn, A., *J. Biol. Chem. 256*, 6729 (1981).
25. Krauss, G., Reisner, D. and Maas, G., *Eur. J. Biochem. 86*, 81 (1976).
26. Holbrook, S.R., Sussman, W.R., Warrant, R.W. and Kim, S.H., *Nucleic Acids Res. 4*, 2811 (1977).
27. Quigley, G.J., Teeter, M.M. and Rich. A., *Proc. Natl. Acad. Sci. 75*, 64 (1978).

Structure & Methods, ISBN 0-940030-32-2
Volume 3: DNA & RNA, ISBN 0-940030-31-4
Eds., Ramaswamy H. Sarma & Mukti H. Sarma, © *Adenine Press 1990*

Path Analysis in NMR Spectra: Application to an RNA Octamer

Mark W. Roggenbuck, Timothy J. Hyman and Philip N. Borer
Syracuse University NMR and Data Processing Laboratory
Center for Science and Technology
Department of Chemistry
Syracuse, New York 13244-4100

Abstract

A promising procedure is outlined for automating assignments of the NOESY spectra of nucleic acids and other biopolymers. The three main components are: (i) *preproccessing* by the use of contrast enhancement and the symmetry properties of the spectrum to accurately locate the "centers" of crosspeaks and create a useful adjacency (connectivity) matrix, (ii) *path analysis* using the Reduced Adjacency Matrix (RAM) or Backtracking (BT) procedures described herein to find all paths consistent with the adjacency matrix, and (iii) *postprocessing* to eliminate paths that do not reflect known chemical information, such as the sequence of residues. Results of a test of the procedures on an RNA octanucleotide duplex are presented and discussed.

Introduciton

Many problems in the assignment of biopolymers can be solved by the use of "walks" through regions of the NMR spectra. This process can be aided if one converts the NMR spectrum to a mathematical graph. Then a path analysis on that graph can be used to help in the assignments. The problem breaks into three parts: (1) find the adjacency matrix (see below) for the spectrum, (2) find all paths through the graph represented by that matrix, and (3) eliminate paths that do not reflect known chemical information. The next few paragraphs explore two solutions for part (2). These solutions can be subsumed under the heading of graph theory. In general, one wants paths that connect only once to a vertex (a diagonal peak in the context of a NOESY spectrum). Mathematically, this is described as finding an elementary edge.

The Adjacency Matrix

The relationship between the NOESY spectrum and the adjacency matrix is illustrated by Figure 1. In this example, there are four protons, corresponding to four diagonal peaks or "vertices" (Figure 1a,b). The presence of the three crosspeaks in Figure 1b is consistent with the connectivities 1-4, 4-2 and 2-3. Figure 1c shows the digraph or "adjacency" matrix, **A**, that conveniently encodes the connectivities. **A** can be broken into four quadrants (Figure 1d) with Q and Q′ being symmetric about the

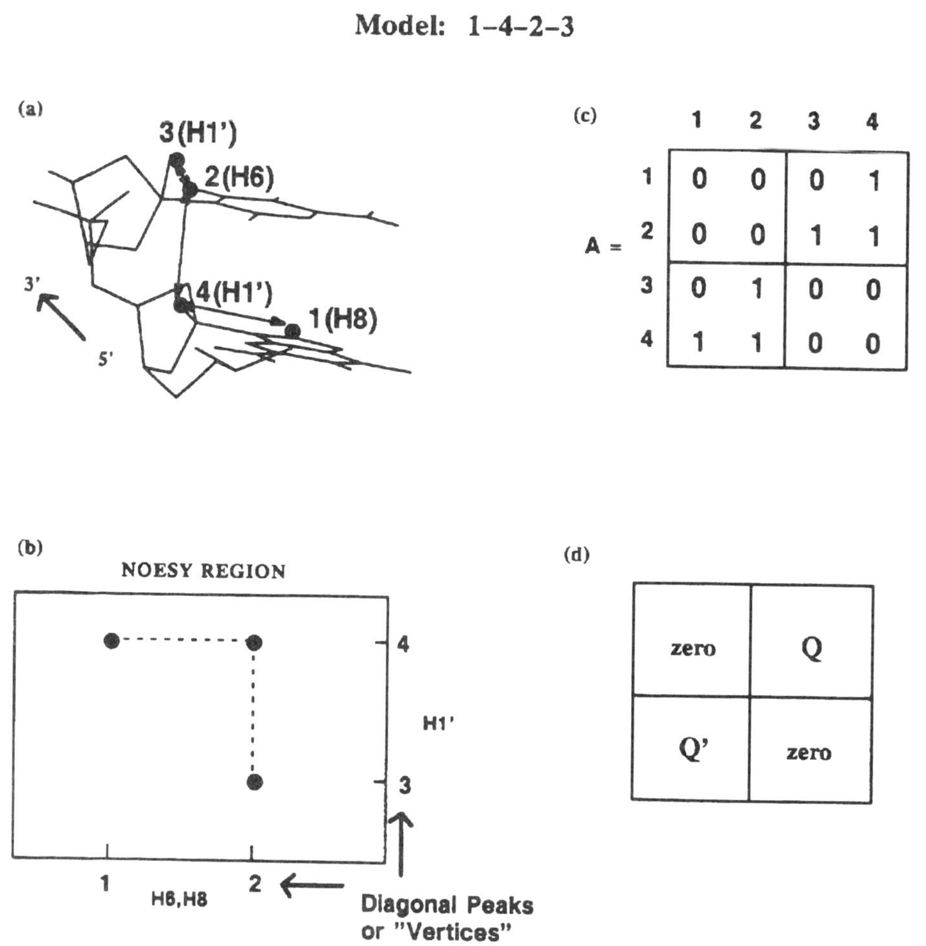

Figure 1: An example of an adjacency matrix. (a) The locations of base and H1′ protons on one strand of a DNA duplex; (b) a NOESY "walk" has *two* steps between *three* crosspeaks that link the *four* diagonal peaks; (c) the adjacency matrix; (d) schematic adjacency matrix.

diagonal for such a spectrum with single-step coherence transfer, and zeroes as indicated when the spectral region does not provide connectivities exemplified by 1-2 or 3-4.

A theorem in linear algebra indicates that the number of n-linked chains between vertices i and j is given by the ij^{th} element of $\mathbf{A}^n$ (1). Since there are n-1 cross-peaks connecting the diagonal peaks in a NOESY spectrum, one should be especially interested in the properties of $\mathbf{A}^{n-1}$.

Figure 2 shows that the 2,3 element of $\mathbf{A}^3$ is 2 (circled), indicating that there are two 3-link chains connecting vertex 2 to vertex 3. A little thought shows that these paths are: 2-4-2-3 and 2-3-2-3, both of which are uninteresting in the context of the NOESY walk since vertex 2 is used more than once. Thus, the elements of $\mathbf{A}^n$ include redundant

MODEL: 1-4-2-3

										PATHS
A^1:	0	0	0	1	R^1:	0	0	0	1	1-4
	0	0	1	1		0	0	1	1	2-3. 2-4
	0	1	0	0		0	1	0	0	3-2
	1	1	0	0		1	1	0	0	4-1. 4-2
A^2:	1	1	0	0	R^2:	0	1	0	0	1-4-2
	1	2	0	0		1	0	0	0	2-4-1
	0	0	1	1		0	0	0	1	3-2-4
	0	0	1	2		0	0	1	0	4-2-3
A^3:	0	0	1	2	R^3:	0	0	1	0	1-4-2-3
	0	0	(2)	3		0	0	0	0	
	1	2	0	0		1	0	0	0	3-2-4-1
	2	3	0	0		0	0	0	0	
A^4:	2	3	0	0	R^4:	0	0	0	0	
	3	5	0	0		0	0	0	0	
	0	0	2	3		0	0	0	0	
	0	0	3	5		0	0	0	0	

Figure 2: Reduced adjacency matrices and associated paths. Powers of **A** are obtained by normal matrix multiplication, powers of **R** are obtained by successive Roggenbuck reductions.

paths, an undesirable property in constructing a matrix representation of the graphical NOESY walk. A second undesirable property is that the elements of $\mathbf{A}^n$ give only the number of n-linked chains, not the paths of these chains. As promised by the above theorem, the 1,3 and 3,1 elements in **A** and $\mathbf{A}^2$ are zero since there are no 1-link or 2-link chains connecting vertices 1 and 3; these elements equal 1 in $\mathbf{A}^3$, however, corresponding to the 3-link chain 1-4-2-3. In a spectrum with 50 diagonal peaks, for example, it would not be worth much to know that a 49-link chain exists, without knowing the path of that chain.

Results and Discussion

Roggenbuck's Reduction

A simple recursion is used to calculate "reduced adjacency matrices," $\mathbf{R}^n$. The so-called "RAM" algorithm: (1) eliminates redundant paths, (2) increases the elements of $\mathbf{R}^n$ by one for each new non-redundant path, and (3) associates proper paths with each non-zero element of $\mathbf{R}^n$. Notice in the simple example above, $\mathbf{R}^3(1,3) = 1$ (path 1-4-2-3) and $\mathbf{R}^3(3,1) = 1$ (path 3-2-4-1). $\mathbf{R}^4 = 0$, since there are no non-redundant 4-link chains connecting any of the four vertices.

Backtracking

A separate, more traditional, procedure offers some advantages over RAM. This "backtracking" (BT) algorithm builds paths from a chosen vertex, one link at a time, consistent with **A**. When this algorithm is applied to all starting vertices, it will find all paths of a certain length as does RAM. BT can be used to find all paths of a certain length from only one starting vertex, an advantage since it is often the case that some chain ends are readily apparent by inspection of the original spectrum. BT can also be used to find all paths that are at least a certain length. This allows for a good deal of flexibility in the analysis when unknown path lengths exist in the graph.

Factors Influencing Efficient Computation of Paths

The particular implementation of BT or RAM depends largely on the user's choice and, to some extent, on the problem under consideration. The main concern has to do with the unmanageable number of paths that can be propagated with (i) too many diagonal peaks or (ii) if the preprocessing step produces an adjacency matrix with a large number of potential connectivities for many of the diagonal peaks. With regard to point (i), a theorem in graph theory is that the number of paths increases exponentially with the number of vertices. Therefore, the path analytic approach may be limited to isolated spectral regions, rather than being applicable to the spectrum as a whole. With regard to point (ii), the number of paths approaches N! as the number of possible connectivities increases. For example, a spectral region, such as the base-H1′, of a "small" nucleic acid or peptide might contain N = 50 diagonal peaks. If each happened to have a connectivity to all 49 of the others, each entry in **A** would equal 1, and there would be 50! (3×10^{64}) non-redundant paths. Thus there is a severe problem when the number of possible paths increases, and the preprocessing should be done with an eye toward producing a sparse (mostly zeroes) adjacency matrix.

We have already encountered some problems with RAM applied to non-sparse matrices (see below). For example, the base-H1′ region of the RNA octanucleotide duplex $(CACAUGUG)_2$ also has cross-peaks connecting to pyrimidine-H5 and adenine-H2 diagonal peaks; these are not part of the usual base-H1′ NOESY walk. In order for RAM to produce the desired 15-link chains from a non-sparse matrix, millions of intermediate length paths can be generated before they are "killed off" to produce long non-redundant chains. In the UNIX operating environment a RAM algorithm incorporating dynamic memory management (to keep track of the chains associated with each element of $\mathbf{R}^n$) will quickly exhaust all of the available computer memory on the SU campus!

The BT algorithm by itself does not require much memory for its path searching; RAM with fixed-size arrays is also a solution to the problem. Preprocessing cannot be overemphasized, however. One key to the success of this approach to automated assignment is the production of a sparse adjacency matrix -- the problem of paths approaching N! quickly causes the situation to get out of hand.

Of course, the RAM and BT algorithms have been written with an eye toward parallelization. Searching through millions of paths lends itself ideally to a parallel architecture computer.

Preprocessing

The example shown in Figure 3a is from the contrast enhanced NOESY spectrum of the octanucleotide duplex, $(CACAUGUG)_2$, (2; Borer, van den Hoogen & Altona, unpublished). The spectrum has sixteen diagonal peaks of interest: the H8,H6 are numbered 1-8 and the H1′ 9-16. Therefore, we are interested in 15-link chains, and the properties of $\mathbf{R}^{15}$. **A** is 16×16 with $a_{ij}=0$ if no crosspeak center exists (within a small tolerance) between base and H1′ protons, and $a_{ij}=1$ if there is a center connecting the vertices. Figure 3b shows the upper-right quadrant, Q, of **A** which corresponds to Figure 3a. Q shows which vertices are connected, e.g., Q(2,13)=1 designates the center connecting the C1,6 and C1,1′ diagonal peaks (circled in Figure 3a).

When $\mathbf{R}^{15}$ is computed from **A** and Q as illustrated in Figure 3b, only one path is found. This path is associated with $\mathbf{R}^{15}(2,11)$ and is congruent with that found when doing the NOESY walk with T-square and triangles. We have also found single paths associated with contrast-enhanced NOESY spectra in the 8-mer duplex $[d(TAGCGCTA)]_2$ and the 10-mer duplex $[d(CGTACGTACG)]_2$.

A modification of the NMR2 program allows easy creation of Q from the peak table in this spectral region. At this stage of its development, our procedure works best after editing the peak table to remove centers involving pyrimidine H5 and adenine H2. The intense H5-H6 cross-peaks are easily identified in the NOESY spectrum (or from a COSY), and the AH2 in AT pairs have large NOEs to the T-N3H imino proton in H_2O, so these can also be clearly distinguished.

It is important to note that the path analytic procedures are completely general as regards the dimensionality of the original spectrum. 3D(or MD)-NMR experiments map equally well to connectivities between diagonal peaks. These path analytic procedures may be of critical importance to the interpretation of MD spectra, where human visualization is no longer useful. It is also worth noting that all of the vital information is combined in Q. **A** conveniently has the appearance of the 2D spectrum, but alternative formulations are possible.

Postprocessing

Figure 3c shows Q that results from the unenhanced NOESY spectrum of $(CACAUGUG)_2$. Note that there are some rows and columns of Q that contain more than two non-zero entries (the new entries are circled). This is the consequence of overlap

(a)

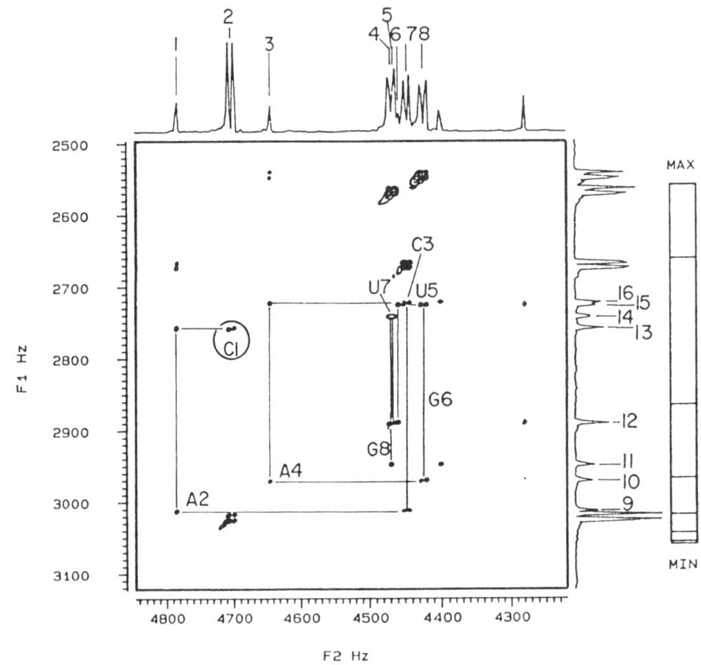

(b)

	9	10	11	12	13	14	15	16
1	1	0	0	0	1	0	0	0
2	0	0	0	0	1	0	0	0
3	0	1	0	0	0	0	0	1
4	0	0	1	0	0	1	0	0
5	0	0	0	1	0	1	0	0
6	0	0	0	1	0	0	1	0
7	1	0	0	0	0	0	0	1
8	0	1	0	0	0	0	1	0

(c)

	9	10	11	12	13	14	15	16
1	1	0	0	0	1	0	0	0
2	0	0	0	0	1	0	0	0
3	0	1	0	0	0	0	0	1
4	0	0	1	(1)	0	1	(1)	0
5	0	0	(1)	1	0	1	(1)	0
6	0	0	0	1	0	(1)	1	(1)
7	1	0	0	0	0	0	(1)	1
8	0	1	0	0	0	0	1	0

Figure 3: (a) The base-H1′ region of the $(CACAUGUG)_2$ NOESY spectrum with diagonal peaks numbered 1-16; (b) **Q** matrix from contrast enhanced spectrum (not shown); (c) **Q** matrix showing additional false connectivities (circled) due to resonance overlap.

POSSIBLE (CACAUGUG)$_2$ NOESY WALKS by PATH ANALYSIS
Base to 1' Region

2	13	1	9	7	16	3	10	8	15	6	14	5	11	4	**12**
2	13	1	9	7	15	8	10	3	16	6	14	5	11	4	**12**
2	13	1	9	7	16	3	10	8	15	6	14	4	11	5	**12**
2	13	1	9	7	15	8	10	3	16	6	14	4	11	5	**12**
2	13	1	9	7	16	3	10	8	15	5	11	4	14	6	**12**
2	13	1	9	7	16	3	10	8	15	4	11	5	14	6	**12**
2	13	1	9	7	16	3	10	8	15	6	12	5	11	4	**14**
2	13	1	9	7	15	8	10	3	16	6	12	5	11	4	**14**
2	13	1	9	7	16	3	10	8	15	6	12	4	11	4	**14**
2	13	1	9	7	15	8	10	3	16	6	12	4	11	5	**14**
2	13	1	9	7	16	3	10	8	15	5	11	4	12	6	**14**
2	13	1	9	7	16	3	10	8	15	4	11	5	12	6	**14**

WRONG endpoints

2	13	1	9	7	16	3	10	8	15	6	14	5	12	4	11
2	13	1	9	7	15	8	10	3	16	6	14	5	12	4	11
2	13	1	9	7	16	3	10	8	15	5	14	6	12	4	11
2	**13**	**1**	**9**	**7**	**16**	**3**	**10**	**8**	**15**	**6**	**12**	**5**	**14**	**4**	**11**
2	13	1	9	7	15	8	10	3	16	6	12	5	14	4	11
2	13	1	9	7	16	3	10	8	15	5	12	6	14	4	11
2	13	1	9	7	16	3	10	8	15	6	14	4	12	5	11
2	13	1	9	7	15	8	10	3	16	6	14	4	12	5	11
2	13	1	9	7	16	3	10	8	15	4	14	6	12	5	11
2	13	1	9	7	16	3	10	8	15	6	12	4	14	5	11
2	13	1	9	7	15	8	10	3	16	6	12	4	14	5	11
2	13	1	9	7	16	3	10	8	15	4	12	6	14	5	11

Consistent with Sequence

ONLY ONE with MLM Processed data

2	13	1	9	7	16	3	10	8	15	6	12	5	14	4	11

Figure 4: Possible NOESY walks connecting the numbered digaonal peaks. Underlined peaks (bottom group) are known to originate from pyrimidine H6.

in the spectrum. In this case, 24 unique paths are distinguished by both the RAM and BT algorithms. These paths are shown in Figure 4. The addition of relatively few non-zero entries to Q (Figure 3b to c) dramatically increases the number of paths as noted in the previous section.

Simple inspection of the spectrum shows that 12 of the paths can be eliminated since they do not include the proper endpoints corresponding to C1,6-C1,1′ and G8,8-G8,1′. The spectrum also shows that peaks 2,5,7,8 correspond to pyrimidine H6′s, and the sequence has alternating purines and pyrimidines. This sequence constraint eliminates all but two of the remaining paths.

The most important feature is that the procedure can find *all paths* consistent with the spectrum. A spectroscopist armed only with T-square, triangles, and intuition is not likely to explore all of the possibilities. This situation is even more true as the complexity of the spectrum and the overlap problems become more severe. Using RAM or BT one can find all paths and systematically eliminate those that are inconsistent with the sequence and other information, such as crosspeaks to the AH2.

We have also shown that the error-free **A** matrices for the different spectral regions (e.g., base-H3′, base-H2′, H1′-H2′), etc., are related by simple linear (unitary) transformations (Wang and Borer, unpublished). We are developing this in an analytical procedure to further constrain the solutions to the NOESY assignments. This is the matrix equivalent of the cross-correlation of regions that a spectroscopist follows, since much of the information in a NOESY spectrum is redundant; this allows error-correction in many cases where overlap occurs in one region but not another.

Finally, if there are breaks in the NOESY walk, this should be manifest in the presence of only zeroes in the higher powers of **R**. For instance if there were a break due to a structural deformation between residues 15-16 in a 25-mer duplex, $\mathbf{R}^{24}$ would contain only zeroes since there would be no non-redundant 24-link chains. However, upon examining successively lower powers of **R**, one would see the reappearance of unique paths in $\mathbf{R}^{14}$. One would then look also at $\mathbf{R}^{9}$ for the other chain fragment.

Summary and Look to the Future

The preprocessing, path analysis and postprocessing modules described here offer a powerful set of procedures for automating the assignments of nucleic acids and proteins. The prospects for handling complex 2D, 3D and MD spectra are especially attractive in that these assignments are tedious at best, and in some cases, impossible for humans. There is also an exciting possibility for using these methods together with the combined ″NOTO″, ″TORO″, etc. procedures (3-11). Finally, the preprocessing, path analytic and postprocessing algorithms, especially the latter, could operate very effectively in a logic programming system environment.

Acknowledgments

This research was supported in part by NIH grants (GM32691, GM35069 an RR01317). M.W. Roggenbuck acknowledges an NSF Graduate Fellowship.

References and Footnotes

1. G. Williams, *Computational Linear Algebra with Models*, 2nd Ed., Allyn & Bacon, Boston, pp. 76-79 (1978).
2. Y. Th. van den Hoogen, C. Erkelens, C., de Vroom, E., van der Marel, G.H., van Boom, J.H. and C. Altona, *Eur. J. Biochem. 173*, 295 (1988).
3. J. Friedrich, S. Davies and R. Freeman, *J. Magn. Reson. 80*, 168 (1988).
4. O.W. Sorensen, C. Griesinger and R.R. Ernst, *Chem. Phys. Lett. 135*, 313 (1987).
5. G. Wagner, *J. Magn. Reson. 57*, 497 (1984).
6. H. Kessler, S. Steuernagel, D. Gillessen and T. Kamiyama, *Helv. Chimica Acta 70*, 726 (1987).
7. H. Kessler, G. Gemmecker and S. Steuernagel, *Angew. Chem., (Int. Ed. English) 27*, 564 (1988).
8. H. Kessler, G. Gemmecker, B. Haase and S. Steuernagel, *Magn. Reson. Chem. 26*, 919 (1988).
9. H. Kessler, G. Gemmecker and B. Haase, *J. Magn. Reson. 77*, 401 (1988).
10. J. Friedrich, S. Davies and R. Freeman, *J. Magn. Reson. 75*, 390 (1987).
11. R. Freeman, J. Friedrich and S. Davies, *Magn. Reson. Chem. 26*, 903 (1988).

Note added in proof: Public domain versions of the RAM and BT algorithms will be made available at a later date. They are also planned for incorporation into NMR2, a commercial software package, available from New Methods Research, Inc., 719 E. Genesee St., Syracuse, N.Y. 13210.

Structure & Methods, ISBN 0 940030 32 2
Volume 3: DNA & RNA, ISBN 0-940030-31-4
Eds., Ramaswamy H. Sarma & Mukti H. Sarma, © Adenine Press 1990

Why Does an Intron Form a Lariat Before the Ligation of 5′- and 3′-Exons in Group II & Nuclear mRNA Splicing? Conformations of Branched Ribonucleotides Modelling the Lariat Intron†

G. Remaud[1], J.-M. Vial[1], N. Balgobin[1], L.H. Koole[2], A. Sandström[1], A.F. Drake[3], X.-X. Zhou[1], C. Glemarec[1] and J. Chattopadhyaya[1]*

[1]Department of Bioorganic Chemistry, Biomedical Centre
University of Uppsala, Box 581
S - 751 23 Uppsala, Sweden

[2]Department of Organic Chemistry
Eindhoven University of Technology, P. O. Box 513
5600 MB Eindhoven, The Netherlands

[3]Department of Chemistry
Birckbeck College, University of London
20 Gordon Street
London WC1, England

Abstract

^{1}H-, ^{31}P-NMR and Circular dichroism studies on the simple naturally-occurring branched trimers **8** and **9** and their comparison with eleven analogous branched trimers **1 - 7** and **10 -13** have shown that all these branched trimers adopt a conformational state closer to the corresponding 2′ → 5′ dimers than the corresponding 3′ → 5′ dimers. The stacking interaction in these trimers however is entirely controlled depending upon the specific location of a particular nucleobase. Conformational studies of branched tetraribonucleotides **14 - 17**, on the other hand, have shown that their overall structures are reminiscent of a distorted linear 3′ → 5′ linked single stranded A-RNA helix fragment. Conformational studies with three branched tetraribonucleotide analogues **18**, **19** and **20**, where the branch-point was either cytidine, uridine, or guanosine have shown that **18** and **19** are in loose conformational states at room temperature. The possibility for C in **18** and especially U in **19** at the branch-point as to be bulged out have been proposed to explain the temperature-dependent ^{1}H chemical shifts. Interestingly, **20** adopts a distorted A-type RNA helix with the distortion being at the 3′ terminal U residue instead of the bulge of the 5′ terminal A residue as in the naturally-occurring

†Dedicated to Professor Lennart Philipson on the ocassion of his 60th birthday.

*Author to whom correspondence should be addressed.

branched tetraribonucleotide **17**. These studies have shown indications why do all lariat RNA introns have adenosine as the branch-point nucleotide! These conformational studies have furthermore established that it is the nature of the 5′-nucleotide residue (5′-pyrimidine in **14** and **15** versus 5′-purine in **16** and **17**) to the branch-point adenosine which dictates the overall conformation due to the intramolecular stackings in the branched RNA. A comparative conformational analysis of tri-, tetra-, penta- and hepta branched ribonucleotides have been subsequently performed by 600 MHz ^{1}H-NMR and 223 MHz ^{31}P-NMR spectroscopy which have revealed that (i) generation of a lariat structure, typical for Group II and nuclear mRNA splicing, can occur with preservation of the A-geometry of the RNA strand, (ii) mimicry of the lariat branch site requires the presence of at least one nucleotide linked to the 5′-site of the branch-point as in tetramer **14** - **17** or heptamer **22**, since the absence of the 5′-nucleotide, in **8**, **9** and **21**, results in an unnatural molecular conformation which is largely dominated by the 2′ → 5′ stacking. These observations suggest that the formation of the lariat-intron does not seriously alter the secondary structure of the single-stranded intron and, therefore, may serve as a recognition signal for the final step of the ligation of 3′- and 5′-exons and the excision of the lariat intron.

Introduction

Protein synthesis in eukaryotic cells is preceded by transcription of DNA into pre-mRNA, and subsequent excission of non-coding nucleotide sequences (introns) (1-5). The scission of the introns from the pre-mRNA and ligation of the 3′- and 5′-coding regions (exons) to form a functional RNA for protein biosynthesis is generally called splicing (3,5) (Figure 1). First, the pre-mRNA is cleaved at the 5′-splice site and a branched (lariat) intermediate is formed in Group II and nuclear mRNA splicing. Second, the cleavage at the 3′-splice site and ligation of the two exons leads to the release of the lariat intron (1-11). These lariat structures have adenosine as the "branch-point" residue, linked *via* a 2′ → 5′ phosphodiester bond to a guanosine residue, and a 3′ → 5′ phosphodiester bond to a pyrimidine residue (1-11). A simple structure of the lariat junction is represented in the structure of the trimeric branched RNAs such as **8** and **9**. Studies on the specificity of the nucleobase requirement at the branch-accepting point have shown that the replacement of the central branch-accepting adenosine residue by any other nucleotide in mutants results in a considerable decrease in efficiency in the splicing as compared to the wild type (12-14). Mutation experiments have shown that all four nucleotides can serve as branch-acceptors, but it is adenosine which fulfils the structural criteria for the second step of splicing optimally, while cytidine residue is prefered to guanosine and uridine residues. Mutation of the normal branch-accepting adenosine nucleotide to guanosine or uridine nucleotide can lead to lariat formation at another adenosine nucleotide residue one nucleotide upstream of the normal branch-site (12,13). Only branches to adenosine or cytidine participate efficiently in the second step of splicing in mutation experiments *in vitro* but the natural splicing in eukaryotes *in vivo* exclusively prefers adenosine as the branch-point for error-free processing of pre-mRNA.

These observations clearly address to a few significant questions regarding the mechanism of splicing: (i) Is there any structural and conformational basis for the evolutionary choice of adenosine as the branch-accepting nucleotide in the splicing reaction? (ii) How and why the conformation of the lariat would be changed when

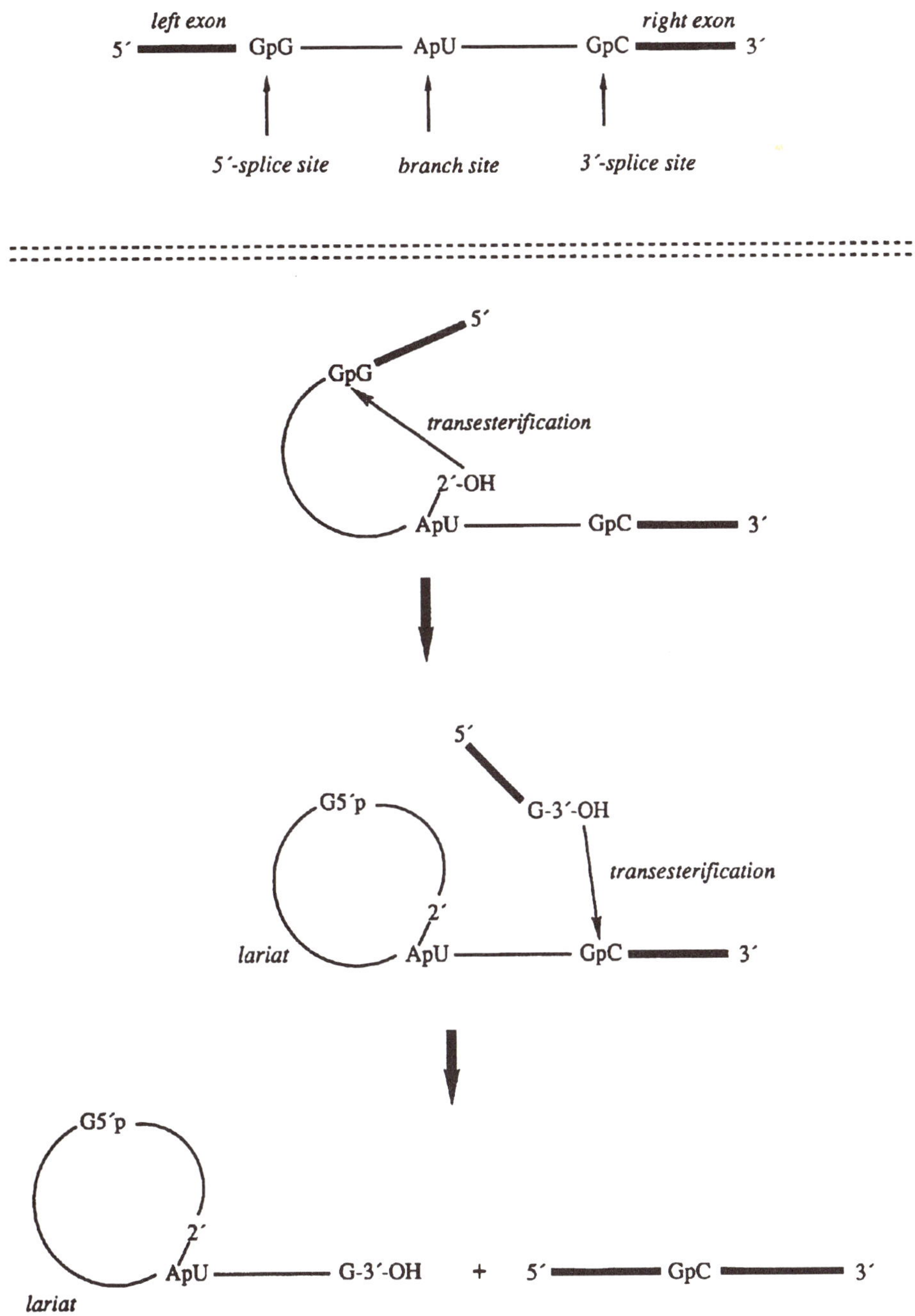

Figure 1: Schematic representation of Group II splicing. Cleavage at the 5′-splice site and formation of lariat occur in the first reaction. The second step comprises cleavage at the 3′-splice site and release of the intron in the lariat form. These transesterification reactions require only Mg^{2+}, no ATP is needed.

the "branch-point" adenosine is replaced with cytidine, guanosine or uridine nucleotide? (iii) Does the chemospecific choice of adenosine nucleotide at the branch-point by Nature give the splicing reaction *in vivo* a thermodynamic or a kinetic advantage that it can not have by having even a cytidine nucleotide (12-14)? We have attempted to answer some of these questions by combining tools of synthetic organic chemistry for regioselective synthesis of relevant model branched RNAs, and then analyzing their conformations by NMR and CD spectroscopy. First, we have tried to understand what are the conformations of simple branched RNA such as **8** and **9**, and how their conformations are different from the 2′ → 5′ or 3′ → 5′ phosphodiester linked dinucleoside monophosphates! This has led us to explore the structural significance of the conserved nucleobases in the lariat junction through the introduction of the selective changes of nucleobases at the branch-point and at the 2′ → 5′, 3′ → 5′ and 5′ → 3′ termini of the "branch-point", and then monitoring the resulting changes by study of their conformations. Next, we have tried to address how the subsequent additions of different nucleobases at three different ends of the natural branched trimer such as **8** and **9** alter and dictate the stabilization of the conformation of the branch-point! Clearly, such conformational studies of different analogues and their comparison with that of the naturally-occurring branched RNA may ultimately show the unique chemical role of branch-accepting adenosine nucleotide in the high-fidelity regulatory processing of m-RNA precursors in eukaryotes and thus explore the chemical basis of natural selection.

Herein, only a brief discussion of the spectroscopic methods used in the present study is included, followed by discussions of our main results on the conformational studies of branched RNAs **1** - **22**. For any detailed information on NMR and CD spectral data on branched RNAs **1** - **22** (21-28), and the chemistry developed in our laboratory for their synthesis (15-20), readers are requested to refer to our original articles cited in the reference section.

Methods

(1) Effect of Temperature on ^1H Chemical Shifts

The chemical shifts in an oligonucleotide molecule are determined (29,30) mainly by (i) the ring-current effect of the nucleobase (the diamagnetic effect under and above the plane of the nucleobase and the paramagnetic effect in its plane), (ii) the diamagnetic anisotropy of electron-rich groups such as C=0 or P=0 bonds, and (iii) other electric effects. In a stacked form, the aromatic and anomeric protons experience an upfield shift due to the ring-current effect of the neighbouring nucleobases. Therefore, the study of the chemical shifts of the aromatic and anomeric protons as a function of the temperature allows the detection of stacking between the two nucleobases under consideration. Theoretical calculations have shown that among the aromatic protons, H2A, H5U and H5C are good probes for detection of stacking since their chemical shifts are solely determined by the ring-current of the neighbouring nucleobases. In a stacked form at a low temperature they experience an upfield shift while in a destacked geometry at a higher temperature they are shifted to a lower

$$\begin{matrix} & \alpha & & \beta & & \gamma & & \delta & & \varepsilon & & \zeta & \\ P & — & O5' & — & C5' & — & C4' & — & C3'\ (2') & — & O3'\ (2') & — & P \end{matrix}$$

Scheme I

field. On the other hand, H8A, H8G, H6U, and H6C have a very strong dependence on the conformation of the glycosidic bond. The H5 of pyrimidine and H2 of adenine are slightly affected by a change in the glycosidic bond angle especially in the range between 200° to 300° (*anti* conformation). On the other hand, H6 and H8 are less shielded when the nucleobase is in *anti* than in *syn* conformation. Only H6 and H8 are sensitive to the value of the angle γ (*gauche-gauche* conformation around C4'-C5' bond). Similarly in an *anti* orientation of the nucleobase, the H6 of pyrimidine and H8 of purine 5'-monophosphates have a large chemical shift dependency with β (angle about C5'-O5' bond) in the range of 60° - 90° corresponding to β^+ (see Scheme I, for the notation of the angles, according to ref. 47). Among the sugar protons H1' is very sensitive to both the glycosidic bond angle and the ring-current effect of the neighbouring bases. A shift of stacking ⇌ destacking equilibria takes place over a large range of temperature, and therefore, a study of chemical shifts of different protons, along with nOe data gives a good approximation of the stereochemical orientation of different nucleobases and their respective sugar moieties within the molecule.

(2) Population of Pseudorotamers of Sugar Residues

The ribose ring conformation can be described as an equilibrium mixture of two puckered modes S (C3'*exo*-C2'*endo*) and N (C3'*endo*-C2'*exo*), undergoing rapid interconversion (31). The conformation of the ribose ring can be determined by various least-square computer programmes developed by Altona and coworkers (32). Thus the N ⇌ S equilibrium constant and the pseudorotation parameters (puckering amplitude and the phase angle) can be estimated from the observed coupling constants. Estimation of the population of pseudorotamers can be conveniently carried out for 2'-deoxyribofuranose sugar, but for ribofuranose sugar different data sets are needed which are usually obtained at different temperatures. It is, however, assumed that only the molar ratio of pseudorotamers (N versus S) changes with the variation of temperature. According to the authors (32c), when the equilibrium constant (N ⇌ S) is nearly invariant over a range of temperatures, one or more parameters must then be constrained, which could make the results unreliable indeed. Our previous studies (21,22,27) have shown that in a branched trimer the N ⇌ S equilibrium is not displaced enough with the temperature and there are severe overlappings of resonances; therefore, the above programmes cannot be used efficiently even for spectra acquired at 500 MHz (23).

Since a detailed pseudorotational analysis of the branched RNAs is not plausible due to overlappings of sugar-proton resonances and an invariant N ⇌ S equilibrium, an estimation of the percentage N conformer can be obtained from $J_{1',2'}$ coupling constants of each sugar residues of **1** to **17** using the procedure described by Altona and coworkers (32). An approximate population of N pseudorotamers at a temperature under consideration has been calculated using the following equation:

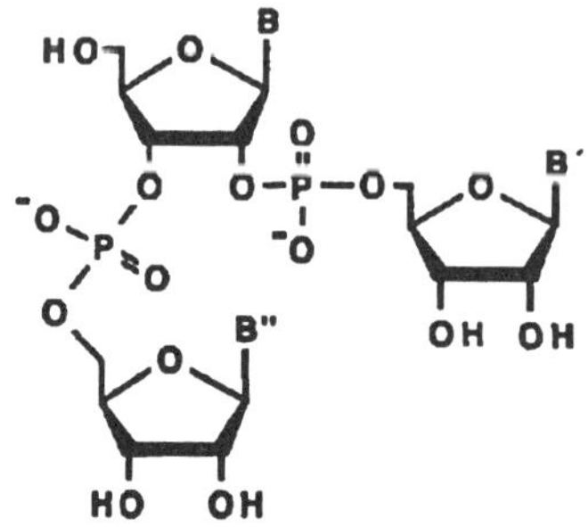

1 : B = U, B′ = G, B″ = C
2 : B = U, B′ = G, B″ = U
3 : B = C, B′ = G, B″ = C
4 : B = C, B′ = G, B″ = U
5 : B = G, B′ = G, B″ = C
6 : B = G, B′ = G, B″ = U
7 : B = A, B′ = C, B″ = U
8 : B = A, B′ = G, B″ = C
9 : B = A, B′ = G, B″ = U
10 : B = A, B′ = C, B″ = G
11 : B = A, B′ = U, B″ = G
12 : B = A, B′ = G, B″ = G
13 : B = B′ = B″ = A

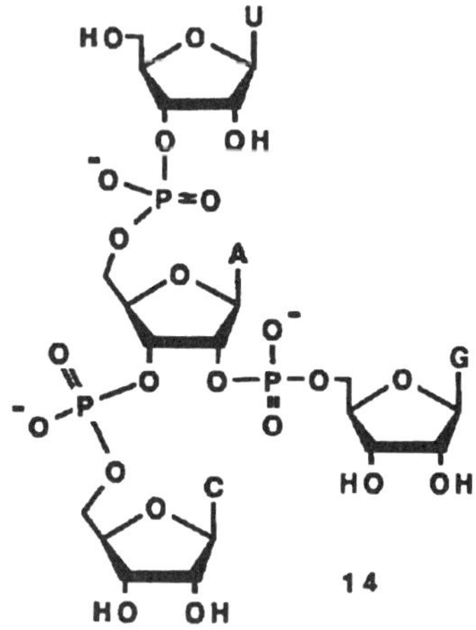

14

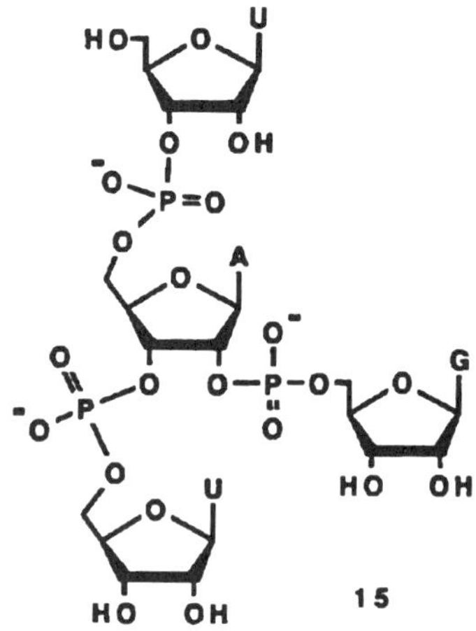

15

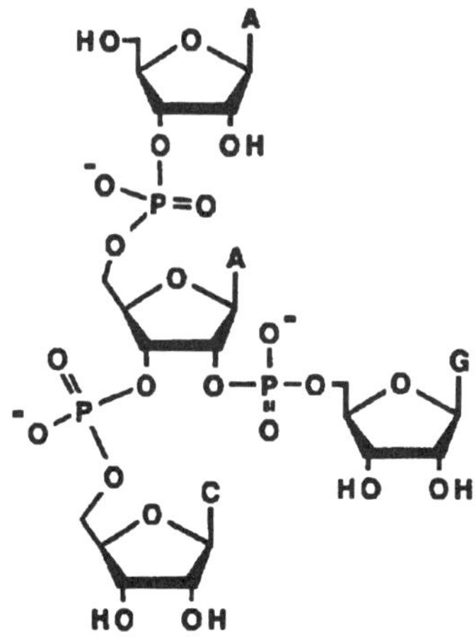

16

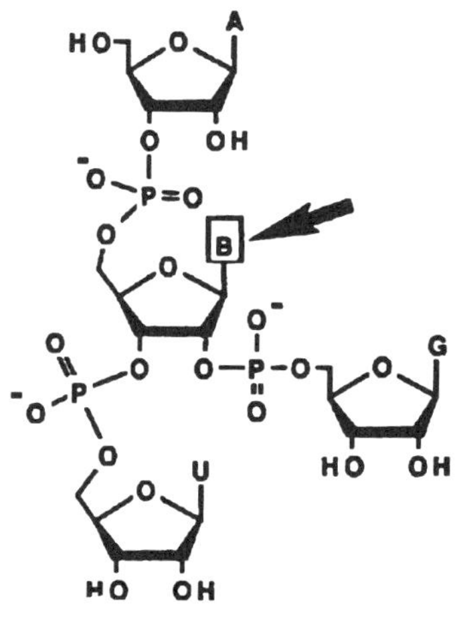

17 : B = A
18 : B = C
19 : B = U
20 : B = G

$$J^{Exp}_{1',2'} = x_N J^N_{1',2'} + (1-x_N) J^S_{1',2'}$$

Where x_N is the molar fraction of the N-type conformers, $J^N_{1',2'}$, $J^S_{1',2'}$ and $J^{Exp}_{1',2'}$ represent the coupling constants between H1′ and H2′ protons for a pure N-type, S-type and for a given compound, respectively. Conventional ranges for the pseudorotational analysis (32c) have been used for the ribose ring, i.e., $P_s = 162°$, $\phi_s = 38°$, $P_N = 9°$, $\phi_N = 38°$, $J^N_{1',2'} = 1$ Hz, $J^S_{1',2'} = 7.8$ Hz (Note that these values representing the pure N- or S-type conformer have an accuracy of ~5% and therefore the apparent $J_{1',2'}$ abstracted directly from the spectra are acceptable). For the percentages of N or S conformers of each sugar in the constitutent sugar moieties of branched RNA molecules **1 - 22**, readers should refer to our original publications. Only conclusions from such pseudorotational analysis would be briefly discussed here.

(3) nOe Studies

2D nOe have been used in the present work to provide two types of data: (i) nOe connectivities have revealed the proximities between the nucleobase and its own sugar unit and therefore the prefered conformation around the glycosidic bond (*syn* ⇌ *anti*) could be assessed, and (ii) the spatial proximities between the aglycones of the nucleotide residues could be determined to confirm stackings. In order to delineate the strength of the nOes and to rule out spin diffusion, different mixing times (700, 500, 350, 200 and 150 ms) have been used (24).

(4) Effect of Temperature on ^{31}P-Chemical Shifts

More recently, we have been able to show (25) that the ^{31}P chemical shift $\delta(^{31}P)$ of the 2′ → 5′ linked phosphodiester in **8** and **9** are more sensitive to temperature changes than the $\delta(^{31}P)$ of the 3′ → 5′ phosphodiester. These observations have also been attributed to a molecular conformation with predominant adenine (2′ → 5′) guanine stacking and a free uracil moiety. These observations have been subsequently confirmed with compound **9** by a detailed pseudorotational analysis, using all vicinal proton-proton, and the proton-phosphorous coupling constants determined at 500 MHz at various sample temperatures (23).

Results

1. Conformation of Naturally Occurring Branched Trimers **8** *and* **9**

The conformational properties of **8** and **9** have been recently investigated by us (21-23,25,27) using variable temperature ^{1}H-, and ^{31}P-NMR at 270 MHz and 109 MHz, respectively and also by the assessment of temperature-dependent shift of N ⇌ S pseudorotamer populations. These studies clearly revealed that adenine (2′ → 5′) guanine stack is the most important structural feature. This has been also confirmed later on by Damha and Ogilvie (33) and Lee *et al.* (34). This 2′ → 5′ stacked state in the branched trimers **8** and **9** makes the branch-point adenosine-sugar adopt a ~65% S conformation at 20°C compared to the adenosine part in A(2′ → 5′)G [~52% S at 20°C]. The sugar part of guanosine residue shows an equal population of

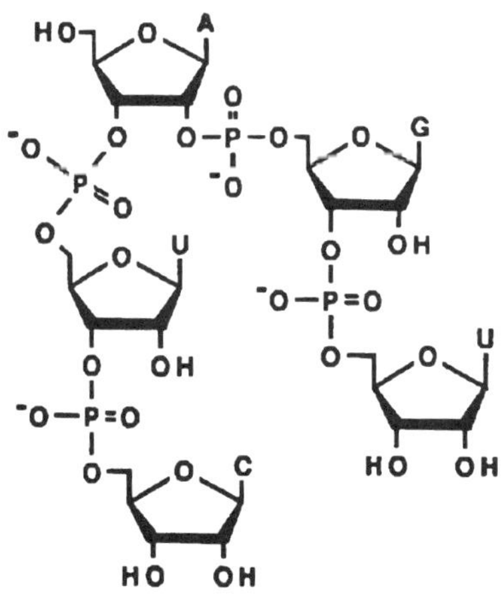

21

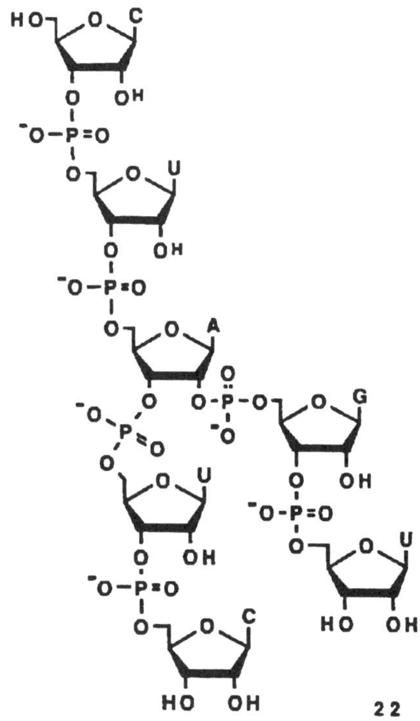

22

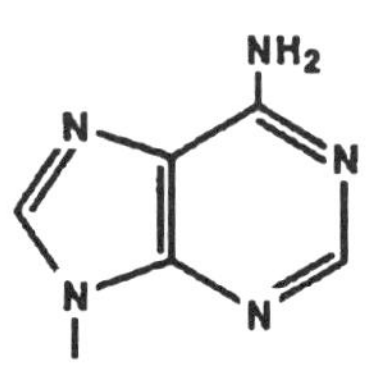

A

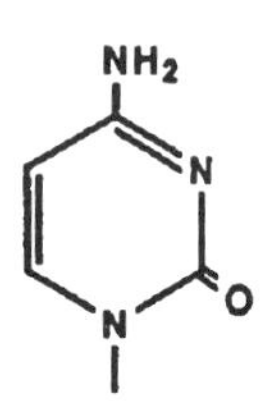

C

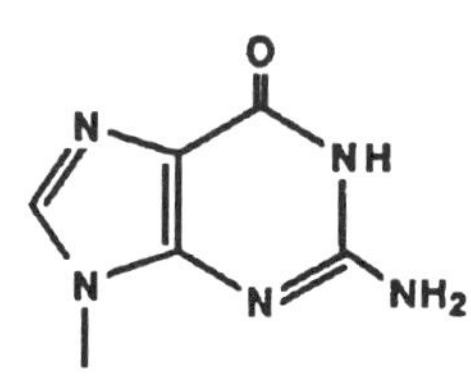

G

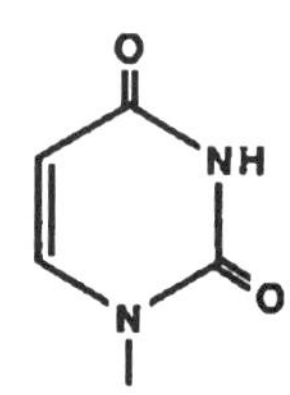

U

S and N conformers in **8** and **9** as in A(2′ → 5′)G. The 3′ → 5′ linked cytosine residue in **8** or uracil residue in **9** are unstacked and located in a coplanar manner with regard to the adenine ring.

1D nOe experiments have shown that the pyrimidine residues in **8** and **9** are in *anti* base-sugar orientation [nOe between H6U/H6C and its H-2′]. We have attributed the deshielding of H8A* [the branch-point nucleobase is herein abbreviated as A*, C*, U*, or G*] by ~0.06 ppm in **8** and **9**, in comparison with that of A(2′ → 5′)G, to the ring-current effect of the coplanar pyrimidine ring. We suggested that a requirement of this model is that the A* should be in *syn* orientation in order to facilitate the coplanarity of A* with the 3′ → 5′ linked pyrimidine. The 1D nOe correlations between adenine and guanine residues are temperature-dependent but they show consistent nOe between their own H8 and H-1′ suggesting that their sugar-base are in *syn* orientation. In the 500 MHz study, along with CD spectroscopy (23), we have also compared the conformation of **9** and **11** in which the positions of 2′ → 5′ and 3′ → 5′ linked nucleobase residues have been reversed. Comparison of the data on trimers **9** and **11** clearly showed that the adenine (2′ → 5′) guanine stacking in **9** results in a more flexible molecular conformation than does the adenine (2′ → 5′) uracil stacking in **11**. This conclusion was in agreement with our recent variable temperature ^{31}P-NMR data on **9** and **11**. The $\Delta\delta$ for the 2′ → 5′ phosphate group of 0.59 ppm for **9**, and the $\Delta\delta$ of 0.65 ppm for **11** also lent support to the fact that the 2′ → 5′ stacking in **11** is more rigid than in **9**. This has also been corroborated by the CD spectroscopy. Thus, addition of ethylene glycol to the aqueous solution of **9** results in clear changes in the CD spectrum as compared to the CD spectrum of **11** which virtually remained unchanged. It should also be noted that the CD spectrum of a given branched trinucleotide matches very well with the CD patterns of its corresponding 2′ → 5′ dinucleoside phosphate.

2. Conformation of Analogous Branched Trimers **1** *-* **7**, **12** *and* **13** *and Their Comparison with the Natural Branched Trimers* **8** *and* **9** *and Constituent Dimers*

Studies (21,22,27) on branched trimers with A at the branch-point have shown that 270 MHz ^{1}H-NMR analysis can indeed reveal their overall conformations. Studies at higher field 400-500 MHz have confirmed (33,34) our initial results by establishing that the 2′ → 5′ stacking is prefered in naturally-occuring branched trimers and also in unnatural analogues. It has been concluded that the conformation of a given branched trimer follows mainly the structure of the constituent (2′ → 5′) bonded dimer. Thus a relative order of conformational constraint (25,27) along the 2′ → 5′ phosphodiester backbone has emerged from studies with different analogous branched trimeric molecules (27). They are as follows:

$$A^{2'p5'U}_{3'p5'G} \geqslant A^{2'p5'C}_{3'p5'G} > A^{2'p5'G}_{3'p5'G} > A^{2'p5'G}_{3'p5'C} > A^{2'p5'G}_{3'p5'U} > A^{2'p5'A}_{3'p5'A} >$$

$$G^{2'p5'G}_{3'p5'U} \geqslant G^{2'p5'G}_{3'p5'C} > U^{2'p5'G}_{3'p5'U} \geqslant C^{2'p5'G}_{3'p5'U} > U^{2'p5'G}_{3'p5'C} \geqslant C^{2'p5'G}_{3'p5'C}.$$

It seems that the preference in stacking is shown along the 3′ → 5′ phosphate linkage when a purine is 3′ → 5′ linked from the branch-point. It thus turned out that A* has a higher tendency to stack with the 3′ → 5′ linked A than with the corresponding U than with C, and than with G. It should be noted that the 2′ → 5′ constraint follows the opposite order. If there is a competition between 3′ → 5′ and 2′ → 5′ stacking, it is the A2′ → 5′Py stacking which is prefered to a normal A3′ → 5′G interaction. It is clear from the data compiled in our laboratory (27) and elsewhere (33,37) that the degree of association among the 2′ → 5′ linked dimers comes in the following order A2′p5′G > G2′p5′G > C2′p5′G > U2′p5′G due to the fact that (i) the deshielding of H1′G and H8G, upon temperature changes, follows the order: U2′p5′G > C2′p5′G > G2′p5′G, (ii) if one assumes that the glycosidic conformation would be identical in U and C, it is clear that H6C in C2′p5′G experiences a larger shielding effect than

H6U in U2′p5′G, (iii) qualitatively, it is true that more stacked forms are associated with more N conformers, at least in 3′ → 5′ linked nucleotides (37), in X2′ → 5′ G (X = A, G, C, U) this observation also seems valid. This classification is in agreement with the commonly accepted model (35) of stacking, i.e., Pu-Py > Py-Pu and C > U. In a stacked geometry the 2′ → 5′ phosphate backbone adopts a specific conformation which is different from a 3′ → 5′ phosphate, especially with regards to the torsion angle of the C2′ - O2′ and C5′ - O5′ bonds (36,37). This can, in turn, specifically "orientates" one H5′ with respect to its geminal H5″. Therefore the influence of the nucleobase on H5′ could be different from that on H5″. This could also be true for a 3′ → 5′ phosphate linked nucleotide but the amplitude of this effect is smaller due to the proximity of the nucleobase to the 2′-position. Qualitatively, it is interesting to note that Δ (δ H5′ - δH5″) is close to zero in C2′p5′C where it was estimated that 35% of stacked species exists at 20°C, while in A2′p5′A, Δ = 0.16 ppm at 83°C and about 50% of stacked states was found. A perusal of values of Δ shows the following magnitude in the dimers [G2′p5′G > C2′p5′G ⩾ U2′p5′G], in the trimers [**7** > **6** > **5** ≫ **4** ⩾ **3** > **2** > **1**] (27).

Interestingly the above order corresponds to the degree of association found in the trimer from the ^{1}H-NMR data (27) which are as follows: (i) H8G in **1** - **4** is deshielded when the temperature decreases, while H8G at the 2′ position in **8**, **9** and **12** is shielded, (ii) H5 of the 3′ → 5′ phosphate bonded pyrimidine has smaller shielding shift in **1** - **4** than the corresponding Py3′ → 5′Py (from high to low temperature) denoting a poor stacking between the branch-point and the 3′ residue in **1** - **4**, (iii) H5 of the branch-point pyrimidine experiences an upfield shift (80° to 7°C) in **4** - **7** whose magnitude is much smaller than in Py2′p- residue in dimers U2′p5′G and C2′p5′G but slightly higher than in Py3′p- in dimers Py3′ → 5′Py, denoting that trimers **1** - **4** do not have any significant base-base interaction along the 2′ → 5′ phosphate linkage, (iv) H8G of the 2′ residue in **5** and **6** is shielded (80° to 7°C), the magnitude being smaller than in **8**, **9** and **12** denoting a weaker stacking in **5** and **6**, (v) H8G* is invariant in **5** but is deshielded by 0.011 ppm in **6** showing a more pronounced interaction between the guanosine branch-point G* and C in **8** than between G* and U in **9**, (vi) H2A* in **7** has a smaller shielding shift upon lowering the temperature than in **10** or **11** (0.12 ppm and ca. 0.14 ppm, respectively). Moreover H5C in **7** experiences a smaller shielding effect than in $A_{3'p5'G}^{2'p5'C}$ (27) (0.041 ppm and 0.074 ppm, respectively), H6U in **7** is moved to higher field (80° to 7°C) by 0.084 ppm while the H6 in $A_{3'p5'U}^{2'p5'G}$ (17) moved by only 0.052 ppm. These data clearly establish that the stacking between A*2′ → 5′C is weaker in **7** than in **10** and similarly A*3′ → 5′U in **10** seems relatively more free than in $A_{3'p5'U}^{2'p5'G}$ **12**. (vii) In all branched trimers **1** - **13**, the branch-point adopts predominantly an S conformation, although A* in **7** is nearly blocked in 95% S conformation which is larger than found in **10** or **11**.

In compounds **1** - **4**, the lack of change in the conformation upon variation of temperature is quite remarkable, compared to that of **7**. This can be attributed to an absence of a noticeable stacking either with the 3′ → 5′ linked or with the 2′ → 5′ linked nucleoside residue (*vide supra*). It should be pointed out that the presence of U at the 3′ → 5′U from the branch point leads to an extra constraint on the 2′ → 5′ phosphodiester linkage due to the weaker ability of 3′ → 5′U to participate in stacking with the branch-point nucleobase residue (27).

A lack of rigidity and internal constraints (such as strong stacking) makes the nOe data scarce. Nevertheless, this can help to identify either the presence or absence of stacking. In this respect, 7 offers the possibility to use nOe data as a confirmation of intramolecular association due to its resemblance to A2′ → 5′C (38) where a strong stacking exists along its 2′ → 5′ phosphate backbone. In order to delineate the strength of the nOes, two NOESY experiments were performed with two different mixing times of 500 ms and 100 ms for **7**. A low mixing time also allows an attenuation of spin diffusion phenomena. Anyway in the present work only qualitative data are retrieved from the 2D nOe. The NOESY spectrum obtained with a mixing time of 100 ms for **7** clearly showed that H8A* has nOes with H6C and H1′A* and H2′A* has nOe with H5C establishing that the spatial proximity between the A* and C in **7** is more pronounced than between A* and U. Some general trends emerged from the nOe studies: (i) H6 or H8 of the branch-point interacts (similar nOe intensity) with H1′ and H2′ of the same nucleotide unit, independent of the nature of the base, (ii) H8G at the 2′ position in **1 - 6** has always a stronger nOe with its H2′ than its H1′, (iii) H6 of the pyrimidine moiety at the 3′-position has a strong nOe with its H2′ almost exclusively. This demonstrates that the branch-point prefers rather an anti conformation, while the 2′ and 3′ nucleotides are definitely in anti conformation. However without quantitative calculations it is hazardous to be specific, especially when contradictory results has been found in 2′ → 5′ dimers (40).

3. Effect of Temperature on ^{31}P Chemical Shifts of Branched Trimers **1 - 13**

It is clear from the studies on the structure and conformation of RNA and DNA that the flexibility of the phosphate backbone comes from the sugar conformation (N ⇌ S) and the stacking gives the overall stability (42). Therefore the change of ^{31}P chemical shift with temperature should be interpreted in terms of *flexibility* or *constraint*. The effect of increasing the temperature is observed (25) for two types of phosphates (2′ → 5′ and 3′ → 5′) in all branched trimers **1 - 13**. which is explained (43) as being due to the change of the O-P-O angle, the torsion angle such as α and ζ (Scheme I), and stacked ⇌ unstacked transition. Although the temperature dependence of ^{31}P chemical shifts can easily be explained by a transition stacked ⇌ unstacked equilibria, there is however no linear relationship between temperature-dependent change of ^{31}P chemical shifts and the percentage of base-base stacking (42). Indeed if one can assume that at a low temperature (stacked state) the phosphate ester conformation is g, g, it is difficult to separate the contribution of g^-, g^- from the total g, g blend. (Note: g^-, g^- produces a ^{31}P chemical shift which is different from g^+, g^-, g^+, g^+, g^-, g^+). We have shown (25) that the $\Delta\delta$ values (difference of ^{31}P chemical shift at high and low temperature) could be *qualitatively* correlated to the flexibility of the phosphate backbones (2′ → 5′ versus 3′ → 5′) in branched trimers, i.e., the higher the $\Delta\delta$ is, the more constrained is the phosphate linkage. ^{1}H-NMR studies, along with such estimation of $\Delta\delta$, can indeed confirm if the stackings or the sugar conformation are the main factor contributing to the phosphate backbone flexibility. Such estimation of $\Delta\delta$ values in compounds **1 - 13** reveals (25,27) that $\Delta\delta$ is always larger for the 2′ → 5′ phosphate than for 3′ → 5′ (similar observations were found in branched tetramers **14 - 17**). The 3′ → 5′ phosphate linked U or C at the branch-point yields a low $\Delta\delta$ value (0.14 - 0.32), the highest values originate when the branch-point is A as in **7 -13**, or G in **5** and **6**. This is primarily due to the ability of A and G to stack with U and C.

In (3′ → 5′) linked dimers, the magnitude of stacking is as follows: ApC > ApU ⩾ GpC > GpU > CpC > CpU ⩾ UpC > UpU. This constraint is even larger when a purine is located at the 3′ position of the branch-point as evident by a comparison of **10**, **11**, **12** and **13**. Despite the fact that A3′p5′A stacks more strongly than A3′p5′G, **13** has a Δδ for the 3′ → 5′ phosphate significantly lower than in **10** and **11** where it is known that the 2′ → 5′ side of the molecule is strongly stacked. This larger constraint on 2′ → 5′ phosphate may force the branch-point sugar pucker to a greater % of S as found in **10** and **11** (~95% S at 7°C) than in **13** (ca. 77% S at 7°C) (27).

Relative Constraint Amongst the Branched Trimers **4 - 13**

We have obtained the *"total amount of constraint"* within a given branched trimer by adding Δδ of the 2′ → 5′ and 3′ → 5′ phosphates (27). In a dilute solution (below 5 mM) this new value of *Relative Constraint* (RC) represents the *intramolecular* associations in a given branched trimer (27). Thus **7**, **10**, **11** and **12** are the trimers where the temperature effect is more pronounced on both 2′ → 5′ and 3′ → 5′ phosphates. On the other hand, in **1 - 4** where a pyrimidine is at the branch-point, intramolecular associations are much poorer, consistent with the fact that pyrimidines are weak "stackers". In agreement with ^{1}H-NMR results, the magnitude of the constraint in 2′ → 5′ phosphate linkage is the predominant stabilizing factor that dictates the conformation of the branched trimers. An interesting point to note is the effect of uridine at the 3′-position of the branch-point. Indeed more constraint is observed in trimers where U is located at the 3′- and G at the 2′-position (compare: **1** and **2**, **3** and **4**, **5** and **6**, **8** and **9**) (25,27).

4. Circular Dichroism (CD) Studies

We have subsequently confirmed these conclusions from ^{1}H- and ^{31}P-NMR studies on stacked ⇌ unstacked transitions and the *"total amount of constraint"* of the branched trimers **1 - 13** by performing both temperature-dependent Circular dichroism (CD) studies and also by comparing the CD spectra in 100% water and 50% water - 50% ethylene glycol, 10% water - 90% ethylene glycol and also in 8M urea. For a more detailed account on our CD studies, readers are refered to our original articles (23,27).

5. Conformational Studies on Naturally-Occurring Branched Tetramers **14 - 17**

Study of variations of ^{1}H chemical shifts of aromatic and anomeric protons from 7° - 80°C in different nucleoside residues of naturally-occurring branched ribonucleotides **14 - 17** show some common features (24): H8A* (branch-point A) moves upfield in these tetraribonucleotides upon temperature change which was not observed with the branched trinucleotides **8** and **9**. Therefore, the observed shifts for H8A* in **14 - 17** are attributed to the presence of a nucleobase at the 5′-terminus of the branch-point adenosine. H2A* is shifted by ~0.13 ppm (0.2 ppm in branched trimers **8** and **9**). H6U of 3′ → 5′ linked pyrimidine in **15** and **17** experienced a downfield shift by ca. 0.09 ppm while in branched trimers **8** and **9** the H6 shift was only 0.05 ppm over the same range of temperature. On the other hand H5U, H6U and H1′U of **15** and **17** are more deshielded compared to the corresponding absorptions in the branched trimer **9**. The 3′ → 5′ linked H5U in **15** and **17** has a steady chemical shift over a temperature range of 7° - 80°C wheras H5C in **14** and **16** moves upfield by ca. 0.12 ppm. In the corresponding branched trimers, they both move upfield by ca. 0.06 ppm. It was noteworthy that H8G in all four branched tetraribonucleotides **14** - **17** moves only ca. 0.03 ppm upfield over the same temperature range studied as compared to its 0.05 ppm upfield shift in the corresponding branched trinucleotides. When A is at the 5′-terminal in branched tetranucleotides such as **16** and **17**, its H2 and H8 move upfield by ca. 0.15 ppm and 0.04 ppm, respectively. On the other hand, the H6U of U3′p located at the 5′-terminal of A* in **14** moves downfield and it has a steady chemical shift in **15** over 7° - 80°C. These features are closely comparable to those of linear (3′ → 5′) linked triribonucleotides such as A3′p5′A3′p5′Py and Py3′p5′A3′p5′Py (48).

We have also estimated the approximate population of pseudorotamers of each sugar moiety of branched tetraribonucleotides **14** - **17** (24) at various temperatures from the $J_{1',2'}$. It emerged that (i) the branch-point A* in **14** - **17** adopts a ~60% N conformation at 20°C and shows a highly temperature dependent N ⇌ S equilibria [~70% N at 7° to ~35% N at 80°C], (ii) the A/U3′ → 5′A* linked residues (5′-terminal to the branch-point) in **14** - **17** show a steady ~65% S conformation and almost no shift of this N ⇌ S equilibria upon temperature change, (iii) the G as the A*2′ → 5′ linked residue prefers an S conformation [45% N at ~7°C and 34% N at ~80°C], (iv) amongst the A*3′ → 5′ Py linked residues (3′-terminal to the branch-point), the C in **14** and **15** shift from 63% N at 7°C to 50% N at 80°C while U in **15** and **17** remains virtually unchanged at ~45% N. This suggested that C as a nucleobase stacks more strongly than the U. These features are closely comparable to those of A3′ → 5′U and A3′ → 5′C. In view of the fact that the A* in the branched trinucleotides **8** and **9** showed almost temperature invariable 70% S conformation (indicative of 2′ → 5′ stacking). The above features of branched tetranucleotides show that (i) their conformations are more flexible than those of **8** and **9**, (ii) the preferential temperature dependent N conformation of A* in **14** - **17**, along with 50% less shielding of H8G, compared to those in **8** and **9**, show a lack of 2′ → 5′ stacking, (iii) 5′-terminal A or U in **14** - **17** is the destabilizing factor for the 2′ → 5′ stacking, and on the contrary it promotes a predominance of 3′ → 5′ stacking between A* and its 3′-terminal pyrimidine residue in **14** - **17**, (iv) a temperature independent ~65% S conformation for the 5′-terminal residue suggests an absence of normal 3′ → 5′ stacking with the A*, on the other hand, a ~65% S conformation of A*2′ → 5′ linked G residue in **14** - **17** suggests that it is likely that the 5′-terminal residue and the A*2′ → 5′ linked G residue are stacked on each other. These suggestions of structures for **14** - **17** are reminiscent of a distorted (3′ → 5′) linear single stranded A-RNA helix fragment (47) since they closely parallel the conformational features found in linear (3′ → 5′) linked tetraribonucleotides, AACC (49), and in triribonucleotides AAC and UAU. It should be noted that the N ⇌ S conformational equilibria of all sugar residues in AACC, AAC and AAU varies from pure N at ~10°C to less N at higher temperatures (48,50), consistent with the destacking caused by an increase of temperature.

Further evidence of the above conclusions have been subsequently obtained (24) by performing 2D nOe studies with mixing times of 700 and 350 ms, and at 5 mM and 9 mM concentrations. Such comparative nOe studies at different conditions have allowed us to make qualitative distinctions of all observed nOe as strong, medium and weak nOe. Following are the general conclusions from our 2D nOe studies: (i) absence of nOe between A* and G residues, suggesting absence of stacking between these two nucleobases, (ii) weak nOe between H8A* and H1′G suggest their spatial proximity owing to the coplanarity of these two nucleobases, (iii) H6 of A*3′ → 5′ linked pyrimidine has always nOe with both H8G and H2A*, suggesting the close proximities of A*, G and pyrimidine residues, (iv) H6 of the pyrimidine is close to its own H2′, suggesting that pyrimidine is in *anti* conformation, (v) H8 of the 5′-terminal A is close to its H1′, suggesting that it is in *syn* conformation, (vi) H8 of both A* and G has nOe with both its H1′ and H2′, suggesting that there is approximately an equal population of *syn* and *anti* conformers, (vii) for tetramers **16** and **17**, nOe connectivities are present between A* and the 5′-terminal A residue, showing their spatial proximities, similar nOe between A* and the H5 of the 5′-terminal U residue in **14** and **15** is much weaker, (viii) presence of strong nOe between H8G and H5 and H6 of the 5′-terminal U residue suggest that these two residues are sufficiently close in space. It thus appears on the basis of 2D nOe connectivities that tetramers **14** and **15** belong to a group of lariat structure where extended stacking in the 3′ → 5′ axis is much weaker, while the tetramers **16** and **17** belong to a separate group where a distorted A-RNA helix along the 3′ → 5′ axis is a dominant conformational feature. This is rationalized by a thermodynamically prefered stacking in A(3′ → 5′)A* than U(3′ → 5′)A* suggesting that the 5′-terminal A in **16** and **17** provides additional energy in stabilizing the short single stranded A-RNA helix which the 5′-terminal U in **14** and **15** can not provide.

Above data are consistent with the ^{31}P chemical shifts and $\Delta\delta$ measurements for different internucleotide phosphates in branched tetramers (25): **14** [U(3′ → 5′)A*: 0.63 ppm, A*(2′ → 5′)G: 0.41, A*(3′ → 5′)C: 0.35]; **15** [U(3′ → 5′)A*: 0.62 ppm, A*(2′ → 5′)G: 0.50, A*(3′ → 5′)U: 0.31]; **16** [A(3′ → 5′)A*: 0.66 ppm, A*(2′ → 5′)G: 0.42, A*(3′ → 5′)C: 0.33]; **17** [A(3′ → 5′)A*: 0.70 ppm, A*(2′ → 5′)G: 0.51, A*(3′ → 5′)U: 0.32].

6. Conformational Studies on Analogous Branched Tetramers **18 - 20**

In view of our above results, we were confronted with what would be the choice of a suitable model "branched" RNA molecules which would be representative of the biologically-occurring lariat structure? We ruled out a simple branched triribonucleotide (21-23,27) since it has been shown by ^{1}H-NMR spectroscopy that the conformation of branched triribonucleotides is completely different from the one of naturally occurring branched tetramers (24). Furthermore no similarities, regarding the conformational state were found between branched trimers with adenosine and with cytidine at the branch-point (27). These observations led us to choose the model system of a tetraribonucleotide for our conformational studies. We therefore prepared (19) and studied the conformations (26) of three other possible branched RNA structures **18 - 20** with identical substituents on the 2′ → 5′, 3′ → 5′ and 5′ → 3′ termini from the branch-point which is however changed to either cytosine (as in **18**), uracil (as in **19**), or guanine (as in **20**).

A study of four branched tetramers with A* at the branch-point, as in **14 - 17**, has shown that their conformational states can be described as a distorted A-type stacking, the distortion coming mainly from the 5′-terminal nucleoside (A or U) (24). But in any case the A* adopted predominantly an N-type conformation, as the U or C at the 3′-terminus does to a small extent. Therefore a 3′ → 5′ stacking is prefered, the 5′-terminal nucleoside, particularly U in **14** and **15**, is oriented away from A*3′p5′ U axis in order to obtain the additional stability by stacking with G at the 2′-terminus. None of branched tetramers **18**, **19** or **20**, however, display such clear features. It turns out that each of them possesses its own structure as described below (26).

Compound **18**: The 5′-terminal A in **18** prefers the stacking with G due to: (i) high percentage of S conformers for A and G, (ii) upfield shift of H8G (80° → 7°C), and (iii) large upfield shifts for H2 and H8 of A. The C* and 3′pU interact through S-N stackings. This interaction is relatively weak due to a poor capacity for stacking of both U and C. This weakness does not impose any strong constraint on the phosphate backbone C*3′ → 5′U (small $\Delta\delta^{31}$P). Therefore other stable conformations could be found (especially at room temperature or above) such as the conformation mimicking the branched trimer $C^{2'p5'G}_{3'p5'U}$ **4** or a conformation similar to a "linear stacking" along the axis A3′p5′C*2′p5′G. The NMR time average conformation of **18** is probably a blend of these three conformations, although we believe that the first one is predominant, at least at a low temperature. In any case, these conformations involve the 2′ → 5′ residue to a large extent, exerting an unexpected large conformational constraint on the 2′ → 5′ phosphate linkage ($\Delta\delta^{31}$P = 0.40).

Compound **19**: An examination of $\Delta\delta^{31}$P of **19** reveals (26) that no strong constraint exists in **19**. The conformation of **19** could be described by three components of almost equal importance at room temperature: (i) as in **18**, a stacking interaction between 5′-terminal and 2′pG is counterbalanced by an interaction between U* and 3′pU, (ii) a possible interaction exists between 5′-terminal A and 3′pU while U* is bulged out to interact with G and (iii) S-S stacking mode is prevalent between 5′-terminal A and U* but weaker than in AUU, such a B-type short helix is further stabilized by a weak interaction with G. In such a case 3′pU can also undergo an interaction with the 5′-terminal A. The large shielding effect of H5 of 3′pU and the relativly smaller shielding of H5U* are in agreement with a bulge out of U*. Such behaviour is well described in the literature but it occurs, however, only in the sequence Pu-U-Pu (51,52). In **19** it is likely that this possible conformation is favoured (even weakly) due to the repulsive interaction between the 2′- and the 3′-phosphates.

Compound **20**: It showed a similar overall conformation as in **17** due to a similar sequence Pu3′p5′$Pu^{2'p5'Pu}_{3'p5'Py}$. However, some sharp differences could be pointed out (26): (i) $\Delta\delta^{31}$P indicate that A3′ → 5′G* and G*2′ → 5′G phosphate backbones are less constrained than in **17** while G*3′ → 5′U in **20** is significantly more constrained than A*3′ → 5′U in **17**, (ii) the 5′-terminal A has a much larger percentage of N conformer in **20** than in **17** and (iii) conversely, 3′-terminal U exhibits an S-type population which is much larger in **20** than in **17**. To rationalize these differences it is likely that the A-type stacked mini helix along the A3′p5′ G*3′p5′ U axis is distorted at the 3′pU level in **20** instead of the 5′-terminal level in **17**. In this hypothetical scheme the main axis of stabilization is A3′p5′ G*2′p5′ G while the 3′pU can interact weakly with A and it is nearly coplanar with G. This is supported by a clear deshielding of H5 and H6 of 3′pU in **3** compared with **14**, **15** and **20** due to the paramagnetic effect of G. These factors increase the constraint of G*3′ → 5′ U (large $\Delta\delta^{31}P$). The presence of G*2′ → 5′ G stacking has already been pointed out when describing the splitting of H5′/5″ of 2′ → 5′G in **3** (*vide supra*).

7. A Comparative 600 MHz ^{1}H- and 143 MHz ^{31}P-NMR Study on Tri-, Tetra-, Penta- and Hepta- Branched Ribonucleotides

We have recently carried out a structural comparison (28) of the branched tri-, tetra-, penta- and heptamer RNAs, **9**, **15**, **21** and **22**, which correspond to the branch site of the Group II intron b11 from yeast mitochondria. We have restricted ourselves to H1′A, H1′G, H2A* and H8A* resonances in all four systems which we have assigned unequivocally. The plot of $J_{1',2'}$ spin-spin coupling constants of H1′A and H1′G against temperature showed that while the trimer **9** and pentamer **21** show a preference for S conformation, the tetramer **15** and heptamer **22** reveal a conformational bias toward an N-type sugar which is normal for the sugar moieties of a usual single stranded RNA. On the other hand, the chemical shift versus temperature profiles of H8G, H2A* and H8A* show a close resemblance for the branched RNA such as **9** and **21** (slightly decreasing dH8A* and markedly increasing dH2A*) on one hand, and **15** and **22** (moderatetly increasing dH8G, dH2A*, and dH8A*), on the other. A consideration of these data along with our previous experiences with temperature dependent N ⇌ S equilibria and chemical shifts with branched tri- and tetranucleotides lead us to conclude that adenine(2′ → 5′) guanine stacking also has a great impact on the conformation of the pentamer **21** (as in trimer **9**); the heptamer **22**, on the other hand, most probably assumes an A-RNA helical structure (as in tetramer **15**) dominated by C3′ → 5′U3′ → 5′A3′ → 5′U3′ → 5′C stacking and a dangling G2′ → 5′U side chain. ^{31}P-NMR data is also consistent with this proposition. Thus the $\Delta\delta^{31}P$ (difference between $\delta^{31}P$ values at 8° and 85°C) for the pentamer **21** at the branch-point 2′ → 5′ and 3′ → 5′ phosphodiester groups are 0.63 and 0.28 ppm, respectively, while for the heptamer **22**, the $\Delta\delta^{31}P$ for A*2′ → 5′G phophodiester group turned out to be 0.38 ppm. Since this value is even lower than the corresponding $\Delta\delta^{31}P$ of 0.50 ppm, measured for the tetramer **15**, we conclude that the 2′ → 5′ linked phosphate in the heptamer **22** is relatively flexible which means that there is no apparent adenine(2′ → 5′)guanine stacking in the heptamer system.

Concluding Remarks

The absence of noticeable nOes between nucleobases indicates a loose conformational state for **20**, and especially for **18** and **19** as found in the corresponding branched trimers. The conformations of **18** and **19** do not resemble an A-type stack helix (as in AUU), but possibly the branch point U* or C* could be bulged out. It also emerged that the conformation of such branched tetramers is strongly dependent on the constituent nucleobases. Recently we reported that the branch core triribonucleotides are not suitable models to understand the structural requirements of the splicing intron. Indeed large conformational differences between branched trimers and tetramers could be observed. The branched trimers, independent of the nucleotide at the branch-point, adopt a conformation biased to the 2′ → 5′ axis leading to an unusually high population of S-type conformers for the sugar residue at the branch-point nucleotide. The strength of the 2′ → 5′ interaction is weak when C or U constitutes the branch-point. An addition of a nucleotide at the 5′ terminal perturbs these conformational features considerably. Thus with A, or to a lesser extent G, at the branch point a 3′ → 5′ stabilization is achieved which is however distorted at the 5′ terminus for A and at the 3′ terminus for G. Finally, enzymes recognized branched tetramers where A was the branch-point as a substrate in enzymatic 5′-phosphorylation reaction but not the corresponding branched trimers (45,46). Splicing is achieved with A, and to a lesser extent with C, at the branch-point *in vitro* experiments. However, the present work does not reveal any strong similarities between branched tetramers with A or with C at the branch-point. It is however noteworthy that in **17** and **18** the conformational constraint along the 2′ → 5′ phosphate linkage is strongest amongst the studied branched tetramers (in **20** a similar constraint is found but it competes with the one along the 3′ → 5′ phosphate linkage). This common structural feature in **17** and **18** may serve as a driving force and a recognition signal for the second step in the splicing. The current study clearly addresses that the length of oligonucleotide residues at the 3′ and 5′ termini is important for the stabilization of the structure of the branch-point in the lariat owing to the stacking of the central core branched structure with the neighbouring residues. It became quite clear by the study of the branched tri-, tetra-, penta- and heptamer RNAs, **9**, **15**, **21** and **22** that the addition of nucleotides at the 5′ termini of the branch-point promote the stabilization of the 3′ → 5′ mini A-RNA helix more significantly through the stabilization of the A-RNA helix by stacking with neighbouring nucleobases along the 3′ → 5′ axis. The comparative conformational studies with the branched tri-, tetra-, penta- and heptamer RNAs, **9**, **15**, **21** and **22** showed that formation of a lariat via generation of a branch with an A2′ → 5′G phosphodiester linkage in Group II or nuclear mRNA splice reactions can occur without substantial distortion of the conformation around the branch-point. In order to mimic the branch, it is apparently necessary to have at least one nucleotide linked to the 5′-site of the branch-point. Thus a tetramer such as **15** is a representative model for the local conformation of the branch, whereas pentamer **21** is not. Comparing pentamer **21** with tetramer **15**, we are faced with the remarkable fact that a larger fragment of the naturally occurring branched system provides poorer representation of the biomolecular structure. Of course, the heptamer **22** is a more improved model than the tetramer **15** due to the fact that the former has higher number of 5′-terminal nucleobase moieties for the thermodynamic stabilization of the branch-point A-RNA termini.

We envisage that after addition of a few more nucleobases at the 5′-, 2′-, and 3′-termini of the heptamer **22**, the conformation of the lariat intron at the branch-point would reach a conformationally stabilized A-RNA like structure mimicking the natural lariat intron, when an additional cyclization of the 5′-terminal nucleobase at the A*5′ → 3′X → 5′-OH end with the 3′-terminal nucleobase at the A*2′ → 5′G3′ → 5′X → 3′-OH end by a phosphodiester linkage would most probably not make any conformational difference at the branch-point. Further work is now in progress in our laboratory to identify the optimum length of such conformationally stabilized branch RNA structure which can be indeed considered as true biological and conformational mimic of the lariat intron.

Acknowledgments

Authors thank the Swedish Board for Technical Development, the Swedish Natural Science Research Council, the Wallenbergsstiftelsen, the Netherlands Foundation for Chemical Research, the Netherlands Organisation for the Advancement of Pure Research and the British Science and Engineering Research Council for financial supports of this research.

References and Footnotes

1. M.M. Konarska, P.J. Grabowski, R.A. Padgett and P.A. Sharp, *Nature 313*, 552-557 (1985).
2. B. Ruskin, A.R. Krainer, T. Maniatis and M.R. Green, *Cell 38*, 317-331 (1984).
3. R.A. Padgett, P.J. Grabowski, M.M. Konarska, S. Seiler and P.A. Sharp, *Ann. Rev. Biochem. 55*, 1119-1150 (1986).
4. B. Ruskin and M.R. Green, *Science 229*, 135-140 (1985).
5. T.R. Cech and B.L. Bass, *Ann. Rev. Biochem. 55*, 599-629 (1986).
6. J.C. Wallace and M. Edmonds, *Proc. Natl. Acad. Sci. USA 80*, 950-954 (1983).
7. P.A. Sharp, *Science 235*, 766-771 (1987).
8. B. Ruskin, C.W. Pikielny, M. Rosbash and M.R. Green, *Proc. Natl. Acad. Sci. USA 83*, 2022-2026 (1986).
9. R. van der Veen, A. Arnberg, G. van der Horst, L. Bonen, H. Tabak and L. Grivell, *Cell 44*, 225-234 (1986).
10. C. Peebles, P. Perlmann, K. Meckenburg, M. Petrillo, J. Tabor, K. Jarrell and H. Cheng, *ibid 44*, 213-223 (1986).
11. K. Jarrell, C. Peebles, R. Dietrich, S. Romiti and P. Perlmann, *J. Biol. Chem. 263*, 3432-3439 (1988).
12. M. Aebi, H. Horning, R.A. Padgett, J. Reiser and C. Weissmann, *Cell 47*, 555-565 (1986).
13. H. Horning, M. Aebi and C. Weissmann, *Nature 324*, 589-591 (1986).
14. G.A. Freyer, J. Arenas, K.K. Perkins, H.M. Furneaux, L. Pick, D. Young, R.J. Roberts and J. Huinitz, *J. Biol. Chem. 262*, 4267-4273 (1987).
15. J.M. Vial, N. Balgobin, G. Remaud, A. Nyilas and J. Chattopadhyaya, *Nucleosides and Nucleotides 6*, 209 (1987).
16. G. Remaud, X.-X. Zhou, B. Öberg and J. Chattopadhyaya, in *Reviews of Heteroatom Chemistry*, Vol. 1 (Ed., S. Oae) MYU Publishing Inc., Tokyo, p. 340-366 (1988).
17. X.-X. Zhou, A. Nyilas, G. Remaud and J. Chattopadhyaya, *Tetrahedron 43*, 4685 (1987).
18. X.-X. Zhou, G. Remaud and J. Chattopadhyaya, *Tetrahedron 44*, 6471 (1988).
19. N. Balgobin, A. Földesi, G. Remaud and J. Chattopadhyaya, *Tetrahedron 44* (22), 6929 (1988).
20. A. Földesi, N. Balgobin and J. Chattopadhyaya, *Tetrahedron Lett. 30*, 881 (1989).
21. G. Remaud, J-M. Vial, A. Nyilas, N. Balgobin and J. Chattopadhyaya, *Tetrahedron 43*, 947 (1987).
22. J-M. Vial, G. Remaud, N. Balgobin and J. Chattopadhyaya, *Tetrahedron 43*, 3997 (1987).
23. L.H. Koole, N. Balgobin, H.M. Buck, W.H.A. Kuijpers, A. Nyilas, G. Remaud and J. Chattopadhyaya, *Recuil des Trav. Chim Pays-bas 107*, 663-667 (1988).
24. X-X. Zhou, A. Nyilas, G. Remaud and J. Chattopadhyaya, *Tetrahedron 44*, 571 (1988).
25. A. Sandström, G. Remaud, J-M. Vial, X-X. Zhou, A. Nyilas, N. Balgobin, and J. Chattopadhyaya, *J.C.S. Chem. Comm.*, 542-544 (1988).
26. G. Remaud, N. Balgobin, C. Glemarec and J. Chattopadhyaya, *Tetrahedron 45*, 1537-1548 (1989).
27. G. Remaud, N. Balgobin, A. Sandström, J-M. Vial, L.H. Koole, H.M. Buck, A.F. Drake, X.-X. Zhou and J. Chattopadhyaya, *J. Biochemical & Biophysical Methods 18*, 1-36 (1989).
28. L.H. Koole, X-X. Zhou, G. Remaud, H. M. Buck and J. Chattopadhyaya, *J.C.S. Chem. Comm.* (in press).
29. C. Altona, *Recl. Trav. Chim. Pays-Bas 101*, 413-433 (1982).
30. C. Giessner-Prettre and B. Pullman, *Quart. Rev. Biophys. 14*, 113-172 (1987).

31. C. Altona and M. Sundaralingam, *J. Am. Chem. Soc. 94*, 8205-8212 (1972) and *ibid, J. Am. Chem. Soc. 95*, 2333-2344 (1973).
32a. C.A.G. Haasnoot, F.A.A.M. de Leeuw and C. Altona, *Tetrahedron 36*, 2783-2792 (1980).
32b. F.A.A.M. De Leeuw and C. Altona, *J. Chem. Soc. Perkin II*, 375-384 (1982).
32c. F.A.A.M. De Leeuw and C. Altona, *J. Comp. Chem. 4*, 428 (1983).
33. M.J. Damha and K.K. Ogilvie, *Biochemistry 27*, 6403 (1988).
34. M. Lee, S. Huss, G. Gosselin, J.-L. Imbach, J.A. Hartley and J.W. Lown, *J. Biomol. Struct. Dyn. 5*, 651-668 (1987).
35. W. Saenger, in *Principles of Nucleic Acid Structure*, Springer-Verlag, New York Inc. (1984).
36. C. Altona, in *Prooceedings 4th Harry Steenback Symposium on Structure and Conformation of Nucleic Acids and Protein - Nucleic Acid Interactions* (Eds., M. Sundaralingam and T. Rao) pp. 613-629, University Press, College Park, MD (1975).
37. A.R. Srinivasan and W.K. Olson, *Nucleic Acids Res. 14*, 5461-5479 (1986).
38. A. Anukanth and P.K. Ponnuswamy, *Biopolymers 25*, 729-752 (1986).
39. P.O.P. Ts'o, N.S. Kondo, M.P. Schweizer and D.P. Hollis, *Biochemistry 8*, 997-1029 (1969).
40. F.S. Ezra, N.S. Kondo, C.F. Ainsworth and S.S. Danyluk, *Nucleic Acids Res. 3*, 2549-2561 (1976).
41. P.J. Cozzone and O. Jardetzky, *Biochemistry 15*, 4853-4954 (1976).
42. M. Sundaralingam and E. Westhof, *Biomol. Stereodyn. Proc. Symp. 1*, 301-326 (1981).
43. D.G. Gorenstein, S.A. Schroeder, M. Miyasaki, J.M. Fu, V. Roangta, P. Abuaf, A. Chang and J.-C. Yang, in *Biophosphates and Their Analogues, Synthesis, Structure, Metabolism and Activity* (Eds., K.S. Bruzik and W.J. Stec) Elsevier pp. 487-502 (1987).
44. C.A.G. Haasnoot and C. Altona, *Nucleic Acids Res. 6*, 1135-1149 (1979).
45. M. Edmonds, personal communication on July 7th, (1987).
46. R. Kierzek, D.W. Kopp, M. Edmonds and M.H. Caruthers, *Nucleic Acids Res. 14*, 4751-4764 (1986).
47. IUPAC-IUB Joint Commission on Biochemical Nomenclature (JCBN), *Eur. J. Biochem. 131*, 9-15 (1983).
48. C.-H. Lee and I. Tinocco, *Biophys. Chem. 11*, 283-294 (1980).
49. J. Doornbos, C.T.J. Wreesman, J.H. van Boom and C. Altona, *Eur. J. Biochem. 131*, 571 (1983).
50. C.H. Lee, *Eur. J. Biochem. 137*, 347, and *idem 137*, 413 (1983).
51. Y.Th. van den Hoogen, C. Erkelens, E. de Vroom, G.A. van der Marel, J.H. van Boom and C. Altona, *Eur. J. Biochem. 173*, 295-303 (1988).
52. Y.Th. van den Hoogen, A.A. van Beuzekom, E. de Vroom, G.A. van der Marel, J.H. van Boom and C. Altona, *Nucleic Acids Res. 16*, 5013-5030 (1988).

Structure & Methods, ISBN 0-940030-32-2
Volume 3: DNA & RNA, ISBN 0-940030-31-4
Eds., Ramaswamy H. Sarma & Mukti H. Sarma, © Adenine Press 1990

Analysis of Mutations in Viroid RNA by Non-Denaturing and Temperature-Gradient Gel Electrophoresis

Rolf Zimmat, Reinhard Gruner, Rolf Hecker, Gerhard Steger and Detlev Riesner*
Heinrich-Heine-Universität Düsseldorf
Institut für Physikalische Biologie
Universitätsstraβe 1
4000 Düsseldorf, F.R.G.

Abstract

Mutations in the potato spindle tuber viroid (PSTVd) were analysed by differend gel electrophoretic techniques. Although PSTVd is a circular single-stranded RNA (359 nucleotides), the first series of experiments were carried out on linear RNA transcripts from different PSTVd-strains. The sequence differences between the different strains were detected by analysing mismatches and loops in heteroduplexes which were formed from (+)- and (−)strands of different strains. The mismatches led to a destabilization in the thermal stability of cooperatively melting domains. The denaturation was simulated by the Poland algorithm and measured by optical melting curves and by temperature-gradient gel electrophoresis (TGGE; Rosenbaum & Riesner, *Biophys. Chem. 26*, 235 (1987)). As a novel experimental approach non-denaturing gel electrophoresis was introduced to the analysis of heteroduplexes, and it was shown that the mobilities of heteroduplexes were smaller than those of the corresponding homoduplexes.

Base substitutions in natural, circular PSTVd strains were studied by three different approaches. In TGGE of non-hybridized viroids only those substitutions were detected, which resulted in a secondary structure with altered thermal stability. If homo- or heteroduplexes were formed between circular viroids and linear transcripts, they could not be analysed in TGGE because curves with well expressed transitions were not obtained. Duplexes of circular viroids and half-size linear transcripts, however, exhibited clear transition curves in which base substitutions could be detected unequivocally. The most simple technique for detection of base substitutions in circular viroids was non-denaturing gel electrophoresis. Heteroduplexes of circular viroid and linear transcripts exhibited a significantly altered electrophoretic mobility (up to 37%) and allowed the discovery of substituted bases in all segments of the circle. It is discussed that TGGE and non-denaturing gel electrophoresis complement each other for the detection of mutants without requireing the determination of the complete nucleotide sequence.

*Author to whom correspondence should be address.

Introduction

Recognition of departures from a prototype nucleic acid sequence without determination of the complete sequence is a present day problem in genetics and molecular biology. For example the diagnosis of genetic diseases is of general interest in medicine. Several human genetic diseases are associated with single-base substitutions (1). RNA viruses like influenza virus (2) and HIV (3) are replicated with low fidelity and exhibit thereby a marked genetic drift. In order to study the evolution of new strains and to determine the extent of sequence variation, methods are required which are faster and more simple than determining the complete sequences of many cloned molecular species. As an other example symptom expression of plant infectious diseases is often modulated by a few or even one base substitutions in small RNA components of the infectious agent. Satellite RNAs (4) or viroids (5) are well known examples of this effect.

In two recent reviews (6,7) several methods for detecting single or few base substitutions were described. The application of denaturing gradient gel electrophoresis was outlined in particular detail and its advantages and limitations were discussed. This method is based on the fact, that mismatches between the genomic strand and a prototype nucleic acid probe alter the thermodynamic stability and are readily detectable by denaturing gradient gel electrophoresis. A denaturing gradient may be established either in form of a concentration gradient of a denaturing solvent such as urea or formamide (8), or may be formed as a temperature-gradient in the gel (9,10).

In the present work we applied different methods to analyse mutations in viroids, in particular in the potato spindle tuber viroid (PSTVd). PSTVd is a single-stranded, circular RNA molecule of 359 nucleotides. PSTVd-strains, which differ only in a few base substitutions, are associated with drastically different virulence; some strains express nearly no symptoms, others are lethal to the host plant (5). Mismatches in hybrids of natural RNA and (−)strand RNA transcript from cloned viroid sequences were detected by temperature-gradient gel electrophoresis. In accordance with the earlier experience (6,7) it was found that base substitutions cannot be detected in all parts of the viroid. If one strand is a circular RNA as the viroid, the limitations for denaturing gradient gel electrophoresis are even more severe. It will be shown, however, that non-denaturing gel electrophoresis is able to monitor the presence of mismatches, also mismatches in those regions which are inaccessible to denaturing gradient gel electrophoresis. The present investigations were performed with different PSTVd-strains of known sequences and served as a model study for future analysis of sequence distributions in natural viroid isolates. Non-denaturing gel electrophoresis may be regarded as a simple, but powerful method to detect mismatches in medium-sized heteroduplexes.

Materials and Methods

PSTVd-Strains

The purification of PSTVd from tomato plants was described elsewhere (11). PSTVd-

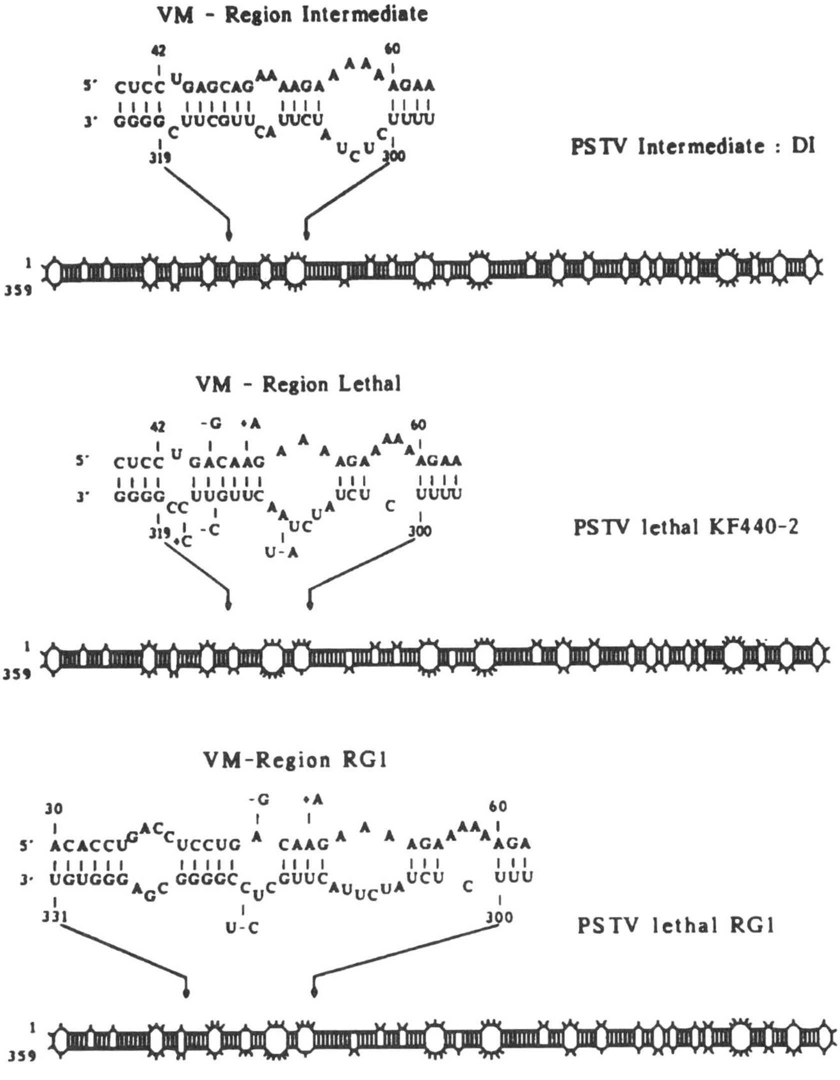

Figure 1: Secondary structures of three PSTVd-strains. The virulence modulating (VM) regions containing the sequence differences are presented in detail according to (5). PSTVd-lethal (RG1) is a new strain.

intermediate (DI) was originally supplied by Dr. T.O. Diener, Beltsville, Maryland. PSTVd-lethal (KF440-2) was obtained by inoculation with dimer (+)strand transcripts (12), the original plasmid was provided by Dr. H.L. Sänger, Munich, FRG (13). PSTVd-lethal (RG1) is a new PSTVd-strain discovered in this laboratory, the sequence is depicted in Figure 1.

RNA Transcripts of PSTVd

Linear RNA with sequences of different PSTVd strains were transcribed from

Table I
Description of RNA Transcripts

PSTVd-strain	original plasimid (reference)	T7-transcription plasmid (14)	polarity of the transcript	start-stop sites of the transcript
intermediate DI	pST-B14 (24)	pRH713	(+)	282-359-1-281
		pRH714	(−)	281-1-359-282
		pRH752	(−)	95-1-359-264
severe DS	pAV401 (25)	pRH703	(+)	282-359-1-281
		pRH704	(−)	281-1-359-282
lethal KF440-2	pMT40 (13)	pRH705	(+)	282-359-1-281
		pRH706	(−)	281-1-359-282
		pRH709	(+)	147-359-1-146
		pRH710	(−)	146-1-359-147

several plasmids (Table I). Cloned cDNA of PSTVd was inserted downstream of the Φ 10 promoter of the T7RNA polymerase in a pBR322 derivative. The construction of these pRH plamids was described earlier (12,14). *In vitro* transcription (15) yielded the corresponding monomeric, single-stranded, linear PSTVd molecules of (+)- and (−) polarity. Short terminal sequences were derived from the vector: at the 5′ end two additional nucleotides (GG) and at the 3′ end seven additional nucleotides (GGGAAUU). Due to the cloning procedure of the circular viroid RNA, the linear (+) transcripts start either at positions 147 or 282 and end either at 146 or 281 (cf. Table I.).

High Performance Liquid Chromatography

RNA transcripts and natural viroid RNA were purified by high performance liquid chromatography (HPLC) on the weak anion-exchanger Nucleogen-DEAE (Macherey-Nagel, FRG). For purification of transcripts the Nucleogen-DEAE 4000-7 column was used, for viroids the Nucleogen DEAE 500 column. The detailed procedures of the purification of transcripts (16) and of viroids (11,17,18) were described before.

Preparation of Homo- and Heteroduplexes

Homo- and heteroduplexes were prepared by hybridization of 500 ng PSTVd or (+)strand transcripts with 500 ng of a (−)strand transcript from the same or another PSTVd-strain in 100 µl buffer (100 mM NaCl, 0.1 mM EDTA, 1 mM Nα-Cacodylate, pH 6.8). The samples were heated to 95°C in a heat-bloc and cooled in an insulation box to 50°C in 2-3 h.

Non-Denaturing Polyacrylamide Gel Electrophoresis (ndPAGE)

Gel electrophoresis was performed in a thermostated apparatus (Bio-Rad, Model 220). Slab gels (140 mm × 100 mm × 1 mm) contained 5% acrylamide, 0.12% bisacrylamide, 0.12% TEMED in "high salt" electrophoresis buffer (89 mM Tris, 89 mM boric acid, 2.5 mM EDTA) with 8 M urea and 0.07% ammoniumperoxydisulfate for starting the polymerization. 10 µl of the sample were filled into one slot. The electrophoresis was carried out under non-denaturing conditions, i.e., at 15°C in the "high salt" electrophoresis buffer. Other conditions are described in the fiugre legends. Staining was carried out with silver (19,20).

Temperature-Gradient Gel Electrophoresis (TGGE)

The technique of temperature-gradient gel electrophoresis was described in detail elsewhere (9). A horizontal slab gel (185 mm × 175 mm × 1) on a film support (FMC Corp. Rockland, Maine, USA) is in thermal contact with a metal plate, but electrically insulated from the metal. A commercially available thermostating plate made of aluminium and coated with PTFE (DIAGEN, Düsseldorf, FRG) was used. Using two independent thermostats, the metal plate was cooled on one side and heated on the other. This permits establishment of a linear temperature gradient between 10°C and 80°C in the gel. In reference runs the linearity of the temperature gradient inside the gel was tested by thermoresistors; the deviation from linearity was smaller than 0.3°C everywhere in the gel. The gel was covered by a plastic film and a glassplate, thus preventing evaporation from the gel and drying out. The device for the temperature-gradient was adapted to a LKB-Multiphor (LKB, Sweden), in the latest experiments a special device (DIAGEN TGGE system; DIAGEN, Düsseldorf, FRG) was used. The direction of the electrophoresis was arranged perpendicular to the direction of the gradient throughout this work. The sample was pipetted into a single slot (130 mm × 5 mm). Gels contained 5% acrylamide, 0.16% bisacrylamide, 0.1% TEMED, 17.8 mM TRIS, 17.8 mM boric acid, 0.4 mM EDTA or 89 mM Tris, 89 mM boric acid, 0.24 mM EDTA and 8 M urea, respectively, and 0.06% ammonium peroxydisulfate for starting the polymerization. The RNA samples were in 17.8 mM TRIS, 17.8 mM borid acid, 0.4 mM EDTA, and 4% glycerol. Between 100 and 300 ng RNA were used for an electrophoretic analysis.

Thermal Transition Curves

The optical, thermal denaturation curves were measured by a two-wave length spectrophotometer (SIGMA-ZWS 11, SIGMA Instruments, Berlin, FRG). Heating of the sample chamber and recording of the absorptions at 260 and 280 mm were controlled by an Apple II+ microcomputer were described earlier (21). The sample solution contained 0.25 A_{260} RNA/ml in 10 mM NaCl, 0.1 mM EDTA, 1 mM Na-cacodylate, pH 6.8; 50 µl were needed for each measurement. The experimental curves had to be extrapolated to reference conditions, i.e., 1 M ionic strength; all theoretical curves refered to these reference conditions.

Calculation of the Helix-Coil Transitions with the Poland Algorithm

Denaturation curves and probability plots were calculated according to the algorithm of Poland (22). Details are described under results.

Results

The detection of base substitutions in viroids was studied by applying different gel electrophoretic methods. The studies could be carried out with three different PSTVd-strains isolated from infected tomato plants. They are depicted in their native secondary structures in Figure 1. For the studies on homo- and heteroduplexes as described later different full length and one half length PSTVd RNA transcripts were available; they are listed in Table I.

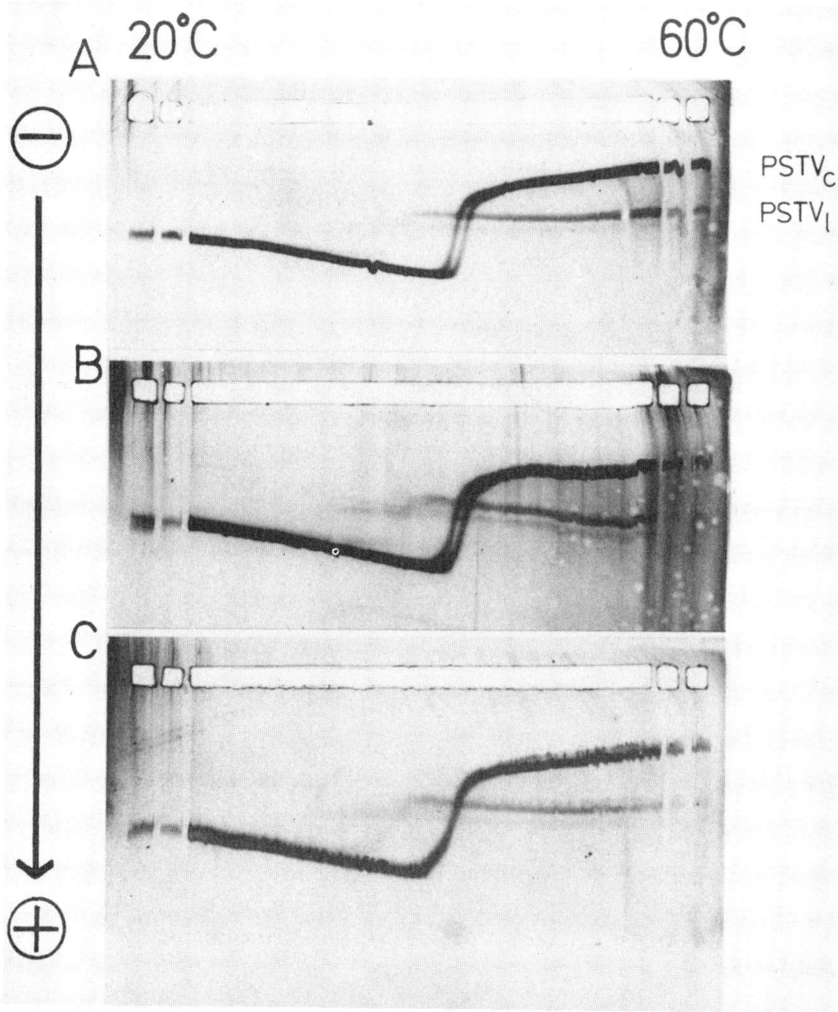

Figure 2: Comparison of native PSTVd-strains in TGGE: (A) PSTVd-lethal (KF440-2) and PSTVd-intermediate (DI); (B) PSTVd-lethal (RG-1) and PSTVd-intermediate (DI); (C) PSTVd-lethal (KF440-2) and PSTVd-lethal (RG1). Direction of electrophoresis is from top to bottom; the linear temperature-gradient is indicated. The gel contained 5% acrylamide, 0.12% bisacrylamide, 0.1% TEMED, 17.8 mM Tris, 17.8 mM boric acid, 0.05 mM EDTA. Electrophoresis was carried out at 300 V for 75 min.

Strain Differentiation by TGGE of Circular PSTVd

Viroids undergo a highly cooperative transition from the native, rod-like structure to a conformation, in which all of the native base pairs are dissociated and a few, stable hairpins are formed, which dissociate at higher temperature. The details of the transitions as studied by thermodynamic and kinetic methods have been summarized earlier (23,26).

In Figure 2 TGGE of different PSTVd-strains is shown. TGGE of PSTVd-intermediate has been reported earlier (26) but had to be included here as a reference. The cooperative denaturation of circular PSTVd is seen as a drastic reduction in mobility to less than a third. In addition to the curves of circular viroids several transition curves of linear viroids, which are derived from the circular molecules by single nicks, were observed as faint lines in accordance with the earlier report (26).

In Figure 2A TGGE of a 1:1 mixture of PSTVd-lethal (KF440-2) and PSTVd-intermediate (DI) is shown, in Figure 2B PSTVd-intermediate (DI) and PSTVd-lethal (RG1). It is obvious that these strains may be differentiated by different thermal stabilities. In Figure 2C, however, it is shown that PSTVd-lethal (KF440-2) and PSTVd-lethal (RG1) could not be differentiated by TGGE. Thus, it was only possible to distinguish between some of the known PSTVd strains, and it was necessary to search for other methods for a differentiation of all known PSTVd strains and hypothetical new mutations.

Strain Differentiation by Forming Heteroduplexes Between PSTVd and Transcripts from PSTVd Clones

The principle of the following studies is based on the fact, that a mismatch in an otherwise homogeneous double-strand represents a fairly large perturbation in structure and stability and may be detected by thermodynamic and hydrodynamic methods. This perturbation is definitely larger than a mere exchange of an A:U-against G:C base pair or *vice versa*. A mismatch is formed if a viroid RNA with a base substitution forms a heteroduplex with the (−)strand RNA of the corresponding strain without the substitution. The influence of mismatches on the stability has been studied earlier by denaturing gradient gel electrophoresis (2,6,7). In the present work similar studies were carried out with TGGE. It will be shown, however, that in many cases denaturing gradient gel electrophoresis was not sufficient for the detection of mismatches but could be combined favorably with non-denaturing gel electrophoresis (ndPAGE).

Three different types of heteroduplexes were investigated. They are depicted in Figure 3. Linear heteroduplexes (Figure 3a) were formed from (+)- and (−)strand RNA transcripts from cloned viroid cDNA. They serve as model system to evaluate quantitatively TGGE and ndPAGE. Natural circular viroid RNA was transformed either into a partial heteroduplex (Figure 3b) by hybridization with less than full length RNA transcripts or into a complete heteroduplex (Figure 3c) with full length RNA transcripts. Obviously, the circular heteroduplex in Figure 3c is covalently

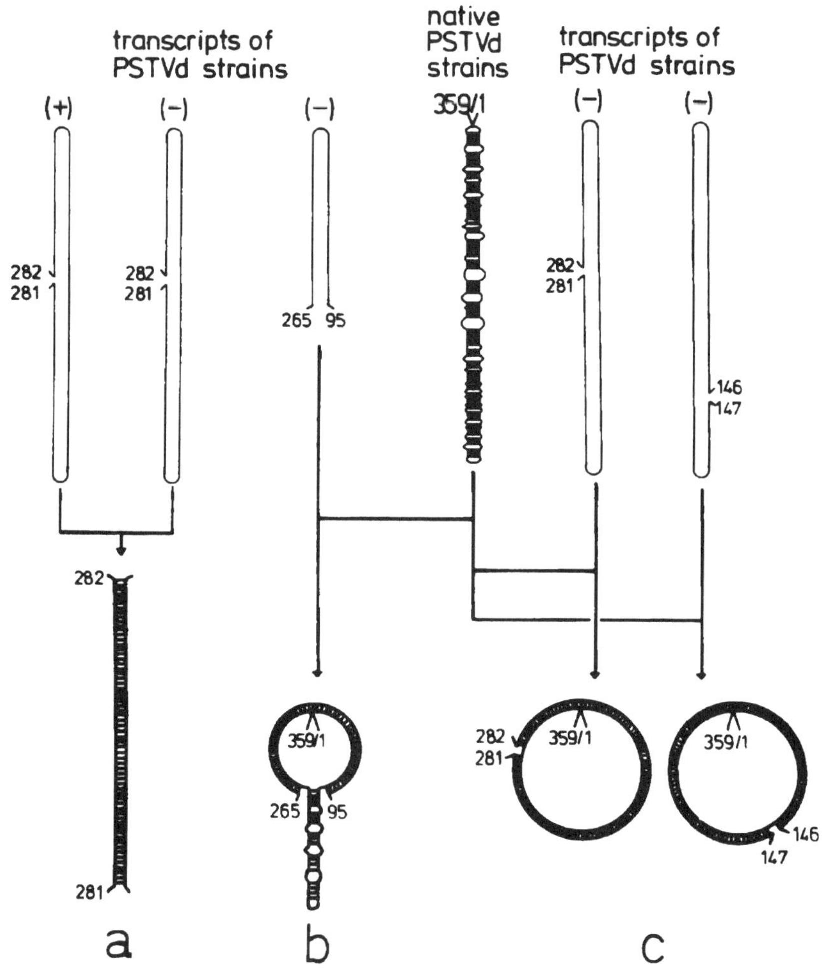

Figure 3: Diagram of the investigated homo- and heteroduplexes. For details see text.

closed only in one strand. All hybrids of Figure 3 were formed also as homoduplexes if (+)- and (−)strand RNA were from the same strain.

Linear Homo- and Heteroduplexes

Calculation of Denaturation Maps

The transition curves from TGGE as well as the optical curves were simulated theoretically on the basis of the known sequences. A modified version (21) of Poland's algorithm (22) was applied. This algorithm allows to calculate the probability of each base pair of the double-stranded nucleic acid to be in the open state at a given temperature. Such a denaturation map with the temperature as the variable in the third dimension is depicted in Figure 4. It shows in a very intuitive manner, which parts of the molecule denature at which temperature. Fraying ends and cooperative units are easy to see.

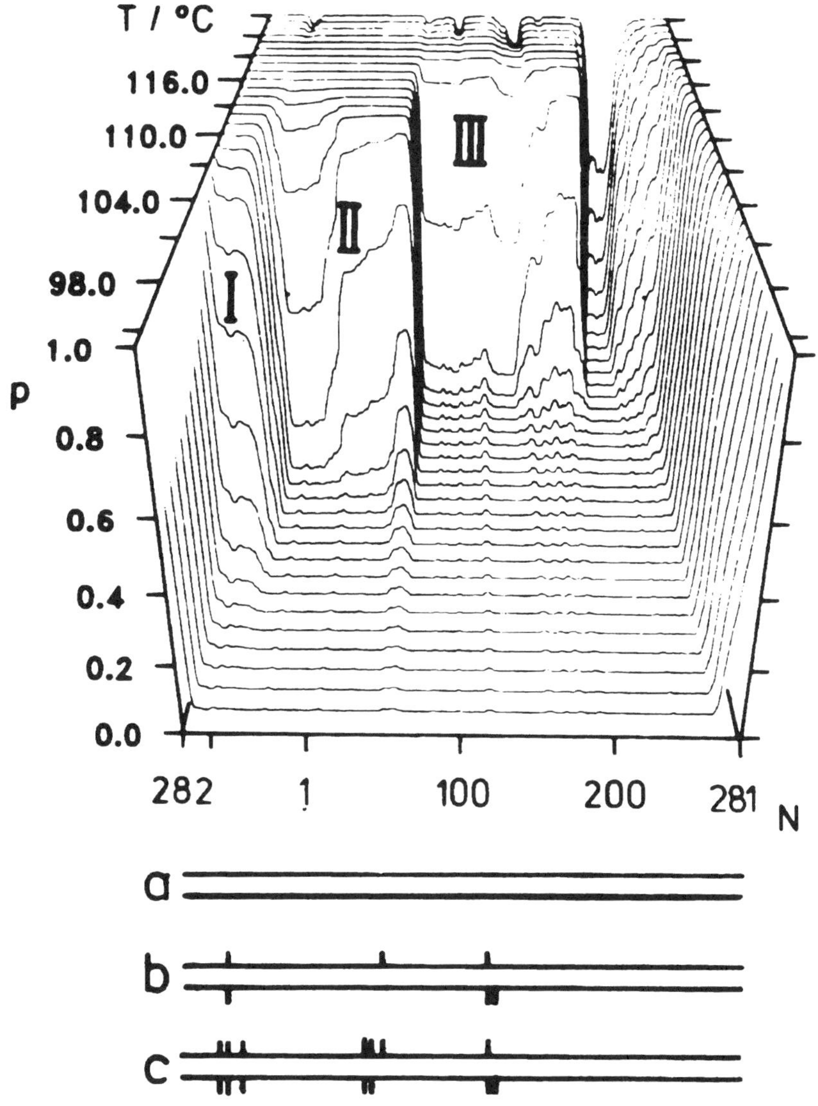

Figure 4: Denaturation map as calculated by the Poland algorithm of a homoduplex formed by the (+)- and (−)strand of linear RNA transcipts of PSTVd-intermediate (DI). The abscissa N denotes the position in the 359 nucleotide long sequence of PSTVd (34). Due to the cloning procedure of the circular viroid RNA, the linear transcript starts at position 282 and ends at 281 (12,24). The ordinate represents the probability for a given base pair to be in the open state (1 = open base pair, 0 = closed base pair). The plots at different temperatures are represented in the third dimension. At the bottom of the figure the different duplexes with the approximate positions of mismatches are depicted. a) (+)strand intermediate/(−)strand intermediate, fully base paired; b) (+)strand severe/(−)strand intermediate, 4 mismatches; c) (+)strand severe/(−)strand lethal (KF440-2), 8 mismatches.

The thermodynamic parameters for helix growth, i.e., parameters for base stacking, were taken from (27), but had to be corrected by 2% in ΔS in the case of A:U stacks and by −2% in the case of G:C/G:C stacks to give optimal fits with optical melting curves. The correction is within the error range of the thermodynamic data. G:U stacks were treated as A:U stacks. Parameters for loop formation were also taken from the literature (28,29). Mismatched base pairs as well as bulge loops were taken into account as internal loops of size 2 using the model of a "virtual stack" (21). For a comparison of experimental and theoretical curves, the experimental curves had to be extrapolated to the conditions used for the calculations, i.e., 1 M ionic strength. This extrapolation was done by a mere shift of 14.3°C per factor of 10 in ionic strength (30). For optical denaturation curves data of the hypochromicity (31,32) and a nucleation constant β of 10^{-3} for strand dissociation were used. For calculation of the relative gel electrophoretic mobility μ/μo of double-stranded and partially denatured molecules the semi-empirical equation of Lerman (8) was taken using a length of the flexible unit L_r of 150 nucleotides (30). Strand separation is not included in the formula.

Figure 4 shows the denaturation map of fully base paired dsRNA, formed by the (+)- and (−)strand of linear RNA transcripts of PSTVd-intermediate strain. The abcissa N denotes the position in the 359 nucleotides long sequence of PSTVd (34). Due to the cloning procedure of the circular viroid RNA, the linear transcript starts at position 282 and ends at 281 (12,24). The ordinate represents the probability for a given base pair to be in the open state (1 = open base pair, 0 = closed base pair). The plots at different temperatures are represented in the third dimension. At the bottom of Figure 4 the homoduplex a and the two deteroduplexes b,c with the positions of the mismatches are depicted in a schematic manner. The sequences are from (5,24,25,34).

The denaturation map shows very clearly that the helix-coil transition of the homoduplex occurs in three well resolved steps. The first denaturation step (I) starts at the left side of the molecule and encloses 30 to 40 base pairs. Obviously this is one region in which mismatches might be detected. In the second step (II) the adjacent sequence of about 100 base pairs denatures. Heteroduplexes b and particularly c contain mismatches in these regions.

The third step (III) leads to complete dissociation into single strands. The segment III and the base pairs of the adjacent groove in the denaturation map (around position 200) denature cooperatively, if the dissociation into single strands were taken into account. The segment which corresponds to step III contains also mismatches.

Experimental Analysis of Linear dsRNA by TGGE and Optical Melting Curves

The experimental analysis of linear homo- and heteroduplexes was performed by TGGE and optical melting curves, and the results are shown together with the computer simulations in Figure 5. The homoduplexes were formed from strands of the intermediate strain (a in Figures 4 and 5), a heteroduplex with 4 mismatches from the (+)strand of the severe strain and the (−)strand of the intermediate strain (b in Figures 4 and 5), and the other heteroduplex with 9 mismatches from the (+)strand

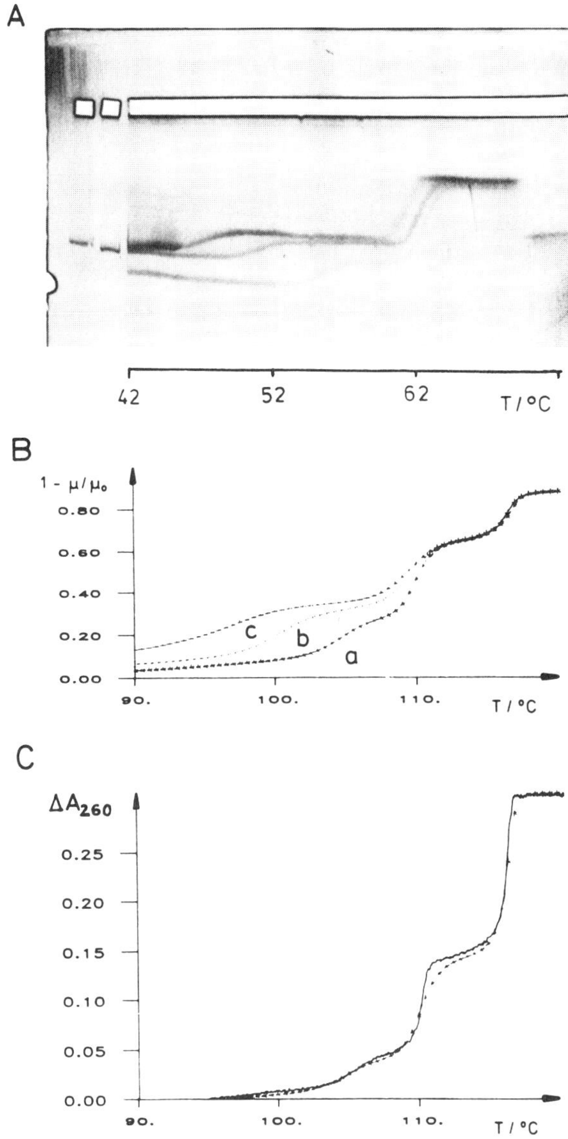

Figure 5: Analysis of homo- and heteroduplexes by TGGE, optical melting curve, and theoretical simulations of the transition curves. (A): TGGE of duplexes a, b, and c as shown in Figure 4. The gel contained 5% acrylamide, 0.12% bisacrylamide, 0.08% TEMED, 89 mM Tris, 89 mM boric acid, 0.24 mM EDTA, 9 M urea and 0.06% ammonium peroxydisulfate for starting the polymerization. Electrophoresis in the presence of the temperature-gradient was carried out at 300 V for 90 min. (B): Calculated transition curves in TGGE for the duplexes a, b, and c as measured in (A). Calculations are carried out as described in the text for the solution conditions of 1 M ionic strength. Strand sparation in the high temperature transition was not taken into account. For the conformational state of the molecules at different temperatures see Figure 4. (C): Experimental and calculated optical transition curve of the homoduplex a. The measurement was carried out in 10 mM NaCl, 0.1 mM EDTA, 1 mM Na-cacodylate, pH 6.9, and the resulting transition curve was shifted by 28.5°C in order to correspond to the solution conditions of 1 M ionic strength as assumed for the calculations.

of the severe strain and the (−)strand of the lethal (KF440-2) strain (c in Figures 4 and 5).

In TGGE three transitions were observed for each of the three duplexes a, b, and c. In the two transitions at lower temperature the mobility decreased with increasing temperature (retardation transitions), in the transition at highest temperatures, which appeared as a discontinuous transition, the mobility increased with temperature. It has been pointed out earlier that the redardation transitions represent partial denaturation, whereas the discontinuous transition at highest temperature is due to strand separation (35). The retardation transitions allowed to differentiate between double-strands without and with mismatches. The depression in the T_m-values amounted up to 9°C. A three-step transition curve was obtained also in optical melting experiments (Figure 5C). Evidently, only one of the duplexes a, b, or c, respectively, may be analysed in one optical experiment. The difference in the T_m-values agreed with those obtained by TGGE, the absolute numbers had to be corrected for the different solution conditions.

The results of Figure 5 demonstrated that mismatches could be detected easily by a shift of the T_m-values in TGGE. Furthermore, the denaturation curves were calculated quite accurately. The comparison of experimental (Figure 5A) and theoretical curves (Figure 5B) of TGGE yielded good agreement not only for the homoduplexes, but also for the influence of mismatches in heteroduplexes. Since the different transitions can be attributed to defined segments representing melting domains of the molecule, a mutation, if its position were not known, could be located in one of these domains. Mismatches are most easy to detect by TGGE if they are in the domain of the first retardation transition. Mismatches in the domain of strand separation are hard to be detected by TGGE, because the transition is discontinuous and does not allow an accurate determination of the T_m-values.

Experimental Analysis by ndPAGE

It was observed already in TGGE of Figure 5, that the three duplexes a, b, and c had different electrophoretic mobilities in the native form although they were exactly the same size. Figure 6 shows a ndPAGE of 3 homo- and 6 heteroduplexes and a diagram of the positions of the mismatches. The homoduplexes contained a few base pair exchanges; they did not exhibit a detectable difference in electrophoretic mobility. The six heteroduplexes with 4 to 9 mismatches could be grouped in three pairs, each of which contained the (+)/(−) and (−)/(+) combination of the same strains. These "inverse" heteroduplexes differed in their ability to form G:U base pairs and in the type of unpaired bases.

As seen from Figure 6, the mismatches induced a remarkable retardation in ndPAGE as compared to the completely homogeneous double strands. The retardation is not only dependent on the number of mismatches. Position and type of mismatch may have an influence as well. Mismatches close to the center of the double strand seemed to have a larger influence; this was obvious from the RNA in lane 4, which

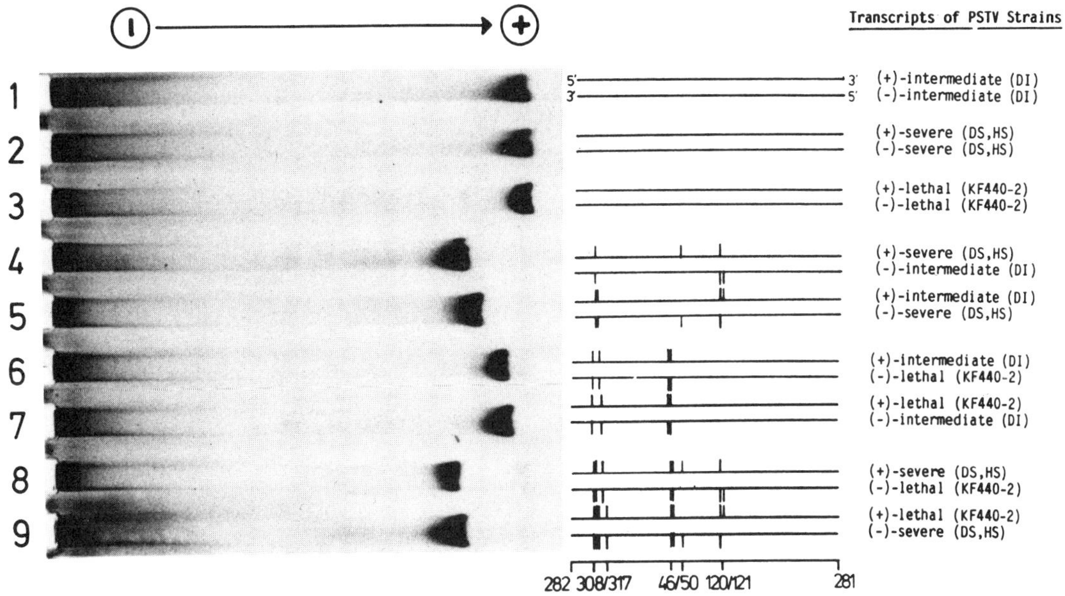

Figure 6: Non-denaturing PAGE of linear homo- and heteroduplexes. The diagram on the right side shows the transcripts with the positions of the mismatches as analysed in the corresponding lanes. The gel contained 5% acrylamide, 0.12% bisacrylamide, 0.1% TEMED, 89 mM Tris, 89 mM boric acid, 0.24 mM EDTA, 4 M urea and 0.06% ammonium peroxydisulfate. Electrophoresis was carried out at 100 V, 20°C for 4 h.

was highly retarded inspite of only four mismatches but two of them in the center. The slight differences in the mobility between "inverse" heteroduplexes indicated particular effects of bulge loops. At present it is not possible, to differentiate between the effects of number, position and type of mismatches; studies on model nucleic acids which are directed to this question are under way.

Homo- and Heteroduplexes of Circular Viroids and Linear, Partial Transcripts

The type of duplex studied in this part of the work is depicted in Figure 3b. Complexes were formed between circular PSTVd of different strains and a linear, partial (−)strand RNA transcript. The transcript was from the intermediate strain. Because the transcript corresponded only to the left half of the native, rod-like structure, it was expected that sequence differences would be detectable only if they were in the segment covered by the transcript. Figure 7 shows the analysis of the duplexes by TGGE. The analysis had to be carried out under two different solution conditions, because the transition of the intramolecular base pairing of the viroid had to be analysed in the absence of urea, whereas the transitions of the two strand complexes were more stable and were shifted into the proper temperature range by 8 M urea (cf. conditions of Figure 5A). In the transition curve of Figure 7A the denaturation of the intramolecular base pairing of PSTVd was observed; it was found at a similar T_m-value as that of PSTVd-denaturation (cf. Figure 2). Differences between different viroid-strains were not visible. The denaturation of the duplex-segment of viroid and transcript is shown in Figure 7B. The homoduplex denatured in a single, dis-

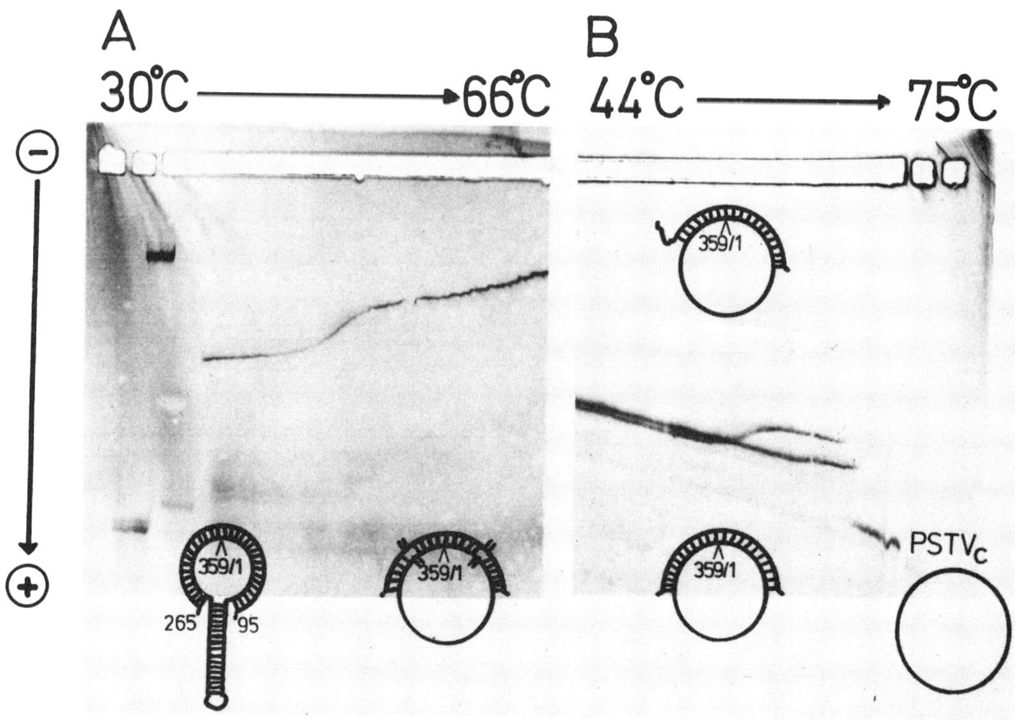

Figure 7: TGGE of homo- and heteroduplexes from circular viroids and half-size, linear transcripts. The duplexes were formed between circular PSTVd-intermediate or PSTVd-lethal (KF440-2), respectively, and half-size, linear (−)strand transcript of the intermediate strain. The conformational states of the duplexes are drawn at the corresponding temperatures. (A): TGGE in 5% polyacrylamide with 89 mM Tris, 89 mM boric acid, 0.24 mM EDTA, and 0.06% ammonium peroxydisulfate. Electrophoresis in the presence of the temperature-gradient was carried out at 300 V for 2.5 h. (B): TGGE of the same samples as in (A), but in a gel containing 8 M urea in addition.

continuous transition including strand separation. Due to the mismatches the heteroduplex underwent first a retardation transition with partial denaturation and then the transition with strand separation. The influence of mismatches could clearly be detected in this experiment.

Homo- and Heteroduplexes of Circular Viroids and Linear, Full Length Transcripts

Duplexes were formed between circular viroids and full length (−)strand RNA transcript (Figure 3c). Thus, circular, relaxed double-stranded RNA molecules without and with mismatches were generated. The (+)strands were the natural circular PSTVd from different strains: intermediate, lethal (RG1), and lethal (KF440-2). The (−)strands were the RNA transcript from the strains intermediate, severe and lethal (KF440-2) as listed in Table I.

The optical melting curves of these circular duplexes and of the corresponding linear duplexes (cf. Figure 5C) were nearly identical (data not shown). In contrast to

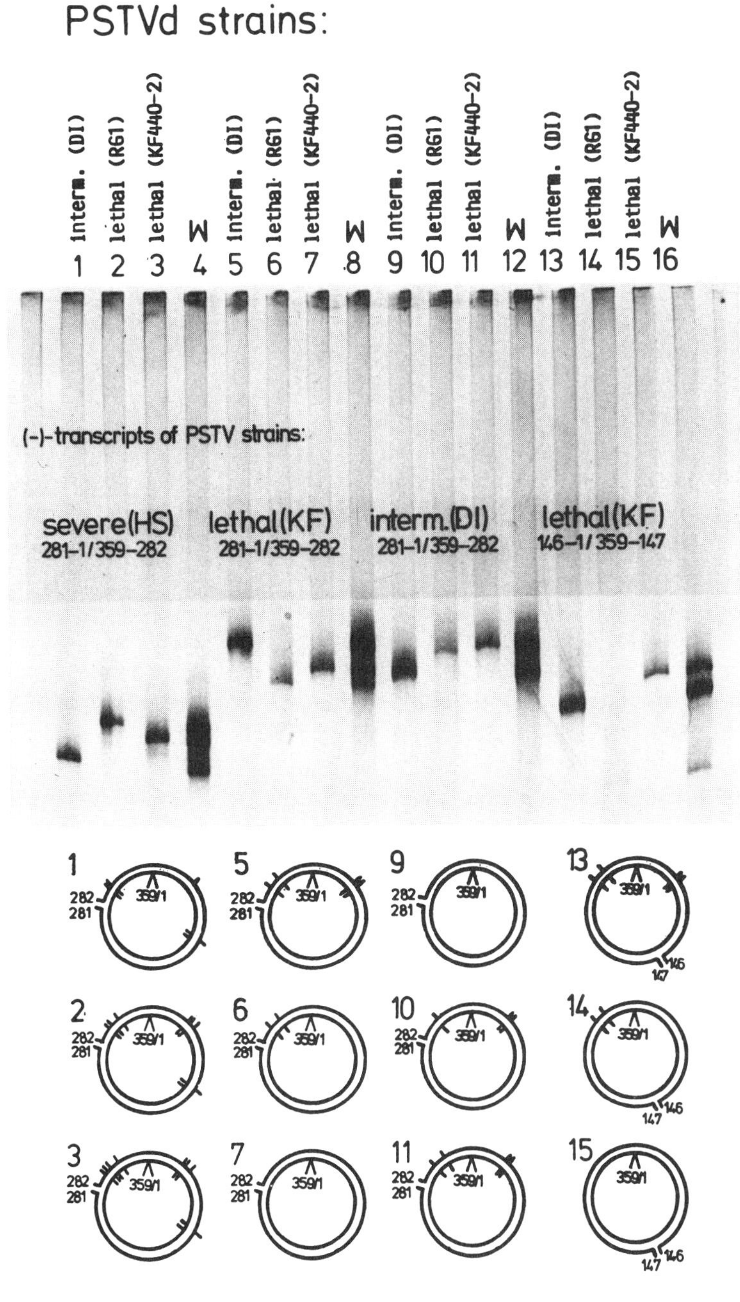

Figure 8: Non-denaturing PAGE of different circular homo- and heteroduplexes. The PSTVd strains and (−)strand transcripts are noted for all lanes and the duplexes with the positions of the mismatches and start/stop sites depicted schematically at the bottom. The gel contained 5% acrylamide, 0.12% bisacrylamide, 0.1% TEMED, 89 mM Tris, 89 mM boric acid, 0.24 mM EDTA, 8 M urea and 0.06% ammonium peroxydisulfate. Electrophoresis was carried out at 150 V, 15°C for 14 h.

the optical melting curves, TGGE of the circular duplexes did not yield results comparable to those of the corresponding linear duplexes. The retardation effect due to partial denaturation of the circular duplexes in TGGE was found to be very small and could not be utilized for a safe detection of mismatches.

Experimental Analysis by ndPAGE

Unlike in TGGE, the different circular duplexes exhibited marked differences in non-denaturing PAGE. The results are shown in Figure 8. In this example all circular homo- and heteroduplexes studied could be compared in one and the same gel. The different combinations of PSTVd-strains and transcripts were arranged in four groups with four lanes each. In every group one transcript was hybridized to three different viroid-strains, and the duplexes analysed separately (left three lanes) and as a mixture (fourth lane). The positions of the mismatches and the start/stop site of the transcript are depicted at the bottom of Figure 8.

The homoduplexes showed similar electrophoretic mobilities for different sequences and different start/stop sites as seen from lanes 7, 9, and 15. In all hybrids studied, the electrophoretic mobilities of all heteroduplexes were clearly different from those of the corresponding homoduplexes. Some of the heteroduplexes studied migrated faster, others slower; the fastest combination (lane 14) was about 37% faster than the slowest (lane 5). Easy rules for the dependence of the electrophoretic mobility upon number, position and type of mismatches were not apparent. In addition, the position of the start/stop site of the linear transcript was relevant; this may be seen most clearly by comparing lanes 5-7 with 13-15, which contained duplexes with different start/stop sites but identical mismatches. As a general tendency, mismatches and/or start/stop site increased the mobility if they were located in the circle by an angular distance of about 180°. This was most obvious with the fastest moving heteroduplex in lane 14. Most probably, the stretched out circle collapses, and the molecule forms two halves, which are arranged more or less in parallel. Heteroduplexes with mismatches and/or start/stop site in only one quarter of the circle were generally slower than those described above; the second (lane 5-7) and third group (lane 9-11) were examples of the second class.

Although the effect of mismatches on the mobility of circular heteroduplexes cannot be described quantitatively, it is obvious from the results described above, that non-denaturing PAGE is an easy and sensitive method to detect mismatches in circular molecules.

Conclusions

Base substitutions in viroid RNA were analysed by different methods. Although the viroid PSTVd is a circular single-stranded RNA of 359 nucleotides, the studies were not restricted to circular RNA but also linear RNA transcripts of the same sequence as the viroid were included in the work. This was for two reasons: First, the advantages and limitations of the different methods could be compared better in the studies on linear RNA, and second, linear nucleic acids are of more general relevance for studies on other nucleic acids.

Base substitutions between two linear RNAs could be detected by forming the heteroduplex between the (+)- and the (−)strands of the two RNAs and analysing the decrease in thermal stability was analysed by calculated denaturation curves, by optical melting and by TGGE. In general, the approach and the results obtained were similar to those reported earlier (2,6,7) on the detection of mismatches in DNA and RNA by denaturing gradient gel electrophoresis: The segment size of 350 nucleotides is well accessible to this type of analysis, but the main limitation is that substitutions in the highest melting domain cannot be detected. In our experience, TGGE offered some advantages as compared to solvent gradient gel electrophoresis; these were mainly easier handling, better comparison with thermodynamic calculations, and more possibilities in chosing solvent conditions, e.g. for analysing protein-nucleic acid complexes (10,36). Also mutations in plasmids were detected successfully with TGGE, and the method was utilized favorably for screening mutant clones after site directed mutagenesis (10).

The main progress of the present work for the detection of base substitution with gel electrophoretic methods was the combination of gradient gel electrophoresis with non-denaturing gel electrophoresis (ndPAGE) under appropriate conditions. Mismatches in linear heteroduplexes alter the electrophoretic mobility in ndPAGE. At present it is not known whether the increased flexibility of the heteroduplex due to the mismatch or the constant bending at the site of the mismatch produces the larger effect in mobility. The influence of the number, position and type of mismatches could not yet be analysed quantitatively, but the comparison of different heteroduplexes showed that mismatches in the center of the heteroduplexes lead to the largest decrease in mobility. A limitation, as concerning the highest melting domain in TGGE does not exist for ndPAGE. For a "normal" sequence, i.e., a sequence in which G:C pairs are not clustered too much, TGGE and ndPAGE are complementary methods. If a double-stranded nucleic acid is melting from the outer to the inner parts, mismatches in the outer parts are detected with TGGE, in the inner with ndPAGE.

The particular advantages of ndPAGE became evident when it was tried to detect base substitutions in natural circular viroids. Only some of the base substitutions were found with TGGE of unhybridized viroids, namely those which resulted in a secondary structure with altered thermal stability. Heteroduplexes formed from circular viroids and full-length linear (−)strand RNA transcripts did not exhibit curves with well expressed transitions in TGGE; therefore, mismatches could not be found in these heteroduplexes. If, however, only half-length transcript were used for heteroduplex formation, clear transitions were measured and the transitions were dependent upon the number and location of mismatches. Thus, it was possible to detect base substitutions in circular viroids by heteroduplex-formation and TGGE but the detection depended upon the right choice of the transcript, and quite a few different transcripts have to be used to detect all base substitutions. In principle, this approach is similar to the differential hybridization of synthetic oligonculeotide probes, where also only a restricted region of a larger sequence may be screened for mutations (37). ndPAGE turned out to be surprisingly simple for the detection of base substitutions in natural circular viroids. Nine different heteroduplexes were formed between three PSTVd strains and four (−)strand transcripts, and all of them could be separated from the homoduplexes, i.e., those dsRNA molecules without mismatches. It has been pointed out above, that it should be possible to screen the whole viroid circle for mutations by chosing one prototype sequence as counter part but with a few different start/stop sites. Although the influence of mismatches in circular heteroduplexes cannot be interpreted quantitatively at present, it is obvious that the structure of a relaxed circle, i.e., one strand circular and one linear, is particularly favorable to detect base substitutions in ndPAGE. At present, studies are under way to analyse sequence distributions in natural isolates of viroids.

Acknowledgments

The skillful technical assistence of Mr. B. Esters and the help of Ms. H. Gruber in preparing the manuscript are highly acknowledged. The work was supported by grants from the Deutsche Forschungsgemeinschaft and the Fonds der Chemischen Industrie.

References and Footnotes

1. S.H. Orkin and H.H. Kazazian, *Ann. Rev. Genet. 18*, 131 (1984).
2. F.J. Smith, J.D. Parvin and P. Palese, *Virology 150*, 55 (1986).
3. V.H. Hahn, G.M. Shaw, S.K. Arya, H. Popovic, R.G. Gallo and F. Wong-Staal, *Nature 312*, 166 (1984).
4. J.M. Kaper and M.E. Tousignant, *Endeavour, New Series 8*, 194 (1984).
5. M. Schnölzer, B. Haas, K. Ramm, H. Hofmann and H.L. Sänger, *EMBO J. 4*, 2181 (1985).
6. L.S. Lerman, K. Silverstein and E. Grinfeld, *Cold Spring Harb. Symp. Quant. Biol. LI*, 285 (1986).
7. R.M. Myers and T. Maniatis, *Cold Spring Harb. Symp. Quant. Biol. LI*, 275 (1986).
8. L.S. Lerman, S.G. Fischer, I. Hurley, K. Silverstein and N. Lumelsky, *Ann. Rev. Biophys. Bioeng. 13*, 399 (1984).
9. V. Rosenbaum and D. Riesner, *Biophys. Chem. 26*, 235 (1987).
10. D. Riesner, G. Steger, R. Zimmat, R.A. Owens, M. Wagenhöfer, W. Hillen, S. Vollbach and K. Henco, *Electrophoresis 10*, 377 (1989).
11. D. Riesner, P. Klaff, G. Steger and R. Hecker, *Ann. N.Y. Acad. Sci. 503*, 212 (1987).
12. R. Hecker, Z. Wang, G. Steger and D. Riesner, *Gene 72*, 59 (1988).
13. M. Tabler and H.L. Sänger, *EMBO J. 3*, 3055 (1984).
14. R. Hecker, Thesis, Heinrich-Heine-Universität Düsseldorf (1989).
15. P. Davanloo, A.H. Rosenberg, J.J. Dunn and F.W. Studier, *Proc. Natl. Acad. Sci. USA 81*, 2035 (1984).
16. R. Hecker and D. Riesner, *J. Chromatogr. 418*, 97 (1987).
17. M. Colpan, J. Schumacher, W. Brüggemann, H.L. Sänger and D. Riesner, *Anal. Biochem. 131*, 257 (1983).
18. M. Colpan and D. Riesner, *J. Chromatogr. 296*, 339 (1984).
19. J. Schumacher, N. Meyer, D. Riesner and H.L. Weidemann, *J. Phytopathol. 115*, 332 (1986).
20. E.A.C. Follett and U. Desselberger, *J. Med. Virol. 11*, 39 (1983).
21. H. Werntges, G. Steger, D. Riesner and H.-J. Fritz, *Nucleic Acids Res. 14*, 3773 (1986).
22. D. Poland, *Biopolymers 13*, 1859 (1974).
23. D. Riesner, in *The Viroids* (T.O. Diener, ed.) Plenum Press, pp. 63-98 (1987).
24. R.A. Owens, R.W. Hammond, R.C. Gardner, M.C. Kiefer, S.M. Thompson and D.E. Cress, *Plant Mol. Biol. 6*, 179 (1986).
25. P. van Wezenbeek, P. Vos, J. van Boom and A. van Kammen, *Nucleic Acids Res. 10*, 7947 (1982).
26. D. Riesner, R. Hecker and G. Steger, in *Structure and Expression* (R.H. Sarma and M.H. Sarma, eds.) Vol. 1, 261 (1988).
27. S.M. Freier, R. Kierzek, J.A. Jaeger, N. Sugimoto, M.H. Caruthers, R. Neilson and D.H. Turner, *Proc. Natl.. Acad. Sci. USA 83*, 9373 (1986).

28. J. Gralla and D.M. Crothers, *J. Mol. Biol. 73*, 497 (1973).
29. H. Jacobson and W.H. Stockmeyer, *J. Chem. Phys. 18*, 1600 (1950).
30. G. Steger, P. Tien, J. Kaper and D. Riesner, *Nucleic Acids Res. 15*, 5085 (1987).
31. J.R. Fresco, L.C. Klotz and E.G. Richards, *Cold Spring Harb. Symp. Quant. Biol. 28*, 83 (1963).
32. S.M. Coutts, *Biochem. Biophys. Acta 232*, 94 (1971).
33. S.F. Fischer and L.S. Lerman, *Proc. Natl. Acad. Sci. USA 80*, 1579 (1982).
34. H.J. Gross, H. Domdey, C. Lossow, P. Jank, M. Raba, H. Alberty and H.L. Sänger, *Nature 273*, 203 (1978).
35. P. Tien, G. Steger, V. Rosenbaum, J. Kaper and D. Riesner, *Nucleic Acids Res. 15*, 5069 (1987).
36. M. Wagenhöfer, D. Hansen and W. Hillen, *Anal. Biochem. 175*, 422 (1988).
37. V.J. Kidd, R.B. Wallace, J. Itakura and S.L.C. Woo, *Nature 304*, 230 (1983).